CIVIL ENGINEERING REFERENCE BOOK
(SECOND EDITION)

ENGLAND:	BUTTERWORTH & CO. (PUBLISHERS) LTD. LONDON: 88 Kingsway, W.C.2
AFRICA:	BUTTERWORTH & CO. (AFRICA) LTD. DURBAN: 33/35 Beach Grove
AUSTRALIA:	BUTTERWORTH & CO. (AUSTRALIA) LTD. SYDNEY: 6-8 O'Connell Street MELBOURNE: 430 Bourke Street BRISBANE: 240 Queen Street
CANADA:	BUTTERWORTH & CO. (CANADA) LTD. TORONTO: 1367 Danforth Avenue, 6
NEW ZEALAND:	BUTTERWORTH & CO. (NEW ZEALAND) LTD. WELLINGTON: 49/51 Ballance Street AUCKLAND: 35 High Street
U.S.A.:	BUTTERWORTH INC. WASHINGTON, D.C.: 7235 Wisconsin Avenue, 14

CIVIL ENGINEERING
REFERENCE BOOK

(Second Edition)

Editor

J. COMRIE, B.Sc., A.M.I.C.E.

First edition edited by

The late E. H. PROBST, D.Eng., M.I.C.E.

J. COMRIE, B.Sc., A.M.I.C.E.

2

LONDON

BUTTERWORTHS

1961

First edition 1951

©

Butterworth & Co. (Publishers) Limited

1961

Printed by The Lewes Press, Wightman & Co. Ltd.
Friars Walk, Lewes, Sussex

CONTENTS

VOLUME 2

VOLUME 3

CONTENTS

CONTENTS

INTRODUCTION TO THE FIRST EDITION

CIVIL ENGINEERING in its widest sense has undergone profound development in the past hundred years.

In all of the many branches into which the subject has necessarily been divided, there exists a great store of knowledge of long-established methods of design and contruction of proved safety and economy. While experience and judgement will always play a large part in civil engineering work, advances in all the related sciences, new inventions and the result of research have produced new conceptions in design and new methods of calculation.

There is a growing need for a concise guide to the best in past practice and to the latest methods and theories. To achieve the highest standards ever greater use must be made of the tools provided by mathematics, mechanics, physics, chemistry and research work, both in the laboratory and in the field.

The increasing use of these aids is to be found in all branches *e.g.* in the design of steel and reinforced concrete structures, in the design of foundations based on soil mechanics research and in the design of harbours and river training works based on the results of tests on models.

In the chapters on general science the essential fundamentals required in the theory of the different subjects, or likely to be needed in the solution of problems, have been gathered together for easy reference.

The chapters on the theory of civil engineering *viz* Mechanics, Strength of Materials, Theory of Structures, Soil Mechanics *etc* give concise explanations of the accepted theories together with the necessary equations, formulae, tables and diagrams. It is hoped that the typical worked examples and the indications of permissible approximations will prove helpful.

The chapters on practice have been arranged into the usual broad divisions and every effort has been made to reduce overlapping to a minimum, though a certain amount is inevitable in closely related branches.

The division of the chapters on structural engineering was decided on after much thought as being the most convenient from the point of view of both contributors to, and the users of, the book.

Economy in design and construction, an essential part of all branches of civil engineering, has been given consideration as far as possible under present economic conditions.

There are chapters on subjects common to several branches *e.g.* Surveying, Building Materials and Works Construction, and short chapters on special subjects such as Explosives, Fire Protection, Legal Notes and Patents.

Much attention has been paid to the Mathematical, Conversion and General Tables. Tables such as logarithms, square roots *etc* which are generally available and tables of steel sections to be found in every structural steel handbook have been omitted to make room for others not so common or entirely new.

It is hoped that the list of conversion factors and the conversion tables will be of value. The metric equivalents of the main dimensions or measures are shown throughout the text wherever it was thought that the conversion would be helpful to the reader.

A reference book of this kind cannot, and it is not intended that it should, replace text-books, design handbooks, Standards, and Codes of Practice. As a guide to fuller information on any subject selected references have been added at the end of each section.

It is becoming increasingly difficult for the civil engineer, who must to some extent specialize, to keep in touch with all modern developments, many of which may possibly be of use in his own branch. More use might be made of proved experience in other fields if the information were more readily available. The aim of this book is therefore to give to the civil engineer, in whatever capacity he may be acting, a concise presentation of the fundamentals of the theory and practice of all branches.

A few chapters have been added on methods derived from experience and developments abroad and it is hoped that this information will prove useful for design and construction.

We wish to express our thanks to the contributors for all their work and ready co-operation; and to many others who have helped by encouragement, advice or suggestions at various stages in the preparation of the book. In particular we wish to acknowledge the valuable help and encouragement we have received from SIR REGINALD E. STRADLING, C.B., M.C., D.Sc., F.R.S., at present Dean of the Military College of Science, formerly Chief Scientific Adviser, Ministry of Works and from SIR CLAUDE C. INGLIS, C.I.E., M.I.C.E., Director of Hydraulics Research. Acknowledgements for material and tables taken from other works, and for the use of diagrams and illustrations are made at the beginning of the *Reference Book*.

Any suggestions and criticisms will be welcome in order to make future editions of the book as useful as possible to civil engineers, architects and contractors in their daily routine work.

E. H. P.
J. C.

London

EDITOR'S NOTE TO THE SECOND EDITION

THOSE familiar with the first edition will find many changes in this new edition. New chapters are included on Hydraulic Power Plants, Overhead Transmission Lines, Structural Concrete, Prestressed Concrete, Masonry and Brickwork and The Aesthetics of Bridge Design. Some chapters have been completely re-written, either by the original contributors or by new contributors. All other chapters retained from the first edition have been thoroughly revised and this has often meant re-writing large sections of the chapter and re-arranging it.

Following the decision to publish in four volumes, the whole book has been re-arranged and it is hoped that the grouping of the chapters will make for convenience.

I have again to express my thanks to all the contributors and to the publishers' editorial and drawing office staff for their kind consideration and help.

J. C.

Kings Langley
November 1960

EDITOR'S NOTE TO THE FIRST EDITION

DR. PROBST began the planning of this *Reference Book* in the summer of 1947. His great experience and wide knowledge of the latest developments in civil engineering practice in many countries are reflected in the general principles which he laid down and in the arrangement and scope of the work. He overcame many initial difficulties and setbacks. The book became one of the ruling interests of his last years and he refused to spare himself in any way up to his untimely death in January, 1950. I had acted as assistant editor during this period and it was then my duty to complete the work that Dr. Probst had begun so well. This task has been made easier by the consideration and help that I continued to receive from the contributors and from the publishers' editorial staff. I take this opportunity to express again to them my grateful thanks.

It was intended to include a chapter on Hydraulic Power Plants in this edition, but I regret that this has not proved possible.

J. C.

London
September 1951

ACKNOWLEDGEMENTS

THE EDITOR AND THE PUBLISHERS wish to thank the following for kindly giving their permission for the reproduction of various diagrams, tables and extracts:

Professor A. Casagrande, Harvard.

Dr. O. L. Davies, Manchester.

Dr. Ian Fox, Cambridge.

Professor N. M. Newmark, Illinois.

Professor A. W. Skempton, Imperial College, London.

Professor K. Terzaghi, Harvard.

Thanks are also due to the following for their kind co-operation in making material available for reproduction:

American Association of State Highway Officials.

American Rail Engineering Association.

American Society of Civil Engineers, New York.

American Society for Testing Materials, Philadelphia.

Appleby-Frodingham Steel Company, Scunthorpe, Lincs.

Blackie & Son Limited, London and Glasgow.

British Cast Iron Research Association, Birmingham.

British Iron and Steel Federation, London.

British Road Tar Association, London.

Bullers Limited, Stoke-on-Trent, Staffs.

Canadian Standards Association, Ottawa.

Cement and Concrete Association, London.

Civil Engineering and Public Works Review, London.

Compressed Air Magazine, Phillipsburg, N.J.

Concrete Publications Limited, London.

Contractors' Record, London.

Department of Scientific and Industrial Research, Building Research Station, Watford, Herts.

Department of Scientific and Industrial Research, Road Research Laboratory, Harmondsworth, Middx.

Dorman, Long & Co. Limited, Middlesbrough, Yorks.

Edward Arnold Limited, London.

E. & F. N. Spon Limited.

E. J. Longyear Co., Minneapolis, Minn.

Electrical Research Association, Leatherhead, Surrey.

The Engineer, London.

English Electric Company Limited.

Federation of Manufacturers of Contractors' Plant, London.

Hercules Powder Co. Limited.

Hilger & Watts Limited, London.

Institution of Civil Engineers, London.

Institution of Structural Engineers, London.

James Williamson & Partners, Glasgow.

John Wiley & Sons Inc., New York.

Longmans Green & Co. Limited, London.

Ministry of Supply, Armaments Research Establishment, Sevenoaks, Kent.

Oliver & Boyd Limited, Edinburgh.

Pilkington Brothers Limited, St. Helens, Lancs.

Ruston-Bucyrus Limited, Lincoln.

Springer-Verlag, Vienna.

Water Power, London.

Vales Plant Register Limited, London.

W. F. Stanley & Co. Limited, London.

W. T. Henley's Telegraph Works Co. Limited, London.

The permission of the Controller of H.M. Stationery Office has been obtained for the reproduction of all material which is Crown copyright.

Extracts from the following British Standards are given by permission of the British Standards Institution, 2 Park Street, London, W.1, from whom full and official copies of these publications may be purchased:

B.S.153: Steel Girder Bridges. Part 3A: 1954, Loads. *Price 7s. 0d.* Parts 3B and 4: 1958, Stresses, Design and Construction. *Price 15s. 0d.*

B.S. 350: 1944. Conversion Factors and Tables. *Price 7s. 6d.*

B.S. 350, Part 1: 1959. Basis of Tables and Conversion Factors. *Price 15s. 0d.*

B.S. 449: 1959. The Structural Use of Steel in Buildings (incorporating B.S. CP 113). *Price 15s. 0d.*

B.S. 600: 1935. Application of Statistical Methods to Industrial Standardization and Quality Control by E. F. Pearson. *Price 17s. 6d.*

B.S. CP 111: 1948. Structural recommendations for Load-bearing Walls. *Price 7s. 6d.*

B.S. CP 112: 1952. The Stuctural Use of Timber in Buildings. *Price 10s. 6d.*

B.S. CP 114: 1957. The Structural Use of Reinforced Concrete in Buildings. *Price 10s.*

B.S. CP 115: 1959. The Structural Use of Prestressed Concrete in Buildings. *Price 8s. 6d.*

SOIL MECHANICS

H. Q. Golder, D.Eng., M.I.C.E. and A. C. Meigh, M.Sc., A.M.I.C.E.

SOIL PROPERTIES AND SOIL TESTING

POROSITY, DENSITY, WATER CONTENT

Definitions

ALL soils consist of solid particles assembled in a relatively open packing. The voids may be filled completely with water (fully saturated soils) or partly with water and partly with air (partially saturated soils).

The relationships between void space and the volume occupied by the particles are fundamental and are characterized by the following definitions.

$$\text{Porosity} \quad n = \frac{\text{volume of voids}}{\text{total volume of soil}}$$

$$\text{Voids ratio} \quad e = \frac{\text{volume of voids}}{\text{volume of soil particles}}$$

$$\text{Hence} \quad e = \frac{n}{1-n} \text{ and } n = \frac{e}{1+e} \qquad \dots\dots\dots(1)$$

$$\text{Degree of saturation} \quad S_r = \frac{\text{volume of water}}{\text{volume of voids}}$$

$$\text{Water content} \quad w = \frac{\text{weight of water}}{\text{weight of soil particles}}$$

Hence if G_s = specific gravity of soil particles

$$w = S_r \frac{e}{G_s}$$

For fully saturated soils $S_r = 1$ and $w = \frac{e}{G_s}$

$$\text{Bulk density} \quad \gamma = \frac{\text{total weight of soil}}{\text{total volume of soil}}$$

$$\text{Hence} \quad \gamma = \frac{G_s + S_r e}{1+e} \gamma_w \qquad \dots\dots\dots(2)$$

where γ_w = density of water = 62·4 lb/cu ft (1 g/cc)

$$\text{For fully saturated soils} \quad \gamma = \frac{G_s + e}{1+e} \gamma_w \qquad \dots\dots\dots(3)$$

$$\text{Dry density} \quad \gamma_d = \frac{\text{weight of soil particles}}{\text{total volume of soil}}$$

$$\text{Hence} \quad \gamma_d = \frac{G_s}{1+e} \gamma_w \qquad \dots\dots\dots(4)$$

$$\text{and} \quad \gamma_d = \frac{\gamma}{1+w} \qquad \dots\dots\dots(5)$$

1

$$\text{also} \quad n = 1 - \frac{1}{G_s} \cdot \frac{\gamma_d}{\gamma_w} \qquad \dots\dots\dots(6)$$

$$\text{and} \quad S_r = w \Big/ \left(\frac{\gamma_w}{\gamma_d} - \frac{1}{G_s} \right) \qquad \dots\dots\dots(7)$$

Submerged density, of soils below the water table

$$\gamma_s = \frac{G_s - 1}{1 + e} \gamma_w \qquad \dots\dots\dots(8)$$

Alternatively,

$$\gamma_s = \frac{\gamma (G_s - 1)}{G_s (1 + w)} \qquad \dots\dots\dots(9)$$

Percentage air voids $A = \dfrac{\text{volume of air}}{\text{total volume of soil}} \times 100$

$$A = 1 - \frac{\gamma_d}{\gamma_w} \left(\frac{1}{G_s} + w \right) \qquad \dots\dots\dots(10)$$

All the foregoing definitions and relationships are in constant use in soil mechanics problems.

Determination of water content

A sample of soil is weighed and then placed in a ventilated oven maintained at a temperature of 105 to 110°C until a constant weight is reached. 24 hours is usually sufficient. Water content = loss in weight/dry weight. Standard methods of determining water content are given in B.S. 1377[1].

The choice of 105 to 110°C as a drying temperature range is arbitrary, since at temperatures above this a higher moisture content results.

Determination of specific gravity

The specific gravity of soil particles smaller than $\frac{1}{4}$ in may be readily determined by the usual pycnometer method, as described in text books on elementary physics. With clays a non-polar liquid such as paraffin should be used and care must be taken to evacuate all air bubbles before filling the pycnometer bottle. The specific gravity of larger particles may be determined by direct volume displacement in a graduated measuring cylinder. Standard methods of determining specific gravity are described in B.S. 1377[1].

Determination of bulk density

In the laboratory, density is readily determined by measuring the volume of a known weight of soil. If in addition the water content is determined the dry density of the sample can immediately be calculated.

For cohesive soils the simplest method is to cut a specimen by pressing in a thin-walled metal cylinder and trimming the ends flush. The cylinder is then weighed and from its known weight and volume the density is found by direct calculation.

For sand samples which have been obtained in the compressed air sand sampler (see chapter on Site Investigation), the density is obtained by carefully trimming the ends (inside the sampler), measuring the length of the sample and pushing it out into a vessel, when its weight can be determined. In general, in laboratory tests on sands and gravel, density is calculated by using a known weight of material and measuring the volume which it occupies in the test apparatus.

In compaction tests the soil is rammed into a mould of known volume and weight, levelled off flush with the top of the mould and weighed.

It is often necessary to measure the density of soil *in situ* in the field. Several methods of doing this are described in B.S. 1377[1]. The two most important methods are the 'sand replacement method' and the 'core cutter method'.

In the sand replacement method a hole about 6 in diameter and 6 in deep is made in the soil whose density is to be determined and all the material taken from the hole is carefully kept and weighed. The volume of the hole is then determined by filling it with sand in a standard manner from a container holding a known weight of sand. The weight of sand required to fill the hole is obtained by difference, and the volume of this weight of sand is known by previous calibration of the sand and method of filling when used to fill standard containers. The method as described is applicable only to fine soils, but by suitable modification of the equipment it can also be used with coarse materials.

In the core cutter method, which is suitable for cohesive and non-stony soils only, a metal cylinder of known volume is forced into the soil and dug out. The soil is then trimmed off flush with the ends of the cylinder and the density determined as described above.

Recently radio-isotopes have been used for *in-situ* measurement of density, both at depth and at the surface. Either the back-scattering or the attenuation of gamma-rays is measured with a Geiger tube (CAMERON and BOURNE[3]). Water content can be measured by using a neutron source and a borontrifluoride proportional counter (GOLDBERG, TRESCONY, CAMPBELL and WHITE[4]).

Determination of porosity, voids ratio and degree of saturation

These properties are rarely measured directly but are deduced from the values for water content, bulk density and specific gravity, by means of the relationships already given.

CLASSIFICATION TESTS

Liquid and plastic limit, plasticity and liquidity indices

The liquid limit is that water content above which a soil behaves as a fluid. Obviously there will be a range of water content over which any soil will become gradually more fluid with increasing water content. Some point must be arbitrarily chosen as the liquid limit; that chosen in B.S. 1377[1], which is in agreement with the practice in most countries, is the water content at which twenty-five small standard shocks will close a standard groove for a length of $\frac{1}{2}$ in. For a description of the apparatus and method of test see AKROYD[2].

The plastic limit is that water content below which a soil ceases to behave in a plastic manner. A sample of the soil is dried by kneading it in the hand until, when rolled out under the palm on a sheet of glass to a thread of $\frac{1}{8}$ in diameter, the thread breaks up into short lengths. The water content is then determined. A repeat test is carried out and if the two results are close the mean water content is taken as the plastic limit. Although this test appears to be rather arbitrary, consistent results are soon obtained by an intelligent operator.

The difference between the liquid limit (L.L.) and the plastic limit (P.L.) is called the plasticity index (P.I.). The liquidity index (L.I.) is the ratio between the water content minus the plastic limit, and the plasticity index: thus

$$\text{L.I.} = \frac{w - \text{P.L.}}{\text{L.L.} - \text{P.L.}} = \frac{w - \text{P.L.}}{\text{P.I.}}$$

When the natural water content of a soil is equal to its liquid limit the L.I. is unity, and when the natural water content is equal to the plastic limit the L.I. is zero.

Activity

Another index property is the activity (SKEMPTON[5])

$$\text{Activity} = \frac{\text{P.I.}}{\mu}$$

where μ is the clay fraction content, *i.e.* the percentage by weight of material finer than $0\cdot002$ mm. Activity is related to the mineralogy and geological history of clays and to the proportion of their shear strength contributed by true cohesion. Experience has shown that difficulty in obtaining undisturbed samples from deep beds is restricted to clays with an activity less than $0\cdot75$.

Relative density, maximum and minimum densities

The classification tests already described apply to predominantly cohesive soils. For granular soils the significant index properties are the maximum and minimum densities. The maximum density, γ_{max}, is the highest dry density at which the soil can exist without a breakdown of the particles, and the minimum density, γ_{min} is the lowest possible dry density. The relative density, which is an important factor governing the strength of granular soils, is expressed as:

$$\text{R.D.} = \frac{\gamma - \gamma_{min}}{\gamma_{max} - \gamma_{min}}$$

Techniques for measurement of maximum and minimum density are discussed by KOLBUSZEWSKI[6].

Mechanical analysis

By mechanical analysis is meant the determination of the sizes of the particles composing a soil and the percentage of particles of a given size present. For particles larger than $0\cdot06$ mm, *i.e.* those particles which are retained by a No. 200 B.S. sieve ($0\cdot07$ mm mesh), the sizing is done by sieving through standard sieves. These sizes comprise the sands and gravels. For particles smaller than $0\cdot06$ mm, *i.e.* the silt and clay range, the sizing is done by measuring the settling velocity v of the particles in water and calculating the particle size from Stoke's law, the assumption being made that the particles are spherical. Stoke's law is

$$v = \frac{\gamma_s - \gamma_w}{18\eta} gD^2 \qquad \qquad \ldots\ldots\ldots\ldots(11)$$

where γ_s=density of soil particles, γ_w=density of liquid (water), $\eta=$ viscosity of liquid, $D=$diameter of the settling sphere, $g=$acceleration due to gravity.

Full details for carrying out the test are given in B.S. 1377[1]. The results are plotted as shown in *Figure 1*.

Shrinkage limit

When a saturated clay soil is allowed to dry out in air it shrinks. At first the loss in volume is equal to the volume of water lost by drying, but finally a point is reached at which the volume ceases to diminish although the weight continues to drop. The water content at which this occurs is called the shrinkage limit. The shrinkage limit is determined by cutting a regularly shaped sample of clay and determining its weight and volume at intervals, the sample being allowed to dry in

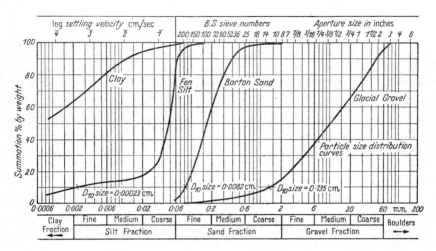

Figure 1. Particle size distribution curves (on standard sheet) showing D_{10} size (The D_{10} size is now given in millimetres)

air between the operations. Finally the sample is oven dried and its water content and dry weight determined. There is no standard shrinkage apparatus. In one type the volume of the sample is obtained by a displacement method using mercury and comparing the sample with a

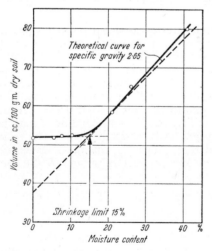

Figure 2. Results of shrinkage test for London clay; liquid limit 66 per cent, plastic limit 20 per cent

metal block of known volume. As the volume of the sample diminishes smaller metal blocks must be used for the comparison. The results are plotted as shown in *Figure 2* which also shows that most soils depart somewhat from the ideal case stated above.

TOTAL PRESSURE, PORE-PRESSURE
AND EFFECTIVE STRESS

Soil can be considered as a two-phase system consisting of a solid phase, the skeleton of soil particles, and a fluid phase, water plus air in a partially saturated soil and water alone in a saturated soil. It follows that the normal stress across a plane within a soil mass will have two components, an intergranular pressure, known as the effective pressure or effective stress (σ') and a fluid pressure, known as the pore pressure or neutral pressure (u). The sum of these will constitute the total normal stress. The volume change characteristics and the strength of a soil are controlled by the effective stress, the pore pressure being significant only in so far as it determines the magnitude of the effective stress for a given total stress.

The simplest illustration of pore pressure and effective stress is given by consideration of the vertical stresses acting on a horizontal plane at depth h under equilibrium conditions with a horizontal water table. The total vertical stress (σ) is given by the weight per unit area of soil and water above the plane

$$\sigma = h\gamma = h \frac{G_s + se}{1+e} \gamma_w$$

The pore pressure will be the water pressure, and if the plane is at a depth h_w below the water table then

$$u = h_w \gamma_w$$

The effective vertical stress is the difference between these:

$$\sigma' = \sigma - u \qquad \ldots\ldots\ldots(12)$$

It should be noted that for positions below the water table the vertical effective stress can also be calculated from the total weight per unit area of material above the water table plus the submerged weight of the material below the water table.

A change in total stresses arising from a change in external loading conditions will give rise to a change in pore-pressure (Δu). The excess pore pressure, positive or negative, will dissipate with time, the rate at which equilibrium pore-pressure conditions are re-established being governed by the permeability of the soil. In coarse-grained granular soils such equilibrium conditions will be achieved immediately and changes in effective stress are equal to changes in total stress. At the other limit, with clays of low permeability, equilibrium conditions may take a considerable time, up to tens of years, to be re-established. The relation between pore-pressure change and the change in principal stresses can be expressed by the use of pore pressure parameters A and B (SKEMPTON[7]). The basic relationship is

$$\Delta u = B [\Delta\sigma_3 + A (\Delta\sigma_1 - \Delta\sigma_3)] \qquad \ldots\ldots\ldots(13)$$

where σ_1 = major principal stress
and σ_3 = minor principal stress.

It is also useful to relate the pore pressure change to the change in deviator stress ($\Delta\sigma_1 - \Delta\sigma_3$) alone and also to the change in the major principal stress ($\Delta\sigma_1$). For these purposes two further parameters $\bar{A}$ and $\bar{B}$ are used as follows:

$$\Delta u = B\Delta\sigma_3 + \bar{A} (\Delta\sigma_1 - \Delta\sigma_3) \qquad \ldots\ldots\ldots(14)$$

$$\Delta u = \bar{B}\Delta\sigma_1 \qquad \ldots\ldots\ldots(15)$$

If the soil structure behaved in an elastic manner the values of the pore pressures could be established theoretically, *e.g. A* would have a value of $\frac{1}{3}$. However, soils behave non-elastically and *A* can have values ranging between $+1\cdot3$ and $-0\cdot7$ (values at failure in a triaxial compression test). Typical values of the pore pressure parameters are given by BISHOP and HENKEL[8]. For a full discussion of the parameters see SKEMPTON[7] and SKEMPTON and BISHOP[9].

PERMEABILITY

Definition
Permeability is that property of a soil which controls the rate of flow of water through the soil. In soil mechanics permeability is defined by the equation (Darcy's law):

$$v = ki \qquad \qquad \dots\dots\dots(16)$$

where *v* is the superficial velocity of flow through the soil, *i* is the hydraulic gradient and *k* is the permeability; *k* therefore has the dimensions of a velocity.

Hazen's law
Typical values of permeability for soils range from 1×10^{-1} cm/sec for a coarse sand to 1×10^{-7} cm/sec for a clay. A very rough estimate of permeability can be obtained for sand from Hazen's law

$$k = D_{10}{}^2$$

where $D_{10} =$ the 10 per cent size or effective size in mm and *k* is in cm/sec.
The 10 per cent size or effective size is the particle size at which the grading curve crosses the 10 per cent line (see *Figure 1*).

Kozeny's formula and Loudon's formula
Research by LOUDON[10] has shown that the permeability of clean sand may be computed from simple soil tests, using Kozeny's formula, with an accuracy of ± 20 per cent

$$kS^2 = 1\cdot5 \times 10^{-4} \frac{n^3}{(1-n)^2} \quad \text{(c.g.s. units)} \quad \dots\dots\dots(17)$$

He suggests an alternative formula which is easier to use and of equal accuracy:

$$\log_{10}(kS^2) = 1\cdot365 + 5\cdot15n \qquad \qquad \dots\dots\dots(18)$$

In both of these formulae $n =$ porosity and *S* denotes specific surface:

$$S = f(x_1 S_1 + x_2 S_2 + \dots \dots x_n S_n) \qquad \qquad \dots\dots\dots(19)$$

where *f* is an angularity factor, varying between $1\cdot1$ for a rounded sand and $1\cdot4$ for an angular sand

$x_1, x_2, \dots =$ fraction in each sieve range
and $S_1, S_2, \dots =$ specific surface for each sieve range; from Loudon's tables.

Measurement of permeability
Permeability is measured in an apparatus known as a permeameter. Two forms are in general use, the falling head permeameter and the constant head permeameter. In general the falling head type is used for soils with relatively low permeability, and the constant head type for soils with high permeability.
It should be remembered that in the ground the horizontal permeability may be very different from (generally higher than) the vertical

permeability. Lamination, or arrangement of the soil particles, which is almost invisible to the naked eye, may multiply the permeability by ten or more. Laboratory measurements should be used with caution in making calculations and should be looked upon as an estimate giving only the order of the permeability. For methods of carrying out permeability tests, see TAYLOR[11], p 101.

SHEAR STRENGTH

Theory of shear strength

Shear strength of a soil is commonly thought of as having two components, cohesion and frictional resistance. Clays are often described as cohesive soils in which the shear strength or cohesion is independent of applied stresses, and sands and gravels are described as non-cohesive or frictional soils in which the shearing resistance along any plane is directly proportional to the normal stress across that plane

$$s = p \tan \phi$$

where ϕ is the 'angle of internal friction.'

The concepts of cohesion and friction were combined in Coulomb's equation for the shear strength of the soil

$$s = c + p \tan \phi \qquad \dots\dots\dots\dots(20)$$

where c = cohesion.

Such simple concepts are, however, inadequate to deal with the complex problem of the shear strength of soils. The early history of the study of shear strength is somewhat confused. Attempts were made to represent the shear strength of a soil by the envelope to a Mohr circle diagram of stress (TAYLOR[11]), the intercept on the vertical axis being taken as cohesion c, and the slope of the envelope being taken as the friction angle ϕ. It was found that except in sands and gravels the results for a given soil varied considerably depending on the test procedure used, particularly the rate of testing and the conditions of drainage of the specimens during test. However, following the realization that the strength of a soil is governed by the effective stress, it was possible to achieve a better understanding of the shear strength characteristics of soils. The shear strength can be expressed as:

$$\tau_f = c' + (\sigma - u) \tan \phi' \qquad \dots\dots\dots\dots(21)$$

where c' and ϕ' are effective stress parameters;

c' = apparent cohesion;

ϕ' = angle of shearing resistance.

The Mohr circle diagram can be plotted in terms of effective stress, with c' as the cohesion intercept and ϕ' as the slope of the envelope (*Figure 3*). It is worth noting that c' and ϕ' are basically nothing more than para-

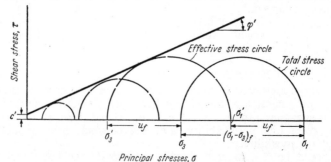

Figure 3. Mohr circle diagram (from SKEMPTON[16]*)*

meters as defined by the envelope of the Mohr circle diagram plotted against effective stress. They do not represent the true cohesion and angle of internal friction of a soil. For a detailed study of true cohesion and angle of internal friction reference should be made to HVORSLEV[12], GIBSON[13] and others. For practical purposes the effective stress parameters, and in some cases the total stress parameters (see below), are sufficient.

Triaxial compression tests
The apparatus generally used for measuring the shear strength of soils is the triaxial compression apparatus, *Figure 4*.

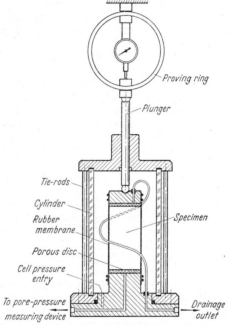

Figure 4. Apparatus for triaxial compression test

In this test a cylindrical specimen of soil is enclosed in a watertight rubber membrane. The specimen is contained within a chamber, the triaxial cell, in which a fluid can be placed under pressure. An axial load is applied at a constant rate of strain by means of a plunger passing vertically through the top of the cell. In normal testing procedures the stress applied by the plunger is the major principal stress (σ_1) and the cell pressure is the minor principal stress σ_3 (the intermediate principal stress $\sigma_2 = \sigma_3$). The value $\sigma_1 - \sigma_3$ is known as the deviator stress, and the value of $\sigma_1 - \sigma_3$ at failure $(\sigma_1 - \sigma_3)_f$ is the diameter of the Mohr circle at failure (*Figure 3*). Density and moisture content are also measured as part of the test procedure, and the stress–strain modulus, E, is obtained from the initial tangent modulus to the stress–strain curve.

Connections to the top and bottom of the sample can be made. One of these is used to control the drainage of the specimen and the other can be connected to the pore pressure measurement device. Two standard sizes of specimen are used, 3 in long × 1½ in diameter and 8 in long × 4 in diameter. Cell pressures are usually up to 120 lb/sq in but higher pressures of up to 1,000 lb/sq in (70 kg/cm²) have been used for the testing of soft rocks and soil–cement specimens (GOLDER and AKROYD[14]).

Three standard test procedures, differing in the drainage conditions which apply are discussed below. For a further description of these tests, and of a number of special tests which can be made in the triaxial apparatus, reference should be made to BISHOP and HENKEL[8].

1. Drained tests—Drainage is allowed throughout the test, and the rate of test is sufficiently slow to ensure that full dissipation of excess pore pressure occurs. The results are plotted in terms of effective stresses (in this case equal to total stresses); the terms c_d and ϕ_d are sometimes used in place of c' and ϕ' in describing the results of these tests.

2. Undrained tests—No drainage is allowed. The results are plotted in terms of total stresses and the parameters are denoted as c_u and ϕ_u. For saturated soils the undrained angle of shearing resistance, ϕ_u, is zero and the apparent cohesion c_u is equal to half the deviator stress. The undrained shear strength c_u is useful in many practical problems, particularly in estimating bearing capacity of clays and in stability analyses for conditions in which no change in pore pressure can take place. This method of analysis is known as the $\phi = 0$ method.

If pore pressures are measured during the test the Mohr circle diagram can be plotted in terms of effective stress and for non-saturated soils the effective-stress parameters can be determined. In addition the pore-pressure measured on application of the cell pressure gives the value of the parameter B, and the value A can be obtained from the pore pressure change during application of the deviator stress. For saturated soils, however, the Mohr circles will be coincident since the change in pore pressure will be equal to the change in cell pressure and the effective stress parameters cannot be determined.

3. Consolidated-undrained tests—In this test the cell pressure is applied and drainage is allowed until the excess pore pressures set up by the application of the cell pressure have dissipated. The deviator stress is then applied without allowing further drainage. If the results are plotted in terms of total stresses the consolidated undrained shear strength parameters c_{cu}, ϕ_{cu} are obtained. These have limited use in practice. If pore pressures are measured during the second stage of the test the results can be plotted in terms of effective stress, and the effective stress shear strength parameters c', ϕ' are obtained. This test is often used in preference to the drained test since it generally requires less time and the results are, for practical purposes, the same.

Unconfined compression test

This test is a particular case of the triaxial test in which the cell pressure is zero. The apparatus is very simple and can be used in the field or the laboratory (COOLING and GOLDER[15]). It can only be used for clay soils. Only one test is done on each sample and the shear strength is assumed to be half the compression strength.

Box shear test

For determining the angle of shearing resistance of free draining granular soils a box shear test is often used. It is also used on some occasions for drained tests on cohesive soils. The sample is contained in a box split horizontally in which the bottom of the box can be moved relative to the top, thus shearing the sample along a horizontal plane. A vertical load is applied to the sample by means of a weighted hanger and a lever arm system.

Sufficient tests (usually four) are carried out under different vertical loads and the results are plotted as shear stress against normal pressure. The cohesion is taken as the intercept of the shear stress axis and the angle of shearing resistance is obtained from the slope of the plot.

Typical shear strength values

Clays fall into two main groups, normally consolidated clays, those which have not been subjected to loads greater than their present overburden pressure, and overconsolidated clays, which have been loaded above their present overburden pressure by the weight of material since eroded away, by ice loading, by desiccation or lowering of the ground water level, or otherwise.

In deposits of normally consolidated clays shear strength increases linearly with depth, although in many cases there is a 'crust' of material which has been subject to drying. The ratio of the undrained shear strength to the effective overburden pressure in a normally consolidated clay $(c/p)_n$ can be related to the liquid limit (SKEMPTON[16]) as shown in *Figure 5*.

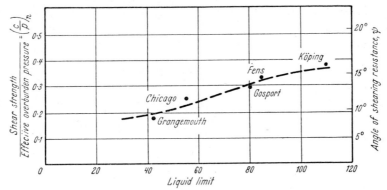

Figure 5. Relation between liquid limit and $(c/p)_n$ for five normally consolidated clay strata

Typically the normally consolidated post-glacial estuarine and marine clays of Great Britain have shear strength values between 150 and 600 lb/sq ft. An example of overconsolidated clay is the London clay. Where the blue London clay occurs below the Thames flood plain gravel it has typically a strength at its upper surface of some 1,500 lb/sq ft, increasing to about 6,000 lb/sq ft at about 90 ft below ground level. Where the blue London clay is overlain by weathered London clay (a brown clay) it has a higher shear strength at its upper surface, usually some 2,500–3,000 lb/sq ft, and at the upper surface of the brown clay the shear strength falls often to about 1,000 lb/sq ft (0·49 kg/sq cm).

CONSOLIDATION

Theory of consolidation

The ultimate change in volume of a soil occurring under a change in applied stress depends on the compressibility of the skeleton of soil particles. However, the water in the voids of a saturated soil is relatively incompressible, and, if no drainage takes place, change in applied stress results in a corresponding change in pore pressure, and the volume change is negligible. As drainage takes place by flow of water from zones of high excess pore pressure to zones of less or zero excess pore pressure, and the excess pore pressures dissipate, the applied stress is transferred to the soil skeleton and volume change takes place. It is this volume change of cohesive soils resulting from dissipation of excess pore pressures which is known as consolidation.

A study of consolidation requires knowledge of the compressibility of the soil skeleton and of the rate at which excess pore pressures dissipate, which is related to the permeability. In Terzaghi's consolidation theory the relation between these factors can be expressed for the one dimensional case as

$$c_v \frac{\partial^2 u}{\partial z^2} = \frac{\partial u}{\partial t}$$

..........(22)

where c_v is a coefficient of consolidation

given by $c_v = \dfrac{k}{m_v \gamma_w}$

..........(23)

u = pressure in pore water
z = thickness of stratum
t = time

and m_v is the modulus of compressibility

given by $m_v = -\dfrac{de}{dp} \cdot \dfrac{1}{1+e}$

..........(24)

where e = voids ratio, and p = effective pressure.

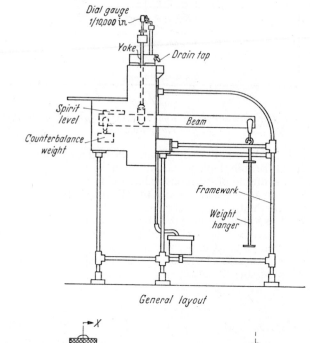

General layout

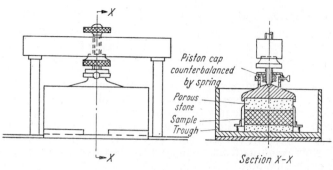

Consolidation pot and floating ring
Figure 6. Oedometer (consolidation) press (from AKROYD[2])

The solution of the consolidation equation has been given by TERZAGHI and FRÖHLICH[17] and values have been tabulated for the degree of consolidation U against the time factor T, where

$$T = \frac{c_v t}{H^2}$$

............(25)

and $H=$ length of drainage path (see p 59)

Values of c_v and m_v are determined by laboratory tests known as oedometer tests or consolidation tests.

Consolidation test

The consolidation test is carried out on clays and silts only. The samples are usually undisturbed, but cases can arise in which tests on remoulded soils are required (*e.g.* assessing the consolidation characteristics of fill for an earth dam). The purpose of the test is to obtain the pressure/voids ratio curve and the coefficient of consolidation for the soil in question. The apparatus is shown in *Figure 6*. The modulus of compressibility, m_v is obtained from the p/e curve (*Figure 7*).

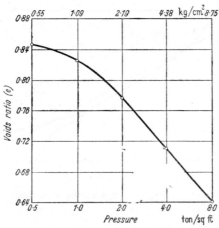

Figure 7. Results of consolidation test:
p/e curve

In the test a specimen contained in a ring, usually 3 in diameter and 2 cm long, is loaded axially between 2 porous discs. In the 'floating ring' apparatus the specimen is tested in the thin-walled sampling ring, which is supported, cutting edge upwards, by 3 lugs on 3 springs. In the older 'fixed ring' apparatus the specimen is extruded from the sampling ring into the thick-walled testing ring.

For a given load increment the settlement with time is measured. When movement has ceased, or virtually ceased, the load is increased and settlement with time is again measured. This is repeated several times until the pressures are greater than any likely to be applied to the soil in the practical problem. Finally the water content of the sample is determined. The initial water content is measured on pieces of soil adjacent to the sample and acts as a check on the calculations.

The pressure/voids ratio curve (*p/e* curve) is calculated by working backwards from the final water content to the equilibrium position under each load. The specific gravity of the soil particles must be known, and the assumption made that the soil is saturated. Then, by means of the relationships given on p 1 the change in voids ratio corresponding to the observed settlement under each load increment can be calculated, and hence the *p/e* curve drawn (*Figure 7*).

The coefficient of consolidation c_v which determines the rate at which settlement occurs is calculated for each load increment and either a mean value is used or that value appropriate to the pressure range in question.

c_v is measured in sq cm/min or sq ft/year. If the deformation under load is plotted against the square root of time, the curve will be a straight line up to about the point of 50 per cent consolidation, and from the slope of this line the value of c_v can be determined, from equation (25), putting a value of 0·848 for T at 90 per cent consolidation,

$$c_v = \frac{0\cdot848H^2}{t_{90}} \text{ sq cm/min} \qquad \ldots\ldots(26)$$

where t_{90} = time in minutes to 90 per cent consolidation,

H = length of drainage path = $\frac{1}{2}$ thickness of sample in cm.

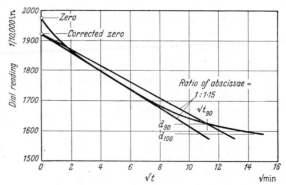

Figure 8.   Time–settlement curve for consolidation test. Square root fitting method

A construction to determine t_{90} is given in *Figure 8* (TAYLOR[11]). In some cases it is preferable to plot time on a log basis, and the construction, in this case to determine t_{100}, is shown in *Figure 9*.

A phenomenon known as the 'secondary time effect' must be taken into account in some cases, but for details of this reference must be made to a textbook on soil mechanics (TERZAGHI and PECK[18] p 75).

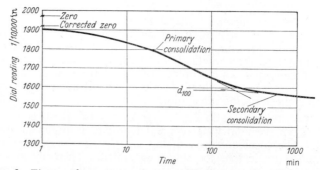

Figure 9.   Time–settlement curve for consolidation test. Log fitting method

PORE-PRESSURE DISSIPATION

For settlement problems the indirect measurement of rate of dissipation obtained from the oedometer test is adequate. For some other problems, however, particularly those involving stability calculations in which strength, and hence the factor of safety, is dependent on the magnitude of the pore pressures, it is important to have a more direct measurement of the pore pressure/time relationship.

In the pore-pressure dissipation test the rate of dissipation is measured directly. A sample is set up as for a triaxial compression test with porous discs at each end. The top disc is connected to an external drainage tube and the bottom disc is connected to a pore-pressure measuring device. For a given cell pressure the pore pressure in the sample is allowed to reach a steady state with the drainage connection shut off. The connection is then opened and the rate of dissipation of the pore pressure is measured. The consolidation coefficient c_v is calculated using the relation

$$T = \frac{c_v t}{H^2}$$

where H is the drainage path (in this case the length of the specimen), t is the time to a given degree of consolidation (usually taken as 50 per cent consolidation), and T is the time factor.

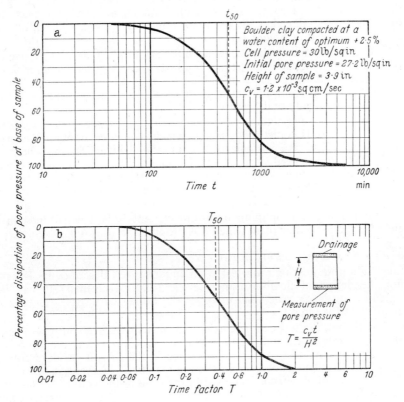

Figure 10. Dissipation test. (a) Percentage dissipation of pore pressure plotted against the logarithm of time for a sample of boulder clay compacted 2½ per cent above the optimum water content. (b) Theoretical relationship between percentage dissipation of pore pressure at base of sample and logarithm of time factor T (from BISHOP and HENKEL[8])

T is evaluated from the theoretical relationship between the time factor and degree of consolidation *U*, from Terzaghi's consolidation theory, as shown in *Figure 10*.

COMPACTION, CALIFORNIA BEARING RATIO, AND
MODULUS OF SUB-GRADE REACTION

Certain other soil properties and the corresponding tests must be considered in relation to problems which arise in the construction of earth dams, roads and runways.

Compaction

When soil is used as a constructional material in earth dams and the base courses and sub-grades of roads and runways it is important to ensure that it is placed in as compact a condition as possible in order to obtain high strength, and a minimum of softening and settlement.

A standard test originally known as the Proctor test and now known in Great Britain as the British standard compaction test is used to determine the compaction characteristics of soils. This test is fully described in B.S. 1377[1].

The test is carried out by compacting the soil in a mould in the standard manner at several different moisture contents and recording the density obtained at each. The moisture content at which the maximum dry density is obtained is the optimum moisture content. The results are plotted as shown in *Figure 11*.

The optimum moisture content and maximum dry density as given by the standard compaction test are looked upon by some authorities as classification tests rather than values to be used in the field. This is because for a different amount of work used in the test the values of these properties obtained are different.

For heavy compaction, particularly with well-graded non-plastic soil, a modified test is sometimes used in which a greater amount of work is employed. This is particularly so in the United States where the A.A.S.H.O. test is used since the results obtained have been found to agree better with the field results on dry soils using the heavy compacting equipment available in that country. There is no British Standard corresponding to this heavier test.

In practice, the optimum moisture content is best determined in the field for the particular plant which it is proposed to use (WILLIAMS[19]).

California bearing ratio (C.B.R.)

The California bearing ratio test is an empirical test described by PORTER[20] for the design of flexible or non-tensile road pavements. It has been extended by large scale tests to cover the design of flexible runways and taxi-tracks for aircraft.

Although the test can be carried out on undisturbed soil it is generally done on compacted soil. The soil is compacted into a mould of 6 in diameter in a manner similar to that used in the British standard compaction test described above, or in the manner used in the A.A.S.H.O. test, but the amount of work is increased in the ratio of the volume of the mould for each of these tests. In its original form the soil was compacted under a static pressure of 2,000 lb/sq in but as this method requires a heavy press it is not used much now.

After compaction a circular plunger of 3 sq in area is forced into the soil (*Figure 12*) at a steady rate of 0·05 in per minute until a penetration of about ¼ in has been obtained. The pressure at various depths of penetration is recorded. The pressure corresponding to a penetration of 0·1 in is read off and is expressed as a percentage of the standard pressure for a material having a C.B.R. of 100 which is defined as 1,000 lb/sq in (70·3 kg/sq cm). The value for a penetration of 0·2 in is also read off and expressed as a percentage of 1,500 lb/sq in (105·5 kg/sq cm). The larger of these two values is taken as the C.B.R. for the soil after confirming the latter value by a repeat test as shown in the following example.

Example—The following tables show the test results on two samples A and B and a repeat on sample B.

Sample A

Time in minutes	zero	1	2	4	6	8	10
Penetration in	0	0·05	0·1	0·2	0·3	0·4	0·5
Load lb	0	193	304	425	498	551	590
C.B.R. per cent	0	—	10·1	9·4	—	—	—

Sample B

Time in minutes	zero	1	2	4	6	8	10
Penetration in	0	0·05	0·1	0·2	0·3	0·4	0·5
Load lb	0	169	358	672	793	884	968
C.B.R. per cent	0	—	11·9	14·9	—	—	—

Sample B (repeat)

Time in minutes	zero	1	2	4	6	8	10
Penetration in	0	0·05	0·1	0·2	0·3	0·4	0·5
Load lb	0	190	366	680	882	980	1,050
C.B.R. per cent	0	—	12·2	15·1	—	—	—

The results are shown plotted against standard C.B.R. percentage curves in *Figure 13*.

The test can be carried out either on the dry soil as compacted or after the soil has been soaked. This latter test is advisable if there is any possibility of the soil on the actual job soaking up water from the water table, or being subjected to heavy rains.

To carry out the soaked test a circular 10 lb weight is placed on top of the sample as a surcharge, and the mould is then placed under water for four days. The expansion of the surface is measured and this is expressed as a percentage of the height of the sample. After four days' soaking the plunger penetration test is carried out as described above, the plunger operating through a suitable circular hole in the centre of the surcharge weight.

Modulus of sub-grade reaction

The design of concrete slabs for airfield runways is usually based on WESTERGAARD'S analysis[21] in which the sub-grade reaction is assumed to be proportional to the vertical deflection. The modulus of sub-grade reaction is measured by a plate loading test in the field. If under a pressure p the plate settles an amount ρ then

$$p = k_s \rho \qquad \qquad \dots \dots \dots (27)$$

where k_s = modulus of sub-grade reaction.

From elastic theory and field bearing tests it is known that k_s has no unique value but depends on the size of the loaded area.

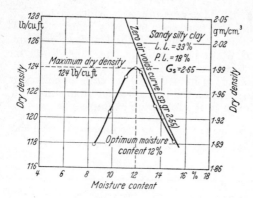

Figure 11. Results of standard compaction test

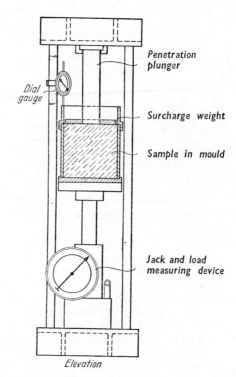

Figure 12. Diagram of California bearing ratio test apparatus

Penetration plunger

Dial gauge

Surcharge weight

Sample in mould

Jack and load measuring device

Elevation

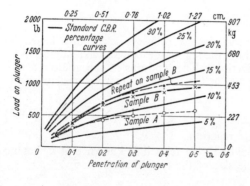

Figure 13. Results of California bearing ratio tests: sample A 10 per cent, sample B 15 per cent, sample B repeat 15 per cent

For roads, 12 in diameter plates are usually used for the test and for runways 30 in diameter plates are used.   When it is impossible to use the larger size a correction can be applied to the results of tests on the smaller plate (STRATTON[22]).   A graph giving this correction is contained in *Figure 14*.

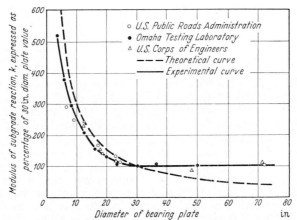

Figure 14.   Relation between modulus of sub-grade reaction and diameter of bearing plate

The test is carried out on the surface of the soil by bedding the plate carefully, using fine sand or plaster of Paris.   The plate is then loaded to 10 lb/sq in (0·7 kg/sq cm) and the settlement is measured. k_s is then equal to $10/\rho$ lb/cu in.

Alternatively, pressure–settlement readings are taken at intervals up to a total settlement of at least 0·07 in.   The pressure in lb/sq in causing a settlement of 0·05 in is then found from the settlement–pressure graph and the value of k_s is obtained from the expression

$$k_s = \frac{p}{0·05} \text{ lb/cu in}$$

To allow for the effect of possible future softening of the sub-grade the U.S. Corps of Engineers[23] recommend that the value of k_s should be corrected as follows.   Two consolidation tests are carried out on samples of the soil, *i* in the condition in which it was loaded, *ii* after soaking under a surcharge pressure equal to the weight of the slab. A pressure of 10 lb/sq in is then applied to each sample, and if the compression of the soaked and unsoaked samples after consolidation are s, and s respectively, the corrected sub-grade modulus is taken to be

$$k_s' = k_s \frac{s}{s_s}$$

...........(28)

STABILITY OF SLOPES

Angle of repose
The problem of the stability of earth slopes has traditionally been approached by the concept of an ' angle of repose ' for the material, in spite of the fact that both experience and some of the earliest work on soil mechanics (COULOMB[24], 1773, FRANÇAIS[25], 1820) showed this to be untrue for cohesive soils.   The application of elegant mathematical solutions to problems in the 19th century, based on the assumption of

an ideal material, led to the assumption that cohesion was non-existent or should be ignored, and that soils had an angle of repose which was the same as their angle of internal friction (assumed constant) and that at this angle a slope would be stable to any height. For clean dry, or clean submerged sands this conception is true, with the qualification that the angle of repose is equal to the lower limit of the angle of internal friction. For cohesive soils, however, the limiting slope is a function of the height of the bank and of time.

Frictional soils

The angle of repose of a frictional soil can be found by (a) observations in the field on existing slopes; (b) laboratory tests—the lower limit of the angle of internal friction; (c) pouring a heap of dry sand from a funnel on to a level surface and measuring the angle of slope.

If a slope is cut or built in a dry frictional soil it should be stable provided that the inclination is less than the angle of repose. Failure of a bank in frictional soil is generally due to the effects of water. For example, seepage through a bank can cause erosion, pore-water pressures due to seepage pressures or arising from sudden drawdown of external water level, give rise to a reduction in effective stress which may lead to failure, and vibration of a loose fine saturated sand can result in a flow slide. Shallow surface troubles are common in these slopes, deep-seated shear slides being due either to sudden drawdown or to heavy external loads applied at the top of the bank. These conditions can be analysed by the circular arc method using the graphical method of slices (see p 21). For simple conditions the ϕ circle method can be used.

Cohesive soils

In cohesive soils, slope and height are interdependent and can only be determined when the shear characteristics of the material are known. In such soils failure usually occurs along curved surfaces of rupture which approximate to cylindrical surfaces, and one method of analysis used is called the circular arc method.

Circular arc method

In principle the method is very simple. An arc is chosen and moments are taken about its centre of the disturbing forces (weight) and the resisting

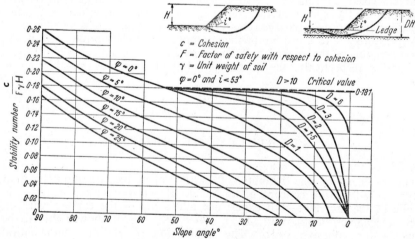

Figure 15. Taylor's curves

forces (strengths). The factor of safety=moments of resisting forces/ moment of disturbing forces. A search is made for the most dangerous circle *i.e.* the one with the lowest factor of safety. This is the factor of safety of the slope. For steep slopes the worst circle goes through the toe; for flatter slopes it goes below the toe, and tends to go as deep as possible, unless shear strength increases rapidly with depth.

Two main cases arise which are known as $\phi = 0$ and c', ϕ' cases.

$\phi = 0$ *case*—In this case the soil is assumed to have a shear strength s which remains constant during the calculation, and the angle of shearing resistance is assumed to be equal to zero. This case applies for 'end of construction' conditions.

c', ϕ' *case*—In this case the soil is assumed to have both friction and cohesion and the effective-stress shear-strength parameters, c' and ϕ' are used. This case represents the conditions for long-term stability. The analysis is known as an effective-stress analysis.

For an analytical solution for simple cases see *Figure 15*, Taylor's curves[11] including the effect of depth factor. For cases in which irregular slope outlines or external loads occur the graphical method must be used, a search being made for the worst circle. The position of this circle is not critical and the work is not onerous. In *Figure 16*, which shows a typical calculation for the $\phi = 0$ case, the factor of safety F is given by the equation

$$F = \frac{slR}{Wd} \qquad \qquad \ldots\ldots\ldots\ldots(29)$$

where W=weight of soil, l=length of arc, s=shear strength.

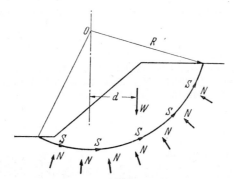

Figure 16. Circular arc method of analysis for cohesive soil ($\phi = 0$)

The reactions across the arc, N, are normal to the surface of rupture (since $\phi = 0$) and therefore have no moment about the centre of the circle.

Method of slices

The above simple method cannot be applied to an effective-stress analysis since the N forces, although they still pass through the centre of the circle, determine the value of the frictional resistance along the surface of rupture which must be included in the moment equation. The wedge of earth bounded by the arc of rupture is divided into vertical slices and the assumption is made that the normal force across the arc is equal to the weight of the slice resolved normally to the arc. The forces between the slices are neglected. In Bishop's improved method these forces are taken into account (BISHOP[26]).

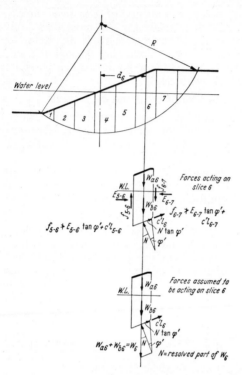

Figure 17. Conventional circular arc method (effective stress analysis)

The forces acting on one slice are then as shown in *Figure 17*, where W_{a6}=weight of slice *6* above water level, W_{b6}=weight of slice *6* below water level, E_{5-6}=normal forces between slices *5* and *6*, f_{5-6}=tangential force between slices *5* and *6*. N=normal reaction at base of slice *6*, l_6=length of arc at base of slice, d_6=lever arm for slice *6*. For slice *6* the disturbing moment=$W_6 . d_6$ and the resisting moment=$(N \tan \phi' + c'l_6) R$. The moments of all these forces about the centre of the arc are calculated and summed for all the slices. The factor of safety is as before,

$$F = \frac{Moment\ of\ resisting\ forces}{Moment\ of\ disturbing\ forces}$$

and for whole bank, ignoring E and f forces, and assuming no excess pore pressures exist,

$$F = \frac{\Sigma (N \tan \phi' + c'l) R}{\Sigma Wd} \qquad ....(30)$$

where c' and ϕ' are the effective-stress shear-strength parameters of the soil. The worst circle must be found by trial and error.

Tension cracks

In a soil possessing cohesion, tension cracks can form and so reduce the length of the arc around which shear strength is resisting the disturbing forces. This should be taken into account in the analysis. The depth z_e to which tension exists in the soil is theoretically

$$z_c = \frac{2\ c}{\gamma}$$

in a purely cohesive soil and

$$z_c = \frac{2\ c}{\gamma} \frac{\cos \phi}{1 - \sin \phi}$$

$\left.\begin{array}{c} \\ \\ \\ \\ \end{array}\right\}$ ....(31)

in a soil possessing both friction and cohesion.

The above formulae can lead to values of the depth of tension crack which are much greater than any observed in the field and in practice a maximum depth of tension crack of 5 to 10 ft is used in analysis.

Water level and drawdown

In using these methods of analysis the weight of the soil below water is reduced by hydrostatic uplift *i.e.* the submerged weight is used even in clay soils. Water pressures do not then enter into the calculation. If this is not done the water pressure must be added to the surface of the bank and its moment must be taken into account in the stability equation. If the water level is part-way up the slope and is suddenly lowered, then the weight of the soil is increased immediately, either to the full saturated weight or to the weight in air, depending on how quickly the soil drains.

But the shear resistance of the soil only increases as the effective pressure increases and with a fine grained soil this may take some considerable time. Therefore the condition may arise in which the weights (disturbing forces) are approximately doubled, while the shear resistance is not increased, thus resulting in a considerable drop in factor of safety and sometimes causing failure. This condition should always be checked in both frictional and cohesive soils, if there is any possibility of water level variation. The conditions of sudden complete drawdown are worse than those for any seepage forces which can occur.

Non-homogeneous banks

The circular arc method is fairly accurate for homogeneous material. Where zones of weaker material occur, however, the slip surface will tend to depart from the circular form and pass through the weaker material. In such cases composite slip surfaces consisting of arcs of two circles of different radii, or of a combination of circular arcs and straight lines, can be used (COOLING and GOLDER[27]).

Simplifying assumptions must be made to ensure that the problem is soluble. A reasonable assumption is that the force acting between any two portions of the slip surface acts either at the lower third point or halfway up the height of the bank at this point, and is normal to the common radius. Moments must be taken for each section separately about its own centre, the effect of the adjacent section being included as an external force. It is important that c and $\tan \phi$ wherever they occur should be divided by F, the factor of safety, and that finally an equation should be obtained which is solved for F. Any attempt to introduce F into the equation for the last section only will give results which are in error.

In Figure 18, W_1=weight on earth in circle I, d_1=lever arm of W_1 about 0_1, $s_1=$ shear strength of soil round circle I, L_1=length of arc of circle I. *Similarly for* circle with suffix 2. The factor of safety F is obtained from the equation

$$\frac{s_2}{F} L_2 R_2 = W_2 d_2 + \frac{a_2}{a_1}\left(W_1 d_1 - \frac{s_1}{F} L_1 R_1\right) \qquad \dots \dots \dots \dots (32)$$

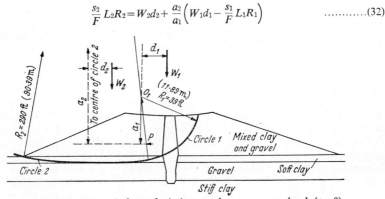

Figure 18. *Two-circle analysis for non-homogeneous bank* $(\phi = 0)$

Stiff-fissured clays

The above methods of analysis are not directly applicable to stiff-fissured clays. Any excavation in these materials allows the fissures to open. Water then penetrates these fissures, causing softening, which gradually increases in extent. Although the cut is stable when made, the factor of safety drops with time until failure occurs, often many years after the cut was first made. For temporary works cuts can often be left very steep, say 45–60 deg but adequate drainage should be provided and the surface of the slope and the ground above the cut should be protected with waterproof material. All heavy loads should be kept away from the top of the cut. A further safeguard is to provide tell-tales to indicate when horizontal or vertical movement of the top or bottom of the cut begins to take place. For permanent work the best measure is to carry out a c', ϕ' analysis using the effective-stress shear-strength parameters in conjunction with effective stresses. This means that the ground water surface in the clay must be known (see HENKEL[28]). Further measures to delay the softening effect referred to above can include grouting of the fissures with an aerated cement grout, which has proved effective in some cases.

Flow slides

Not all slides are deep-seated shear slides. For a classification of land slides see WARD[29]. A fairly common type which should be mentioned is the flow slide. Flow slides take place in saturated masses of loosely compacted, fairly impervious soils such as fine sands, silts or silty clays. They can occur on quite flat slopes and can travel long distances. The soil and water flows as a liquid mass. They are caused by a sudden reduction of the shear strength to zero, or close to it, by the transfer of all the pressure to the water in the voids. They can occur under a variety of circumstances, the chief of which is a sudden disturbance of a loose saturated soil by a heavy vibration. Drainage and compaction are the two main remedial and preventive measures.

Sensitive clays

In some cases the existing undisturbed strength is much greater than the strength after remoulding. The ratio of these two strengths is called the sensitivity of the clay. In general, the undisturbed strength is measured *in situ* by means of a vane test. (See p 101). Much work on this problem has been done in Norway and Sweden (SKEMPTON and NORTHEY[30]). In England sensitivities are usually below 10 and in these cases an analysis can be made using the unconfined compression strength and the $\phi=0$ method. The small disturbance which occurs due to sampling and testing is apparently approximately equivalent to the progressive failure effect which occurs due to the fact that the analysis assumes an average shear strength around the surface of failure, but in fact failures take place progressively (GOLDER and PALMER[31]).

With clays of high sensitivity, that is over 20 and up to 100, such as occur in southern Norway and Sweden, experience shows that an analysis based on the $\phi=0$ case and the undisturbed strength of the clay measured by a vane test gives results which agree with practice. This problem is not yet completely understood and some aspects of it are controversial. When failure takes place in a clay of high sensitivity the result is in many respects similar to a flow slide described in the paragraph above, the clay becoming practically fluid and flowing through quite small apertures down flat valleys or hillsides for a long distance. The formation of these very sensitive clays is believed to be due to the clay being laid down in salt water, then being raised above water level by tectonic forces, the salt later being leached out by the percolation of fresh water; thus the liquid limit of the clay is reduced but the moisture content remains high. On disturbance therefore the moisture content greatly exceeds the liquid limit and the clay acts as a heavy fluid.

Protective and remedial measures

Certain protective and remedial measures can be taken to prevent a slip or to stabilize a slip which has occurred. Of these the most important is drainage. The majority of troubles are due to water; well designed and adequately maintained drainage can prevent the ingress of water to a bank and so stop or considerably delay any softening which may take place and prevent the build-up of high pore pressures.

On sidelong ground a drain should be installed at the top of the slope to catch surface water. Water from the slope itself should be caught in a toe drain and led away from the toe. On a long slope it may be necessary to catch surface water in chevron drains or even to lead it to a longitudinal drain on a berm halfway up the slope. It is important to line the inverts of these drains.

A considerable degree of protection can be obtained by grassing the slope and the level area at the top where shrinkage cracks are likely to appear. Cracks once formed can become filled with water the pressure of which exerts a considerable disturbing force on the bank. A good carpet of grass prevents not only drying and cracking but also surface erosion. Bushes and trees with strong root systems can also be of help, but trees which grow rapidly and absorb large amounts of water from the soil should be avoided *e.g.* poplars, elms[32].

A bank or cutting may be more stable after a slip has occurred than before it, but the attempt to clear away the spoil may reduce the stability again if material is first removed from the toe.

Deep seated slides can be stabilized either by reducing the disturbing forces or by increasing the resisting forces, by one or other of the following methods

(*a*) Reducing the disturbing forces by loading the toe, or removing material from the top, or replacing material at the top by lighter material, or altering the bank profile *e.g.* introducing berms

(*b*) Increasing the resisting forces by increasing the shear strength by drying or drainage, or adding frictional counterforts or keys through the slip surface

EARTH DAMS AND EMBANKMENTS

The slope stability of an earth dam or embankment can be examined using the methods outlined in the previous section. In addition the following aspects of the problem must be considered.

(*a*) The stability of the foundation material under the weight of the bank

(*b*) The strength properties of the material which will be placed artificially in a remoulded condition

(*c*) In the case of earth dams, which must be watertight, the watertightness of the foundation material and of the bank itself must be considered and the strength properties of the material in the submerged condition must be investigated

(*d*) The effect of seepage forces on earth dams must also be investigated

Foundations of dam or bank

Where an earth fill dam is to be placed on a rock surface no foundation stability problem arises. However, care must be exercized in bonding the fill to the rock and in some cases cut-off walls extending up into the fill are necessary to reduce the danger of seepage along the junction between fill and foundation.

Where a fill is to be placed on a foundation of strength of the same order or less than that of the fill, it is necessary to examine the possibility of failure on deep-seated surfaces passing down into the foundation material. Surfaces of this type are analysed as deep circles in the case of stability of slopes (p 21) or for a non-homogeneous bank (p 23) where the foundation layer of clay is thin in comparison with the size of the cross section of the dam, or in the manner described for the overall stability of a retaining wall (p 43).

For foundations on soft clay the strength may be increased by the use of sand drains, which, if properly installed, accelerate greatly the rate of consolidation under the fill.

Stability of slopes

The stability of the slopes of the dam can be investigated by the methods described on pp 19-25, bearing in mind that several different conditions must be considered, namely:

(a) The conditions during construction and at the end of construction, *i.e.* before filling the reservoir

(b) The condition immediately after filling when the dam is flooded for the first time

(c) The condition of rapid drawdown after the dam has been flooded for some time

(d) The long term stability when the soil in the dam and the foundation have come to equilibrium under the stresses imposed on them with the dam flooded

For any important dam an effective stress analysis using the parameters c' and ϕ' must be carried out for each of the conditions given above. This is only possible if the pore water pressure is known or can be estimated. The pore water pressures can be measured during construction by the methods described later (p 28) either in the dam itself or in a trial bank or both, or they can be estimated from the results of pore pressure measurements made during consolidated undrained triaxial compression tests carried out on soil compacted to the condition at which it should be placed in the dam. This method involves the use of the parameters A and B described by SKEMPTON and BISHOP[7, 9]. (See also p 6.)

The condition for long term stability is analysed using c' and ϕ' obtained either from drained triaxial compression tests or from consolidated-undrained tests in which pore pressures are measured.

In the absence of the necessary testing equipment, or for a small dam, the conditions during construction can be analysed using the results of undrained tests or even unconfined compression tests on clay material. The case of sudden drawdown can be analysed using the full weight of the saturated soil for the disturbing forces, but resisting forces determined by effective stresses due to the submerged weight of the soil. In most cases this method will prove conservative. Neither of these methods is recommended for a high or an important dam or embankment.

Drawdown

This condition is extremely important on the upstream slope of earth dams. The stability under drawdown conditions can often be improved by using suitably placed layers of rapidly draining material, at or near the upstream face of the dam.

Watertightness—Foundation

The best way of ensuring a watertight foundation is to choose a good site for the dam (see following chapter on Site Investigation). In many cases, however, the foundation material must be treated to make it watertight. This can be done by means of a cut-off which must be complete, *i.e.* it must reach down to impervious material to be of much use. The cut-off can be formed by a trench filled with clay or concrete or other impervious material, or it can be formed by driving steel sheet piles down through the pervious layer to the impervious layer, or by placing a row of 'continuous' bored cast-*in-situ* piles down to the impervious layer. Alternatively it can be formed by grouting up the pervious material or fissured material to reduce its permeability. (See Geotechnical Processes, p 63).) In some cases it is impossible to reach an impervious layer and then the cut-off must be formed to a depth such that the loss of water below it is not serious and that the stability of the dam is not endangered by the exit velocities of the water.

Watertightness—Dam

The traditional method of rendering an earth dam watertight is to place a core wall of impervious material in the middle of the dam. Puddle clay is often used and there are traditional laboratory tests to determine the suitability of a given clay (AKROYD[2]). Flexible concrete walls have been used to some extent.

An alternative method is to place an impervious blanket on the upstream face of the dam. This can be formed of concrete or bituminous concrete, or clay materials suitably protected. In some climates the question of ice damage must be borne in mind.

In a rolled-fill dam the whole of the dam is relatively impervious and no core wall is used. It is important in this case to keep the phreatic line, which is the free water surface within the dam, well below the surface of the slope, otherwise erosion will occur where it emerges. This line is controlled by placing a filter drain at the toe of the dam (see *Figure 19*).

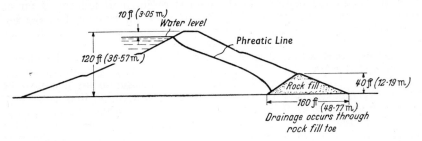

Figure 19. Section of rolled-fill dam showing line of saturation and internal toe drain

The seepage forces should be considered in this case when carrying out a stability analysis. (See Flow Nets, p 29.)

In many cases the materials available for construction of a rolled-fill dam will vary over a wide range of permeability when placed. The dam is then zoned with the less permeable material in the centre and the fill becoming progressively coarser and more permeable towards the outer faces, in some cases merging, via transition zones, into rock fill zones.

MATERIAL

The material in an earth dam or an embankment can be chosen and can be controlled to some extent. Obviously some soils such as peats and soft clays are unsuitable and must normally be rejected. The material which can be accepted depends on the height of the dam since soil which can be used in a low dam cannot economically be used in a high dam; the higher the dam the more critically must the soil be chosen. The choice of soil must always be a compromise between availability, compactability, strength when compacted and impermeability.

For a high dam considerable testing of the soils, both from foundation and fill, is necessary. This will start by laboratory testing, including triaxial tests in which the parameters A and B are measured, and thus an estimate of the pore water pressures occurring in the dam during construction can be made (see p 6). The compaction characteristics are examined by means of laboratory compaction tests. For an important dam field tests are frequently carried out, including the construction of a small section of embankment using the plant which will be used in the actual construction in order to determine the best moisture content for placing and the compaction which can be achieved. Laboratory tests on samples taken from this bank will be required.

The choice of placement moisture content is often critical (KNIGHT[33]). A placement moisture content above optimum moisture content will give relatively high pore-pressures. On the other hand a placement moisture content considerably below optimum may lead to excessive settlement on saturation and possibly to cracking. In wet-weather areas it is often necessary to accept a high placement moisture content and to design accordingly.

In addition to strength, the weight of the material must be measured and in most cases an estimate of permeability must also be made.

CONSTRUCTION

When a dam is designed the specification for its construction will be written. This specification must be a possible one which is why it is best in the case of a large dam to do field trials with the plant available. Compaction of the material in the dam is essential to reduce, as far as possible, the air contained in the soil. The less air contained in the soil and the greater its weight, in general the stronger it will be both when placed and after submergence.

During construction strict control must be maintained on the placing and compacting procedure. This is done by density and moisture content measurements of the material placed. These measurements can now be made very quickly using radioactive probes. In addition it is now usual in an important dam to install apparatus for measuring the pore water pressure in the soil at a number of points during the construction of the dam. Each point consists essentially of a porous plug about 3 in diameter placed in the dam and connected by two lines of polythene tubing to a manometer. The whole of the apparatus is filled with air-free water and the pressure in the water is measured on the manometer. The apparatus must also include some means of circulating the water through the polythene tubes in order to remove any air which collects in the system. If the water pressure is known at any point then, if the total vertical pressure at that point is assumed to be equal to the total weight of the material above it, the effective pressure is known and a stability calculation can be carried out. Thus a check on stability can be maintained throughout the construction period. This very useful device can be extended to check stability when the dam is first filled, and if necessary, during the first drawdown.

If stability calculations during construction show that the strengths expected are not being attained, construction procedure can be altered in one of the following ways.

(a) The speed of construction can be reduced. This allows the strength to increase slowly as the pore water pressures dissipate due to drainage.

(b) The method of placing can be altered, for instance, heavier compacting machines can be used. This must be carefully checked since in some soils heavier machines may cause even greater pore water pressures.

(c) The type of material can be changed, for instance, a more frictional material will generally give better results than clay. With clay fill the placement moisture content can be altered.

(d) The side slopes can be flattened to reduce the shear stresses in the material.

(e) A lower factor of safety may be accepted. The factor of safety in most earth dams is never much more than 1·5, but where the conditions are carefully controlled and the pore water pressure is known at a number of places throughout the dam, a factor as low as 1·25 may sometimes be acceptable, depending on the consequence of a failure.

Good bonding between layers of rolled fill is essential. This is usually achieved by harrowing or otherwise loosening the top inch or two of a compacted layer before the next layer is spread.

Fill is not placed during rain. The embankment is usually given a fall away from the centre-line during construction so that rain will not pond on the fill. When rain is expected the fill is ' sealed ' with a smooth-wheeled roller. After rain any softened material is either removed or harrowed to dry and re-compacted.

SETTLEMENT OF DAMS

The settlement of the top of an earth dam consists of two parts: (a) settlement of the foundation of the dam due to consolidation; (b) settlement of the material in the dam itself.

Settlement of the foundation can be calculated in exactly the same way as for buildings (see p 11). The settlement of the dam itself can also be calculated, but in a well compacted material this will usually be quite small and is not a serious problem.

FLOW NETS

A flow net is a graphical representation of the pattern of the seepage or flow of water through a permeable soil. By means of a flow net it is possible amongst other things to calculate the hydrostatic uplift on a structure such as a dam or barrage, the amount of seepage through an earth dam or under a barrage, or to estimate the probability of piping occurring in a cofferdam.

A flow line is the path followed by a particle of water flowing through a soil mass. Flow lines are always smooth even curves as shown in *Figure 20*. An equipotential line is a line joining points at which the hydraulic head is equal; therefore if standpipes are inserted into any two points on an equipotential line the water will rise to the same level in each standpipe. Flow lines and equipotential lines are always at right angles to each other.

Theory of flow nets

Consider the two-dimensional case shown in *Figure 20*(a). Let the components of velocity be u and v in the x and y directions respectively. Then from D'Arcy's law

$$u = k \frac{\partial h}{\partial x} \qquad \text{and} \qquad v = k \frac{\partial h}{\partial y}$$

where h = loss in head and k = permeability.

Consider the element shaded:
Let the entrance velocity be u and v and the exit velocity be

$$u + \frac{\partial u}{\partial x} \quad \text{and} \quad v + \frac{\partial v}{\partial y}$$

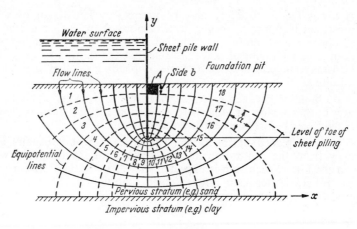

a

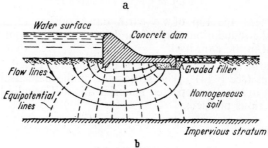

b

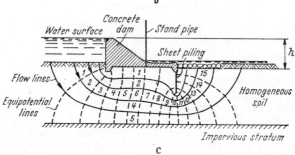

c

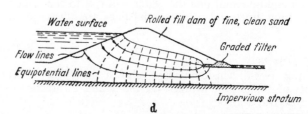

d

Figure 20.   Examples of flow nets for simple cases
a *beneath sheet pile wall*   **b** *beneath concrete dam on sand*
c *beneath concrete dam on sand with sheet pile cut-off wall*
d *through rolled fill dam with toe drain*

The quantity of water flowing into the element is equal to the quantity flowing out and

$$\text{Quantity} = \text{velocity} \times At \qquad\qquad A = \text{area} \quad t = \text{time}$$

Therefore $\quad \dfrac{\partial u}{\partial x} + \dfrac{\partial v}{\partial y} = 0$

Hence $\quad \dfrac{\partial^2 h}{\partial x^2} + \dfrac{\partial^2 h}{\partial y^2} = 0 = \text{operator of Laplace} \qquad\qquad$ ....(33)

This is the equation of two sets of orthogonal curves, the flow lines and the equipotential lines.

Construction of flow nets

Four methods of constructing flow nets are in general use.

(*a*) *Mathematical*—For simple boundary conditions the above equation can be solved mathematically. With the increasing use of electronic computers allied with relaxation methods quite complicated cases can be tackled (see McNAMEE[34]).

(*b*) *Electrical analogy*—The differential equation for flow nets is the same as that for flow of electricity and flow nets can be drawn by using an electrical model and tracing lines of equal potential with a wandering probe. The soil is represented by a suitably shaped card coated with graphite, strips of copper represent water surfaces and an insulating material represents an impervious surface. Once the equipotential lines are drawn, the flow lines can easily be drawn in at right angles to them.

(*c*) *Hydraulic models*—An obvious approach is to construct a model of the problem in sand behind glass, to allow water to flow through it and to trace the flow lines by inserting a small drop of dye at the soil surface. The flow of the water can be clearly seen by the streak left by the dye as it flows through the soil. This trace is then drawn on the glass with a wax pencil and the procedure repeated from a different point.

(*d*) *Graphical method*—After a little practice it is quite possible to sketch a flow net for many problems which is quite accurate enough for most practical purposes. The cross-section is drawn and the boundary conditions are clearly marked. The flow net is then tentatively sketched in, bearing in mind that flow lines and equipotential lines are at right angles to each other, that flow lines always start at right angles to a free water surface and equipotential lines start or finish at right angles to an impervious surface. The number of flow and equipotential lines is chosen to divide the seepage area into shapes which are approximately square and which are bounded by two flow lines and two equipotential lines.

Solution of hydraulic problems by flow nets

(*a*) *Uplift pressure*—In *Figure* 20(c) let the number of squares along a flow line be n (=15) and the number along an equipotential line be f (=5).

Then if the total drop in head = h

The drop in head across each square $= h/n$

At a borehole through the concrete at the number 6 equipotential line the loss in head will be

$$\frac{h}{n} \times 6 = h\frac{6}{15} = h\frac{2}{5}$$

The uplift pressure at this point will be the remaining head × density of water

$$= \left(h - h \frac{2}{5} \right) \gamma_w$$

$$= h . \gamma_w \left(1 - \frac{2}{5} \right) = \frac{3}{5} h \gamma_w$$

Note that this result is independent of the number of squares in the flow net, since if $n=30$ instead of 15 the borehole in the position shown would be on the 12th equipotential and loss in head $= \dfrac{h}{30} \times 12 = h\dfrac{2}{5}$

(b) *Amount of seepage*—Let the amount of water flowing under the dam in *Figure 20* (c) be Q.

Then if $v =$ velocity of flow, $v = \dfrac{Q}{A\,t}$ where $A =$ area of flow and $t =$ time.

But $v = k\,i$ by D'Arcy's law

therefore $\qquad\qquad\qquad\qquad Q = A\,t\,k\,i \qquad\qquad\qquad$ ....(34)

Consider any square in the flow net—let its side be b

Then drop in head across the square $= \dfrac{h}{n}$

and therefore i for the square $= \dfrac{h}{n} \Big/ b = \dfrac{h}{n\,b}$

therefore flow through one square $Q = b\,k\,\dfrac{h}{n\,b}$ in unit time

therefore total flow per unit length in unit time $= k\dfrac{h}{n}f$

where $f =$ number of flow compartments

$$Q = k\,h\,f/n$$

where f/n is independent of the size of the squares.

(c) *Factor of safety against piping*—The factor of safety against piping is the ratio of the critical hydraulic gradient to the existing hydraulic gradient at exit.

In *Figure 20* (a) piping will occur at A when the upward force of the water issuing at A is greater than the weight of the particles.

The upward force of the water $= \gamma_w i$

the weight of the particles $= \gamma_w \dfrac{\rho - 1}{1 + e}$

therefore piping occurs when $i = \dfrac{\rho - 1}{1 + e}$

For a loose sand ρ is commonly $2 \cdot 7$ and e about $0 \cdot 7$, therefore

$$\frac{\rho - 1}{1 + e} = \frac{2 \cdot 7 - 1}{1 + 0 \cdot 7} = 1$$

i.e. the critical hydraulic gradient is about unity.

The exit hydraulic gradient at A, *Figure 20*(a) is $(h/n)/b$.
Therefore the factor of safety against piping is

$$\frac{1}{\dfrac{h}{n\,b}} = \frac{n\,b}{h} \qquad \dots\dots\dots(35)$$

Note that $n\,b$ is independent of the number of squares.

It is generally considered that the value of the factor of safety against piping should be 4 or greater.

EARTH PRESSURE

Active and passive pressure

The problem of earth pressure is the oldest soil mechanics problem. The lowest pressure which a retaining structure must be capable of resisting to prevent a bank of earth from collapsing is the active pressure. The highest pressure which a structure can exert on a bank of earth without causing it to move in the direction of the pressure is the passive pressure or passive resistance. Examples of both are given in *Figure 21*.

Below a level ground surface, the horizontal pressure is known as the 'pressure at rest'. This pressure lies between the active and passive pressures and is usually designated by the factor K_0 which is the ratio of the horizontal and vertical pressures at any given depth. The factors K_a and K_p similarly relate the active and passive horizontal pressures to the vertical pressure.

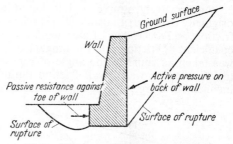

Figure 21. Active pressure and passive resistance

Not much is known about the values of K_0 but in normally consolidated soils its value probably lies between 0·4 and 0·75 and in over consolidated soils it is probably not less than unity.

TABLES 1 and 2 from the Civil Engineering Code of Practice No. 2[39], give typical values for K_a and K_p for cohesionless materials, vertical walls with horizontal ground where ϕ=angle of friction for the soil and δ=angle of wall friction.

TABLE 1

VALUES OF K_a FOR COHESIONLESS MATERIALS, VERTICAL WALLS WITH HORIZONTAL GROUND

Values of δ	Values of ϕ				
	25°	30°	35°	40°	45°
	Values of K_a				
0°	0·41	0·33	0·27	0·22	0·17
10°	0·37	0·31	0·25	0·20	0·16
20°	0·34	0·28	0·23	0·19	0·15
30°	—	0·26	0·21	0·17	0·14

TABLE 2

VALUES OF K_p FOR COHESIONLESS SOILS, VERTICAL WALLS AND HORIZONTAL GROUND

Values of δ	*Values of ϕ*			
	25°	30°	35°	40°
	Values of K_p			
0°	2·5	3·0	3·7	4·6
10°	3·1	4·0	4·8	6·5
20°	3·7	4·9	6·0	8·8
30°	—	5·8	7·3	11·4

In order that the lateral pressure may change from the pressure at rest to either the active or the passive value movement must take place to mobilize shear forces. This generally occurs during the construction of the retaining structure.

ACTIVE PRESSURE

For an ideal material the problem of determining the total active pressure is comparatively simple and is based on the wedge theory which was originally due to COULOMB[35] (1773) who solved it for a material having both friction and cohesion. Later workers omitted the cohesion, changed the coefficient of friction into the tangent of the angle of internal friction, which was taken as equal to the angle of repose, and extended the expression to include sloping walls, wall friction (anticipated in part by Coulomb), and inclined surcharges. Not all of these changes were improvements.

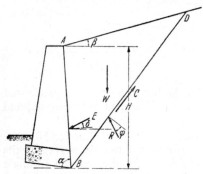

Figure 22. Coulomb or general wedge theory

In the wedge theory it is assumed that the pressure on the wall is due to a wedge of earth which tends to slip down an inclined plane as shown in *Figure 22*. The forces acting on the wedge are also shown in the figure. The inclination of the plane BD is altered until the position which gives the greatest value for the force E is found. This can either be done analytically or graphically.

The general formula for the total pressure over depth H exerted by a frictional material having no cohesion is

$$E = \tfrac{1}{2} \cdot \gamma H^2 \left(\frac{K_a}{\sin \alpha \cos \delta} \right) \qquad \dots\dots\dots(36)$$

where the coefficient of active earth pressure

$$K_a = \frac{\sin^2 (\alpha + \phi) \cos \delta}{\sin \alpha \sin (\alpha - \delta) \left[1 + \sqrt{ \left\{ \frac{\sin (\phi + \delta) \sin (\phi - \beta)}{\sin (\alpha - \delta) \sin (\alpha + \beta)} \right\} } \right]^2}$$

$$\dots\dots\dots(37)$$

ϕ=angle of friction, δ=angle of wall friction, α, β and H are as shown in *Figure 22*.

For the case of a vertical wall and horizontal backfill, the values of K_a to be used in equation 36 are as in TABLE 1.

For the special case of no wall friction, vertical wall and horizontal backfill this reduces to the Rankine formula

$$E = \tfrac{1}{2} \gamma H^2 \left(\frac{1 - \sin \phi}{1 + \sin \phi} \right) \qquad \ldots\ldots\ldots\ldots(38)$$

No analytical solution exists for the general case of a soil having both friction and cohesion, but for the special case of a vertical wall, horizontal backfill and no wall friction or adhesion, the total pressure is given by the FRANÇAIS[36] equation

$$E = \tfrac{1}{2} \gamma H^2 \ \tan^2 \left(\frac{\pi}{4} - \frac{\phi}{2} \right) - 2 cH \tan \left(\frac{\pi}{4} - \frac{\phi}{2} \right) \qquad \ldots\ldots\ldots\ldots(39)$$

This is the same as the solution given by BELL[37] in 1915. For a purely cohesive material equation 39 reduces to $E = \tfrac{1}{2} \gamma H^2 - 2cH$ for the case of no wall adhesion, or if wall adhesion is taken as equal to the cohesion the formula becomes $E = \tfrac{1}{2} \gamma H^2 - 2 (\sqrt{2}) cH$.

Equation 40, which gives the intensity of active pressure at any level, can be applied to simple cases of layered systems by calculating the pressure at the top and bottom of each layer, treating the layers above as a surcharge.

$$p_a = \gamma \ z \ \tan^2 \left(\frac{\pi}{4} - \frac{\phi}{2} \right) - 2c \tan \left(\frac{\pi}{4} - \frac{\phi}{2} \right) \qquad \ldots\ldots\ldots\ldots(40)$$

Below water the earth pressure is calculated using the submerged weight of the soil, but the full water pressure is added to this.

Example—To find the total pressure for the layered system and soil conditions shown in *Figure 23*.

The pressure p_a at any depth z in soil of weight γ is

$\gamma z \dfrac{1 - \sin \phi}{1 + \sin \phi}$ * in sand and $\gamma z - 2c$ in clay, where ϕ=angle of internal friction and

c=cohesion.

At $z = 10$ ft (sand)	$p_a = 10 \times 110 \times \tfrac{1}{3}$	$= +370$ lb/sq ft
$= 10$ ft (clay)	$= 1,100 - 5,400$	$= -4,300$ lb/sq ft
$= 13$ ft (clay)	$= (1,100 + 3 \times 126) - 5,400$	$= -3,920$ lb/sq ft
$= 13$ ft (clay)	$= (1,100 + 3 \times 126) - 1,840$	$= -360$ lb/sq ft
$= 35$ ft (clay)	$= (1,100 + 3 \times 126) + (22 \times 126) - 1,840 = +2,410$ lb/sq ft

Total area (positive areas only)$= \left(10 \times \dfrac{370}{2} \right) + \left(19 \cdot 1 \times \dfrac{2,410}{2} \right) = 1,850 + 23,100$

Total pressure $= 25,000$ lb/ft run

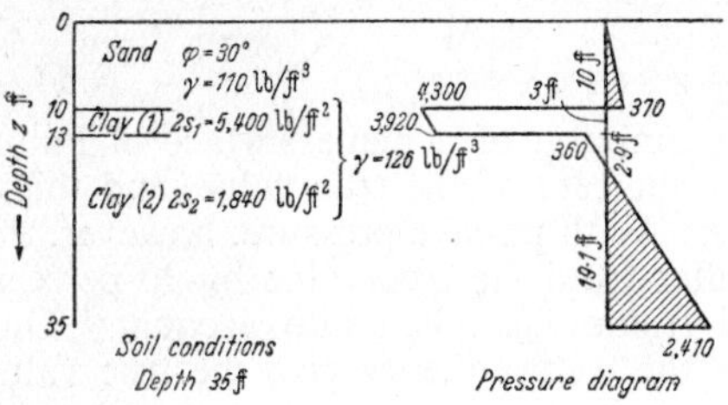

Soil conditions
Depth 35 ft

Pressure diagram

Figure 23. Earth pressure in layered
system (pressure in lb/sq ft)

$*\dfrac{1 - \sin \phi}{1 + \sin \phi} = \tan^2 \left(\frac{\pi}{4} - \frac{\phi}{2} \right)$

Analytical solutions of these simple cases have been published in graphical form by PACKSHAW[38].

It must be clearly understood that although the above formulae give an approximation to the total pressure which will be exerted on a wall, and that this is given by the total area of the pressure diagram, they do not necessarily give any idea of the actual distribution of the pressure.

Graphical method

A simple graphical solution can be used for walls with irregular outlines, for irregular backfills, external loads on the backfill, and variation in the properties of the backfill. The principle is that of the wedge theory, the most dangerous surface of slip being found by trial.

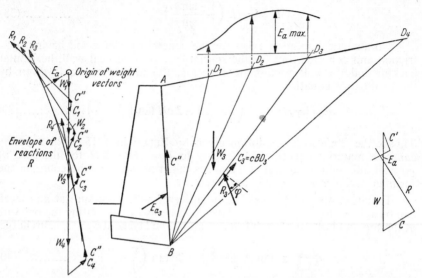

Figure 24. Engesser's method for determination of active pressure

The polygons of forces are drawn for a number of wedges ABD_1, ABD_2, etc as shown in *Figure 24*. The forces acting on each wedge are: its weight W, the reaction R across the plane BD, the cohesion C acting up the plane BD, and the earth pressure E which it is required to find. For limiting equilibrium R is inclined at ϕ to the normal to the plane BD, and $C = c \cdot BD$. If the direction of E is assumed, the polygon of forces can be completed, giving the value of E. It is convenient to plot all the polygons from a common origin of W as shown. The maximum value of E is then given by the point at which the envelope of the R lines cuts the line representing E. This E line can be drawn from the origin in any assumed direction, thus allowing for wall friction. Wall adhesion (cohesion) can be included by subtracting it from the weight of the wedge.

Alternatively the force polygons can be drawn separately for each wedge and the value of E_a can be plotted above the position of the corresponding slip surface.

PASSIVE RESISTANCE

In the case of active pressure the assumption of a plane surface of failure gives results which are within 3 or 4 per cent of the true value, and this is close enough for all practical purposes. With passive pressure, however, this assumption leads to results which differ from the true value by 30 per cent or more on the unsafe side if wall friction is taken into account. Only for the case of no wall friction does the wedge theory give the true value. The passive pressure in this case is given by the formula

$$E = \tfrac{1}{2} \gamma H^2 \tan^2 \left(\frac{\pi}{4} + \frac{\phi}{2} \right) + 2cH \tan \left(\frac{\pi}{4} + \frac{\phi}{2} \right) \quad \ldots\ldots\ldots\ldots(41)$$

Wall friction adds greatly to the passive resistance, but not so much as the wedge theory indicates; it is seldom, therefore, that it can be neglected.

The reason why the wedge theory does not give the right answer is that the surface of failure is not a plane but is curved, as shown in *Figure 25*. Although rigorous methods of solution of the problem exist they are of little use in practical problems. Their use lies in checking the approximate graphical methods which are used in practice. Two such graphical methods are in use *viz* the logarithmic spiral method and the ϕ-circle method; both give results within 5 per cent of the true value. Only the latter will be described here.

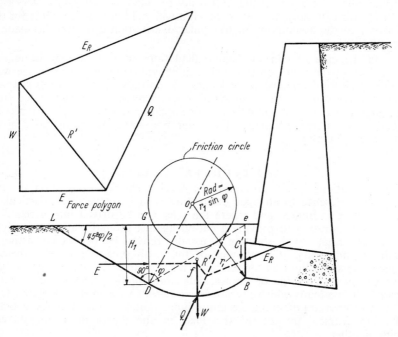

Figure 25. Determination of passive pressure. $E=\frac{1}{2}\gamma H_1^2 \tan^2(\pi/4+\phi/2)$

In the ϕ-circle method the surface of failure is assumed to be a portion of a circle extending from the bottom of the foundation to the point where it becomes tangential to a line making an angle of $\pi/4-\phi/2$ to the horizontal as shown in *Figure 25*, where $E=\frac{1}{2}\gamma H_1^2 \tan^2\left(\dfrac{\pi}{4}+\dfrac{\phi}{2}\right)$.

The forces acting on the quadrant of earth are *i* the horizontal thrust E from the triangular section of earth GDL which can be taken as equal to the Rankine or Coulomb value as this force is horizontal, *ii* the weight of the quadrant W, *iii* the passive resistance E_R which is required, *iv* the wall adhesion C' which is known, *v* the cohesion C round the arc BD, *vi* the reaction across the arc DB

By making the assumption that the reaction Q is tangential to a circle with centre O and radius $r\sin\phi$ it is possible to solve the problem graphically.

For the simple case of horizontal ground and vertical wall, in cohesionless soil, *Figure 26*, gives values of the passive earth-pressure coefficient, K_p, for use in the equation

$$E=\frac{1}{2}\gamma H^2 K_p \sec\delta \qquad\qquad\ldots\ldots\ldots\ldots(42)$$

DISTRIBUTION OF PRESSURE

It is generally assumed that pressure increases uniformly with depth. This is only true in certain special cases although the assumption is not unreasonable in some other cases for which it is not strictly true. Cases in which the assumption should not be made are dealt with below.

The wedge theory gives the total pressure; the distribution of pressure cannot be obtained from this theory as it depends on the way in which the wall yields and will only be triangular (hydraulic) if the wall yields by turning about its base. If the wall is not founded on rock and is very rigid in itself this is usually the way in which it will yield in practice. It is for this reason that the assumption of triangular distribution can often be made in practice.

In the case of cohesive soils calculations indicate a zone of tension at the top of the wall. In this region there will be no pressure on the wall, and in practice deep tension cracks are often observed behind walls supporting cohesive soils. The value of this tension must not be subtracted from the pressure diagram. If it is possible for the tension cracks to become filled with water, the value of the water pressure must be included in the pressure calculations.

STRUTTED EXCAVATIONS

For excavations below ground water level a sheeted excavation is often used in preference to an open excavation with battered sides, particularly where space is limited and where the piles can be driven into a relatively impervious stratum to provide a cut-off against ground water in overlying pervious strata. Such sheeting is usually braced by frames consisting of walings and struts. Calculations of the earth pressures on the sheeting follow the same lines as for retaining walls. However, during progressive excavation and placing of frames, deflections of the sheeting occur which lead to frame loads which are not in agreement with those calculated from the earth pressure diagram, assuming hinge points at all frame levels below the top frame. In general the load in the struts does not increase with depth.

For sands Terzaghi has proposed an empirical design rule, based on a number of field observations, as shown in *Figure 27*(a), and the same rule

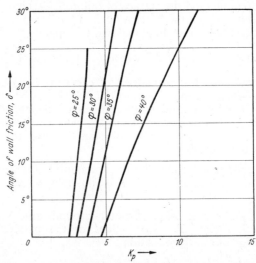

Figure 26. Values of passive earth-pressure coefficient

with a modification for use in clay, has been adopted in the Civil Engineering Code of Practice No. 2 (C.P. 2)[39]. A pressure redistribution suggested by PECK[40] for use in clays, based on measurements carried out in Chicago, is shown in *Figure 27*(b).

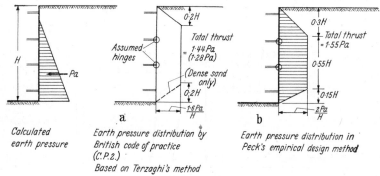

a

b

| Calculated earth pressure | Earth pressure distribution by British code of practice (C.P.2.) Based on Terzaghi's method | Earth pressure distribution in Peck's empirical design method |

Figure 27. Earth pressure on strutted excavations

It should be emphasized that the redistributed pressure diagrams described above are in effect design devices for obtaining frame loads and do not necessarily imply any actual redistribution of earth pressure. In fact SKEMPTON and WARD[41] have described the results of strut and waling load measurements in a cofferdam at Shellhaven and have interpreted results to show that the observed frame loads can be accounted for in terms of deflections of the sheet piling prior to placing the struts in position and without the need for assuming any redistribution of earth pressure.

Two useful rules in determining levels at which frames should be placed have been given by WARD[42] as follows:

(a) In a deep deposit of normally consolidated clay the uppermost frame of struts should be placed across a cofferdam before the depth of excavation (H_1) reaches a value given by $H_1 = 2c/\gamma$ and

(b) the second frame of struts should be placed before the depth of excavation reaches a depth H_2 given by $H_2 = 4c/\gamma$.

ANCHORED BULKHEADS

An anchored bulkhead is usually in the form of a steel sheet-pile wall supported by ties at one level only and by passive pressure against the toe. However, anchored bulkheads may also be constructed with timber, precast reinforced concrete sheet piles, or continuous bored piles. Calculations of active and passive earth pressures follow the same lines as for retaining walls but analysis of the stability of an anchored bulkhead requires the determination of bending moments in the piling and of the magnitude of the anchor pull.

The magnitude of the maximum bending moment occurring in the bulkhead will be influenced by the conditions of fixity at the toe. If there is no fixity, *i.e.* with 'free earth support', the maximum bending moment will be at its highest value. With increasing end fixity the maximum bending moment is reduced. It has been shown by ROWE[43] that the maximum bending moment is greatly influenced by the flexibility of the wall and the density of the material into which the wall penetrates. In his method Rowe uses a flexibility number $\rho = H^4/EI$, where H is the overall height of the bulkhead, E is the Young's modulus of the bulkhead material, and I is the second moment of inertia of the bulkhead section.

The various dimensions and forces entering into a bulkhead calculation are indicated in *Figure 28*. A design procedure based on Rowe's method, and similar to that described by TERZAGHI[44], is as follows:

(a) *Forces acting on faces of bulkhead*

The active and passive pressures are first calculated. The active pressure calculations must allow for the maximum possible unbalanced water pressure and for any surcharge in the form of distributed, line or point loads supported directly on the backfill.

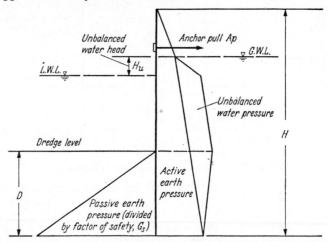

Figure 28. Dimensions and forces in anchored bulkhead calculation. Earth pressure diagrams illustrated are for homogeneous cohesionless soil. No pressures from surcharge loads have been shown

Strictly speaking the water pressures should be calculated from a flow net (*Figure 29*(a)) taking into account the effects of stratification in the soils present. However, if the soils do not vary widely in their permeabilities it

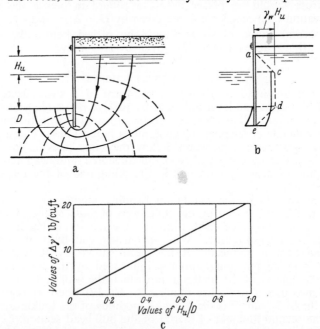

Figure 29. Unbalanced water pressure. (a) Flow net. (b) Distribution of unbalanced water pressure. (c) Average reduction of effective unit weight of passive wedge due to seepage pressure exerted by the upward flow of water (from TERZAGHI[44]*)*

is sufficient to use the simplified pressure distribution shown in *Figure 29*(b). Allowance must also be made, where the passive pressure is provided by a permeable stratum, for a reduction in passive pressure due to the seepage gradients (*Figure 29*(c)).

The effect of a distributed surcharge of magnitude W_u is to increase the earth pressure over the whole height of the bulkhead by an amount $W_u K_a$, in the case of granular backfills, and by an amount W_u in the case of cohesive backfills. The effect of a line load W_l can be estimated with sufficient accuracy for most designs by the construction shown in *Figure 30*.

The effect of a point load W_i on the backfill is more difficult to estimate. The problem has been investigated by GERBER[45] and by SPANGLER[46]. An approximate method which is given in Civil Engineering Code of Practice No. 2, (C.P. 2), is to assume that the load is spread through the backing at an angle of dispersion of 45° on each side of the load. The lateral pressure at any point due to the surcharge is then taken as K_a times the vertical pressure at the point. This method, however, tends to give results on the unsafe side. The following tentative approximate method is suggested.

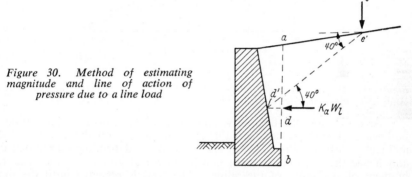

Figure 30. Method of estimating magnitude and line of action of pressure due to a line load

The line of action of the resultant force is obtained by a construction similar to that for a line load (*Figure 30*), the 40° line being constructed from the centre of the loaded area. It is assumed that, if the length of the loaded area be L and the distance between the back of the wall and the near edge of that area be x, the resultant lateral thrust will be distributed along a length of wall equal to $L+x$. Then, if W_i be the load on the area, the resultant thrust per unit length of wall will be $K_a W_i/(L+x)$.

(b) Computation of depth of penetration

A diagram of active and passive pressures is drawn as shown in *Figure 28* for a trial penetration of the piling. Before passive pressures are plotted a factor of safety G_s is applied. For granular soils it is applied to the whole of the passive pressure and for cohesive soils it is applied to the shear strength component. The choice of a value for this factor of safety for a given design depends on the accuracy of the data on which the earth pressures have been based, but in general it should not be less than 2.

The earth pressure diagram is then divided up into a number of convenient areas and the total load on each of these areas and its point of application is estimated. Moments of these loads are then taken about the line of action of the anchor pull. This is repeated for other trial depths of penetration until a depth giving zero total moment is obtained. Alternatively the pressures below dredge level may be expressed in terms of the penetration, D, and the required depth found analytically. It is usual to increase the calculated depth of penetration by 20 per cent to allow for the possibility of scour or overdredging.

(c) Computation of maximum bending moments

The bending moments are first calculated on the assumption of 'free earth support', and the maximum bending moment is determined. This is a straightforward calculation based on the resultant forces of the areas into which the pressure diagram has been divided, using either analytical or graphical methods.

If the sheet piles are to be driven into a fairly homogeneous stratum of clean sand with a known relative density the calculated maximum bending moment for free earth support can be reduced on the basis of Rowe's investigations, as illustrated in *Figure 31*.

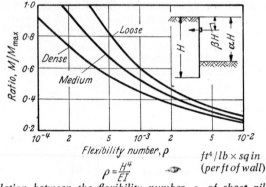

$$\rho = \frac{H^4}{EI}$$

Figure 31. Relation between the flexibility number, ρ, of sheet piles, and bending moment ratio M/M_{max} (logarithmic scale) (from TERZAGHI[44])

As a first step the flexibility number is calculated for a trial section of bulkhead. For the calculated value of the flexibility number a value of the moment reduction ratio M/M_{max} can be read off, depending on the density, and hence the reduced moment can be obtained and compared with the moment of resistance of the piling. The trial is repeated until the most suitable section of the bulkhead is obtained, *i.e.* until the reduced moment is equal to or just less than the moment of resistance of the section. If required the calculation can be extended to cover alternative construction materials.

If the sheet piles are to be driven into a homogeneous stratum of dense or medium-dense silty sand, the moment reduction curves for medium and loose sand should be used instead of those for dense and medium dense sand. Sheet piles to be driven into loose silty sand should be calculated

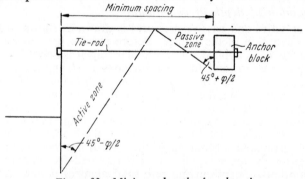

Figure 32. Minimum length of anchor ties

on the figure for free earth support, since compressibility of such sands may be high. Recent work by ROWE[47] has shown that in some cases moment reduction can be made where piles penetrate clay below dredge level.

(*d*) *Anchor pull*

The anchor pull is determined by resolving horizontally all the forces acting on the bulkhead. There are, however, a number of factors which may lead to an anchor pull somewhat greater than that computed, and conservative design stresses should therefore be adopted.

Where the ties are taken back to blocks or beams the position of these should be such that no overlapping of active and passive zones occurs, as illustrated in *Figure 32*.

OVERALL STABILITY

The design of a retaining wall, whether a mass wall or a sheet pile wall, should always be considered from the point of view of overall stability *i.e.* failure as a bank of earth. The forces are shown in *Figure 33*.

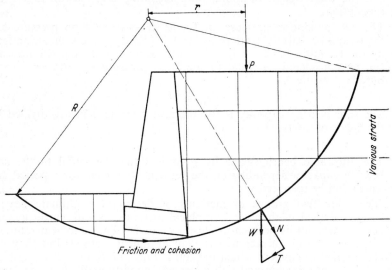

Figure 33. Overall stability of a retaining wall

$$\text{Disturbing moment} = \Sigma \, TR + Pr \qquad \qquad \dots\dots\dots\dots(43)$$

$$\text{Resisting moment} = (\Sigma \, N \cdot \tan\phi + \Sigma \, cL) \, R \qquad \dots\dots\dots\dots(44)$$

where L is the length of the arc over which c acts and T and N are the tangential and normal components of W

$$\text{Factor of safety} = \frac{(\Sigma \, N \cdot \tan\phi + \Sigma \, cL) \, R}{\Sigma \, TR + Pr} \qquad \dots\dots\dots\dots(45)$$

The methods described on p 19 *et seq* are directly applicable.

FOUNDATIONS

BEARING CAPACITY AND SETTLEMENT

There are two ways in which a foundation can fail; by shear failure and by settlement. In the first case a surface of rupture is formed in the soil, the foundation settles considerably and probably tilts to one side, and heaving of the soil occurs on one or both sides of the foundation. In the second case failure of the soil in shear does not occur, but the existing deformations are large enough to cause failure of the structure which the foundation is supporting.

Failure by settlement is therefore a function of the particular structure as well as the underlying soil. SKEMPTON and MACDONALD[48] have given a criterion for framed buildings based on angular distortion, which is expressed by the ratio of differential settlement, δ, to the distance, l, between two points, usually the column positions. From a detailed study of field data a limiting value of $\delta/l = 1/300$ has been determined. More flexible structures, oil tanks for example, may undergo considerably greater settlements without sustaining damage. At the other limit some sensitive machinery will tolerate very little settlement.

The ultimate bearing capacity of a foundation is the value of the net loading intensity at which the ground fails in shear. Before discussing bearing capacity several definitions are necessary:

1. The gross foundation pressure is the pressure due to the applied load and the total weight of foundation, including any backfill above the foundation.

2. The net foundation pressure, p_n, is the gross foundation pressure less the weight of material (soil and water) displaced by the foundation (and by the backfill above the foundation). Alternatively the net pressure can be considered as equal to the gross pressure less the total overburden pressure

$$p_n = p - p_0$$

3. The safe bearing capacity is the ultimate bearing capacity divided by the factor of safety.

$$q_s = q_u/F$$

4. The allowable bearing capacity q_a is less than or equal to the safe bearing capacity depending on the settlements which are expected and which can be tolerated.

There are two groups of methods of determining ultimate bearing capacity, analytical methods and graphical methods, as with earth pressure problems to which this problem is closely related. The analytical solutions are often easier and quicker to use than graphical methods but they can only be applied to cases in which the soil is fairly uniform. The graphical methods are very flexible and will cover any conditions likely to be found in practice.

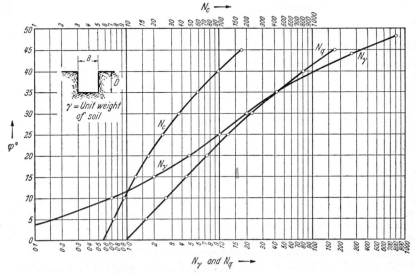

Figure 34. Terzaghi's bearing capacity coefficients for shallow footings

The most general formula for net ultimate bearing capacity of a strip footing is that given by TERZAGHI[49]

$$q = cN_c + 0.5\gamma BN_\gamma + \gamma D (N_q - 1) \qquad \ldots\ldots\ldots(46)$$

where N_c, N_γ, and N_q are bearing capacity factors depending on the angle of shearing resistance ϕ (*Figure 34*).

For a circular footing of diameter D:

$$q = 1.3cN_c + 0.3\gamma BN_\gamma + \gamma D (N_q - 1) \qquad \ldots\ldots\ldots(47)$$

For a square footing of width B:

$$q = 1.3cN_c + 0.4\gamma BN_\gamma + \gamma D (N_q - 1) \qquad \ldots\ldots\ldots(48)$$

Although the Terzaghi formula is a useful summary of factors governing ultimate bearing capacity, in its full form it is not used in practice. The methods for calculating both ultimate bearing capacity and settlements are generally related to the type of ground involved under three main groups, rocks, granular soils (sands and gravels) and cohesive soils (clays).

FOUNDATIONS ON ROCK

The bearing capacity of rock is not readily determined by tests on specimens and mathematical analysis, since it is greatly dependent on the large-scale structural features of the rock stratum. Some guidance concerning safe bearing capacity of rocks is given in Civil Engineering Code of Practice No. 4—Foundations[50], which gives a range of values between 6 ton/sq ft for hard solid chalk and 100 ton/sq ft (109·4 kg/sq cm) for igneous and gneissic rocks in sound condition. For small loaded areas plate bearing tests are useful provided that they are carefully related to the structural features of the rock. For large loaded areas plate bearing tests do not provide satisfactory design data and judgment must be used to take account of the structural features and the possibility, in some cases, of mining subsidence.

FOUNDATIONS ON SAND

For uncomplicated ground conditions an analytical solution is used and this is described in detail below. For complicated conditions graphical methods are necessary and the simplest of these is the circular arc method developed by KREY[51], although the log-spiral method first suggested by RENDULIC[52] is also quite good.

Shallow footings on sand
In granular soils the cohesion is negligible; putting $c = 0$ in Terzaghi's formula, for a strip footing, it reduces to

$$q = 0.5\gamma BN_\gamma + \gamma D (N_q - 1) \qquad \ldots\ldots\ldots(49)$$

in which the first term represents the effect of the strength of the sand below foundation level and the second term represents the effect of the surcharge of material above foundation level. This is often used as a basis for calculation of the net ultimate bearing capacity of shallow footings on sand or gravel. In order to determine the values of the bearing capacity factors N_γ and N_q it is, however, necessary to determine the angle of shearing resistance, ϕ. With sand and gravels it is unfortunately difficult and expensive to obtain an adequate number of undisturbed samples, except at very shallow depths, on which to carry out the necessary shear testing in the laboratory*. For this reason it is common practice to determine the approximate relative density of granular materials by means of dynamic penetration tests (the Standard Penetration Test, see next chapter on Site Investigation). From these an approximate value of ϕ can be obtained for use in the bearing capacity formula. Values of the number of blows to drive the standard tool a distance of 12 in using the standard equipment and procedure, N values, are determined over a range of levels below the proposed foundation level in a number of boreholes. The average value for each borehole is obtained and the minimum average value is used in the calculation. The empirical correlation between N value and relative density and ϕ is given in *Figure 35*.

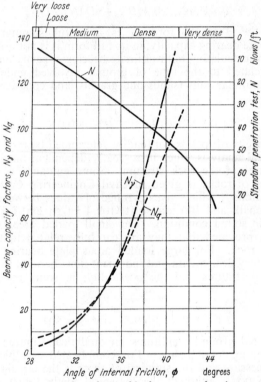

Figure 35. *Curves showing the relationship between ϕ, bearing capacity factors, and values of N from the standard penetration test*

However, the procedure has been further simplified by PECK, HANSON and THORBURN[53] who have drawn graphs of safe bearing capacity directly against N values. These assume a bulk density of 100 lb/cu ft and a factor of safety of 3. The values of safe bearing capacity are given in two components corresponding to the two terms in the bearing capacity formula, one relating to strength and hence relative density, and the other to overburden, in *Figures 36*(a) and *36*(b).

The values are based on a level of the water table at a depth below foundation level at least equal to the width of the footing. If ground water level is at foundation level the component of safe bearing capacity corresponding to the first term (*Figure 36*(a)) is halved, and for intermediate positions of the water table a linear interpolation is used. For ground water level at ground level the component of bearing capacity corresponding

---

* Even if 'undisturbed' samples are obtained it is often virtually impossible to prepare an undisturbed test specimen; recompaction of the specimen is usually necessary.

to the second term (*Figure 36*(b)) is also halved. Where fine sand exists below water table the corrected value of N must be used. Where the measured N is greater than 15

$$N_{corr.} = 15 + \tfrac{1}{2}(N - 15) \qquad \dots\dots\dots(50)$$

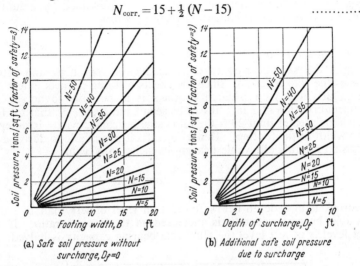

(a) *Safe soil pressure without surcharge, $D_f = 0$*

(b) *Additional safe soil pressure due to surcharge*

Charts based on water table not closer than B below base of footing

Figure 36. *Safe soil pressures beneath footings on sand, as determined by bearing capacity*

The dominant part of equation 49 is the first term, $0.5\gamma BN_\gamma$, which is directly proportional to the width of the footing. For all but the very narrow footings the safe load is high and the limiting factor is settlement. Peck, Hanson and Thorburn have also prepared graphs of allowable bearing capacity against N values (*Figure 37*). These are based partly on theoretical considerations and partly on a study of field data; the criterion is that of 1 in settlement being tolerable. Again it is assumed that ground

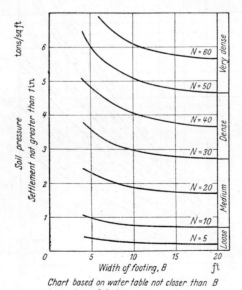

Chart based on water table not closer than B below base of footing

Figure 37. *Soil pressure corresponding to 1 in settlement of footings on sand*

water level is at a depth below foundation level at least equal to the width of the foundation. If water level is at foundation level the allowable bearing capacity must be halved. Allowable bearing capacities corresponding to other settlement criteria can be obtained by assuming the settlement to be proportional to bearing pressure.

Shallow rafts on sand

For rafts the safe bearing capacity is always very high and settlement becomes the sole criterion. Since the effects of loose pockets is less marked with a raft than with isolated footings it is possible to accept a total settlement criterion of 2 in. It can be seen from *Figure 37* that for foundation widths greater than 20 ft the allowable bearing capacity is independent of the width of the footing. Hence for rafts it is possible to derive a simple expression relating allowable bearing capacity to N value

$$q_a = \frac{N-3}{5} \text{ tons/sq ft} \qquad \ldots\ldots\ldots\ldots(51)$$

If bedrock is at a depth below foundation level of less than $B/2$ then the allowable bearing capacity is increased in the inverse ratio. If ground water level is at raft level the allowable bearing capacity is halved.

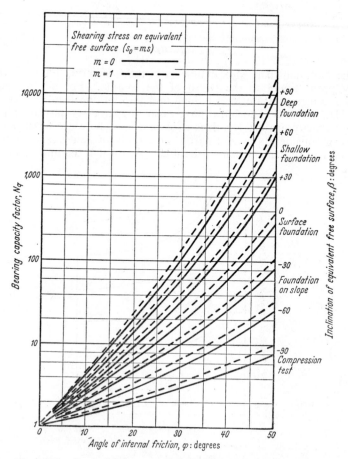

Figure 38. General bearing capacity factor N_q for strip foundation

Deep foundations in sand

The Terzaghi bearing capacity factors are known to be somewhat conservative when applied to shallow footings but they are a sufficient guide for practical purposes. For deep foundations, however, they are

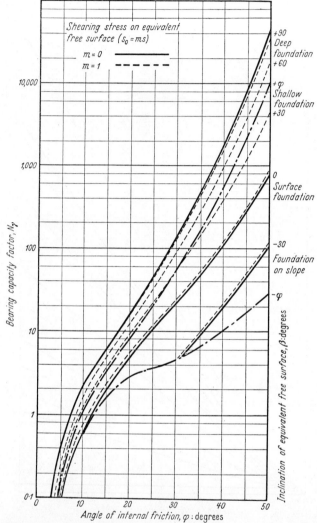

Figure 39. General bearing capacity factor N_γ for strip foundation

too conservative to be applicable and it is necessary to use bearing capacity factors given by MEYERHOF[54]. For deep footings it is feasible to determine ϕ from N values (standard penetration test values) and to use this to evaluate the Meyerhof bearing capacity factors. For piles, however, the small width in relation to the depth leads to dominance of the depth term $\gamma D (N_q - 1)$ in the bearing capacity formula and it is then simplest to determine end-bearing capacity directly from the results of static penetration tests such as Dutch deep sounding tests (HUIZINGA[55]).

In *Figures 38* and *39* Meyerhof's values of N_q and N_γ are plotted against ϕ, for various values of a parameter β which is the 'inclination of the equivalent free surface' and for limiting values of the mobilization of shear strength on this equivalent free surface. These curves are not directly usable over their full range without extensive computation to determine the stresses on the equivalent free surface, and its slope. For the cases which are given by the curves, namely surface foundations ($\beta=0$) and foundations on a slope ($-90° < \beta < 0°$), corrections are required to allow for local shear failure and for the shape of the foundations, as described below.

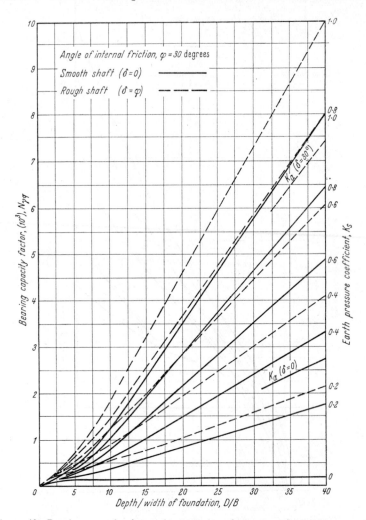

Figure 40. Bearing capacity factor for strip foundation in cohesionless material

To avoid the lengthy computations, Meyerhof has given an alternative method using a composite bearing capacity value factor $N_{\gamma q}$ in the expression

$$q = 0 \cdot 5 \gamma B N_{\gamma q} \qquad \ldots\ldots\ldots\ldots(52)$$

Values of $N_{\gamma q}$ are tabulated in *Figures 40* and *41* against the depth/ width ratio D/B for values of $\phi = 30°$ and $\phi = 40°$ respectively.

The values are for a strip footing with a rough base and for the two limiting conditions of a perfectly smooth shaft ($\delta=0$) and a perfectly rough shaft ($\delta=\phi$). To use these curves it is necessary to assume a value for K_s, the earth pressure coefficient on the shaft within the failure zone. In practice K_s varies between 0·5 for loose sand and 1·0 for dense sand. It is also necessary to use a corrected value of ϕ to take into account the effects of local shear failure arising from the compressibility of the sand. The friction angle ϕ is reduced by means of an empirical compressibility factor K so that

$$\tan \phi_{\text{corr.}} = K \tan \phi \qquad \ldots\ldots\ldots\ldots(53)$$

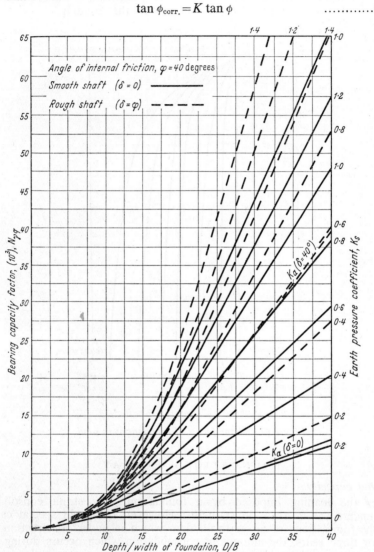

Figure 41. *Bearing capacity factor for strip foundation in cohesionless material*

For buried foundations K varies between 1·0 for shallow foundations and 0·85 for deep foundations ($D/B > 5$). For driven foundations K varies between 1·0 for shallow foundations and 0·95 for deep foundations.

In order to calculate the net bearing load of a foundation a shape factor λ must be applied in the expression

$$Q = \lambda A q \qquad \ldots\ldots\ldots\ldots(54)$$

Values of λ are given in *Figure 42*.

It must be emphasized that the discussion above has been concerned with the net ultimate bearing capacity of a foundation, not the gross bearing capacity. To determine the gross ultimate bearing capacity an addition must be made of the weight of material (soil and water) displaced by the foundation, and for bearing capacity arising from the mobilization of shear forces on the sides of the foundation. This is particularly important in the case of piles, and is discussed more fully under that heading.

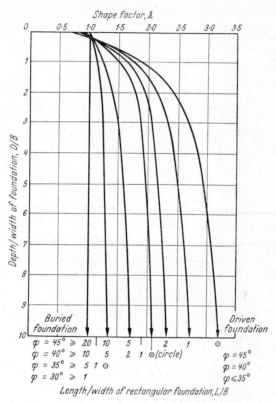

Figure 42. Shape factor of foundations in sand

FOUNDATIONS ON CLAY

Bearing capacity

Under the loading imposed by a foundation, clay strata consolidate and undergo an increase in strength. However, except in special cases, *e.g.* the foundations of an earth-fill dam which is under construction for two or three years, the amount of consolidation which occurs during the construction and first loading period is negligible, so that calculations of ultimate bearing capacity can be more easily made in terms of the total applied stresses, and not the effective stresses, and the angle of shearing resistance with respect to these applied stresses is zero for saturated clays, $\phi = 0$. This is a direct parallel with the $\phi = 0$ method for 'end of construction' stability analysis of slopes; in fact the circular arc method of analysis is applicable, as discussed below.

Putting $\phi = 0$ in the general bearing capacity formula eliminates the terms involving N_γ and N_q, leaving the simple expression

$$q = cN_c \qquad \qquad \qquad \dots\dots\dots\dots(55)$$

where c, the undrained shear strength, is obtained from triaxial compression tests; N_c is a function of the shape and depth of the footing and values of N_c have been obtained by both analytical and graphical methods. PRANDTL[56] in 1920 gave a solution for surface strip footings which he developed originally for metals in a plastic state, and which was produced independently by CAQUOT[57],

$$N_c = (\pi + 2) = 5 \cdot 14 \qquad \ldots\ldots\ldots\ldots(56)$$

The analysis has been extended to cover circular footings, both shallow and deep, by ISHLINGSKY[58], HENCKY[59], MEYERHOF[54], and others. In addition, the circular arc method has been employed. This was introduced by FELLENIUS[60] and has been fully explained by WILSON[61]. Wilson's curves give the centre of the worst circle and the bearing capacity. The former can be a very useful guide in starting a graphical analysis for a problem which is too complicated for the application of a formula. These curves are given in *Figure 43*.

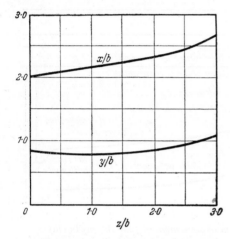
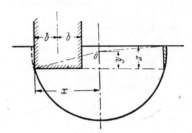

Figure 43. *Circular arc method (after Guthlac Wilson)*

The results of the analytical solutions have been combined by SKEMPTON[62] into two expressions for the bearing capacity factor N_c in terms of the depth, length and width of a foundation. He has also shown that the resulting values are in good agreement with field data and with results of laboratory tests.

For a depth/width ratio, $D/B < 2\frac{1}{2}$

$$N_c = 5 \left(1 + \frac{D}{5B}\right)\left(1 + \frac{B}{5L}\right) \qquad \ldots\ldots\ldots\ldots(57)$$

in which the term in the first bracket is the depth factor and the term in the second bracket is the shape factor.

For deep footings $D/B \geqslant 2\frac{1}{2}$

$$N_c = 7 \cdot 5 \left(1 + \frac{B}{5L}\right) \qquad \ldots\ldots\ldots\ldots(58)$$

Circular footings have the same N_c values as square footings ($B/L = 1$) and hence for deep circular or square footings, and for piles, $N_c = 9$.

In using the values of ultimate bearing capacity given by equations 57 and 58 it is necessary to apply a factor of safety (F), usually 3, in arriving at the net safe bearing capacity. The value of c taken in the calculation is the average value for a depth below foundation level equal to about $\frac{2}{3}$ B provided that the shear strength within this depth does not vary more than about ± 50 per cent of this average value. Overstressing will occur where the net applied pressure p_n is greater than πc_{min}, where c_{min} is the minimum shear strength within a depth equal to $B/2$. Except in special cases applied pressure should not exceed πc_{min} or $c_{av} N_c / F$ whichever is the less. As mentioned, with complex foundation conditions graphical analysis may be the more appropriate.

SETTLEMENT

An idealized representation of settlement of foundations in clays is given in *Figure 44*.

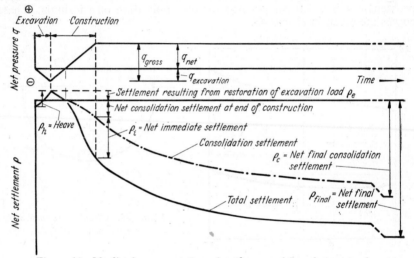

Figure 44. Idealized representation of settlement of foundations in clay

On excavation, heave occurs and the majority of this is recovered when the original total overburden pressure p_0 is replaced. This recovery of heave is often neglected in settlement calculations. With further application of load, *i.e.* with increase in the net applied pressure, an immediate settlement occurs without volume change of the clay, followed by consolidation settlement as the excess pore pressures set up by the applied load dissipate. In practice, the consolidation settlement starts immediately the net pressure is greater than zero, but at a very slow rate, so that it is convenient to ignore the consolidation settlement occurring during construction or, alternatively, to consider it as starting at halfway through the construction period.

The net final settlement is the sum of the immediate settlement and the consolidation settlement:

$$\rho_{final} = \rho_i + \rho_c \qquad \qquad \dots\dots\dots\dots(59)$$

The net settlement at any time t, is given by:

$$\rho_t = \rho_i + \bar{U}\rho_c \qquad \qquad \dots\dots\dots\dots(60)$$

where $\bar{U}$ is the degree of consolidation after time t.

The consolidation settlement can be related to the oedometer settlement, ρ_{oed} (the settlement obtained by the straightforward application of the oedometer tests results, see p 13, by a coefficient μ (SKEMPTON and BJERRUM[63]). Equation 60 then becomes

$$\rho_t = \rho_i + \overline{U} \mu \, \rho_{\text{oed}} \qquad \dots\dots\dots(61)$$

Immediate settlement

The immediate settlement below the corner of a uniformly loaded rectangular area can be calculated from elastic theory using the STEINBRENNER[64] equation:

$$\rho_i = \frac{3}{4} q \frac{B}{E} I_\rho \qquad \dots\dots\dots(62)$$

where E is Young's modulus for the clay, as measured by the initial tangent modulus of stress–strain curves from triaxial tests, and I_ρ is an influence factor which is a function of the length and width of the foundation and the thickness of the compressible layer below foundation level. Values of I_ρ are given in *Figure 45*.

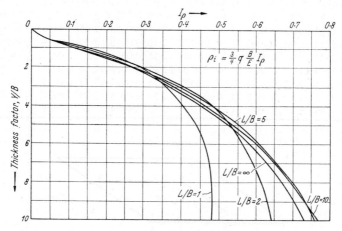

Figure 45. Steinbrenner's influence factors for loaded area $L \times B$ on compressible stratum of thickness Y

Settlements at other points below a rectangular area can be calculated by splitting the area into a number of rectangles and using the principle of superposition.

Consolidation settlement

The oedometer settlement is calculated from the equation:

$$\rho_{\text{oed}} = \int_0^z m_v \Delta\sigma_1 dz \qquad \dots\dots\dots(63)$$

In practice this expression is evaluated by dividing the compressible strata into layers and the oedometer settlement of each layer is calculated using the average stress increment $\Delta\sigma_1$ in that layer and the average value of the modulus of compressibility m_v in that layer. The total oedometer settlement is then the sum of the settlements of the layers. The increment of vertical stress in any layer can be calculated from elastic theory. BOUSSINESQ[65] gave the following equation for the vertical stress increase at depth z due to a point load P on the surface of a semi-infinite solid:

$$\sigma_z = \frac{P}{z^2} \cdot \frac{3}{2\pi} \left[\frac{1}{\{1 + (r/z)^2\}^{5/2}} \right] \qquad \ldots\ldots\ldots\ldots(64)$$

where z and r are defined in *Figure 46*. This can be written

$$\sigma_z = PK/z^2 \qquad \ldots\ldots\ldots\ldots(65)$$

Values of K are given in TABLE 3.

TABLE 3

VALUES OF COEFFICIENT K IN EQUATION 65

Ratio $\frac{r}{z}$	Coefficient K	Ratio $\frac{r}{z}$	Coefficient K	Ratio $\frac{r}{z}$	Coefficient K	Ratio $\frac{r}{z}$	Coefficient K	Ratio $\frac{r}{z}$	Coefficient K	Ratio $\frac{r}{z}$	Coefficient K
0·00	0·4775	0·60	0·2214	1·20	0·0513	1·80	0·0129	2·40	0·0040	2·84	0·0019
0·05	0·4745	0·65	0·1978	1·25	0·0454	1·85	0·0116	2·45	0·0037	2·91	0·0017
0·10	0·4657	0·70	0·1762	1·30	0·0402	1·90	0·0105	2·50	0·0034	2·99	0·0015
0·15	0·4516	0·75	0·1565	1·35	0·0357	1·95	0·0095	2·55	0·0031	3·08	0·0013
0·20	0·4329	0·80	0·1386	1·40	0·0317	2·00	0·0085	2·60	0·0029	3·19	0·0011
0·25	0·4103	0·85	0·1226	1·45	0·0282	2·05	0·0078	2·65	0·0026	3·31	0·0009
0·30	0·3849	0·90	0·1083	1·50	0·0251	2·10	0·0070	2·70	0·0024	3·50	0·0007
0·35	0·3577	0·95	0·0956	1·55	0·0224	2·15	0·0064	2·72	0·0023	3·75	0·0005
0·40	0·3294	1·00	0·0844	1·60	0·0200	2·20	0·0058	2·74	0·0023	4·13	0·0003
0·45	0·3011	1·05	0·0744	1·65	0·0179	2·25	0·0053	2·76	0·0022	4·91	0·0001
0·50	0·2733	1·10	0·0658	1·70	0·0160	2·30	0·0048	2·78	0·0021	6·15	0·0001
0·55	0·2466	1·15	0·0581	1·75	0·0144	2·35	0·0044	2·80	0·0021		

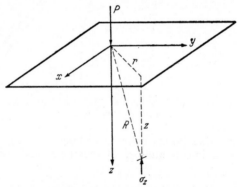

*Figure 46. Diagram showing z and r in
Boussinesq equation for concentrated load*

This equation has been integrated and tabulated by NEWMARK[66] to give
the pressure below the corner of a rectangle uniformly loaded at the surface
and the values are given in TABLE 4. In order to obtain the pressure below
any other point it is necessary to regard that point as the corner of four
adjoining rectangles, not necessarily the same shape or size, to calculate the
pressure below the corner of each and add these pressures; *e.g.* the pressure
below the centre of a rectangle is four times the pressure beneath the corner
of a rectangle whose sides are half the sides of the original rectangle. The
principle can be extended to points outside the original rectangle by addition
and subtraction of rectangles. It is implied in the above that the pressure
is uniformly distributed at the surface of the ground. This in turn is an
assumption that the foundation is quite flexible, which is in general not true

TABLE 4.   VERTICAL PRESSURE σ_z UNDER CORNER OF RECTANGLE $a \times b$ LOADED UNIFORMLY WITH INTENSITY q. σ_z/q FOR VALUES OF $\alpha = a/z$ AND $\beta = b/z$

α/β	0·1	0·2	0·3	0·4	0·5	0·6	0·7	0·8	0·9	1·0	1·2	1·4	1·6	1·8	2·0	2·5	3·0	4·0	5·0	6·0	8·0	10·0	∞
0·1	0·0047	0·0092	0·0132	0·0168	0·0198	0·0222	0·0242	0·0258	0·0270	0·0279	0·0293	0·0301	0·0306	0·0309	0·0311	0·0314	0·0315	0·0316	0·0316	0·0316	0·0316	0·0316	0·0316
0·2	0·0092	0·0179	0·0259	0·0328	0·0387	0·0435	0·0474	0·0504	0·0528	0·0547	0·0573	0·0589	0·0599	0·0606	0·0610	0·0616	0·0618	0·0619	0·0620	0·0620	0·0620	0·0620	0·0620
0·3	0·0132	0·0259	0·0374	0·0474	0·0559	0·0629	0·0686	0·0731	0·0766	0·0794	0·0832	0·0856	0·0871	0·0880	0·0887	0·0895	0·0898	0·0901	0·0901	0·0902	0·0902	0·0902	0·0902
0·4	0·0168	0·0328	0·0474	0·0602	0·0711	0·0801	0·0873	0·0931	0·0977	0·1013	0·1063	0·1094	0·1114	0·1126	0·1134	0·1145	0·1150	0·1153	0·1154	0·1154	0·1154	0·1154	0·1154
0·5	0·0198	0·0387	0·0559	0·0711	0·0840	0·0947	0·1034	0·1104	0·1158	0·1202	0·1263	0·1300	0·1324	0·1340	0·1350	0·1363	0·1368	0·1372	0·1374	0·1374	0·1375	0·1375	0·1375
0·6	0·0222	0·0435	0·0629	0·0801	0·0947	0·1069	0·1168	0·1247	0·1311	0·1361	0·1431	0·1475	0·1503	0·1521	0·1533	0·1548	0·1555	0·1560	0·1561	0·1561	0·1562	0·1562	0·1562
0·7	0·0242	0·0474	0·0686	0·0873	0·1034	0·1168	0·1277	0·1365	0·1436	0·1491	0·1570	0·1620	0·1652	0·1672	0·1686	0·1704	0·1711	0·1717	0·1719	0·1719	0·1720	0·1720	0·1720
0·8	0·0258	0·0504	0·0731	0·0931	0·1104	0·1247	0·1365	0·1461	0·1537	0·1598	0·1684	0·1739	0·1774	0·1797	0·1812	0·1832	0·1841	0·1847	0·1849	0·1850	0·1850	0·1850	0·1850
0·9	0·0270	0·0528	0·0766	0·0977	0·1158	0·1311	0·1436	0·1537	0·1619	0·1684	0·1777	0·1836	0·1874	0·1899	0·1915	0·1938	0·1947	0·1954	0·1956	0·1957	0·1957	0·1958	0·1958
1·0	0·0279	0·0547	0·0794	0·1013	0·1202	0·1361	0·1491	0·1598	0·1684	0·1752	0·1851	0·1914	0·1955	0·1981	0·1999	0·2024	0·2034	0·2042	0·2044	0·2045	0·2046	0·2046	0·2046
1·2	0·0293	0·0573	0·0832	0·1063	0·1263	0·1431	0·1570	0·1684	0·1777	0·1851	0·1958	0·2028	0·2073	0·2103	0·2124	0·2151	0·2163	0·2172	0·2175	0·2176	0·2177	0·2177	0·2177
1·4	0·0301	0·0589	0·0856	0·1094	0·1300	0·1475	0·1620	0·1739	0·1836	0·1914	0·2028	0·2102	0·2151	0·2184	0·2206	0·2236	0·2250	0·2260	0·2263	0·2264	0·2265	0·2265	0·2266
1·6	0·0306	0·0599	0·0871	0·1114	0·1324	0·1503	0·1652	0·1774	0·1874	0·1955	0·2073	0·2151	0·2203	0·2237	0·2261	0·2294	0·2309	0·2320	0·2324	0·2325	0·2326	0·2326	0·2326
1·8	0·0309	0·0606	0·0880	0·1126	0·1340	0·1521	0·1672	0·1797	0·1899	0·1981	0·2103	0·2184	0·2237	0·2274	0·2299	0·2333	0·2350	0·2360	0·2364	0·2367	0·2368	0·2368	0·2369
2	0·0311	0·0610	0·0887	0·1134	0·1350	0·1533	0·1686	0·1812	0·1915	0·1999	0·2124	0·2206	0·2261	0·2299	0·2355	0·2361	0·2378	0·2391	0·2395	0·2397	0·2398	0·2399	0·2399
2·5	0·0314	0·0616	0·0895	0·1145	0·1363	0·1548	0·1704	0·1832	0·1938	0·2024	0·2151	0·2236	0·2294	0·2333	0·2362	0·2404	0·2420	0·2434	0·2439	0·2441	0·2443	0·2443	0·2443
3	0·0315	0·0618	0·0898	0·1150	0·1368	0·1555	0·1711	0·1841	0·1947	0·2034	0·2163	0·2250	0·2309	0·2350	0·2378	0·2420	0·2439	0·2455	0·2461	0·2463	0·2465	0·2465	0·246
4	0·0316	0·0619	0·0901	0·1153	0·1372	0·1560	0·1717	0·1847	0·1954	0·2042	0·2172	0·2260	0·2320	0·2360	0·2391	0·2434	0·2455	0·2473	0·2479	0·2482	0·2484	0·2484	0·248
5	0·0316	0·0620	0·0901	0·1154	0·1374	0·1561	0·1719	0·1849	0·1956	0·2044	0·2175	0·2263	0·2324	0·2364	0·2395	0·2439	0·2461	0·2479	0·2486	0·2489	0·2491	0·2491	0·2492
6	0·0316	0·0620	0·0902	0·1154	0·1374	0·1562	0·1719	0·1850	0·1957	0·2045	0·2176	0·2264	0·2325	0·2367	0·2397	0·2441	0·2463	0·2482	0·2489	0·2492	0·2494	0·2495	0·2495
8	0·0316	0·0620	0·0902	0·1154	0·1374	0·1562	0·1720	0·1850	0·1957	0·2046	0·2177	0·2265	0·2326	0·2368	0·2398	0·2443	0·2465	0·2484	0·2491	0·2494	0·2496	0·2497	0·2498
10	0·0316	0·0620	0·0902	0·1154	0·1375	0·1562	0·1720	0·1850	0·1958	0·2046	0·2177	0·2265	0·2326	0·2368	0·2399	0·2443	0·2465	0·2484	0·2492	0·2495	0·2497	0·2498	0·2499
∞	0·0316	0·0620	0·0902	0·1154	0·1375	0·1562	0·1720	0·1850	0·1958	0·2046	0·2177	0·2266	0·2326	0·2369	0·2399	0·2443	0·2465	0·2485	0·2492	0·2495	0·2498	0·2499	0·2500

(*After* NEWARK[60])

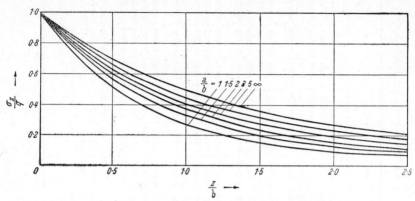

Figure 47. Mean pressure under stiff foundation (after Fox[67]*)*

but gives a limit for the pressure distribution which is not far from the truth. The other limit is given by the assumption that the foundation is quite stiff *i.e.* that the same settlement occurs at every point. The pressure distribution for this case has been worked out by Fox[67], who gives a series of curves, *Figure 47,* for the mean vertical stress σ_z at a depth z beneath a rectangular area $a \times b$ uniformly loaded with a pressure q, the rectangle being on the surface.

JURGENSON[68] has tabulated influence values for grids of points below a variety of flexible loaded areas, with uniform, triangular and 'terrace' loadings.

The coefficient μ in the equation $\rho_c = \mu \cdot \rho_{oed}$ is related to the pore pressure coefficient A by the equation

$$\mu = A + \alpha (1 - A) \qquad \ldots\ldots\ldots\ldots (66)$$

where α is a coefficient depending on the geometry of the problem. It has been computed for circular and strip footings, with various ratios of the thickness of the clay z to the width of the footing B. The results are given in TABLE 5.

TABLE 5

VALUES OF α IN THE EQUATION $\mu = A + \alpha (1 - A)$

Z/B	*Circlar footing* α	*Strip footing* α
0	1·00	1·00
0·25	0·67	0·74
0·5	0·50	0·53
1	0·38	0·37
2	0·30	0·26
4	0·28	0·20
10	0·26	0·14
∞	0·25	0

Depth correction

Where foundations are below ground level a correction must be made to allow for the effect of the surcharge in reducing settlement. The values to be used are given by Fox's correction curves (*Figure 48*).

Time settlement

The basis of the Terzaghi one dimensional consolidation theory has been discussed on p 12. Once the total consolidation settlement has been determined and a value of the coefficient of consolidation, c_v, has been

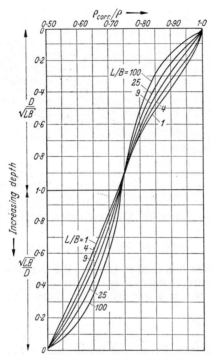

Figure 48. Fox's correction curves for settlements of flexible rectangular footings of area $L \times B$ at depth D

selected, it remains to determine the relation between the degree of consolidation and time. This can be obtained from the expression

$$T = c_v \frac{t}{H^2} \qquad \qquad \ldots\ldots\ldots\ldots(67)$$

where c_v is the consolidation coefficient in square feet per year, t is the time in years and H is the length of the drainage path in feet, and from the relation between U and t. This relationship is dependent on the initial distribution of excess pore pressure. *Figure 49* gives a plot of U versus t for various ratios of the initial excess pore pressure at the top and bottom of the compressible stratum u_1/u_2. The cases given are all for single drainage.

For double drainage, *i.e.* where drainage can take place at the top and bottom of the layer, values corresponding to $u_1/u_2 = 1$ can be used for all ratios of initial pore pressure, but it should be noted that in the double drainage case H is taken as only half of the layer thickness.

One-dimensional drainage is seldom fully realized in practice and for important calculations, particularly where the loaded area is small in comparison with the thickness of the compressible stratum, two- or three-dimensional consolidation should be considered (see GIBSON and LUMB[69]).

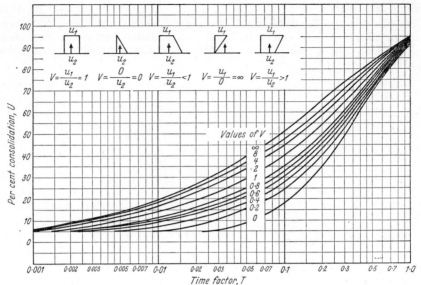

Figure 49. Values of time factor T

PILED FOUNDATIONS

A pile is a column which is used to transfer the foundation load to a deeper stratum when the surface material is not strong enough to carry the load. The oldest type of pile is a tree trunk, but there are now many different varieties.

Types of piles

Piles can be divided into driven and bored piles. The difference between a driven pile and a bored pile from the engineering point of view is that the driven pile compacts the ground by vibration and displacement, whereas the bored pile causes no compaction and vibration is avoided. Obviously the merits of either system depend on the conditions of the problem.

Driven piles can be pre-formed and made either of wood, concrete or steel, or they can be formed *in situ* when they are nearly always made of concrete. Bored piles are generally formed *in situ* of concrete, but can be pre-formed and dropped into a hole previously bored.

Pre-formed steel piles can be either H beams, box piles, sheet piles, steel tubes, or even steel rods. Pre-formed concrete piles can be either ordinary reinforced concrete or pre-stressed concrete. For all pre-formed piles the handling and driving stresses are usually the greatest which the pile will ever sustain.

There are many varieties, usually under proprietary names, of concrete piles formed *in situ*. In some cases mandrels are used, and some incorporate pre-formed concrete sections which are grouted up when in the ground.

For further information on pile types see chapter on Foundations and Earthworks.

Groups of piles

A piled foundation generally consists of a group of several piles, the behaviour of which must be considered as an entity.

The piled group will consist of either point-bearing piles which transfer their load to a hard stratum of soil on which their points bear, *e.g.* piles to rock, or friction piles which transfer their load mainly by friction on the sides of the piles to a firm stratum into which they penetrate. Friction piles into a firm clay stratum will usually penetrate about 20 to 30 times the pile diameter into the clay. Piles driven through soft material into compact sand or gravel will usually penetrate about 5 times the diameter and will be partly point-bearing and partly frictional.

When friction piles are used in conditions in which the increase in strength of the soil with depth is only gradual, they must be of a length comparable to the size of the building to be of much advantage. This is shown in *Figure 50* in which the stress distribution with and without piles

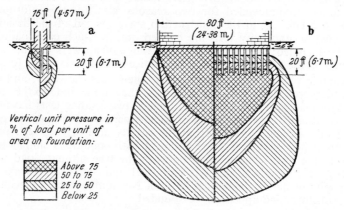

Figure 50. *Diagram illustrating increase of vertical pressure in soil beneath friction pile foundations having piles of equal lengths carrying equal loads. In* a *width of foundation small compared to pile length; in* b *width of foundation large compared to pile length*

is shown for two buildings of different widths but with piles of the same length. Unless the use of piles changes the stress pattern radically they are probably not economic.

The design of a foundation on friction piles should always be checked from the point of view of overall stability as described in the section on Foundations, and assuming that the whole of the load is distributed uniformly over the area of the building and acts at the foot of the piles. The friction round the circumference of the block of soil containing the piles should be subtracted from the foundation load.

If the foundation on friction piles is supported by a bed of clay, consolidation settlements will occur which can be estimated as described for deep foundations above.

Single piles

Although the carrying capacity of a group of piles is not that of a single pile times the number of piles in the group, it is useful to know the load which a single pile will carry.

Pile bearing on rock

For a point bearing pile to rock, the bearing capacity is usually no problem. If the rock surface is steeply sloping it may be necessary to provide the pile with a special point to make sure that it is adequately toed in (BJERRUM[70]) and if the pile passes through very soft clay and is a slender column its stability against buckling must be investigated.

Pile bearing in sand and gravel

The bearing capacity of a pile in sand and gravel can be estimated from the results of a static penetration test or Dutch deep sounding test. This is carried out by pushing a steel tube with a cone-shaped point into the ground at a slow but steady rate and measuring the resistance of the point and the wall separately. The point resistance of a full-scale pile is greater than the cone resistance in the ratio of the areas since in equation 46 (p 45) for a deep foundation the depth term far outweighs the others.

When it is possible to carry out a loading test on a full-scale pile this should be done, the test being carried to failure, *i.e.* until settlement continues under constant load.

The use of dynamic pile driving formulae to calculate the ultimate load is not to be recommended for two reasons viz: (*a*) the information is obtained too late, *i.e.* at the construction stage instead of the design stage unless previous expensive tests are carried out, in which case loading tests should be included; and (*b*) a very wide range of answers can be obtained depending on the formula used and the choice of constants in the formula.

Dynamic pile driving formulae have their uses, however, and records of set and energy should always be kept as they are a guide to the variation in ultimate load over a site on which one or two loading tests have already been carried out. Also engineers of wide experience can make an estimate of the load carrying capacity from the results of a driving test, provided always that their experience was obtained with conditions similar to those relating to the test. The relation between the true ultimate load and that given by the dynamic formula is empirical and should be recognized as such in spite of the mathematical basis of Newtonian impact mechanics on which such formulae appear to be founded.

Pile bearing in clay

A pile in clay will in general be a friction pile, only 10–20 per cent of the load being taken by the point. A loading test will give the best indication of the bearing capacity and of the settlement under load. If the pile is driven into the clay it should not be test-loaded immediately since the true bearing capacity will only be attained some 2–4 weeks after driving, that is after the hydrostatic pressures caused by the driving have dissipated.

The bearing capacity of a pile in clay can be estimated from the shear strength s of the clay ($\frac{1}{2}$ compression strength) by the formula

$$Q = 9A_1s + kA_2s \qquad \dots\dots\dots\dots(68)$$

where Q = bearing capacity

      A_1 = area of point

      A_2 = area of pile wall in contact with clay

      k = an empirical factor which varies with the type of pile and the clay and is between 0·45 and 0·6 for a well constructed bored pile in blue London clay (SKEMPTON[71]).

The working load is Q/F where F = factor of safety, usually 2 to $2\frac{1}{2}$.

The settlement of a single pile under the working load can really be determined only from a loading test or from extensive experience of piles in similar conditions.

When a pile is driven into a sensitive clay a considerable drop in strength of the clay may occur. Test-loading should not be carried out for at least a month after driving, by which time the clay will have recovered most of its strength and the bearing capacity will be found to agree approximately with that given by equation 68 where s is the undisturbed shear strength of the clay measured *in situ* with the vane apparatus.

Negative skin friction

When a pile is driven through a soft sensitive clay to a harder stratum, reconsolidation of the soft clay under its own weight following disturbance will cause a downward drag on the shaft of the pile which will be at least as great as the remoulded shear strength of the clay times the shaft surface in the clay, and may approach the undisturbed shear strength times the shaft surface as the clay regains its strength. This phenomenon exerts a real load on the pile which must be added to the building load to give the total applied load on the pile.

GEOTECHNICAL PROCESSES

In order to solve some engineering problems it is necessary or convenient to change the properties of the soil concerned. These changes are effected by geotechnical processes, which include compaction, both deep and superficial, injection processes, drainage and waterlowering, freezing, and the use of compressed air (see GLOSSOP[72]).

SUPERFICIAL COMPACTION AND SOIL STABILIZATION

These processes are used mainly in the construction of earth dams, embankments, and the subgrades of roads and runways. The principle of the compaction process is that mechanical work applied to a soil will reduce the air voids and so give greater strength and mechanical stability. Stabilization with Portland cement or other additives will then maintain the stability under adverse conditions.

Plant

Compaction plant varies from hand punners to heavy vibrating plates and jumping frog rammers, and comprises also many types of rollers, rubber-tyred, wobbly wheel, sheepsfoot and smooth steel-tyred. Some rollers can be ballasted by water or broken stone, and some incorporate vibrators.

Stabilization plant includes all the above compaction plant and in addition pulverizing and mixing plant which can vary from simple ploughs, harrows and disc cultivators to impressive single-pass machines, some of which pulverize, moisten, mix, lay and compact the soil in one pass of the machine.

Grading

It is easier to compact or to stabilize a soil satisfactorily if the grading approximates to that of a naturally stable material (see *Figure 51*). The

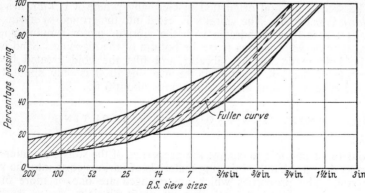

Figure 51. Suggested particle-size limits for bases. $1\frac{1}{2}$ *in maximum aggregate size*

grading of a soil which departs from this can be corrected by mixing another soil with it, provided always that the soil is such that mechanical mixing is possible *e.g.* it is not always possible to mix another soil with some very sticky or very hard clays. But a stiff clay can sometimes be stabilized with cement by using a machine with a high-speed rotor which cuts the clay into flakes which then act as an aggregate and are coated with cement and compacted.

Moisture content

The moisture content of the soil must be close to the optimum for the particular compaction plant and process used. This is often best determined by field trials based on preliminary laboratory tests.

Compaction

The soil should always be compacted to the maximum possible density. This will not only give it greater immediate strength, but will greatly reduce any future softening which may take place. There is an obvious economic limit to the degree of compaction which can be obtained with the plant available, since the increase in density per pass of the roller drops off rapidly after 8 or 10 passes.

Stabilizer

A stabilizing agent may be mixed with the soil before compaction. The purpose of this is to waterproof or to cement the soil, or to prevent the pick-up of water and thus reduce softening. Various substances can be and have been used as stabilizers, amongst which are cement, resins (sodium rosinate, *Vinsol*), bituminous emulsions, chemicals (calcium chloride, common salt), molasses, oils (Shell stabilizing oil), (see ROBINSON[73]). A recent development is the construction of impervious soil blankets by soil stabilization methods, used to line reservoirs. The permeability of the soil can be very greatly reduced by mixing in quite small amounts of certain chemicals such as sodium tetraphosphate (see LAMBE[74]).

DEEP COMPACTION

This process is used to increase the density of sandy and gravelly soils before building on them. The method relies on vibration as the compacting agency.

Two methods exist. The first is the simpler and consists of driving piles into the soil. The vibration compacts the soil and the pile occupies the void resulting from the compaction. Driven *in situ* piles can be used; it is unnecessary to add cement to the pile, an inert filler being used since the pile is not required to carry a load. This is an advantage in acid soils.

The second method originated in Germany, where it is known as the *Rutteldruckvervahren*. The vibrator is jetted into the ground by means of a water jet. It is then withdrawn with the vibrator motor running and an upward flow of water issuing from the bottom of the machine. Sand is fed into the hole made by the vibrator and fills the void created by the compaction of the soil. Although the machine itself is only about 12 in diam, the effective radius of the vibration is about 3 ft.

INJECTION PROCESSES—GROUTING

Purpose

It is sometimes possible to change the properties of the soils encountered in an engineering problem by injecting materials of various sorts into the voids of the soil. The properties which are changed are one or more of the following: permeability, strength, compressibility, weight.

Cases in which the change in permeability is important include the formation of grouted cut-offs under dams, grouting fissured rocks, grouting sand and gravel to reduce air losses during construction work in compressed air, and sealing gaps in sheet piling. The increase in strength is important in underpinning problems, in support of excavation in tunnelling, and in stabilizing clay embankments. Injection processes can also be used to lift tanks and pavement slabs by hydraulic pressure, the grout later setting and supporting the structure in the raised position.

Soils which can be grouted

Grouts can be injected into the fissures in a rock. This is probably one of the earliest applications of the process. Rock fill and rubble masonry can also be grouted. Usually cement grouts are used in these cases since the voids are fairly large.

Gravels and sands can be grouted successfully by a variety of different processes as described below, but clays and silts cannot be grouted because their voids are too small and their permeabilities are too low (GLOSSOP and SKEMPTON[75]).

Soils such as peat can sometimes be grouted successfully but the mechanism is probably somewhat different from that in sands and gravels and may involve compression and displacement of the soil.

The fissures in stiff fissured clays have been grouted on occasion, and a recent successful development is the grouting of clay embankments using the Aerocem process which employs aerated cement grouts. (See PURBRICK and AYRES[76]).

Materials used as grouts

Grouts generally consist of suspensions but emulsions and solutions, or mixtures of these, can be used.

Suspensions

The majority of grouts are suspensions of cement in water. If the voids to be filled are large then sand is also used to reduce the cost and the shrinkage on setting. Fly-ash is now sometimes used when available cheaply. Powdered clay can be used, generally in the form of a thixotropic gel; bentonitic clays such as fullers' earth are very suitable.

The particles of cement and clay will not penetrate into the voids of a soil finer than fine gravel or possibly coarse sand, but in a mixed soil the grouting is often accompanied by compression and compaction of the soil due to the penetration of the grout along the coarser layers since most soils of this type are stratified to some extent.

Emulsions

Bituminous emulsions can be used as grouts. When used alone, as in the Shell-Perm process, they can be injected into soils down to the fine sand range. They reduce the permeability considerably and are therefore used to form cut-offs under dams and barrages; but they add practically nothing to the strength of the soil and are therefore of no use in underpinning problems.

Bituminous emulsions can also be used mixed with sand for filling large voids under pavement slabs and floors. In this case cut-back emulsions are used which coagulate and set, developing considerable strength.

Solutions

There are several grouting processes in which solutions of chemicals are injected. Although these vary quite a lot they all use sodium silicate in one form or another.   The chemical processes can be used down to the fine sand range.   They divide into the two-solution and the single-solution processes.

In the two-solution processes (Joosten and Guttman processes) the first chemical injected is sodium silicate, and this is followed immediately by calcium chloride or some such salt.   The reaction is almost immediate and for this reason the solutions cannot penetrate far from the injection pipes which are therefore spaced at about 2 ft centres.   The process gives considerable strength to the soil and also reduces the permeability to a very small fraction of its previous value.

In the single-solution processes the two chemicals are mixed before injection with a third chemical which delays the setting action for some time.   The injection pipes can therefore be at greater centres.   The processes reduce the permeability but do not give strengths comparable to the two-solution process.

Method of injection

In nearly all grouting work the injections are made by driving pipes into the ground and pumping the grout in under pressure through hoses attached to the pipes.

The spacing of the pipes varies widely with the process and the conditions from 2 ft for the two-solution chemical process in sand, to about 10 ft for clay injections in alluvium, and up to 30 ft or more for cement grouts in fissured rocks.

When filling fissures in rock with cement grout it is usual to use piston pumps which will give a pressure up to 1,000 lb/sq in (70 kg/cm²).   The same pumps can be used for clay injections with alluvial sands and gravels but the pressures must be carefully controlled and should not greatly exceed the overburden pressure to avoid lifting the ground surface.

In the Joosten and Guttman two-solution chemical processes the amount of grout required to fill the voids in the soil between injection pipes is pumped in irrespective of the pressure, subject to a maximum pressure of 400 lb/sq in (28 kg/cm²).   Piston pumps are used.

In the Aerocem process the grout is compressible and a pump of the continuous screw type such as a Monopump is used, pressures ranging up to 150 lb/sq in (10·5 kg/cm²).

For very simple grouting jobs a grout pan is used.   The cement grout is mixed in the pan by a paddle driven by hand or by a compressed air motor, an air pressure up to 100 lb/sq in (7 kg/cm²) is then applied to the surface of the grout in the pan and this drives the grout through the hose into the injection pipe and so into the ground.

In general grouting work is not simple and damage can be caused by the indiscriminate use of high pressures by inexperienced operators.   The work should be planned and carried out by engineers and operators experienced in the use of grouting methods.

DRAINAGE AND WATER LOWERING

Ordinary methods of drainage, although correctly classed as a geotechnical process, are so well known that they need not be considered here.

Water lowering can be used in sands and gravels to allow an excavation to be carried out in the dry below the water table, or to reduce the water pressure either on the side or the bottom of an excavation.   It is not normally of use in silts owing to the long time required to drain a silt.   It differs from pumping from sumps in that the flow of water is away from the excavation, thus increasing the stability and minimizing the danger of 'blows'.

Water lowering, unlike the other processes so far mentioned, is a temporary expedient. Continuous pumping is required during the lowering period. The spacing of the wells and capacity of the pumps is theoretically calculable provided that the permeability of the ground is known, see GLOSSOP and COLLINGRIDGE[77], but a great deal of experience and judgment is also called for. In practice, provision should always be made for more wells than are theoretically needed, and these should be installed if found necessary.

Permeability and filters

The determination of the permeability of the ground is part of the site investigation without which no water lowering project should ever be considered (see chapter on Site Investigations).

Pumping tests give the most reliable value for k but much can be done from grading curves (see LOUDON[10]). Undisturbed samples of fine sands are essential in order to see if the material is laminated—a fact which naturally can have a marked effect on the horizontal permeability.

Grading curves are also used to choose suitable sand as a filter medium using Terzaghi's empirical rule which states that the grading curve for the filter material should be the same shape as that for the material to be filtered, and the point at which it crosses the 15 per cent line should lie between four times the 15 per cent size and four times the 85 per cent size for the latter (see *Figure 52*).

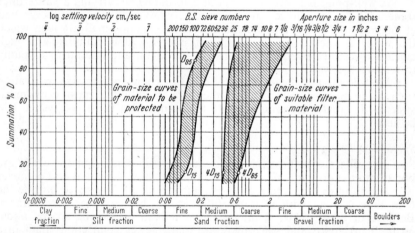

Figure 52. Diagram illustrating Terzaghi's rule for filter materials. Left-hand zone encloses particle size distribution curves of material to be protected; right-hand zone encloses particle size distribution curves of filter material

Pumping capacity

The quantity of water to be pumped can be calculated from the equation

$$Q = \frac{16 \cdot 75k \, (H^2 - h^2)}{\log_{10} R / A} \, (\text{gal/min}) \qquad \ldots\ldots\ldots\ldots(69)$$

where k = permeability (cm/sec)

H = depth from normal water level to an impermeable stratum (ft)

h = depth from lowered water level to an impermeable stratum (ft)

R = radius of cone of depression (ft)

A = radius of circle of area equal to area surrounded by wells (ft)

R can be obtained from the relation

$$R \, (\text{ft}) = 300 \, (H - h) \, (k \, \text{cm/sec})^{\frac{1}{2}} \qquad \ldots\ldots\ldots\ldots(70)$$

The number of wells required can be obtained from the empirical relationship

$$Q = 52 r_0 h_0 n k^{\frac{1}{2}} \text{ (gal/min)} \qquad \ldots\ldots\ldots\ldots(71)$$

where r_0 = radius of a well (ft)

h_0 = water level outside a well (ft)

k = permeability in cm/sec

n = number of wells required.

The expression $2\pi r_0 h_0 n$ is the immersed area required. h_0 is generally fixed by the geometry of the problem, but r_0 and n can be varied together at will (see GLOSSOP and COLLINGRIDGE[77]).

Well-points, suction wells and deep wells

Three systems of water lowering are in common use and each has certain advantages and disadvantages.

Well-points

When the lowering of the water level required is 15 ft (4·5 m) or less a well-point system can be used. If the system operates very efficiently greater lowering can be obtained, but this should not be assumed at the planning stage.

A well-point is a steel tube about 2 in diameter carrying a gauze filter some 3 ft long at its lower end. The well-points are jetted into the ground at intervals of 3 to 6 ft and then connected to a suction main through which the water is sucked out by a special pumping unit comprising a high efficiency vacuum pump for exhausting the main, and a centrifugal pump to remove the water.

Well-points are cheap to install and for a long progressive excavation such as a pipe or sewer trench they are usually the most economical system. If greater lowering than 15 ft is required a two-stage system can be used.

Suction wells

Suction wells are in principle the same as well points but the wells are bored into the ground. The wells are usually about 12 in (30 cm) diameter with a 6 in filter tube and a 3 or 4 in suction pipe. The space outside the 6 in tube is filled with a gravel filter as the boring tube is withdrawn. Because of their greater diameter the wells can usually be spaced about 30 ft (9 m) apart, and since there are many fewer connections than in a well-point system the efficiency is greater and lowering of 20 to 22 ft (6 to 6·7 m) can be expected. The wells are connected to a ring main and a pumping and vacuum plant as in the case of well-points.

The cost of pumping is much the same for a given lowering of the water level from either a well-point or a suction well system, but the cost of installation of the suction wells is higher. The suction well installation is often to be preferred for an excavation of rectangular shape (as opposed to a long trench) where pumping must continue for many months, in fine sands where a graded filter is necessary or in laminated soils where a definite vertical connection between the aquifers is required.

As in the case of well-points two-stage systems can be used for a lowering of more than 22 ft but in general deep wells will prove cheaper.

Deep wells

With the deep well system any required lowering of the water level can be achieved in one stage. This is because the pumps are placed at the bottom of the wells and deliver the water against pressure; there is no suction in the system. The pumps used are electrically driven submersible pumps. They require a 12 in diameter filter tube to accommodate them and the ring main is 4 to 6 in diameter. The well cannot be less than 18 in diameter, which allows a 3 in thickness of filter gravel, and if a two-stage filter is desired the well will be 24 in (61 cm) diameter. For this reason the capacity of the wells is much greater than in the case of suction wells and they can therefore be spaced further apart, in general 70 to 100 ft, but this will vary considerably on different installations.

The cost of a deep well system is high but it gives safe dry excavation and can often reduce the time of construction considerably. For safety, two independent sources of electric power must be provided for the pumps, since once they have started pumping it might be disastrous if they failed.

Vacuum drainage

In soils of low permeability such as coarse silts, drainage can sometimes be effected by sealing the wells or well-points and exhausting the air from them. The pressure of the atmosphere then acts as a surcharge on the soil causing it to consolidate, and water is squeezed out of the soil into the filters of the wells. The amount of water removed is very small but the increase in strength of the silt is marked, and excavation into it is greatly facilitated.

Electro-osmosis

Electro-osmosis is a further drainage process which can be used in silts. It is based on the principle that if a direct electric current is passed through the soil a flow of water takes place from anode to cathode. The cathode is made into a well and the water which reaches it is pumped out; the amount of water removed is small. As with the vacuum method the success of the method depends on the fact that the flow of water is away from the excavation, the free water surface is lowered and the water which remains in the soil above this surface is in tension, and that the capillary tensions add greatly to the strength of a silt. To some extent also the water content of the soil is reduced, thus resulting in an increased strength. Electro-osmosis is an expensive process and should only be considered if more normal methods of construction are inapplicable. In many silts the vacuum method of drainage is probably nearly as effective and much cheaper.

Settlements caused by water-lowering

When the water level is lowered the effective weight of the soil between the original and the lowered water levels is increased because the buoyancy effect has been removed. Where the soil concerned is sand and gravel any settlements due to this increase in weight are normally negligible, but where silt, clay or peat occurs in the zone referred to, settlement will occur with time due to the consolidation of this material under its own increased weight.

Before installing a ground-water lowering system it is essential therefore to consider what effect such settlements may have on structures within the zone of influence. Important structures will probably be founded below the compressible material, either directly or on piles, and will be unaffected. For structures founded on the compressible strata it is necessary to calculate the probable settlement and to estimate what damage, if any, to the structure would result.

In some cases the zone of influence can be reduced in size at a particular point so as not to include a given structure, by pumping water back into the ground through well-points on the perimeter of the structure.

Sand drains

Sand drains are used to accelerate the settlement of layers of soft clay or silt under applied loads. In many cases settlement can be tolerated provided it occurs quickly, preferably during the construction period, *e.g.* road embankments on soft clay.

The rate at which a clay layer consolidates is inversely proportional to the square of the drainage path, which is either the thickness or half the thickness of the layer depending on the drainage conditions. The principle of the sand drain method is to provide vertical drains of sand in the clay. The drainage path is then reduced to half the spacing of the drains. When the load, for example a fill, is applied, the settlements take place quickly, in say a few months instead of many months or even years. It is important to note that sand drains do not reduce the amount of settlement.

The consolidation of the clay under load increases its strength, a fact which can sometimes be made use of by construction, in stages, of a fill which would cause foundation failure if placed in one operation.

Such drains are usually 10 to 18 in (25 to 45 cm) diameter and spaced anything between 6 to 20 ft (2 to 6 m) centres depending on the conditions. They are particularly effective in laminated soils, where the horizontal permeability is very large in comparison to the vertical permeability. They are constructed by making a vertical hole in the clay and filling it with sand. Methods of installation of the drains which cause remoulding of sensitive soil should be avoided. A horizontal drainage blanket must be provided at ground level to link the drains together before the fill is placed, unless the fill itself is permeable.

COMPRESSED AIR

The use of compressed air is well known in underground work. It again is a temporary process used during construction only. It can be used in sands and gravels, silts and clays. The air pressure, acting on the surface of the soil in the excavation, or more correctly on the water surfaces in the voids of the soil, prevents the flow of water through the soil and acts as a support. Theoretically the air pressure must be equal to the water pressure, *i.e.* 15 lb/sq in of air = 1 atmosphere = 30 ft head of water. In practice a pressure somewhat lower than the theoretical is often satisfactory. In gravels the losses of air through the gravel may be serious and these can sometimes be cut down by injections of clay suspensions into the gravel before commencing excavation in order to reduce the permeability. For a detailed treatment see HEWETT and JOHANNESSON[78], also the chapter on Works Construction, Vol. 4, for the physiological effects.

FREEZING

Another temporary method of preventing the access of ground water to excavations is by freezing the water. This is normally done by boring vertical holes into the ground, installing pipes in them and circulating brine, cooled to below the freezing point of water, through the pipes. The freezing process is expensive and slow but once the water is frozen excavation can safely take place inside the frozen ring. The freezing must, of course, be continued until the permanent work is completed. One of the disadvantages of this method is that if a leak occurs in the pipes brine will escape into the ground water and it may then prove impossible to freeze it. To overcome this objection the Dehottay process was introduced. In this process liquid carbon dioxide is circulated instead of brine. In general the freezing process is applied to narrow deep excavations such as mine shafts, but cases are on record of its use in foundation work, see DAXHELHOFER[79] and MUSSCHE and WADDINGTON[80].

REFERENCES

Soil properties

[1]B.S. 1377: 1948. *Methods of Test for Soil Classification and compaction*

[2]AKROYD, T. N. W. *Laboratory Testing in Soil Engineering,* Soil Mechanics Limited, London

[3]CAMERON, J. F. and BOURNE, M. S. A Gamma-scattering Soil Density Gauge for Subsurface Measurements. *International Journal of Applied Radiation and Isotopes* Vol. 3, No. 1, 1958

[4]GOLDBERG, I., TRESCONY, L. J., CAMPBELL, J. S. and WHITE, G. J. Measurement of Moisture Content and Density of Soil Masses using Radio Activity Methods. Clays and Clay Minerals *Proc. and 3rd Nat. Conf. on Clay and Clay Minerals for Location 395* National Academy of Sciences, National Research Council, Washington D.C. (1955) 516

[5]SKEMPTON, A. W. The Colloidal 'Activity' of Clays, *Proc. 3rd Int. Conf. Soil Mech. and Foundation Engng* Vol. 1, p 57, Zurich 1953

[6]KOLBUSZEWSKI, J. J. An Experimental Study of the Maximum and Minimum Porosities of Sands *Proc. 2nd Int. Conf. Soil Mech. and Foundation Engng* Vol. 1, p 158, Rotterdam 1948

[7]SKEMPTON, A. W. The Pore-Pressure Coefficients A and B *Géotechnique* 4 (1954) 143

[8]BISHOP, A. W. and HENKEL, D. J. *The Measurement of Soil Properties in the Triaxial Test* London, 1957

[9]SKEMPTON, A. W. and BISHOP, A. W. *Soils. Building Materials: Their Elasticity and Inelasticity* Pt D, Ch. 10, Amsterdam, 1954

[10]LOUDON, A. G. The Computation of Permeability from Simple Soil Tests *Géotechnique* 3 (1952) 165

[11]TAYLOR, D. W. *Fundamentals of Soil Mechanics* New York, 1948

[12]HVORSLEV, M. J. Über die Festigkeitseigenschaften gestörter bindiger Böden. *Ingen. Vidensk. Skr. A.* No. 45, Copenhagen, 1937

[13]GIBSON, R. E. Experimental Determination of the True Cohesion and True Angle of Internal Friction in Clays *Proc. 3rd Int. Conf. Soil Mech. and Foundation Engng* Vol. 1, p. 126, Zurich, 1953

[14]GOLDER, H. Q. and AKROYD, T. N. W. An Apparatus for Triaxial Compression Tests at High Pressures *Géotechnique* 4 (1954) 131

[15]COOLING, L. F. and GOLDER, H. Q. A Portable Apparatus for Compression Tests on Clay Soils *Engineering Lond.* 149 (1940) 57

[16]SKEMPTON, A. W. Vane Tests in the Alluvial Plain of the River Forth near Grangemouth *Géotechnique* 1 (1948) 111

[17]TERZAGHI, K. and FRÖHLICH, O. K. *Theorie der Setzung von Tonschichten* Vienna, 1936

[18]TERZAGHI, K. and PECK, R. B. *Soil Mechanics in Engineering Practice* New York, 1948

[19]WILLIAMS, F. H. P. Compaction of Soils *J. Instn civ. Engrs* 33 (1949) 73

[20]PORTER, A. J. The Preparation of the Subgrade *Proc. Highway Res. Board* 18 (1938) 324

[21]WESTERGAARD, H. M. Stresses in Concrete Pavements Computed by Theoretical Analysis *Public Roads* 7 (1926) 25

[22]STRATTON, J. H. Military Airfields, a symposium. Construction and Design Problems *Proc. Amer. Soc. civ. Engrs* 1944, 70 (1) (1944) 28–54

[23]*U.S. Corps of Engineers Engineering Manual* part 12 ch. 3, 1946

Stability of slopes

[24]COULOMB, C. A. Essai sur une Application des Règles de Maximis et Minimis à quelques Problèmes de Statique relatifs á l'Architecture *Mem. Div. Sav. Acad. des Sciences* 7 (1776) 343

[25]FRANÇAIS. Recherches sur la Poussée des Terres, sur la Forme et les Dimensions des Revêtements et sur les Talus d'Excavations *Mem. de l'Officier du Génie* 4 (1820) 157

[26]BISHOP, A. W. The Use of the Slip Circle in the Stability Analysis of Slopes *Géotechnique* 5 (1955) 7

[27]COOLING, L. F. and GOLDER, H. Q. The Analysis of the Failure of an Earth Dam during Construction *J. Instn civ. Engrs* 19 (1942) 38

[28]HENKEL, D. J. Discussion on paper by J. D. Watson: Earth Movement Affecting L.T.E. Railway in Deep Cutting East of Uxbridge *J. Instn civ. Engrs* 5, No. 3 (1956)

[29]WARD, W. H. The Stability of Natural Slopes *Geograph. J.* 105 (1945) 170

[30]SKEMPTON, A. W. and NORTHEY, R. D. The Sensitivity of Clays *Géotechnique* 3 (1952-3) 30

[31]GOLDER, H. Q. and PALMER, D. J. Investigation of a Bank Failure at Scrapsgate, Isle of Sheppey, *European Reg. Conf. on Stability of Slopes* Stockholm, 1954

[32]*Proc. Conf. Biology and Civil Engineering Instn Civil Engineers,* London, 1948

[33]KNIGHT, R. G. Dams and Reservoirs. Some Aspects of Investigation and Design *Proc. Engng Conf.* Melbourne, 1953

[34]McNAMEE, J. Seepage into a Sheeted Excavation *Géotechnique* 1, No. 4 (1949) 229

Earth pressures

[35]COULOMB, C. A. Essai sur une Application des Règles de Maximis et Minimis à des Revêtements et sur les Talus d'Excavations *Mem. de l'Officier du Génie des Sciences* 7 (1776) 343

[36]FRANÇAIS. Recherches sur la Poussée des Terres, sur la Forme et les Dimensions des Revêtements et sur les Talus d'Excavations *Mem. de l'Officier du Génie* 4 (1820) 157

[37]BELL, A. L. The Lateral Pressure and Resistance of Clay and the Supporting Power of Clay Foundations *Min. Proc. Instn civ. Engrs* 199 (1915) 233

[38]PACKSHAW, S. Earth Pressure and Earth Resistance *J. Instn civ. Engrs* 25 (1946) 233

[39]Civil Engineering Code of Practice No. 2 *Earth Retaining Structures*

[40]PECK, R. B. Earth Pressure Measurements in Open Cuts, Chicago Subway *Trans. Amer. Soc. civ. Engrs* 108 (1943) 1008

[41]SKEMPTON, A. W. and WARD, W. H. Investigations Concerning a Deep Cofferdam in the Thames Estuary Clay at Shellhaven *Géotechnique* 3 (1952) 119

[42]WARD, W. H. Experiences with Some Sheet-pile Cofferdams at Tilbury *Géotechnique* 5 (1955) 327

[43]ROWE, P. W. Anchored Sheet Pile Walls *J. Instn civ. Engrs.* 1, No. 1 (1952) 27

[44]TERZAGHI, K. Anchored Bulkheads *Proc. Amer. Soc. civ. Engrs* 79 (1953) 262

[45]GERBER, E. *Untersuchungen über die Druckverteilung im örtlich belasteten Sand* Zürich, 1929

[46]SPANGLER, M. G. Horizontal Pressures on Retaining Walls due to Concentrated Surface Loads *Iowa Eng. Expt. Stn. Bull.* No. 140

[47]ROWE, P. W. Sheet-pile Walls in Clay. *J. Instn civ. Engrs* 7 (1959) 629

Foundations

[48]SKEMPTON, A. W. and MACDONALD, D. H. The Allowable Settlements of Buildings. *J. Instn civ. Engrs* 5, Pt III, No. 3 (1956) 727

[49]TERZAGHI, K. *Theoretical Soil Mechanics* London, 1943

[50]Civil Engineering Code of Practice No. 4 *Foundations*

[51]KREY, H. *Erddruck, Erdwiderstand* 143, 146, 197, 5th ed. Berlin, 1936

[52]RENDULIC, L. Ein Beitrag zur Bestimmung der Gleitsicherheit *Bauingenieur* 16 (1935) 230

[53]PECK, R. B., HANSON, W. E. and THORNBURN, T. H. *Foundation Engineering* New York, 1953

[54]MEYERHOF, G. G. The Bearing Capacity of Foundations *Géotechnique* 2 (1951) 301

[55]HUIZINGA, T. K. Application of Results of Deep Penetration Tests to Foundation Piles *Building Research Congress* Div. 1, Pt. III (1951) 173

[56]PRANDTL, L. Ueber die Härte plastischer Körper. *Nachr. Kgl. Gesell. Wiss. Göttingen, Math-phys. Klasse* p 74, 1920

[57]CAQUOT, A. *Equilibre des Massifs à Frottement Interne, Stabilité des Terres pulverulents et cohérentes* Paris, 1934

[58]ISHLINSKY, A. J. The Axial Symmetrical Problem in Plasticity and the Brinell Test *J. Appl. Math. Mech. U.S.S.R.* 8 (1944) 201

[59]HENCKY, H. Über einige statisch bestimmte Fälle des Gleichgewichts in plastischen Koerpern *Z. angew. Math. Mech.* 3 (1923) 241

[60]FELLENIUS, W. Jordstatiska Beräkningar för vertikal Belastning pá horisontal Mark under Antagande av cirkulär-cylindriska Glidytor *Tekn. Tidskr.* 59 (1929) 57, 75

[61]WILSON, G. The Calculation of the Bearing Capacity of Footings on Clay *J. Instn civ. Engrs.* 17 (1942) 87

[62]SKEMPTON, A. W. The Bearing Capacity of Clays. *Building Research Congress* Div. 1, Pt III (1951) 180

[63]SKEMPTON, A. W. and BJERRUM, L. A Contribution to the Settlement Analysis of Foundations on Clay *Géotechnique* 7 (1957) 168

[64]STEINBRENNER, W. Tafeln zur Setzungsberechnung *Die Strasse* 1 (1934) 121

[65]BOUSSINESQ, J. *Application des Potentiels à l'Étude de l'Équilibre et du Mouvement des Solides Elastiques* Paris, 1885

[66]NEWMARK, N. M. Simplified Computation of Vertical Pressures in Elastic Foundations *Circ. Univ. Ill. Eng. Expt. Stn Bull.* No. 24, 1935

[67]FOX, E. N. The Mean Elastic Settlement of a Uniformly Loaded Area at a Depth Below the Ground Surface *Proc. 2nd Int. Conf. Soil Mech.* 1 (1948) 192

[68]JURGENSON, L. The Application of Theories of Elasticity and Plasticity to Foundation Problems *J. Boston Soc. civ. Engrs* 21 (1934) 206

[69]GIBSON, R. E. and LUMB, P. Numerical Solution of Some Problems in the Consolidation of Clay *J. Instn civ. Engrs* 2, Pt I (1953) 182

[70]BJERRUM, L. Norwegian Experiences with Steel Piles to Rock *Géotechnique,* 7 (1957) 73

[71]SKEMPTON, A. W. Cast in-situ Bored Piles in London Clay, *Géotechnique* 9 (1959)

Geotechnical processes

[72]GLOSSOP, R. Classification of Geotechnical Process *Géotechnique* 2 (1950) 3

[72]ROBINSON, W. P. *Practical Soil Stabilization* London, 1948

[74]LAMBE, T. W. The Improvement of Soil Properties with Dispersants. *J. Boston Soc. civ. Engrs* April 1954

[75]GLOSSOP, R. and SKEMPTON, A. W. Particle-size in Silts and Sands *J. Instn civ. Engrs* 25 (1945) 81

[76]PURBRICK, M. C. and AYRES, D. J. Uses of Aerated Cement Grout and Mortar in Stabilization of Slips in Embankments, Large-scale Tunnel Repairs and Other Works. *J. Instn civ. Engrs* 5, Pt II (1956)

[77]GLOSSOP, R. and COLLINGRIDGE, V. H. Notes on Groundwater Lowering by Means of Filter Wells *Proc. 2nd Int. Conf. Soil Mech.* 2 (1948) 320

[78]HEWETT, B. H. M. and JOHANNESSON, S. *Shield and Compressed Air Tunnelling* New York, 1922

[79]DAXHELHOFER, J. P. Un nouveau procédé de congélation et ses possibilités d'application *Erdbaukurs der Eidg. Techn. Hochschule Section 17* Zürich, 1938

[80]MUSSCHE, H. E. and WADDINGTON, J. C. Applications of the Freezing Process to Civil Engineering Works *Instn civ. Engrs Works Construction Paper No. 5,* 1946

SITE INVESTIGATION

R. GLOSSOP, B.Sc., M.I.C.E. and I. K. NIXON, A.M.I.C.E.

GENERAL

Site investigation may be divided into a preliminary stage leading to the choice of a site suitable to the proposed works, followed by a more detailed examination of the chosen site for design data *etc.*

Choice of site

Choice of site may be influenced chiefly by economic, or in Great Britain by administrative, considerations, though in certain instances natural features may be decisive. Thus topography may strictly control the siting of a bridge, and a sufficient water supply that of a steam power station. The preliminary examination should include location, restrictions, natural features and resources, and public services.

Location—The identification of the site must be made on existing maps together with the establishment of property and building lines.

Restrictions—Legal restrictions are as follows.

Under the Town and Country Planning Acts 1947 to 1954 proposals and an outline development plan should be submitted to the local planning authority (county or county borough) and an application made for approval to 'use of land' before the preparation of a detailed scheme.

Inquiries should be made as to the existence of mineral rights, mine workings, tunnels, ancient monuments, burial grounds and rights of light, support and way including any easements.

Natural features and resources—Amongst these are water supply, raw materials, climate, hydrology, and waste disposal.

Details of the water supply should be obtained from the local authority or water supply company. The possibility of increased supply either from the authority or by sinking wells *etc* should be investigated.

Raw materials include building stone, bricks, concrete aggregate, cement, road metal, timber, earth fill and puddle clay.

Study of climatic conditions involves investigation of rainfall, range of temperatures and humidity, prevailing winds and fog.

River and tide levels, stream flow, heights of floods and details of catchment area are classified as hydrological measurements.

Facilities for disposal of waste should be known.

Public services—Under this heading are grouped access by road, railway, water, air; electricity, gas, sewerage; land drainage; heating; and telephone.

Detailed examination

Surface survey—The first step in a detailed site examination is to prepare an accurate survey from which plots on any required scale may be made. All levels should be referred to the Newlyn Ordnance datum, and if possible the site should be related to the Ordnance Survey grid. In plotting surveys a north point should be clearly drawn and marked 'astronomical meridian' or 'magnetic meridian' as the case may be; the date of establishment should be noted on the plan using a magnetic north.

On large sites it is often convenient to set up a local graticule of coordinates. Solid and permanent beacons should be established clear of the works to which the setting out engineers may refer. These should have their coordinates relative to the local origin recorded on the plan.

Underground survey—This should include all geological data which may influence the design of structures or the choice of construction methods. The methods employed are fully described in the following pages.

INVESTIGATION OF UNDERGROUND CONDITIONS

A knowledge of the geological conditions beneath a site may be necessary *1* to locate materials of construction such as earth fill, freestone and concrete aggregates; *2* to find a supply of water; *3* to provide data on bearing capacity, lateral pressures and probable settlements such as are necessary for the design of structures; *4* in shafts, tunnels, docks and other deep excavations, to aid in the choice of a suitable construction method[1-5].

The solution of these problems is only possible if sufficient accurate information has been collected; it is probably correct to say that more engineering failures may be attributed to inadequate site investigation than to any other cause.

Methods of investigation

Four methods of investigation are in general use. First, the classical method of geology[6], the structure in depth being inferred from accurate mapping of the features exposed at the surface. This is always valuable but may fail to reveal minor geological features having a decisive influence on the safety of the work. It should be supplemented wherever possible by the second method, which is exploration by means of boreholes, trial pits, or adits, in which the ground is exposed for examination and samples are taken for testing. The third is the measurement *in situ* of the mechanical properties of soils and weak rocks. The fourth is geophysics.

Four geophysical methods are in general use, gravitational, magnetic, seismic and electrical. All these methods are widely and successfully employed in the search for oil and minerals. Increasing use is now made of them in civil engineering, the most suitable being the seismic and electrical methods.

Choice of method

Choice of method is influenced by the type of engineering structure and the nature of the site conditions. TABLE 1 summarizes the relation between structure, geology and method of investigation.

So far as structures in, or founded on, rock are concerned there are few alternatives, and geological methods aided by trial pits and core borings will generally suffice. Borings may be supplemented by pressure tests in zones of jointing. Shear strength and permeability tests, either *in situ* or in the laboratory, may be necessary where large dams are to be built on weak and permeable rocks.

Soil deposits may be investigated in many ways and several countries have developed tests suited to their most common soil types. Choice of method should depend upon the nature of the soil[7].

In situ methods may be divided into those which measure a fundamental soil property *e.g.* the vane test, which determines shear strength, and those which are empirical *e.g.* the various penetration tests. The latter, which are most useful in the case of non-cohesive soils, should be used with caution

TABLE 1

ENGINEERING PROBLEMS AND SITE INVESTIGATION

NATURE OF WORKS	PROBLEM	GEOLOGY	FIELD INVESTIGATION	LABORATORY TESTS	METHODS AND PROCESSES
1 FOUNDATIONS 1 Shallow foundations a Rafts, footings	Safe bearing capacity	Soft, recent clay	Borings and undisturbed samples taken, preferably with a piston sampler. Vane tests for sensitive clays, particularly below 30 ft	Index properties. Undrained triaxial and unconfined compression tests	Foundation should always be below the zone of seasonal variations. Investigate to a depth equal to the least plan dimension of the foundation×1·5, allow a factor of safety of 2 to 3 on the ultimate bearing capacity. Note that soft recent clay is sometimes overlain by a crust of stiffer clay
		Firm to stiff clay	Borings and undisturbed samples	Index properties. Undrained triaxial test on fissured clays	Foundation should always be below the zone of seasonal variations. Investigate to a depth equal to the least plan dimension of the foundation×1·5, allow a factor of safety of 2 to 3 on the ultimate bearing capacity
		Stoney clay	Field bearing tests	Index properties of 8 mesh fraction. Unconfined compression tests on soil binder	Test by boring and penetration tests for softer deposits in depth
		Sand and gravel	Borings and penetration tests. Field bearing tests	Shear tests on undisturbed or disturbed samples recompacted to original densities	Ultimate bearing capacity is based upon theory and small scale tests, also on penetration tests
	Settlements	Clay	Borings and undisturbed samples. Use piston samplers in soft clays	Consolidation tests	Settlement analysis based on Terzaghi's theory of consolidation
		Sand and gravel	Field bearing test	Consolidation test may be applied to saturated micaceous sands	Note possibility of a 'Quick' condition being caused by shock o. vibration in loose, saturated sands; also internal erosion
b Dams	Safe bearing capacity	Rock	In situ shear strength of weak shale. Use of seismic to obtain Young's modulus. Location of rock beneath superficial deposits by borings into rock co-ordinated by geophysics	Compression tests on cores. High pressure triaxial tests	Cement grouting of fissures if required
		Soils	See 1, 1a	See 1, 1a	See 1, 1a
	Settlements	Soils	See 1, 1a	See 1, 1a	See 1, 1a
	Flow of water beneath foundations affecting bearing capacity and seepage losses	Rock	Core borings and pressure tests	Permeability of sandstones	Decide depth of cut off. Consider use of cement or other injections
		Sand and gravel	In situ permeability tests. Borings and undisturbed samples	Permeability of recompacted samples or undisturbed samples. Note variation between vertical and horizontal permeability	Submergence reduces bearing capacity of frictional materials. Investigate danger of piping by construction of flow nets. Design and use of inverted filters

c Roads and runways	Thickness of base	Clay	Posthole auger. Undisturbed samples	Unconfined compression test	Analyse by shear strength method
		Sand and composite soils	Boring and sampling. In situ plate bearing tests	California bearing ratio	California bearing ratio curves for flexible pavements. Westergaard for concrete pavements
	Frost heave	Silts and silty clays	Boring and sampling. Location of ground water level	Particle size analysis, freezing tests	Identification of certain soil types known to heave under suitable conditions. Removal of doubtful materials
2 Deep foundations					
a Cylinders, caissons, bridge piers	Safe bearing capacity / Settlements	All soils	Boring and undisturbed sampling. Use piston sampler in soft clays and vane tests for sensitive clays below 30 ft	See I, 1a	Theory of shallow foundations is conservative. Meyerhof has proposed general theory of deep foundations
	Safety against scour	Sand, silt and gravel	Boring and sampling	Model tests	
	Choice of method / Skin friction etc	All soils	Boring and undisturbed sampling. Use piston sampler in soft clays and vane tests for sensitive clays below 30 ft	See I, 1a	Estimate of friction between skin and soil. Resistance against bottom heave
b Point bearing piles	Length of pile and safe bearing capacity	Soft recent clay over firm stratum	In suitable cases bearing stratum may be located by pilot boreholes and geophysical survey. Explore by boring for bearing stratum which should be sampled. Extend by Dutch deep sounding test	Index properties / Shear strength / Consolidation characteristics	Treat bearing stratum as for I, 1a, and explore for softer material beneath. Consider effect of negative skin friction in soft clay. Bearing capacity cannot be forecast from 'piling formulae'. Static load tests only safe way. Bearing capacity of group of X piles may be less than X times single pile
	Settlements	Sand	Test piles. Dutch soundings		
		Bearing stratum of clay	Borings and undisturbed samples	Measure consolidation characteristics	Settlements from Terzaghi's consolidation theory
		Bearing stratum of sand	Test piles. Dutch deep sounding test extended below piles		Ratio of settlement between individual test pile and a group suggested by Skempton. Explore for more compressible soil beneath bearing stratum
c Friction piles	Safe load and length of piles	All soils	Borings and undisturbed samples. Loading and pulling tests. Dutch deep sounding test	Measure index properties and shear strength	See I, 2b
	Settlements	Clay and silt	Borings and undisturbed samples	Consolidation tests	Settlement analysis based on properties of soil around and beneath the piles
II EXCAVATIONS					
a Shallow unsupported excavations of large area basins, docks, canals, cuttings	Stability of slopes	Stiff fissured clays	Borings and undisturbed samples. Observation wells or Dutch pore water pressure device to determine ground water level for effective stress analysis. Observations on existing slopes	Effective stress tests, drained triaxial tests or undrained with pore water pressure measurement	Effective stress analysis. Note possibility of failure after interval of time, short or long
		Soft recent clays	Borings and undisturbed samples. Vane test	Unconfined compression tests or undrained triaxial tests	$\phi = 0$ analysis for slips. Gives right value for factor of safety but wrong position of failure surface
	Inflow of water, internal erosion, piping	Sand and silt	Borings and undisturbed samples. Observation of ground water levels and their seasonal variations	Dry density. Particle size analysis. Permeability	Calculations for ground water lowering if required. Design of permanent filter drains for cuttings

TABLE 1—continued

NATURE OF WORKS	PROBLEM	GEOLOGY	FIELD INVESTIGATION	LABORATORY TESTS	METHODS AND PROCESSES
b Supported excavations of moderate depth	Lateral pressures	Clay	Borings and undisturbed samples. Ground water level observations	Bulk density. Triaxial shear tests	Choice between timber, sheet piles, etc. Pressure distribution by the method of Terzaghi and Peck
		Sand	Borings and undisturbed samples. Ground water level observations	Value of ϕ for various densities	Wedge theory
	Safety against piping	Sand and silt	Borings and undisturbed samples. In situ permeability tests. Ground water level observations	Permeability of undisturbed samples or recompacted samples. Particle size analysis	Flow net analysis. Use of ground water lowering or caissons
	Safety against bottom heave	Soft clay	Borings and undisturbed samples below bottom of excavation vane tests. Ground water level observations	Unconfined compression tests	Use of sheet piles with adequate penetration. Analysis by Terzaghi's method and Bjerrum
c Deep excavations shafts	Inflow of water	Rock	Core borings. Pressure tests to locate water bearing fissures	Permeability tests on porous sandstone	Use of cement grouting for fissured rocks. Silicate injections for permeable sandstones
	Inflow of water sand and silt	All soils	Boring, sampling. Ground water observation	Particle size analysis permeability	Choice between compressed air, or freezing. Drop shaft or some form of bored shaft
d Tunnels	Support	Rock	Geological survey aided by core borings and geophysics	Examination of rock specimens for swelling, softening etc	Design of permanent lining and of temporary supports if necessary
	Overbreak	Rock	Geological survey aided by core borings and geophysics	Examination of rock specimens for schistosity etc	
	Method of tunnelling	All soils	Borings and undisturbed samples. Ground water level observations	Shear strength. Index properties of clays. Permeability of sands. Bulk density, all soils	Choice of shield. Use of compressed air, chemical consolidation etc. Assume full over-burden pressure in clay
III EARTHEN STRUCTURES	Foundations and thickness of base	All soils	See I, 1c	See I, 1c	
a Earth roads	Stabilization	All soils	Representative samples from borrow pits	Compaction and optimum moisture content tests. Tests of stabilizers	Choice of cement, bitumen, oils, waxes, resins etc
b Earth dams	Watertightness	All soils	Representative samples from borrow pits	Permeability of compacted material	Flow nets
	Stability	All soils	Representative samples from borrow pits	Compaction and optimum moisture content, triaxial tests (softened triaxial). Effective stress tests. Pore water pressure dissipation tests	Stability of foundation material, c, ϕ analysis allowing free pore water pressures. Effect of vibration on sand fills, earthquakes
IV GROUND WATER	Effect on concrete	All soils and ground water	Samples from boreholes	Analysis for sulphates. pH value and temporary hardness	Comparison of measured concentrations with previous observed results
V CORROSION OF IRON AND STEEL	Corrosion of steel piles, pipes etc	All soils	Samples for bacteriological tests. Probes to measure resistivity and polarization. Surface resistivity surveys	Preparation of cultures to test for sulphate reducing bacteria, e.g. desulphovibrio desulphuricans. pH on soil and ground water	

for they can only be relied upon if they have been checked over a long period, under all sorts of site conditions, against laboratory measurements and field observations.

In general it can be said that clay soils are best investigated by laboratory tests on undisturbed samples, except for highly sensitive, recent clays, for these the shear strength should be measured *in situ* by the vane test.

The field bearing test remains the only method for the determination of the bearing capacity of weathered rock. It is useful for shallow foundations where soil conditions near the surface are exceptionally complex. The Dutch deep sounding method is widely used to determine the safe bearing capacity of pile foundations in sandy deltaic deposits.

GEOLOGICAL METHODS

Scope

The geological examination of an engineering site is carried out in four stages:

a recognition and classification of the types of rock and soil occurring in the area

b elucidation of the geological structure, and hence of the disposition of these rocks and soils in depth, which may be inferred from surface mapping with or without the help of borings, or geophysical measurements; here the position of faults, zones of fracturing *etc* is of particular importance. Mapping should generally be left to the geologist.

c description of the physical properties of the rocks, including such measurements of strength and permeability as may be necessary, and in certain cases Young's modulus.

d consideration of the engineering problems which arise.

Examination and description of rocks and soils

In geology all materials found within the earth's crust are described by the term 'rock'; the subdivision of rock, known as 'soil', is defined as the outermost layer of the mantle of rock waste in which the physical and chemical processes of weathering are in progress and are usually associated with biological activity. This use of the word 'soil' is also that of common speech and of the science of pedology.

In civil engineering it has been found convenient to group all geological materials in two classes according to their mechanical properties, namely 'rocks' and 'soils'. Rocks are typically massive, brittle and elastic; their constituent minerals are rigidly interlocked, as in granite, or are bound together by a cement of solid matter, as in sandstones. Soils are materials such as gravel, sand, silt or clay, which are composed of discrete solid particles, the voids between them containing only water or air. There is no sharp division between these classes.

Physical properties of rocks—The properties to be observed and recorded when examining rocks on engineering sites are strength, elasticity, permeability, degree of chemical alteration and susceptibility to weathering.

Strength. The inherent strength of a rock depends upon the hardness and cleavage of its constituent minerals and upon their texture, that is to say their orientation and the manner in which they are interlocked or cemented together. Hardness greatly influences the cost of excavation; weak rocks such as chalk, slightly cemented sandstones and shales can be excavated without the use of explosives. For hard rocks the cost of drill steel and explosives varies considerably with the degree of hardness. Hardness is generally estimated from previous experience: where structures, such as large dams, will exert high compressive and shear stresses on weak rocks, such as shale, actual strength measurements are desirable[8]. These may be made by high pressure triaxial compression tests on core samples[28].

In deep tunnels and mines weak shales may encroach on the workings by plastic flow set up by the high overburden pressure; such 'squeezing rocks' require very strong support[9].

Quite apart from the inherent strength of the rock substance the over-all strength of a mass of rock is greatly influenced by the occurrence of bedding, jointing, cleavage and other natural planes of weakness. These also influence the amount of support required in shafts and tunnels and the percentage of overbreak in excavations. The degree of stratification of sedimentary rocks may be described as 'laminated', 'thinly bedded', or 'massive', according to the thickness of the beds. A stratified rock with two well developed systems of joints is known as 'blocky'.

To describe jointing the frequency ('closely jointed', 'moderately jointed' and 'intact') may be used; and the width ('tight' or 'open' joints) should be noted. The dip and strike at the principal joint systems should also be observed and noted.

Zones of crushed rock or breccia are commonly associated with faults and may be most troublesome in excavations. Faults beneath large structures, such as dams, are a potential source of danger and should, if possible, be avoided particularly where mining is projected or has been carried out.

Permeability. The permeability of rock controls the flow of water into tunnels and excavations and the amount of leakage to be expected beneath dams[10]. As a rule intact and moderately jointed rocks present no problems, except where the joints are open due to weathering near the surface or to folding, but slightly cemented sandstones may be sufficiently permeable to need grouting where they occur beneath dams. Zones of open jointing and brecciation may carry very heavy flows of water; this is often so in limestone. Limestone is soluble in water which carries carbon dioxide in solution, so that joint and bedding planes may have been greatly enlarged by circulating water, and caverns are thus formed[11].

Weathering and chemical alteration. The depth to which bed rock may be affected by the chemical effects of weathering is extremely variable and in the tropics may amount to over a hundred feet. In tunnels, weathering may be encountered along zones of faulting and brecciation at a great depth below the surface at a level where the unfractured rock is perfectly sound. Since clay minerals are among the most common products of weathering, heavy pressure on tunnels may be set up in such zones by their property of swelling[9].

The chemical alteration of rocks, due to the action of solutions ascending from a great depth (hydrothermal action), is not uncommon in the vicinity of faults; these zones of chemical alteration may prove troublesome in tunnelling.

In sedimentary formations swelling pressures are also caused by the conversion of the mineral anhydrite ($CaSO_4$) into gypsum ($CaSO_4 . 2H_2O$) with a consequent increase in volume. The conversion of olivine to serpentine in basic igneous rock also involves an increase in volume, and heavy rock pressures have been attributed to the existence of internal stresses due to this reaction.

Many sedimentary rocks have lower strengths when wet. Sandstones with a cement of clay or glauconite are reported of which the compressive strength was 3,500 lb/sq in (250 kg/sq cm) when dry and 850 lb/sq in (60 kg/sq cm) when wet[12]. In order to ensure that their *in situ* strength can be measured, care should always be taken to preserve such rock specimens, or cores, in the natural state by sealing them with a coating of wax immediately after they have been obtained. Shales deteriorate rapidly when exposed to alternate wetting and drying.

British Standard classification of soils for engineering purposes—The system of soil classification adopted in Great Britain[1] is set out in TABLE 3. It is based upon grain size, strength, and structure. The simple non-organic soil types are divided into five classes in decreasing order of grain size; stones, gravels, sands, silts and clays. The limits of these classes correspond approximately to important changes in the engineering properties of the soils[13]. The principal soil types in TABLE 3 usually occur in nature as siliceous sands and silts and as alumino-siliceous clays, but varieties very different chemically and mineralogically also occur. These may give rise to peculiar mechanical and chemical characteristics which, from the engineering standpoint, may be of sufficient importance to require special consideration. The following are examples. Lateritic weathering may give rise to deposits with unusually low silica contents, which are either soft nodular gravels or clays; but intermediate grades are rare. Volcanic ash may give rise to deposits of very variable composition which may come under any of the principal soil types. Deposits of sand grains may be composed of calcareous material (*e.g.* shell sand, coral sand) or may contain considerable proportions of mica (where grain shape is important) or glauconite (where softness of individual grains is important). Deposits of silt and clay may contain a large proportion of organic matter (organic silts, clays, or muds) and clays may be calcareous (marls).

Clays are further subdivided into seven classes according to strength, see TABLE 2.

TABLE 2

SUBDIVISION OF CLAYS

Consistency	Shear strength	
	lb/sq ft	*kg/sq cm*
Very soft	< 375	< 0·18
Soft	375–750	0·18–0·35
Soft to firm	750–1,000	0·35–0·50
Firm	1,000–1,500	0·50–0·75
Firm to stiff	1,500–2,000	0·75–1·0
Stiff	2,000–3,000	1·0 –1·5
Very stiff or hard	> 3,000	> 1·5

Sensitivity of clay—Certain recent clays which have been deposited in sea water and, following geological uplift, have been subjected to leaching by fresh water, exhibit the phenomenon of sensitivity. In a sensitive clay the remoulded shear strength is much less than the shear strength of the undisturbed material. Sensitive clays have been classified by Skempton and NORTHEY[31].

Class	Sensitivity
Insensitive clays	*c.* 1·0
Clays of low sensitivity	1 to 2
Clays of medium sensitivity	2 to 4
Sensitive clays	4 to 8
Extra-sensitive clays	> 8
Quick-clays	> 16

Sensitive clays are most commonly found in areas subjected to isostatic uplift at the end of the Pleistocene period, for example, the coasts of Scandinavia and the valley of the St. Lawrence River.

TABLE 3

GENERAL BASIS FOR FIELD IDENTIFICATION AND CLASSIFICATION OF SOILS

	Size and nature of particles			Strength and structural characteristics			
	Principal soil types		Composite types	Strength		Structure	
	Types	Field identification		Term	Field test	Term	Field identification
Coarse grained, non-cohesive — Boulders, Cobbles	Boulders Cobbles	Larger than 8 in diam. Mostly between 8 in and 3 in	Boulder gravels, Hoggin	Loose	Can be excavated with spade. 2 in wooden peg can be easily driven	Homogeneous	Deposit consisting essentially of one type
Gravels	Gravels	Mostly between 3 in and No. 7 B.S. sieve	Sandy gravels	Compact	Requires pick for excavation. 2 in wooden peg hard to drive more than a few inches		
Sands — Uniform	Uniform	Composed of particles mostly between No. 7 and 200 B.S. sieves, and visible to the naked eye. Very little or no cohesion when dry. Sands may be classified as uniform or well graded according to the distribution of particle size. Uniform sands may be divided into coarse sands between Nos. 7 and 25 B.S. sieves, medium sands between Nos. 25 and 72 B.S. sieves and fine sands between Nos. 72 and 200 B.S. sieves	Silty sands, Micaceous sands	Slightly cemented	Visual examination. Pick removes soil in lumps which can be abraded with thumb	Stratified	Alternating layers of varying types
Sands — Graded	Graded		Lateritic sands, Clayey sands				
Fine grained, cohesive — Silts, Low plasticity	Silts — Low plasticity	Particles mostly passing No. 200 B.S. sieve. Particles mostly invisible or barely visible to the naked eye. Some plasticity and exhibits marked dilatancy. Dries moderately quickly and can be dusted off the fingers. Dry lumps possess cohesion but can be powdered easily in the fingers	Loams, Clayey silts, Organic silts, Micaceous silts	Soft	Easily moulded in the fingers	Homogeneous	Deposit consisting essentially of one type
				Firm	Can be moulded by strong pressure in the fingers	Stratified	Alternating layers of varying types

Table 3—continued

				Soil type	Consistency	Field test	Structure	Structure description
Fine grained, cohesive—continued	Medium plasticity		Dry lumps can be broken but not powdered. They also distintegrate under water	Boulder clays	Very soft	Exudes between fingers when squeezed in fist	Fissured	Breaks into polyhedral fragments along fissure planes
				Sandy clays	Soft	Easily moulded in fingers	Intact	No fissures
	High plasticity	Clays	Smooth touch and plastic, no dilatancy. Sticks to the fingers and dries slowly	Silty clays	Firm	Can be moulded by strong pressure in the fingers	Homogeneous	Deposits consisting essentially of one type
			Shrinks appreciably on drying, usually showing cracks	Marls			Stratified	Alternating layers of varying types. If layers are thin the soil may be described as laminated
			Lean and fat clays show those properties to a moderate and high degree respectively	Organic clays	Stiff	Cannot be moulded in fingers		
				Lateritic clays	Hard	Brittle or very tough	Weathered	Usually exhibits crumb or columnar structure
Organic	Peats		Fibrous organic material, usually brown or black in colour	Sandy, silty or clayey peats	Firm	Fibres compressed together		
					Spongy	Very compressible and open structure		

The principal soil types in the above table usually occur in nature as siliceous sands and silts and as alumino-siliceous clays, but varieties very different chemically and mineralogically also occur. These may give rise to peculiar mechanical and chemical characteristics which, from the engineering standpoint, may be of sufficient importance to require special consideration. The following are examples:

Lateritic weathering may give rise to deposits with unusually low silica contents, which are either gravels or clays; but intermediate grades are rare.

Volcanic ash may give rise to deposits of very variable composition which may come under any of the principal soil types as regards grain size.

Deposits of sand grade may be composed of calcareous material (e.g., shell sand, coral sand) or may contain considerable proportions of mica (where grain shape is important) or glauconite (where softness of individual grains is important).

Deposits of silt and clay grade may contain a large proportion of organic matter (organic silts, clays, or muds) and clays may be calcareous (marls).

Description of soils—Since in a limited area soil types with the same fundamental mechanical properties are likely to be similar in appearance, colour, odour, texture *etc*, soils should be described in accordance with a simple system and the use of local and dialect terms, however apt, should be discouraged.   Such a system may be found in the British Code of Practice[1] which recommends that soils should be described by density and structural characteristics; colour; type of particles.   For example: ' stiff, fissured, grey clay ', ' coarse, shelly, loose, stratified, brown sand '.

By the use of such a system the various strata are at once recognized and may be represented in sections drawn through adjacent boreholes.

EXPLORATION BY TRIAL PITS, ADITS AND BOREHOLES

In this method the ground is exposed for examination.

Depth of exploration

The depth to which bores should be taken is governed by the depth of the structure itself and by the depth below the base of the structure to which exploration is considered necessary; this is influenced by geological considerations.   Thus in glacial deposits large boulders may be mistaken for bed rock; to avoid this the rock should be tested by core boring to a depth appreciably greater than the largest boulder observed in the district.

Under certain conditions a very soft stratum may occur beneath firm material; four examples are quite common:

i beds of peat or soft clay are sometimes found in the river gravels of southern England; it is thus unwise to stop a boring on penetrating a bed of gravel on the assumption that it is certain to be homogeneous

ii sand dunes fringing a coast may block the outlet of streams and great depths of swamp deposits (soft clay and peat) may accumulate on the landward side of the dunes.   The dunes may then advance over the swamp and conceal it, see *Figure 1*.

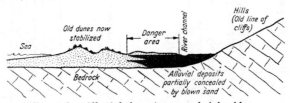

Figure 1.   Alluvial deposit concealed by blown
sand

iii reclaimed marsh lands of British estuaries have a characteristic soil section.   Bedrock is usually overlain by gravel, above which is found a thick bed of soft clay with lenses of peat.   At the surface, and to a depth of as much as 8 ft ($2\frac{1}{2}$ m), the properties of this clay have been greatly altered by field drainage and the transpiration of plants.   The moisture content has been reduced and the shear strength greatly increased.

iv waste dumps are often placed in old ponds or excavations, where silt has accumulated, or on swampy valley bottoms.   Hence quite apart from the undesirable qualities of fill as a foundation there is often the danger of very soft clay, silt, or peat between the bottom of the fill and bedrock, *Figure 2*.

Figure 2. Alluvial deposit concealed by fill

Buried channels—Old river channels cut deep into the bedrock and subsequently filled in and completely masked by alluvial deposits are found beneath the estuaries of many British rivers. Such channels should always be sought when planning tunnels and large bridges. Mountain valleys once occupied by glaciers have often been over-deepened *i.e.* bedrock has been scoured out locally by glacial action to a far greater depth than would be the case in a valley formed by the erosive action of a river. The existence of over-deepened areas is of course concealed by alluvium. The extent of over-deepening may be very great and disastrous accidents have been caused by tunnels encountering such valleys.

Recognition of bedrock

In certain localities bedrock is overlain by a fragmentary deposit known as *head*. This was formed by alternate cycles of freezing and thawing during the Pleistocene glaciations. The rock surface was then disrupted and a mantle of disturbed material was formed. On slopes downward transport of this material may occur when charged with water, a phenomenon known as *solifluxion*.

Head deposits are characterized by lack of structure or sorting and are composed of local materials. In such deposits it is difficult and sometimes impossible to locate bedrock by means of boreholes or by geophysical methods. This is particularly the case where the bedrock is itself frost shattered *in situ*. The only certain method of recognizing bedrock in such cases is by examination from a trial pit. In some cases, *e.g.* the cut-off trench for a dam, a deep trial pit may be of use later as a sump during excavation.

Solifluxion deposits of chalk lying on chalk bedrock are common and are difficult to detect. They may lead to engineering difficulties if not recognized as, for example, chalk head may occur to a considerable depth and give comparatively little support to piles driven into it. Cases have also been known where a rubbly chalk head was the source of very heavy flows of water into excavation.

Head deposits can also occur when bedrock, in the geological sense, is unlithified (*e.g.* London clay and Thanet sand) and gives rise to a mantle of softened clay or loosened granular material.

Lateral extent of exploration

No general rule can be given as to the number of borings required since this will depend upon the complexity of the structure in rocks and degree of lateral variation in soils. As a rule the first few borings should be widely spaced so as to cover the whole area; further borings can be added as found necessary. The possibility of dangerous conditions originating on adjacent property, for example landslips, internal erosion and the erosion of river banks, should not be overlooked.

Cost of site exploration

The ratio between the cost of site exploration and the total cost of the works varies with the nature and extent of the project and the ground conditions[14].

The following table gives the cost of site investigation work expressed as a percentage of the civil engineering and building costs for different kinds of projects based on a review of a number of actual cases.

Type of Project	Range of values of civil engineering and building	Per cent cost of site investigation work
(a) *Road schemes and associated structures*	£1·5m–£10·2m	0·10–0·40
(b) *Oil refineries*	£1·5m–£3·7m	0·30
(c) *Large buildings and industrial plants*	£0·5m–£2·7m	0·04–0·10
(d) *Power stations*	£2·4m–£7·1m	0·10–0·20
(e) *Dams*	£0·7m–£12·0m	0·06–1·00

Note: The minimum and maximum figures for cost and percentage are not related.

On smaller works and in difficult cases 1 to 2 per cent is a usual figure, but figures as high as 4 and 7 per cent have been quoted[15].

Exploration by trial pits and adits

Boreholes in soil yield complete records of strata but in rock no core may be recovered from precisely those zones of close jointing, shearing and brecciation where information is most needed. Hence, although trial pits are expensive, particularly where pumping is necessary, borings are sometimes supplemented by trial pits in which the structure of the rock can be examined *in situ*.

Adits are less expensive than pits since they are self draining and no winding is required. They are generally used to explore the abutments of dams. In hilly country, steeply inclined strata are more effectively explored by adits and horizontal strata by pits or boreholes.

Boring

Methods of boring—Three methods, differing in principle, are used to sink boreholes: *1* jetting or wash boring in which the soil is displaced and brought to the surface by a jet of water; *2* rotary boring in which either the rotating tool cuts and retains the soil as with the auger, or in which the rotating tool is armed so as to abrade rock and may or may not be designed to retain a core; and *3* percussion boring, in which rock is broken by repeated blows from a chisel and fragmental material is subsequently recovered by means of a sand pump or 'shell', *Figure 3*b. In practice all three methods are often used in the same borehole. Thus wash boring or percussion boring may be used to sink a stand pipe through overburden to bedrock, preparatory to diamond drilling.

Methods suited to soils only—Such methods include wash boring and use of shell and auger gear.

Wash boring. In wash boring the only tool used is a chisel, or chopping bit, with a water outlet in the cutting edge. This is attached to a string of hollow rods. High pressure water is pumped through the bit as it breaks up the ground and the cuttings are carried to the surface with the return water. Simultaneously the boring tube is driven ahead with a heavy monkey. This method, though quick and cheap, has serious limitations and can be very unreliable. The reason for this is that the water jet causes different soils to mix and changes in strata are imprecisely located. Samples taken from the return water are generally sorted while the disturbance below the base of the borehole interferes with undisturbed sampling.

Shell and auger gear. The use of shell and auger gear is the oldest and most primitive method of boring and remains the best for holes of moderate depth in soil where careful sampling is required.

A typical outfit is shown in *Figure 3*. The four legged derrick, *Figure 3*a, is 18 to 20 ft high. The boring tube is square threaded, flush jointed and manufactured to B.S. 879 : 1939. The lower end is fitted with a cutting shoe of external diameter slightly greater than that of the tube and the upper end with a driving head of internal diameter equal to that of the tube but of external diameter large enough to give a thickness of metal at least twice that of the tube so as to withstand driving.

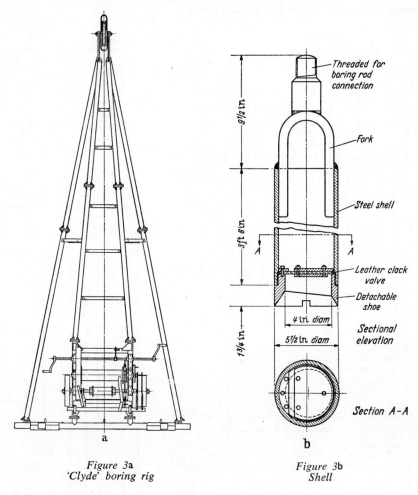

Figure 3a
'Clyde' boring rig

Figure 3b
Shell

Boring tools are of two types; the percussive, generally raised or lowered on a rope or wire bond, and the rotary, attached to steel boring rods and rotated by hand. The principal percussive tools are:

a 'the shell', *Figure 3*b, which is used for boring in non-cohesive soils below water level;

b 'the clay cutter', *Figure 3*c, which is a cylinder with a cutting edge of internal diameter slightly less than that of the tube. The tool is dropped to the bottom of the hole and cuts a clay core which it retains when withdrawn to the surface; and *c* 'the chisel', which is used for breaking up soft rock or cemented gravel. The fragments are subsequently removed in the 'shell'.

Rotary tools are:

i 'the auger', *Figure 3*d, consisting of a hollow cylinder small enough to pass easily into the boring tube, with a connection for the boring rods at the upper end, and one or two cutters at the lower end. Openings are formed in the cylinder for the removal of soil from it

ii 'the miser', a short receptacle with an external helical vane, used for boring in dry sand and gravel

iii 'boring rods', *Figure 3*e, usually $1\frac{1}{2}$ in square with a male thread at one end and a female thread at the other.

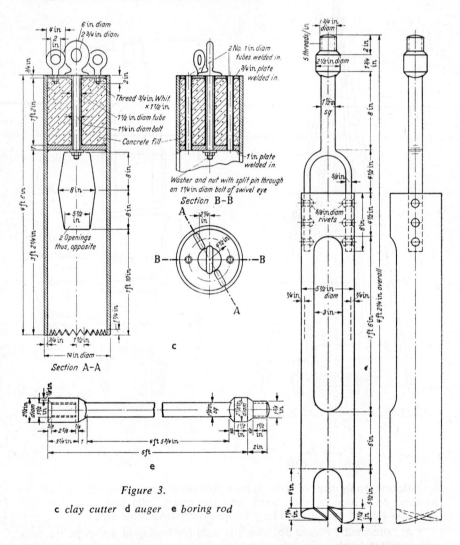

Figure 3.

c *clay cutter* d *auger* e *boring rod*

Methods suited to rocks and soils—Methods suited to both rocks and soils are percussion drilling and rotary mud flush boring.

Percussion drilling. There are many types of percussion rigs but all are similar in principle. The string of tools is carried on a wire rope which passes over a sheave on the derrick and is attached to a beam which is oscillated by means of a crank. The tools consist of a 'chisel', of which many types exist for use in different types of ground, and 'sinker bars' and 'jars' give weight and elasticity to the stroke. In a typical mobile unit the weight of the tools is 1,500 lb (680 kg) and the stroke 3 ft (*c* 1 m). As the hole deepens, the stretch in the rope increases the efficiency of the blow. Cuttings are recovered from the hole by a bailer fitted with a clack valve. In site exploration this method is useful for penetrating boulder deposits where accurate sampling is not of importance.

Rotary mud flush boring. This is widely used in drilling for water and oil in sedimentary rocks. Continuous cores are not recovered and the hard metal bit operates by abrasion. The characteristic feature is the use of a circulating fluid of high specific gravity, usually a suspension of clay containing powdered barytes. This fluid supports the sides of the hole during drilling so that casing can be placed in long lengths. This is probably the quickest and cheapest method of deep drilling, but it is rarely used in site exploration.

Methods suited to rocks only

Diamond drilling. The cutting edge or 'bit' of the diamond drill is set with fragments of diamond which, when pressed against the bottom of the hole and rotated at high speed, cut an annular groove, leaving a cylindrical core of rock which passes through the bit, past a core lifter, into a core barrel where it is retained, *Figure 4*. The bit is carried on heavy, solid drawn, steel tube drill rods, flush jointed with internal nipples. Water is passed down the hollow rods and escapes through channels cut in the face of the bit, returning to the surface outside the rods; this cools the diamonds and carries the cuttings to the surface. In modern practice African crystalline diamond, *boart*, is used. Small stones are cast set at the factory, in a tungsten alloy. These bits are returned to the maker when worn and the useful stones are recovered. Rotational speeds vary from 100 to 1,500 r.p.m. depending upon the diameter of the bit and the formation being drilled.

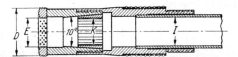

Figure 4. Diamond drilling bit, reaming bit and inner tube of double core barrel

Core recovery. In hard, intact rocks the core recovered may approach 100 per cent of the footage drilled and normally a double tube core barrel with a fixed inner barrel would be used. In soft sandstones, limestones and shale and in zones of brecciation and faulting it may be difficult or impossible to recover any core at all. Such adverse conditions require larger core barrels or those specially made for such formations, for example, swivelling inner barrel, thin wall bits, bottom discharge bits and the use of mud or compressed air instead of water for flushing. More skill is required and the core barrel should be withdrawn at frequent intervals to prevent the core being worn away.

Rate of drilling. This depends upon the bit diameter, the nature of the rock (fractured rocks may cause jamming in the core barrel and more frequent withdrawals) and the depth of the hole. For holes up to 1,000 ft (300 m) typical figures are between 5 ft and 20 ft (1·5 and 6 m) per shift.

Precautions. After labour costs the highest cost item is that of diamond wear. Much depends upon the skill of the operator; precautions to be observed include a sufficient and constant supply of circulating water, the correct rate of feed and the reduction of vibration to a minimum. When the wear of a bit reaches a certain stage deterioration becomes very rapid and overrunning is probably the commonest cause of high drilling costs. Bits should be returned for resetting as soon as 15 per cent of the stones are fractured or badly worn.

Advantages of diamond drill. The fact that the cores are of small diameter is of no disadvantage as they yield as much information to the geologist as those of 6 or 8 in diam can do, and have the advantage of being easily handled. The drilling unit itself is comparatively light and compact and can be adapted for use under all sorts of conditions both on the surface and underground. With this type of drill holes can be drilled at any angle from the vertical.

Chilled shot boring. In this method of core boring, chilled steel shot of $\frac{1}{8}$ in diam is the cutting agent. There is a plain steel bit in which are cut two diagonal slots which allow the wash water to escape without displacing the shot. The shot is fed into the hollow drill rods with the circulating water, carried into the slots and thus under the bit. For exploration work bits of 6 in diam are common, but holes up to 6 ft in diam have been used. The rods are always of much smaller diameter than the bit, hence it is not possible to maintain a rising current of water in the hole of sufficient velocity to carry away the coarse cuttings. For this reason a cup, or 'calyx', is fitted above the core barrel and into it the cuttings settle. The speed of rotation is low, 50 to 100 r.p.m., and the pressure is applied by the weight of the rods alone. To grip the core before withdrawing the rods a handful of quartz gravel known as 'grout' is fed in with the wash water. This lodges between the core and the side of the core barrel. The top rod or 'kelly' which carries a water swivel is square in section and passes through a square hole in a turn-table rotated through gearing. Holes are as a rule vertical but may be drilled to as much as 35° from the vertical. Broken ground must be grouted with cement, or the shot will be lost in fissures.

Records

Trial pits and adits—Plans and sections should be prepared showing all geological details such as the distribution of rock types; the dip and strike of contacts, faults, joint systems and zones of mineralization; the position and quantity of any inflows of ground water; and the location of samples taken. The location and level of the workings should be noted together with the scale, the direction of true north, the name of the firm carrying out the work and of the engineer or geologist responsible for the observations, and the date.

Boreholes—The following data should be recorded for each borehole.

General. *a* name of boring contractor *b* name of client *c* serial number of borehole *d* location *e* level of ground surface relative to Newlyn or Liverpool Ordnance Survey datum *f* inclination and bearing of hole if not vertical *g* diameter of borehole *h* method of boring *i* date of start and completion of work.

Geology. *i* description of each type of soil or rock encountered *ii* thickness of each formation *iii* position of contacts between formations, as depth below surface and relative to O.D. *iv* notes on position and attitude of joints, schistosity, zones of mineralization.

Samples. *i* levels, types and reference numbers of soil samples *ii* levels of drill runs and core recovery of rock drilling *iii* levels and reference numbers of water samples.

Hydrology. The levels at which water is struck should be noted and the rate and extent of any rise in level due to artesian pressure. Such observations may be necessary in a number of water bearing strata separated by impermeable beds.

If records of tidal or seasonal variations in level are required a sounding tube of 2 in diam should be lowered into the boring to such a depth that perforations in the lower end coincide with the stratum to be investigated. Filter gravel is placed round the perforated portion and as the boring tube is withdrawn puddle clay is passed into the hole and lightly tamped to cut off water from the surface or from overlying strata.

When boring in rock, levels at which the circulating water fails to return should be noted as this denotes the existence of open fissures.

Borehole data are best recorded graphically on a standard form. Standard symbols will be found in the British Standard Code of Practice[1].

METHODS OF PROCURING AND HANDLING SAMPLES
Rock samples

Rock core samples—Diamond drill cores of small diameter are preserved in wooden core boxes 5 ft long divided by fixed battens to take ten rows of core. The depth of the box should be barely greater than the diameter of the core so that no movement is possible when the lid is closed. Depths below ground level should be recorded in indelible pencil on small wooden blocks inserted at intervals denoting when the core barrel was withdrawn. The location and number of the borehole should be painted on the outside and inside of the lid. If specimens are required for examination the core should be divided longitudinally, using a core splitter, and one half preserved in the box.

Rock sludge samples—When core drilling in rock, it is advisable to collect and preserve the cuttings brought to the surface by the return water so that, if no core is recovered, the rock may be identified by the microscope. The sludge from each 5 ft of drilling is dried and packed in a labelled canvas bag. A borehole camera[29] has been devised for photographing the walls of unlined holes which is particularly useful when proving the presence of voids in cavernous formations or old mine workings.

Soil samples

These are of two types, disturbed samples taken by methods which destroy the original structure of the material, although the natural moisture content may be preserved, and undisturbed samples which preserve the original structure.

Disturbed samples—To retain the natural moisture content samples should at once be placed in an airtight jar and labelled. The jar should be filled to the top so as to leave a minimum of air space. In taking disturbed samples of sand for mechanical analysis from borings, the fine fractions brought up in suspension with water in the shell should be allowed to settle out, and added to the sample.

Undisturbed clay samples—Hard samples of clay may be cut out with a sharp knife as soon as a clay is exposed in excavation. From the moment it is exposed the clay must be protected from contact with water and from the direct rays of the sun. The sample should be coated with paraffin wax and packed in a box with damp sand.

The simplest form of sample tool for obtaining core samples of clay, called an open-drive sampler, consists of a tube fitted at one end with a cutting shoe, and at the other with a driving head. The inside diameter of the shoe should be slightly less than that of the tube, and the external diameter of the shoe should be rather greater than that of the tube. To ensure a minimum remoulding effect the interior of the sampler must be truly cylindrical and concentric with the cutting edge; the area ratio should be kept as low as is consistent with strength. The area ratio is defined as follows

$$\text{Area ratio} = \frac{D_w{}^2 - D_c{}^2}{D_c{}^2} \times 100 \text{ per cent} \qquad \ldots\ldots\ldots\ldots(1)$$

where D_w is the external diameter of the nose of the cutting shoe and D_c the minimum internal diameter of the shoe.

The sampler[16] most generally used in Great Britain is shown in *Figure 5*a. The complete sampler consists of the tube, the driving head, the cutting shoe, and two caps for the tube which enable it to be used as a container for the transport of samples.

The sampler is lowered in the borehole and is then driven into the ground by repeated blows from a hammer weighing about 100 lb (45 kg). After driving the sampler is given a complete turn to shear off the sample and is then withdrawn. The head and shoe are removed, the ends of the sample levelled off slightly below the ends of the tube, a label is then placed on one end of the sample and both exposed ends are covered with paraffin wax. If the sample is short and the clay soft, a layer of plaster of Paris should be added on top of the wax to support the sample in the tube. The caps are then screwed on and the sample is ready for transport to the laboratory. Constant use has shown that remoulding of the clay is limited to a zone $\frac{1}{4}$ in thick at the edge of the sample. A humid store room has been found unnecessary and samples may be kept in the tube for several months without appreciable alteration in their properties.

Experience has shown that some disturbance is inevitable when using open-drive samplers in soft clays. In order to obtain cores of high quality from such soils, it is necessary to use piston samplers. The stationary piston type, an example of which is given in *Figure 5*b is usually preferred because it provides positive control of the piston at all stages. Initially, the piston is fixed at the base of the sampler, which is then lowered down the borehole by adding lengths of tubes and rod to the sampler and piston respectively. The assembly should be pushed into the soil at the base of the borehole for a distance at least equal to the width of the borehole to penetrate disturbed ground, after which the piston is freed by rotating it half a turn. The piston is then held stationary by means of the rods while the sampler is driven forward. Before withdrawing the sampler, the piston is again fixed at its upper limit by rotating it half a turn. Thereafter the sample is prepared for transport in the same manner as for that from an open-drive sampler.

Undisturbed sand samples—Before excavation for trial pits in sand is started the ground should be drained by well points or filter wells, for if pumping is carried out from a sump within the excavation the flow of water to it may alter the density of the sand. Samples may be taken by the method illustrated in *Figure 6*. Sampling from trial pits is preferable to the use of borings since the ground can be carefully examined, the presence of stratification, thin clay layers *etc* noted, and samples taken from which the permeability may be measured both in the vertical and horizontal direction.

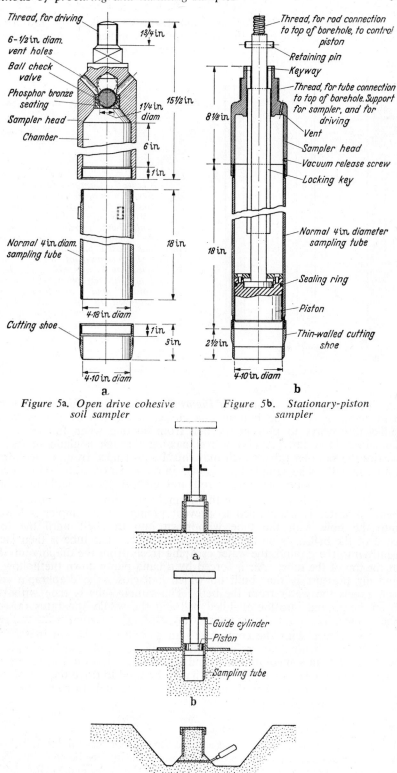

Figure 5a. *Open drive cohesive soil sampler*

Figure 5b. *Stationary-piston sampler*

Figure 6. *Method of taking undisturbed samples of sand, after Loos*
a *start of sampling* b *sampling tube filled with soil* c *cutting sample free*

Four methods of sampling sand from boreholes, by bituminous injections, by freezing, by the use of piston sampler and mud[5], and by compressed air, have been successfully used. Only the last has been employed in Great Britain[17].

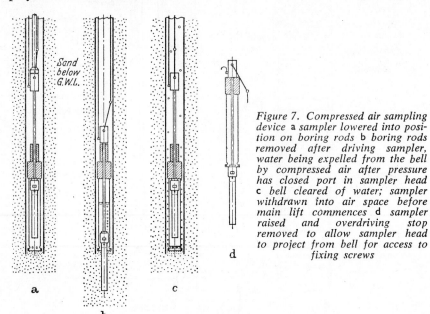

Figure 7. *Compressed air sampling device* a *sampler lowered into position on boring rods* b *boring rods removed after driving sampler, water being expelled from the bell by compressed air after pressure has closed port in sampler head* c *bell cleared of water; sampler withdrawn into air space before main lift commences* d *sampler raised and overdriving stop removed to allow sampler head to project from bell for access to fixing screws*

The compressed air sampler *Figure 7* consists of an outer tube or bell, 5 in diam, open at the bottom and closed at the top by a massive cap sufficiently heavy to prevent the bell from floating when full of air and immersed in water. A hollow rod passing through a gland in the cap carries the sampler tube, which may thus be protruded from, or withdrawn into, the bell. The sample tube is of 3 in diam, and is attached to a head communicating with the hollow rod and embodying a diaphragm valve.

The boring is put down in the normal way with a shell and an excess head of water is maintained to prevent piping. The sampler is lowered into the hole with the tube withdrawn into the bell until the lower edge of the bell rests on the bottom of the hole. The tube is then jacked gently into the ground, the water escaping freely from the diaphragm valve at the top of the tube. Air is forced by a hand pump down the hollow rod and air pressure is thus built up which first closes the diaphragm valve, and expels the water from the bell. The sample tube is then withdrawn from the ground into the air-filled bell and the whole apparatus raised to the surface, the sample being retained by capillary tensions in the wet sand.

Experience with the compressed air sampler has shown that natural sands with a distinctive grain structure may be satisfactorily sampled as well as sands in a medium dense and loose state. It would appear that if the sand is so dense that a monkey has to be used to drive the sampler, the measured density is lower than the *in situ* value and, in such cases, it is better to be guided by penetration tests (NIXON[30]).

Frequency of sampling in boreholes

Ideally a continuous undisturbed sample throughout the full depth of boring should be obtained. This is sometimes achieved in core borings in rock; in soft and plastic clays it is partially achieved by the American Shelby method, and by the Kjellman sampler[18]. In Great Britain, where soil profiles are generally complex, it is usual to take an undisturbed sample with every change in soil type and at 5 ft intervals in homogeneous soil. However, the number of cores desirable will vary with the nature of the problem and no general rule can be given.

Size of samples

The size of a sample is governed by the nature of the soil and the type and number of tests which are to be made upon it, see TABLE 4.

TABLE 4. SIZE OF SOIL SAMPLES*

Purpose of sample	Soil type	Minimum weight of sample required	
		lb	kg
Soil identification, natural moisture content and chemical tests	Cohesive soils and sands	1½	0·7
	Gravels	7	3·0
Compaction tests	Cohesive soils and sands.	25	11
	Gravelly soils	50	22
Comprehensive examinations of construction materials including soil stabilization	Cohesive soils and sands	50-100	22·5-45
	Gravelly soils	100-200	45-90

*British Standard Code of Practice, CP 2001:1957, Site Investigations.

Labelling samples

Samples should be labelled as soon as taken and the following records kept: No. of sample, No. of trial pit or boring, container No., type of sample, contract or site, position of sample relative to ground level, and date.

Ground water samples

Samples of water may be required to test its fitness for domestic purposes, for boiler water or industrial processes, or for making concrete. Samples may also be taken if it is suspected that the water is corrosive and will attack underground structures of metal and concrete. Sulphates when present may seriously damage concrete, and water from foundation sites on strata which may contain the mineral gypsum, such as the Keuper marl and the London clay, should always be tested. TABLE 5 gives a classification of sulphate soil conditions and precautionary measures[19].

In obtaining samples of ground water from boreholes every precaution must be taken to prevent their dilution by surface water or rain water. Thus samples should not be taken during a rain storm; before sampling the boreholes should be bailed out and the sample taken after the water in it has risen to its former level. The container should be well rinsed with the water before filling.

IN SITU TESTS

In situ tests may include dynamic penetration tests, static penetration or loading tests, shear tests, permeability and bulk density measurements.

Dynamic penetration tests

Simple probing tests—Where it is only required to find the depth of soil above bedrock, and where this depth is not more than 20 to 30 ft (6 to 9 m), it may be sufficient to drive down a pointed steel rod and to note the depth

TABLE 5

CLASSIFICATION OF SULPHATE SOIL CONDITIONS AFFECTING CONCRETE AND RECOMMENDED PRECAUTIONARY MEASURES

Classification of soil conditions	Sulphur trioxide in ground water, parts SO_3 per 100,000	Sulphur trioxide in clay, per cent SO_3	Precautionary measures		
			Pre-cast concrete products	Cast in situ concrete	
				Buried concrete surrounded by clay	Concrete exposed to one-sided water pressure or concrete of thin section
1	Less than 30	Less than 0·2	No special measures	*No special measures except that use of lean concretes (e.g. 1:7 or leaner ballast concrete) is inadvisable if SO_3 in water exceeds about 20 parts per 100,000. Where the latter is the case Portland cement mixes not leaner than 1:2:4, or, if special precautions desired, pozzolanic cement or sulphate resisting Portland cement mixes not leaner than 1:2:4 should be used*	*No special measures except that when SO_3 in water is above 20 parts per 100,000 special care should be taken to ensure high quality of Portland cement concrete, using if necessary 1:1½:3 mixes. Alternatively pozzolanic cements or sulphate resisting Portland cement may be used in mixes not leaner than 1:2:4*
2	30 to 100	0·2 to 0·5	*Rich Portland cement concretes, e.g. 1:1½:3, not likely to suffer seriously except over a very long period of years. Alternatively either pozzolanic, sulphate resisting Portland cement, high alumina or supersulphated cement should be used*	*Rich Portland cement concretes, e.g. 1:1½:3, unlikely to suffer seriously over a short period of years provided care is taken to ensure that a very dense and homogeneous mass is obtained. For most work, and particularly if the predominant salts are magnesium or sodium sulphates, concrete made with either pozzolanic cement, sulphate resisting Portland cement, high alumina cement, or supersulphated cement (1:2:4) is advisable*	*Use of Portland cement concrete not advisable. Pozzolanic cement or preferably high alumina cement recommended*
3	Above 100	Above 0·5	*The densest Portland cement concrete is not likely to suffer seriously over periods up to say 10-20 years unless conditions are very severe. Alternatively sulphate resisting, high alumina or supersulphated cement concrete should be used*	*The use of high alumina or supersulphated cement concretes is recommended*	*The use of high alumina or supersulphated cement concretes is recommended*

Where 1:2:4 concrete is mentioned other mixes of equivalent weight ratio of cement to total aggregate but with somewhat increased ratio of sand to coarse aggregate (e.g. 1:2½:3¾ or even 1:2½:3¾) may of course be used, sometimes with advantage. It may be necessary when using supersulphated cement to employ mixes somewhat richer than 1:2:4 in order to obtain adequate workability.

at which there is a great and sudden increase in the resistance to driving. This method should never be used where boulders may occur in the overburden, and it must be remembered that it gives no information as to the nature or degree of weathering of the bedrock.

Cone penetration tests—Slightly more information may be gained by probing if a rod with a conical end of standard dimensions is driven by successive blows from a hammer of known weight dropped from a standard height. The number of blows per inch of advance is then plotted against the depth of the point below the surface and a curve is thus obtained which bears occasionally some relation to soil strength. This method should be used with caution and may be dangerous unless checked by a boring.

Standard (Raymond) penetration test—This method which is now being used all over the world was first developed in the United States and has been applied there for many years. It is based on the resistance to driving of a tube and is intended to compare the results of different boreholes on the same site and for obtaining an indication of the bearing value of non-cohesive soils. A borehole is sunk to the level at which a test is required, taking care to prevent any upward seepage by adding water to a level above the water table. The tube is then lowered into the hole and forced six inches into the soil before the test blows are given. During the test the tube is driven by means of a hammer weighing 140 lb (63·5 kg) and falling freely from a height of 30 in (76 cm). The number of blows to drive the tube 12 in into the ground is recorded. The sample tube has an external diam of 2 in, an internal diam of 1½ in and a length of 2 ft (0·6 m). It consists of a pipe split longitudinally and threaded at each end, one end being screwed into a socket which is sharpened to form a cutting edge and the other into an adapter which is attached to the boring rods.

TERZAGHI[20] gives, for footings resting on sand, graphs relating the number of blows in the standard penetration test to the width of footing, and the allowable bearing pressure.

This method is purely empirical but it has two important advantages over the probing tests described above. In the first place, samples of the soil are recovered which, although partially disturbed, may be examined and their index properties measured. Secondly, the method of interpretation is based upon wide experience of foundation engineering in the United States. In saturated clays direct methods of investigation are preferable, but the Raymond method is undoubtedly valuable in deposits of fine sand and silt. It has also been applied to gravelly soils because of the lack of other more suitable methods, and the results indicate that the design data for its use in sands leads to conservative estimates of allowable bearing pressures in sandy gravels(PALMER and STUART[32]).

Test piles—In driving and testing piles the following precautions should be observed[21]; see also chapter on Foundations and Earthworks.

In driving: *1* at least one boring should be put down and the strata accurately described; the boring should be deep enough to ensure that no weak strata exist beneath the proposed bearing stratum; *2* as soon as the point of the pile reaches the bearing stratum the number of blows for a constant drop per inch of advance should be noted and the results plotted against depth until driving is completed; *3* the type of pile driving gear should be similar to that which it is intended to use on the works.

In testing: *a* the most convenient method of testing is by means of a hydraulic jack reacting on a suitably loaded kentledge frame (*Figure 8*) with a separate pump outside the area of the kentledge for safety reasons; *b* the settlement is observed by means of a scale securely fixed to the head of the pile and readings are taken with an engineers' level; *c* the load should be applied in a series of increasing steps and each increment should be maintained particularly when in cohesive soil to observe the change in settlement with time and succeeding increments should only be added after the pile has reached equilibrium. At least once, generally after the application of the working load, the load should be reduced to zero to observe the permanent settlement. The results are plotted, load in tons against settlement in inches, as shown in *Figure 9*; *d* it is most desirable that loading should be carried to failure when continuous settlement takes place under constant load, or at least to a settlement equivalent to 10 per cent of the nominal width of the pile. This is the ultimate load and a factor of safety of $2\frac{1}{2}$ should be allowed on it.

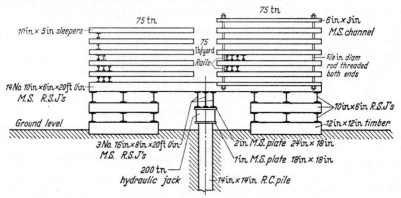

Figure 8. *Kentledge frame for pile test*

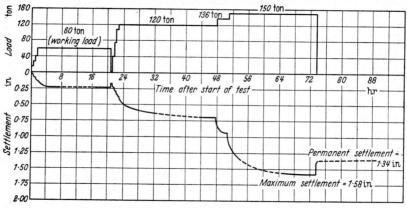

Figure 9. *Load/time/settlement diagram for pile test*

Static penetration or loading tests

Field bearing tests[22]—Plate loading tests are the oldest and most widely used method for measuring the safe bearing capacity of a soil, but they can be most misleading unless correctly interpreted. *Figure 10* illustrates the apparatus required; it should be noted that the dead load should be well clear of the excavation so as not to influence the result.

In carrying out a bearing test the following precautions should be observed. The surface soil should be removed to the depth of the proposed foundation, and the bottom of the excavation must be protected from rain while the test is in progress. The loading plate must be sufficiently stiff so as not to deflect under the maximum load applied to it. After each increase in load, settlement of the plate should be observed as accurately as possible

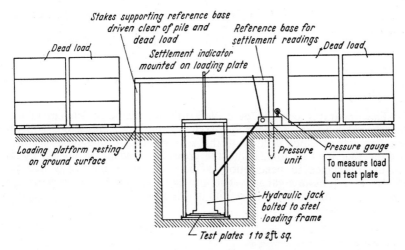

Figure 10. *Apparatus for plate bearing test*

and the results plotted as for a pile test (*Figure 9*). It is advisable to increase the load to a point at which actual failure of the soil occurs; this is indicated by a rapid increase in the amount of settlement.

Conditions of use. A bearing test should always be supplemented by at least one boring, for the soil in this test is only significantly stressed to a depth of about $1\frac{1}{2}$ times the breadth of the plate; no indication is given of the nature of the deeper layers which will be stressed by a large foundation. Where soft strata occur in depth, bearing tests alone can be most misleading and dangerous.

On homogeneous clay a bearing test measures the ultimate bearing capacity but this can be found more accurately and at less cost by means of auger borings and measurements of the shear strength. It gives no indication whatever of the settlements which may be caused by consolidation. It does give a measure of the elastic settlement, and this is proportional to the square of the loaded area but is, as a rule, relatively unimportant as a cause of settlement.

Bearing tests are of value for investigating the bearing capacity of weathered rock, stony clay and other materials to which ordinary methods of sampling and testing cannot be applied.

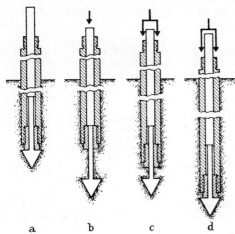

Figure 11. *Principle of Dutch deep sounding device* a *commencement of driving cone—cone resistance measured* b *limit of cone movement* c *penetration of hollow rods* d *pushing cone to new depth: 'total resistance' measured*

a   b   c   d

Dutch deep sounding test—This type of probing test is most effective in determining the bearing capacity of piles driven into deltaic deposits, and in particular, of strata of fine sand of varying density[23]. It should not be used in soft clays; for these the standard procedure of sampling and testing, together with vane tests, is preferable. It is useful to determine the existence of an adequate thickness of gravel soils below 50 ft alluvium for end-bearing piles.

The apparatus consists of a steel tube of diameter 3·6 cm (1·4 in), through which passes a steel rod carrying at its lower end a 60° cone, the base diameter of which is equal to that of the tube. Either tube or cone or both together may be forced into the ground by means of a jack; in each case the resistance to penetration is measured by means of a hydraulic cylinder and pressure gauge. The principle of the test is illustrated in *Figure 11* and an example of results is given in *Figure 12*.

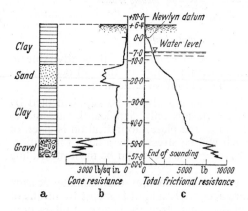

Figure 12. *Results of Dutch deep sounding device* a *soil profile from boring* b *values of maximum resistance when driving cone* c *values of 'total resistance' minus previous 'cone resistance'*

In operation the cone is forced into the soil for a distance of 8 cm (3·2 in) and the maximum resistance recorded; this is proportional to the point bearing capacity of a pile in sand at the same depth. The tube is then pushed up to the cone, and both together are forced down a further 20 cm (7·9 in). The resistance, in this instance the point bearing resistance plus the frictional resistance of the rods, is measured and recorded. This cycle of operations is repeated until a suitable bearing stratum is reached. The method is very widely used in the Low Countries where it may be described as standard practice.

Proctor needle—This is a light, easily portable, spring loaded penetration device, illustrated in *Figure 13*. It is chiefly used for the field control of the consistency of fine grained soils during the construction of rolled fill embankments.

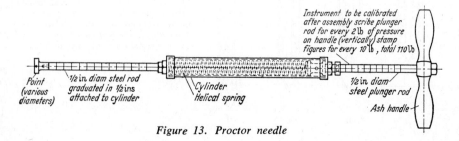

Figure 13. *Proctor needle*

The needle is forced into the soil at the rate of about ½ in/sec (13 mm/sec), the maximum force required being registered by the amount of compression of the spring and recorded on the upper graduated rod by means of a simple cursor. For any soil type the needle can be calibrated on specimens prepared under known conditions in the Proctor compaction apparatus (see chapter on Soil Mechanics).

Shear tests

Box shear tests—The shear strength of shale has been measured *in situ* by means of a large shear box[5].

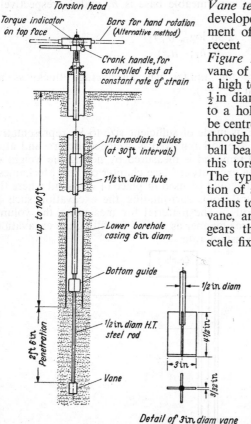

Figure 14. Vane test

Vane test—The vane test has been developed for the *in situ* measurement of the shear strength of soft recent clays[24]. The apparatus, *Figure 14*, consists of a cruciform vane of 2 in or 3 in diam carried on a high tensile steel rod 3 ft long and ½ in diam. This in turn is attached to a hollow torsion rod which may be centred in the borehole by guides, through which the rod is carried in ball bearings. At the upper end of this torsion rod is a torsion head. The type shown utilizes the deflection of a proving bar at a constant radius to measure the torsion on the vane, and by means of a series of gears the moment is shown on a scale fixed in the head.

In use the rod is lowered down the borehole to such a depth that the vane is forced into the clay about 3 ft ahead of the boring tube. The torsion head is then rotated with a velocity of about 0·1°/sec, and the maximum reading on the scale is observed.

The moment required to mobilize the shear strength of the clay is given by the equation

$$M = c\frac{D^2 H}{2}\left(1 + \frac{1}{3}\frac{D}{H}\right)\pi \qquad \ldots\ldots\ldots\ldots(2)$$

where D and H are the diameter and height of the vane and c is the shear strength of the clay.

Permeability

This may be measured *in situ* by observations on the yield from a pumped well[25]. The well should penetrate to the full depth of the aquifer. Pumping should be carried on at a constant rate until comparative equilibrium is established. The depth to water level is noted before and during pumping. Then

$$K = \frac{2\cdot3q \log_{10}\left(\dfrac{R}{r_w}\right)}{\pi\,(H^2 - h^2)} \qquad \ldots\ldots\ldots\ldots(3)$$

where K is the permeability in ft/sec, q the discharge in cusec, R the radius of influence, r_w the effective radius of well, H the depth of water above the impermeable base before pumping, and h the depth after pumping, measured preferably immediately outside the well. As a first approximation R may be taken as 500 in many cases. In fact R depends upon the draw-down and permeability. SLICHTER[33] suggests the following relationship:

$$R = 300 \ (H-h) \ \sqrt{K}$$

Where possible, it will normally be better to take observations in two adjacent wells at distances r_1 and r_2 from the pumped well where the equilibrium depth above the impermeable base is h_1 and h_2 respectively. Then:

$$K = \frac{2 \cdot 3q \ \log_{10} \ (r_1/r_2)}{\pi \ (h_1{}^2 - h_2{}^2)}$$

In the artesian case where the aquifer has an average thickness m, $(h_1{}^2 - h_2{}^2)$ is replaced by $2m \ (h_1 - h_2)$.

Bulk density

As a rule a small excavation is made of sufficient size to be representative of the local conditions, and the soil removed is weighed before and after drying. The volume of soil removed is measured by noting the weight of dry sand required to refill the excavation[26] (see chapter on Soil Mechanics). Carefully selected pea gravel should be used in place of dry sand where the latter might enter into natural voids surrounding the excavation such as may be present in gravel soils. The material for measuring the volume should be calibrated in the same manner as is used for filling the excavation, usually by pouring it at a constant rate.

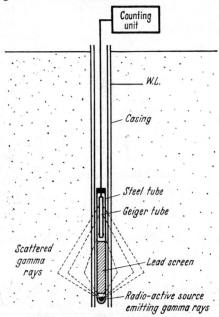

Figure 15. Radioactive density probe

A more recent method that has been developed commercially is the use of radioactive isotopes[34, 35]. A cobalt 60 or caesium 137 source is placed in the soil and gamma rays are emitted, which are scattered back to a geiger tube placed at an optimum distance from the source. The higher the bulk density, the fewer are the gamma rays which reach the detector. The instruments are calibrated by testing them in materials of known density. The radiation hazard is kept to a minimum by a careful design of the equipment but nevertheless it should only be used by experienced personnel.

The instrument illustrated in *Figure 15* is used for measuring the density of soils at depth in a lined hole in the ground. This application is particularly useful for measuring the density of granular materials under water, where normal sampling methods cannot be used.

A second instrument, illustrated in *Figure 16*, is used to measure the bulk density of soils at the surface. In this instrument the source is housed in a steel probe which is forced into the soil to a predetermined depth, and the gamma radiation is detected by a geiger tube at the surface. With both these instruments, the density measurements take about two minutes and can be accurate to within ± 1 per cent.

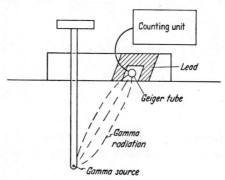

Figure 16. *Radioactive surface density meter*

Moisture content

Equipment has been developed commercially to measure moisture content *in situ*, using a radioactive source of radium–beryllium[36]. Neutrons emitted from this source are slowed down in a soil in proportion to the hydrogen content, and are counted using a slow neutron detector. As most of the hydrogen is in the form of water, the count will be proportional to the moisture content of the soil. This equipment has been combined with the density instrument illustrated in *Figure 16* for surface measurements.

GEOPHYSICS[27, 37]

There are four geophysical methods in general use, namely, gravitational, magnetic, electrical, and seismic. Each method involves the measurement of a particular physical property at the ground surface that can be associated with variations in the sub-surface geology. Although, using modern instruments, there are no great difficulties in carrying out the site measurements, experience and a geological knowledge are essential in interpreting the data correctly.

The main applications of a geophysical survey for a site investigation are to determine the depth to bedrock and to locate the extent and thickness of constructional materials in borrow pits. It is particularly advisable to have a survey on a site where there may be a buried channel, as a continuous profile of the bedrock surface can be obtained. It is considered essential to have boreholes on the site to correlate the geophysical results.

The two main methods applicable to site investigation are the electrical resistivity and the seismic refraction. The equipment for both these methods is portable, and the site work can be carried out quickly.

Electrical resistivity method

In this method four steel electrodes are placed in line, usually at equal distances apart. An alternating electrical current is passed into the ground through the outer two electrodes and the resultant potential drop is recorded between the inner two electrodes. From the current and voltage readings the ground resistivity can be calculated for a depth approximately equal to the electrode spacing. By increasing the electrode spacing the resistivity of the ground can be measured to a greater depth, thus indicating any geological changes that occur in depth. This is illustrated in *Figure 17* where the overburden resistivity is recorded with the electrode in position (*a*) An increased resistivity value is recorded in position (*b*) where the electrode spacing is larger and rock is contained within the measurement.

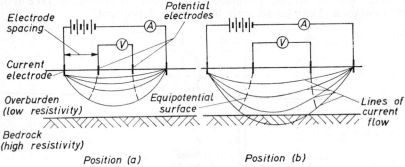

Figure 17. Measurement of resistivity of ground

This method is called the expanding electrode technique. Readings of resistivity are taken at increasing values of the electrode spacing and from the resistivity/spacing curve the depth to bedrock can be determined. The accuracy of the determination depends on the uniformity of the ground conditions but is usually within 10 per cent of the correct depth.

An alternative method of operation is the lateral traversing technique in which the electrode system is moved along a traverse whilst the electrode spacing is kept constant. The resistivity is measured at successive points along the traverse and any changes in the ground within the depth of investigation are indicated by changes in the observed resistivity values. This technique is very useful in locating the extent and thickness of construction materials such as sand and gravel.

The cost of a resistivity survey is about £50 per day on site including the subsequent interpretation of the results. In a day it is possible to carry out up to 10 expanding electrode tests or 2,000–5,000 ft of lateral traverse depending on the number of readings to be taken and the site conditions.

Seismic refraction method

A small charge of gelignite is fired near the ground surface and the resulting seismic waves transmitted through the ground are picked up by a number of vibration detectors placed on the ground in line with the shot point. The detectors transform the ground vibrations into electrical impulses which are amplified and recorded on a moving photographic paper. From the photographic record, the interval of time can be measured between the instant of explosion and the arrival of the first seismic impulse at each detector. These time intervals are plotted against the distances of the detectors from the shot point, and from the resultant graph the velocities of transmission of the elastic waves in the ground can be measured. This is illustrated in *Figure 18*, which shows the seismic wave ray diagram and time–distance graph for a two-layer structure.

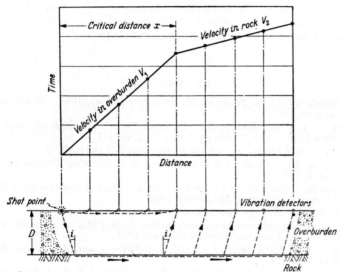

Figure 18.   *Time–distance graph for two-layer structure and section showing refracted wave rays*

Close to the shot point the vibration that has travelled directly through the overburden is the first to arrive at the detectors. However, beyond a certain critical distance from the shot point the first vibration to reach the detector is one that has travelled down to the bedrock surface, been refracted along the bedrock, and has re-emerged to the surface. This refraction will always take place when the velocity of transmission in the rock is greater than in the overburden, and the angle at which it occurs is given by the expression:

$$\sin i = \frac{V_1}{V_2}$$

where V_1 and V_2 are the velocities of transmission in the overburden and rock respectively. These velocities are calculated from the reciprocal slopes of the time-distance graph. The depth to the rock surface is given by the formula

$$D = \frac{x}{2}\left(\frac{V_2 - V_1}{V_2 + V_1}\right)^{\frac{1}{2}}$$

In practice a shot is fired at each end of the spread of detectors and then by an extension of the above formula it is possible to calculate the depths along a sloping rock surface.

This method of exploration is normally used for determining the bedrock profile between boreholes. It is considered more accurate than the resistivity method, but is more expensive. A survey costs about £90 a day on site including the interpretation. About 1,000–3,000 ft of traverse can be surveyed each day, depending on site conditions and the depth of investigation.

DOWSING AND WATER DIVINING

Since many worthy people accept the reality of this phenomenon their claims should not be dismissed as mere self deception; nevertheless, in the present state of our knowledge and so far as civil engineering is concerned, it is better to rely on the evidence of boreholes. For those who wish to explore this obscure borderland of physics and psychology there is only one guide: *entia non sunt multiplicanda praeter necessitatem!*

REFERENCES

[1]British Standard Code of Practice C.P. 2001: *Site Investigations.* British Standards Institution, 1957

[2]HARDING, H. J. B. Site Investigations including Boring and other Methods of Sub-Surface Exploration *J. Instn civ. Engrs* 32 (1949) 111

[3]COOLING, L. F. Soil Mechanics and Site Exploration *ibid* 18 (1942) 37

[4]MOHR, H. A. *Exploration of Soil Conditions and Sampling Operations,* 2nd ed. Harvard, 1940

[5]HVORSLEV, M. J. *Sub-Surface Exploration and Sampling of Soils for Civil Engineering Purposes* Vicksburg, Mississippi, 1948

[6]LAHEE, F. H. *Field Geology* 4th ed. New York, 1941

[7]GOLDER, H. Q. The Influence of Geology on Soil Testing Methods in Western Europe *Proc. 2nd Int. Conf. Soil Mech.* Rotterdam, 1948

[8]NIEDERHOF, A. E. Field Tests of a Shale Foundation *Trans. Amer. Soc. civ. Engrs* 105 (1940) 1519

[9]TERZAGHI, K. Introduction to Tunnel Geology, published in *Rock Tunnelling with Steel Supports* by R. V. PROCTOR and T. L. WHITE Youngstown, Ohio, 1946

[10]DROUHIN, M. Essais Géotechniques des Terrains de Fondations *Trans. 2nd Congr. Large Dams,* vol. IV, 1936

[11]FRINK, J. W. The Foundation of Hales Bar Dam *Econom. Geol.* 41 (1946) 576

[12]REEVES, F. and ROSS, C. P. A Geologic Study of the Madden Dam Project *U.S. Geol. Survey Bull. 821-B,* 1930

[13]GLOSSOP, R. and SKEMPTON, A. W. Particle Size in Silts and Sands *J. Instn civ. Engrs* 25 (1945) 81

[14]GUTHRIE BROWN, J., in discussion on paper of H. J. B. HARDING[2]

[15]LEGGETT, R. F. *Geology and Engineering* New York, 1939

[16]LONGSDON, A. E. C. An Improved Clay Sampler *Engineer* 180 (1945) 97

[17]BISHOP, A. W. A New Sampling Tool for Use in Cohesionless Sands Below Ground Water Level *Géotechnique* 1 (1948) 125

[18]KJELLMAN, W. and KALLSTENIUS, T. A Method of Extracting Long Continuous Cores of Undisturbed Soil *Proc. 2nd Int. Conf. Soil Mech.* Rotterdam, 1948

[19]Concrete in Sulphate Bearing Clays and Ground Waters, *Build. Res. Sta. Dig.* No. 31 (1951)

[20]TERZAGHI, K. and PECK, R. B. *Soil Mechanics in Engineering Practice* New York, 1948

[21]BISHOP, A. W., COLLINGRIDGE, V. H. and O'SULLIVAN, T. P. Driving and Loading Tests on Six Pre-cast Piles in Gravel *Géotechnique* 1 (1948) 49

[22]GOLDER, H. Q. Soil Bearing Tests and Foundation Design *Trans. Liverpool Engng Soc.* 67 (1946) 15

[23]See papers in *Proc. 2nd Int. Conf. Soil Mech.* Rotterdam, 1948

[24]SKEMPTON, A. W. Vane Tests in the Alluvial Plain of the River Forth near Grangemouth *Géotechnique* 1 (1948) 111

[25]WENZEL. L. K. Methods for Determining the Permeability of Water Bearing Materials with Special Reference to the Discharging Well Methods *Water Supply Paper 887, U.S.A.S.,* 1942

[26]B.S. 1377:1948. *Methods of Test for Soil Classification and Compaction*

[27]HEILAND, C. A. *Geophysical Exploration* Prentice Hall, New York, 1946

[28]GOLDER, H. Q. and AKROYD, T. N. W. An Apparatus for triaxial compression tests at High Pressures *Géotechnique* 4 (1954) 131-6

[29]Anon. Borehole Camera Aids Foundations. *Engng News Rec.* 146 (1952)

[30]NIXON, I. K. Some Investigations on Granular Soils with particular reference to the Compressed Air Sand Sampler *Géotechnique* 4 (1954) 16-31

[31]SKEMPTON, A. W. and NORTHEY, R. D. The Sensitivity of Clays *Géotechnique* 31 (1952) 30-53

[32]PALMER, D. J. and STUART, J. A. Some Observations on the Standard Penetration Test and on a correlation of the Test with a new Penetrometer. *Proc. 4th Int. Conf. Soil Mech. & Found. Eng.* I. pp. 231-6 (1957)

[33]SLICHTER, C. S. Theoretical Investigation of the Motion of Ground Waters. *U.S. Geol. Surv.* 19th Ann Part 2 pp. 295-384 (1899)

[34]CAMERON, J. F. and BOURNE, M. S. A gamma scattering soil density gauge for sub-surface measurements. *Int. J. Appl. Rad. Isotope* 3 (1957) 15-19

[35]BELCHER, D. J., CUYKENDALL, T. R. and SACK, H. S. The measurement of soil moisture and density by neutrons and gamma ray scattering. *Amer. Civ. Aero. Admin. Tech. Dev. Report 127* (1950)

[36]MEIGH, A. C. and SKIPP, B. O. Gamma-ray and Neutron Methods of Measuring Soil Density and Moisture, *Géotechnique* 10, No. 2 (1960)

[37]ROBERTSHAW, J. and BROWN, P. D. Geophysical Methods of Exploration and their Application to Civil Engineering Problems. *J. Instn civ. Engrs* 4, No. 5 (1955)

FOUNDATIONS AND EARTHWORKS

Guthlac Wilson, S.M., D.Sc., M.I.C.E., M.I.Struct.E., MASCE

Revised by E. O. Measor, A.C.G.I., B.Sc., M.I.C.E., M.I.Struct.E.

GENERAL

The object of a foundation is to carry the loads imposed upon it and to restrict the total and relative settlements within the limits that may be permitted by the nature and use of the structure which it supports.

There are three independent factors: minimum depth, stability and settlement (over-all and relative). There have been instances of foundation failure due to each of these causes, see *Figures 1, 2* and *3*.

The selection of the most appropriate type of foundation depends upon the type and sequence of ground at the site of the structure, upon any special circumstances prevailing and upon the class of structure.

Type of ground

Types of ground may be broadly divided into two main groups: soils and rocks. TABLE 2 in B.S. Code of Practice C.P. 2001:1957—Site Investigations, is an excellent basis for the classification of various types of soils. See also other sections of that code.

From the point of view of foundation design, rocks and soils may be grouped as shown in TABLE 1 below:

TABLE 1

MAIN TYPES OF GROUND

Class	Type of rock or soil	Remarks
H = Hard	Solid rock, varying from granite to virgin chalk Dense gravels and sands Compacted sand and gravel fills Slag heaps	
	Loose gravels and sands Tipped sand and gravel fills	Unstable, may need compaction or stabilization
	Hard clays	Consolidation under heavy loads may have to be considered
Borderline	Medium clays Compacted fills of clay	Consolidation settlement must be considered
S = Soft	Soft clays Chalk marls Silts Compacted fills of silt	Consolidation settlement must be considered
	Tipped fills of clay and silt	Not to be relied upon unless of such age that settlement is complete
	Peat	Must be removed or load must be carried to lower strata, or settlement must be specially allowed for in design

Chemical waste deposits should be subjected to mechanical tests and ascribed to the same class as the soil to which they correspond most closely. All soils, but particularly clays, and ground water may require to be

108

chemically analysed in order that any chemicals deleterious to concrete or other foundation materials may be detected.

Figure 1. Insufficiently deep foundation on clay (from photograph in Proc. Conf. Biol. and Civil Engrs., 1948)

Sequence of ground

The sequence of strata (or ground) which is found within the depth to which significant increase of stress is transmitted by the foundation is as important as are the types of ground. There are four important sequences: these are set out in TABLE 2.

TABLE 2. SEQUENCES OF GROUND

Sequence	Description
H-H = Hard on hard	*A series of consistently hard strata*
S-S = Soft on soft	*A series of consistently soft strata (even if including relatively thin layers of harder soil)*
S-H = soft on hard	*Soft strata overlying hard sub-strata*
H-S = Hard on soft	*A hard crust on a deep soft stratum, or series of soft strata*

Illustrative examples of these sequences are given in *Figures* 4a to h.

Special regional circumstances

In certain regions there exist special circumstances which affect the design of foundations and may also have a fundamental effect upon the design of structures. The most important special circumstances are mine workings (including pumping of brine), earthquakes and permafrost. The modifications of foundation technique required under these circumstances are considered on p 151. General regional subsidence due to consolidation of incompletely consolidated strata, or further consolidation due to ground water lowering, may require that such subsidence be taken into account but will not require modification of the normal foundation technique.

Figure 2.   General shear failure

Class of structure

When considering foundations the engineer should classify structures according to their relative flexibility. It is not, however, sufficient to consider a scale ranging from '100 per cent flexible' at one end to '100 per cent stiff' at the other. It is also necessary to distinguish structures which are 'stiff-brittle' from those which are 'stiff-strong'. A '100 per cent stiff-strong' structure may be defined as one which is sufficiently strong and stiff to re-distribute foundation loads as may be required by the nature of the ground, without damage to itself: in the limit, such a structure should be capable of being supported on three points. A '100 per cent stiff-brittle' structure may be defined as a building that cannot be distorted without suffering damage, one that is stiff without being strong, stiff by reason of its finishes, as a framed building cased in marble, plastered, or provided with partitions that cannot be deformed without cracking, or a

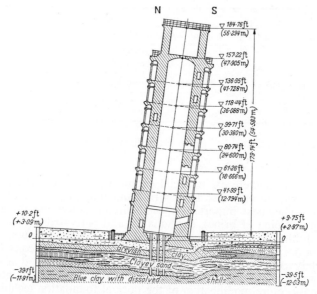

Figure 3.   Unequal consolidation settlement, Tower of Pisa

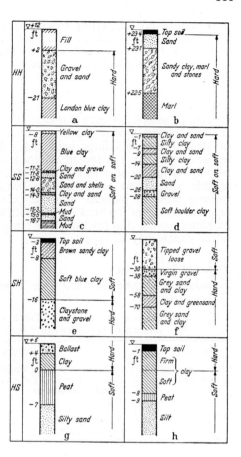

Figure 4. Typical examples of ground sequence, see TABLE 2. a *London* b *Pontypool* c *Shanghai* d *Hull* e *Leek* f *Southampton* g *Charlton* h *Avonmouth*

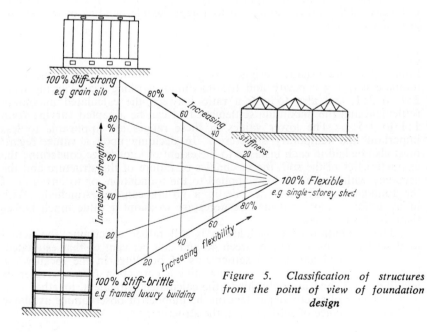

Figure 5. Classification of structures from the point of view of foundation design

flexible structure supporting machinery that must be kept strictly in alignment. In this class would also be placed a continuous bridge which would be
endangered by a relative settlement of the piers. Any structure can then be
plotted in the mind's eye somewhere on a triangular diagram such as that in
Figure 5.

The type of trouble that may be expected to result from settlement
varies according to the type of building. In luxury buildings clad with
veneers of marble, or even Portland stone, general cracking and spalling of
the finishes may occur. In heavy brick buildings of the old factory type,
or steel framed buildings with heavy brick infilling, the structure may
act as a rigid box and spread the load over the whole of the base, instead
of only on the footings as intended. In such instances the earliest signs of
trouble will appear at the corners owing to the heavy concentrations of
bearing pressure induced in these positions: these are likely to cause
diagonal cracks in the brickwork. With steel-framed or reinforced concrete
buildings having thin brickwork or other brittle panelling, general cracking
of the panels may be expected.

Types of foundation
Foundations may be classified as in TABLE 3 below:

TABLE 3

INDEX TO TREATMENT OF VARIOUS TYPES OF FOUNDATION

Main type	Sub-type	Refer to pages
Direct bearing foundations	Pad and strip foundations	116, 118, 121
	Trench, pier and cylinder foundations	121, 130
	Floating basement	122
	Rafts	121
Piled foundations	Bearing piles	142
	Friction piles	142

Figure 6 indicates the applicability of the various types of foundation
to a heavy stiff-brittle building and to a light flexible building under various
ground conditions.

Factor of safety
Foundations are usually designed to give a ratio between the calculated
ultimate carrying capacity and the maximum working load varying from
2:1 to 3:1, and also to give a ratio between the calculated maximum
settlement and the maximum settlement that can be accepted varying from
1:1 to 1·5:1. The lower values in these ranges are applicable to less
important and temporary structures. In deciding upon a value, regard
must also be had in each instance to the extent of knowledge concerning the
characteristics of the soil, the mechanics of failure of the structure and the
accuracy with which the load applied to the foundation, or to any unit of
the foundation, such as one pile in a group, can be estimated. With
unfavourable examples it may be necessary to adopt a value much higher
than those suggested.

The estimation of consolidation is still rather uncertain: the actual
total settlement may range between 40 and 200 per cent of that estimated.
If the theoretical and actual settlements of buildings in the locality are
known, it should be possible to determine a correction factor, greater or
less than unity, and to apply this to the calculated settlement, together with
a small factor of safety, dependent on the number of observations available
and the importance of settlement to the structure.

In the case of cohesive soils, settlements should always be calculated from the maximum average load on the foundations for a long period, which may be much less than the maximum instantaneous load, which latter value should be used in calculations of ultimate failure.

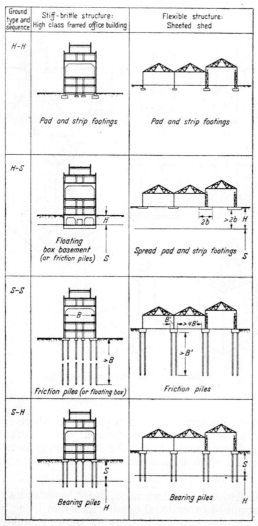

Figure 6. *Types of foundation to stiff-brittle and flexible buildings for various ground sequences*

DIRECT BEARING FOUNDATIONS APPLIED TO BUILDINGS

Figures 7, 8 and *9* show examples of the main types of direct bearing foundations which are considered in the following sections.

TYPES OF DIRECT BEARING BUILDING FOUNDATIONS

All strip footings are derived from the original wall footing, *Figure 7*a, which was supported on soft ground by a layer of compacted sand or chalk,

Figure 7b, or by a layer of wooden planks or baulks, *Figure* 7c; alternatively the wall base was thickened out to spread the load, *Figure* 7d, and later the thickening of the masonry wall was supplemented or replaced, *Figure* 7e, by mass concrete which was in turn followed by the reinforced concrete footing, *Figure* 7f.

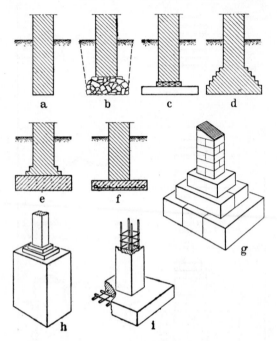

Figure 7. Pad and strip footings

Pad, or block, footings may be regarded as short sections of strip footings as far as the ground is concerned, but as structures they are essentially three dimensional whereas the strip footing is two dimensional. *Figures* 7g, h and i show typical masonry, mass concrete and reinforced concrete block footings.

Trench foundations and pier and cylinder foundations are really strip and pad foundations of exceptional depth called into being by the necessity to reach a hard bearing stratum. *Figure* 8a shows a building with trench foundations through fill to Thames ballast; *Figure* 8b shows a typical cylinder excavated by hand. Various machines have been developed recently for sinking cylinders rapidly which in many cases can be done without the necessity and expense of using a lining.

A raft foundation is a foundation that occupies the whole area of the building, *Figure* 9a: the necessity for such a foundation arises when the sizes of the requisite pad and strip foundations are so great that they merge into one another.

A 'floating basement' foundation is one in which such a volume of ground is excavated that little or no change of vertical pressure is induced in the ground at foundation level. Such foundations are useful in very bad ground and a typical example is illustrated in *Figure* 9b.

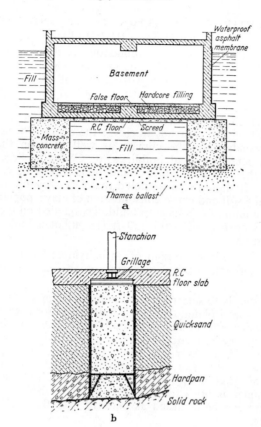

Figure 8. *Trench, pier and cylinder foundations* **a** *pier and trench foundations* (*London*) **b** *cylinder foundation* (*New York*)

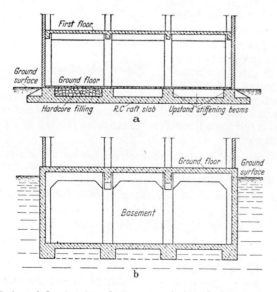

Figure 9. *Raft and floating foundations* **a** *raft foundation* **b** *floating basement*

PAD AND STRIP FOUNDATIONS: THE INDIVIDUAL PAD
OR BLOCK, FOUNDATION

The first step in the design of any foundation is the determination of the minimum depth to which it should be carried below the finished ground surface. This depth must be such that the base of the foundation is below the depth to which soil volume changes are caused by alternate drying and swelling, or by frost heave. Such volume changes do not occur in soils containing less than 3 per cent of grains under 0·02 mm diam. Alternate drying and swelling occurs mainly in clays: the depth to which this process takes place depends upon the climate as well as upon the soil. Local knowledge, the study of local buildings, or Codes of Practice may give guidance as to the depths to which foundations should be carried to avoid these troubles. It should also be noted that fast growing trees draw a lot of water from the soil and cause consolidation of clay: poplars have caused a considerable amount of damage to buildings founded on the London clay, and should not be planted within 60 ft (18 m) of a building carried on shallow foundations.

The second step in the design of an individual block foundation is to determine the ultimate bearing capacity of the ground in which it is supported.

The third step is to select the minimum factor of safety, see p 111. If the foundation is an isolated one *e.g.* a foundation for a small water tower situated at a distance from any other building, the design bearing pressure can generally be the ultimate bearing pressure divided by the minimum factor of safety. If, however, the foundation is one of a group it may be necessary to use a lower bearing pressure determined from consideration of the settlement of the group, p 117. In some instances it is necessary to check that the settlement is not excessive, even with an isolated footing. The bearing pressure can be regarded as uniform over the area of the base of a block footing.

A brick footing or an unreinforced concrete footing is designed on the assumption of an 'angle of spread' of load from the edges of the baseplate or column foot to the sides of the base, *Figures 10*a and b. The angle of spread may be taken as four vertical to three horizontal for a brick footing and 45° for

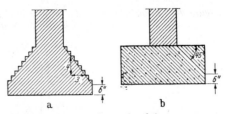

Figure 10. Brick and plain concrete footings a brick b mass concrete

a concrete footing. The depth of the footing should be such that the base is about 6 in below the intersection of the angle of spread with the sides. The design of a reinforced concrete rectangular footing is illustrated in the following example.

Example—A rectangular reinforced concrete footing for a reinforced concrete column, 20 in × 20 in cross section, carrying a load of 200 ton. Subsoil: stiff marl, having a cohesion of 1 ton/sq ft.

Design. Minimum effective thickness of base, for punching shear

$$t = \frac{448,000}{4\,(20 + 2 \times 0{\cdot}875t) \times 100} = \frac{1,120}{20 + 1{\cdot}75t}$$

$$1{\cdot}75t^2 + 20t - 1,120 = 0$$

$$t = 21 \text{ in}$$

The over-all depth will therefore be about 24 in and the increase in bearing capacity due to depth is negligible.

Bearing capacity. The column spacing is such that adjacent columns need not be considered. Safe bearing capacity$=3c=3$ ton/sq ft.

Area of footing$=200/3=67$ sq ft$=8$ ft 3 in sq.

$$\text{Bending moment (B.M.)} = \frac{200}{4}\left\{\frac{8\cdot25}{3} - \frac{1\cdot67}{3}\right\}$$

$$= \frac{200\times6\cdot58}{3\times4} = 109\cdot8 \text{ ft ton}$$

This may be spread over the full 99 in width, so bending moment per in width is given by

$$\text{B.M.} = \frac{109\cdot8}{99} = 1\cdot11 \text{ ft ton} = 29,900 \text{ in lb} = Rbd^2$$

and

$$R = \frac{29,900}{1\times21^2} = 68$$

which is amply safe.

The reinforcement should be spread over the width of $(20 \text{ in} + 2\times25 \text{ in}) = 70$ in in each direction (see *Figure 11*a).

If the load in the column is not axial there are two possible cases: *i* if the load passes within the kern of the base, or *ii* if it passes outside the kern.

As an illustration of the first of these cases, let there be a bending moment of 200 ft ton at the base of the column in the example given above *i.e.* eccentricity about one axis$=1$ ft (*Figure 11*b) *i.e.* less than 1/6th of the side of the smallest allowable square foundation.

Then: Maximum bearing stress$=3$ ton sq ft and let the side of square base$=a$

$$3 = \frac{200}{a^2} + \frac{200}{a^3/6}$$

and $3a^3 - 200a - 1,200 = 0$

by trial and error $a = 10\cdot3$ ft$=10$ ft 4 in

The distribution of bearing pressure is triangular (*Figure 11*b) and the bending moment at the critical section is:

$$\text{B.M.} = 1\cdot5\times\frac{10\cdot33^2}{4} \times \frac{10\cdot33}{3} + 1\cdot5\times10\cdot33 \times \frac{10\cdot33}{6} \times 3 \times \frac{10\cdot33}{4\times2}$$

$$= 1\cdot5\times\frac{10\cdot33^3}{12} + 1\cdot5\times\frac{10\cdot33^3}{16}$$

$$= 242\cdot4 \text{ ft ton}$$

For safety against punching shear, the depth should be chosen so that a total load of 3 ton/sq ft all over the base can be resisted.

The second case is when the eccentricity is such that there will not be bearing over the whole of the base. Under these conditions *1* the bearing pressure will act on part of the base and will vary from zero along some line *AB* (*Figure 11*c) to a maximum, not exceeding the safe bearing pressure, at *C*, *2* the total bearing pressure will be equal to the total load and *3* the centre of gravity of the bearing pressure must be under *D*, the point of action of the load.

GROUPS OF PAD OR BLOCK FOUNDATIONS

With groups of foundations all the considerations necessary in the design of individual foundations arise and, in addition, those of group failure and relative settlement. Group failure may occur where a group of individually safe foundations rest on a relatively strong layer overlying a thick layer of weaker material. The settlement of a foundation which would take place if it were so far from other foundations that its settlement was not affected by the loads upon them, termed 'inherent' settlement, must be distinguished from the additional settlement caused by loads on neighbouring foundations, termed 'interference' settlement.

It has long been assumed that uniform settlement of the parts of a structure is ensured by adopting a uniform bearing pressure for all the foundations. The only instance in which this is even approximately true is that of the inherent settlement of geometrically similar foundations in sand and gravel. It can never be true when interference settlement is involved.

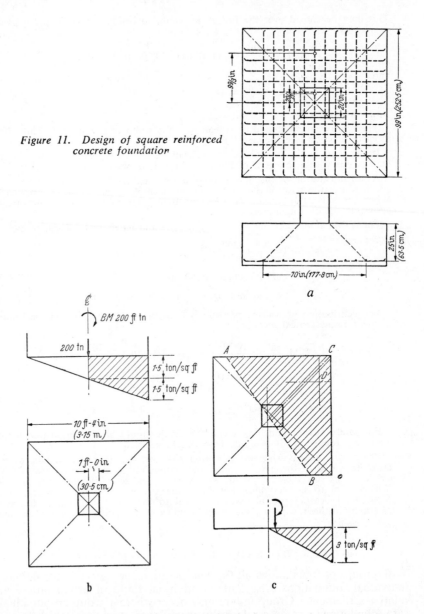

Figure 11. Design of square reinforced concrete foundation

TAYLOR[1] gives an excellent discussion on the variation of inherent settlement with foundation size and loading, which is summarized in TABLE 4. This table only holds for geometrically similar foundations, see *Figure 12*, in soil which is uniform to a great depth *i.e.* *H-H* or *S-S* sequences.

TABLE 4

VARIATION OF INHERENT SETTLEMENT OF GEOMETRICALLY SIMILAR FOUNDATIONS

Nature of ground	Sand or gravel (modulus of elasticity varies with stress)		Clay (modulus of elasticity approximately constant)	
Size of foundation	$b \times l$	$n . b \times n . l$	$b \times l$	$n . b \times n . l$
Bearing pressure	q	nq	q	nq
	q	nq	q	q/n	q	q/n
Bearing pressure Total load Settlement	q / $qbl*$ / δ	nq / $nqbl$ / $n\delta$	q / n^2qbl / δ	nq / n^3qbl* / $n\delta$	q / $qbl\dagger$ / δ	q/n / qbl/n / δ/n	q / $n^2qbl\dagger$ / $n\delta$	q/n / $nqbl$ / δ

*These total loads have an equal factor of safety against structural failure of the soil for sand or gravel.
†These total loads have an equal factor of safety against structural failure of the soil for clay.

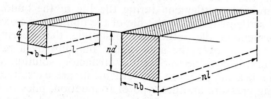

Figure 12. Geometrically similar foundations

Thus for equal inherent settlement the typical linear dimension should be proportional to the square root of the total load for sand or gravel but to the total load for clay. The relation between load and inherent settlement in the general case can be expressed by the equation

$$\frac{q}{\delta} = c_1 \left(1 + \frac{2d}{b}\right) + \frac{c_2}{b} \qquad \ldots\ldots\ldots(1)$$

or,

$$\delta = \frac{qb}{c_1(b+2d)+c_2}$$

where b is the breadth and d the depth of foundation, c_1 and c_2 being constants depending on the soil properties.

In completely cohesionless soils $c_2=0$ and in highly cohesive soils c_2 is very great compared with c_1, which may be taken to be zero.

The interference settlement can be calculated by determining the distribution of vertical stress under a given foundation due to the loads on the surrounding foundations and then summing the amounts by which the underlying soil layers are compressed. An approximate idea of the amount of the interference settlement may be arrived at as follows: the settlement δ of a rigid circular disc of diameter b on the surface of an elastic medium due to a total load P is given by the equation

$$\delta = \frac{(1-\mu^2)P}{Eb}$$

where E is the modulus of elasticity and μ is Poisson's ratio. The settlement of the surface at a radius r from the centre of the disc is

$$\delta_f = \frac{2(1-\mu^2)P}{\pi Eb} \sin^{-1} \frac{b}{2r}$$

$$\therefore \quad \frac{\delta_f}{\delta} = \frac{2}{\pi} \sin^{-1} \frac{b}{2r} \quad \text{or approximately}$$

$$\frac{\delta_f}{\delta} = \frac{1}{\pi} \cdot \frac{b}{r} \qquad \ldots\ldots\ldots(2)$$

If the foundations have been so designed that the inherent settlements δ are equal the approximate total settlement will be

$$\delta_t = \delta + \delta_f = \delta\left(1 + \frac{1}{\pi}\Sigma\frac{b}{r}\right) \qquad \ldots\ldots\ldots\ldots(3)$$

and the relative settlements will be the difference between the various values of the second term in the bracket, corresponding to different foundations.

When designing foundations for a structure, the ultimate settlement at the middle of the loaded area should first be estimated. If this is excessive, the time required for 90 per cent of settlement to take place should be computed. If this time considerably exceeds the probable life of the building the probable settlement during the life of the building should be calculated. If settlement during the life of the building is excessive the next step is to re-calculate the settlement, assuming that bearing pressure is distributed uniformly over the area of the building by a raft. This will indicate whether it is possible to obtain a satisfactory solution of the problem by reducing the bearing pressure. If settlements are excessive at the lowest possible bearing pressure another type of foundation, piles or floating base-ment, will have to be adopted. If, on the other hand, it appears that the maximum settlements will not be excessive if plain footings are used, the next step is to estimate whether the probable relative settlement is excessive. SKEMPTON and MACDONALD[43] have indicated criteria for permissible relative settlements.

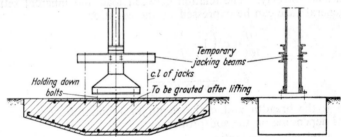

Figure 13. Shallow foundations including means for jacking up stanchion of light shed structures: note 'thin edge' to preserve as much as possible of resistance of 'H' crust to punching shear

Relative settlements will not usually be important, except in buildings founded on clay. Methods of reducing relative settlement of individual shallow foundations are:

   i introducing means of levelling up building by jacking up stanchions

   ii making the building, as a whole, stiff-strong. There are objections to both methods as summarized below:

to *i* the trouble and expense of periodic jacking up. This method is most suitable for light shed structures that may require to be maintained in a level condition because of crane gantries *etc.* An example of such a foundation is shown in *Figure 13*

to *ii* the expense and inconvenience of making the structure efficiently stiff and strong.

LONG STRIP FOUNDATION

The long strip foundation may be regarded as a special case of a group of foundations placed immediately side by side. If a strip foundation of finite length settles uniformly there must be a concentration of bearing pressure at the ends. If such a strip foundation supports a wall it may be necessary to check that the wall is capable of resisting the induced diagonal tension, otherwise diagonal cracks may appear as sketched in *Figure 14*. An alternative method is to make the strip foundation narrower towards the ends so that the bearing pressure per ft run remains constant, although the intensity is increased.

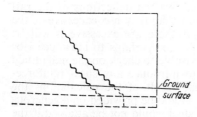

Figure 14. Cracks due to induced diagonal tension

An example that often arises is that of a number of columns resting on a continuous strip foundation; it is usually desired that the settlement of these columns should be equal. Much has been written on this subject from the assumption that the soil reaction at any point of the foundation is directly proportional to the settlement at that point, but the results are complicated and of little practical use.

If the ground settlements are large in comparison with the deflections of the foundation as a beam, the beam can be regarded as rigid relative to the soil and the bearing pressure may vary from about half the average at the centre to about four times the cohesion at the ends (it will be clear that this is the case of a compressible cohesive soil). If on the other hand the foundation is relatively flexible as a beam it is likely that the bearing pressure will be concentrated under the loads. It will then be safe to design the foundation as a uniformly loaded continuous beam. If there is freedom to extend the foundation beyond the end stanchions an estimate of a suitable length for the foundation may be made by imagining it to be inverted, acting as a uniformly loaded continuous beam on level supports at the column positions, and choosing the overlength at the ends so that the reactions are as close as possible to the column loads. The foundation may then be imagined as divided into a number of lengths and the settlements may be computed. If the foundation cannot be extended beyond the end stanchions the necessary uniformity of settlement can only be secured by making the foundation sufficiently stiff.

TRENCH, PIER AND CYLINDER FOUNDATIONS

These types of foundation are used to carry heavily loaded structures down to a bearing on the hard stratum in an *S-H* sequence. If the depth to the hard stratum is at all great an economic comparison should be made with an alternative design using piles. Trench foundations can be economical up to a depth of 15 ft (4·5 m) in favourable circumstances and cylinder foundations can be carried to considerable depths.

If the hard stratum to which a trench or cylinder is carried is a clay or other non-frictional material the allowable bearing pressure is only greater than it would be near the surface of a similar stratum by the weight of the soft stratum displaced by the foundation. If on the other hand the hard stratum is a frictional material such as sand or gravel the internal frictional resistance is greatly increased by the intergranular pressure at the base of the soft stratum. It is never permissible to assume that any support is afforded to the foundation by friction between it and the soft stratum.

RAFT FOUNDATIONS

A raft foundation may be regarded in the first place as a group of foundations of such size that they all touch. If settlement is to be uniform the bearing pressure will be greatest at the corners, least at the centre, and will have an intermediate value at the centre of the sides. The distribution of bearing pressure can only be found by trial and error, imagining the raft split into a suitable number of units and calculating the deflections consequent on an assumed distribution of bearing pressure. When the distribution of bearing pressure has been determined the bending moments in the slab, which are induced by the transmission of the wall and column loads to the soil, are calculated. As a final test the deflections of the raft should be checked as it will often be found that they are excessive if the slab is designed on a stress basis alone. If these are excessive it will be necessary to make the raft thicker and stiffer, or perhaps to introduce ribs as shown in *Figure 9*a. It is also always advisable to check on the magnitude of the shear stresses in the raft slab and to introduce any shear reinforcement that may be required. Whatever the result of the calculations the reinforcement, both for bending and shear, should be provided on a generous scale at least so that the yield point in the steel would not be attained if the bending moment were doubled. The slab should everywhere be doubly reinforced with equal steel in the top and bottom surfaces.

BASEMENT FOUNDATIONS, INCLUDING FLOATING FOUNDATIONS

The application of this type of foundation is to *S-S* or *H-S* sequences. The minimum depth of basement necessary is found by making the weight of excavated soil, less the dead weight of the basement together with the superload on it, at least equal to the excess of the average weight per square foot of the building over the allowable bearing pressure per square foot. It is often advisable to make the 'net' bearing pressure, found in this way, zero.

If there is an appreciable variation in the average weight per square foot of different parts of the building as, for example, in a building with a high or heavy tower, the depth of the basement, or the number of basements, should be varied so that the net bearing pressure is the same all over the area of the building. The actual foundation is designed as a raft distributing the gross bearing pressure to the walls and columns founded upon it. If necessary this 'raft' may consist, structurally, of Vierendeel trusses or cross walls of height equal to the total depth of the basement, the ground floor and basement slabs being taken as flanges, although each is also subject to local bending due to the superload in one case and the bearing pressure in the other.

If the weight of soil excavated is everywhere equal to the weight of the building above, so that the 'net' bearing pressure is equal to zero, the gross bearing pressure may be assumed to be uniformly distributed over the base of the raft. If the net bearing pressure is not zero its distribution should be calculated as for a raft, or alternatively assumed to be carried by friction acting upwards on the basement walls, up to the limit of the cohesion of the soil, and the balance of the gross bearing pressure should be assumed to be uniformly distributed. The same remarks apply to the design of reinforcement of the raft as applied to that of surface rafts. The basement walls must be designed as retaining walls to resist the earth pressure at rest which, in a soft clay or silt, may be assumed to be equal to the vertical pressure. The design of such walls is treated on p 166.

INSPECTION OF DIRECT BEARING BUILDING FOUNDATIONS

The points to be noted in the inspection of direct bearing building foundations are set out in TABLE 5.

TABLE 5

INSPECTION OF DIRECT BEARING BUILDING FOUNDATIONS

Stage of construction	Type of foundation	Check that
Setting out	All	All lines, levels and reference marks are in agreement with approved drawings
Before excavation	All	Check levels and condition of adjacent structures
Excavation	All	Excavated material is as anticipated from trial borings: notify engineers immediately of any change. Watch for any signs of subsidence of adjacent structures
	Floating basements	Excavation is so carried out that swelling of soil in bottom is avoided or minimized
Timbering etc	All	Sheeting is driven without such vibration as would cause damage to adjacent structures Walings and struts are placed as early as possible, are wedged up tight, and show no signs of distress
Pumping	All	Pumping is carried out from properly filtered sumps or well points There is no excessive local seepage and no signs of impending ' blows ' such as fine sand being washed into the excavation
Bottoming	All	Bottom is in anticipated stratum Last 3 in of clay stratum is only removed immediately before placing concrete screed There is no seepage through gravel or sand stratum during placing of concrete screed and no water pressure is allowed to build up until there is sufficient weight of concrete to resist it

DIRECT BEARING FOUNDATIONS APPLIED TO BRIDGES AND WHARVES

Foundations for bridges and wharves are usually considered to include the foundation proper, which transmits the load to the ground, the pier shaft and the cap, which receives the load from the superstructure. The principles governing the design of the foundation proper are the same as those governing the design of building foundations and will not be repeated here: reference should be made to pp 116-121. Examples of design as applied to bridges and wharves will be found below and on p 130. This section deals with the design of the whole of direct bearing substructures of bridges and wharves, with the exception of abutments and those wharves which resist earth pressure, see p 154.

Unlike building foundations, where the vertical forces are generally so great in comparison with the horizontal forces that the latter can be neglected, the design of foundations for bridges and wharves involves the consideration of horizontal forces due to a variety of types of load. The loads that require consideration in the design of bridges and wharves are as follows:

1 dead load—vertical and horizontal thrust in arches *etc*

2 live load—vertical, horizontal thrust in arches *etc* and braking forces and tractive effort of vehicles on superstructure

3 wind load on superstructure, on live load and on substructure

4 loads due to water current (rivers, tides *etc*), on substructure

5 loads due to impact of waves on substructure, conceivably also on superstructure, in wharves

6 temperature stresses

7 earthquake loads—see p 150

For wharves, the following additional loads must be considered:

8 pull of mooring ropes equal to breaking strain of strongest rope in use

9 thrust of ships against wharf when mooring.

TYPES OF DIRECT BEARING BRIDGE PIER

Pier caps

The function of the pier cap of a masonry pier is to distribute the load from the superstructure, if concentrated on bearings, evenly over the area of the shaft. Before the advent of reinforced concrete, pier caps were built of massive masonry pad stones; sometimes this may still be the best form of construction. It is now normal practice to use plain or reinforced concrete caps when steel or reinforced concrete superstructures are used. Reinforced concrete caps should be provided with reinforcing bars running in two perpendicular directions just below the bearings and covering an area slightly greater than that of the bearings. If the bearing pressure under the bearings is high it may be advisable to provide intersecting steel spirals for the full depth of the cap under the bearings. It is often advisable, as with other massive concrete structures, to provide light anti-crack reinforcement just beneath all exposed surfaces. A cap with spiral and anti-crack reinforcement is illustrated in *Figure 15.* Caps may join the tops of twin or multiple cylinder piers, and must be reinforced to resist the bending moments due to their own weight and to the portal action of the pier as a whole when resisting transverse forces, temperature changes *etc* as well as those due to any loads that may be applied to the cap between piers. Masonry and plain concrete caps should be designed to spread the load from the bearings at an angle of 45° until the compressive stress on horizontal planes is within that allowable in the pier shaft. Reinforced concrete caps should be designed according to the rules for reinforced concrete structures. Allowable bearing pressures between bearings and pier caps are given in TABLE 6. See also chapter on Bridge Bearings, vol. 3.

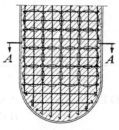

Section A–A

Figure 15. Spiral and anti-crack reinforcement

TABLE 6

ALLOWABLE PRESSURES UNDER BEARINGS

(From Code of Practice for Simply Supported Steel Bridges Instn of Civil Engineers and Instn of Structural Engineers 1949)

Material of pier cap	Allowable bearing pressure	
	ton/sq ft	*kg/sq cm*
Granite	50	54·6
Sandstone, or similar	25	27·3
Cement concrete	The direct compressive stresses laid down in the Code of Practice for the Structural Use of Normal Reinforced Concrete	

Where cement concrete suitably and adequately reinforced is used, the pressures for this material may be increased by 50 per cent. These limits may, at the discretion of the engineer, be exceeded by 20 per cent when the maximum possible combination of loads is taken into account.

Pier shafts

Pier shafts may be of stone masonry, brickwork, mass concrete or reinforced concrete. Shafts on dry land may be rectangular in plan, while those in water should have rounded noses, either semi-circular, conical, or of two arcs, the radius of which is commonly equal to the pier thickness. Short piers may have vertical sides or may be built with a convex batter if it is desired to give an appearance of stumpy sturdiness. Tall piers should be battered: a concave batter may give a graceful appearance and so may be chosen although difficult to construct. Economy may sometimes be secured, especially in wide bridges with two main girders, by the use of twin piers, usually of cylindrical form.

Other factors

Except for reinforced concrete piers the resultant load should always pass through the kern of the section. In connection with arch bridges of varying span it may be possible to equalize the dead load horizontal thrust from two adjoining spans by decreasing the rise to span ratio of the smaller span arch relative to that of the larger span arch, *Figure 16*.

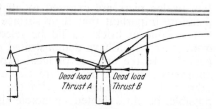

Figure 16. *Equalization of dead load thrust. With suitable design,* $A = B$

Figure 17 gives kern sizes for various sections. Permissible compressive stresses for various kinds of masonry and reduction factors for slenderness ratio, from B.S. C.P. 111:1948, are given in the chapter on Masonry and

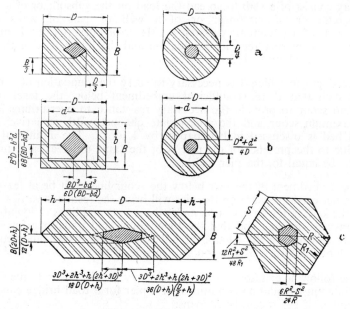

Figure 17. **a** *solid rectangle and cylinder* **b** *hollow rectangle and hollow cylinder* **c** *irregular and regular hexagon*

Brickwork, vol. 3; for permissible stresses in reinforced concrete see chapter on Reinforced Concrete Building Structures, vol. 3.

The slenderness ratio is equal to the least lateral dimension divided by the effective height. If the pier is uniformly battered the lateral dimension may be taken at the top of the foundation. The effective height is defined as follows in B.S. C.P. 111:1948.

> *Columns.* Where a column is provided with complete support at the bottom and lateral support parallel to the line of one of the horizontal surface dimensions at the top, its effective height relative to the direction of the top support should be taken as the height between supports: its effective height at right angles to this should be taken as twice its height above the lower support. In the absence of top support its effective height relative to both directions should be taken as twice its height above the lower support.

> *Walls.* Where a wall is laterally supported top and bottom, its effective height should be taken as three fourths of the height between such lateral supports: in the absence of top lateral support the effective height should be taken as one and a half times the height of the walling above the bottom lateral support.

Bridge piers are exposed to all the disruptive forces of nature; it is therefore important that their surface should be of material that weathers well. Stone or brick should be selected on the basis of local experience from those which have demonstrated good weathering properties over long periods. In the absence of local experience only materials of undoubted durability should be used. Great care should be taken in the selection of a mortar that is compatible with the material used. Masonry should, if possible, be close jointed: concrete should be dense and hard. Where ice forms in the winter it is often necessary to have specially formed upstream ends to the piers which will cause the ice sheet to lift and break; and these icebreaks may have to be reinforced with steel rails[2].

The foundation proper may be no more than the bearing area of the shaft if it rests on solid rock on which the allowable bearing pressure is at least equal to the allowable compressive stress in the material of the pier; or it may consist of a slab to spread the load on the subsoil; or of a block of concrete; or of masonry; or of a well or pair of wells (open caissons); or of a pneumatic caisson, p 131; or of piles, p 135. It may be necessary to construct the pier foundation and the lower part of the pier shaft in a coffer dam, p. 135.

The depth to which it is necessary to carry the foundation of a bridge pier is such that there is sufficient embedment below the level of the maximum scour to provide the necessary resistance to overturning forces. The maximum scour and the appropriate channel width of a river in an alluvial bed is discussed in two papers by LACEY[3]. The additional local scour due to the presence of the pier is of the same order as, and may be taken to be equal to, the pier width.

The embedment of the pier below the scour line must be at least such that the net earth pressure on the pier will bring the resultant vertical force within the kern of the base section under the worst conditions of longitudinal and transverse loading and that the longitudinal and transverse forces can be safely resisted by the friction or adhesion on the base combined with the available passive resistance on the lee side of the pier.

The following examples and *Figures 18, 19* and *20* illustrate the design, under different foundation conditions, of a pier for a road bridge consisting of a number of 125 ft cantilever spans.

Example—Design of pier on hard rock foundation (*Figure 18*).

There are two conditions to be satisfied:

a maximum compression on the underlying strata not to exceed the permissible bearing pressure,

b no tension to be developed in the masonry or concrete faces of the pier

Calculations about lateral axis, span loaded
Weight of pier $= 20 \times 15 \times 5 \times 140 = 210{,}000$ lb
$= 96$ ton

∴ Total vertical load (DL+LL) $= 2 \times 127 \cdot 5$
$+96 = 351$ ton

Total horizontal load due to wind pressure $=$ 19·3 ton

The maximum and minimum pressures are given by

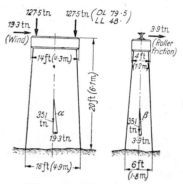

Figure 18. Pier on hard rock foundation

$$\frac{W}{A} \pm \frac{M}{Z} = \frac{351}{16 \times 8} \pm \frac{19 \cdot 3 \times 20 \times 6}{8 \times 16^2} = 2 \cdot 74 \pm 1 \cdot 13$$

$= 3 \cdot 87$ ton/sq ft compression or $1 \cdot 61$ ton/sq ft compression

Calculations about longitudinal axis, span loaded
Total horizontal load due to roller friction $= 3 \cdot 9$ ton

As before the maximum and minimum bearing pressures are given by $\dfrac{W}{A} \pm \dfrac{M}{Z}$

$$= \frac{351}{16 \times 8} \pm \frac{3 \cdot 9 \times 20 \times 6}{16 \times 8^2} = 2 \cdot 74 \pm 0 \cdot 46$$

$= 3 \cdot 20$ ton/sq ft compression or $2 \cdot 28$ ton/sq ft compression
The total maximum pressure is $3 \cdot 87$ ton/sq ft plus that load due to roller friction and will occur under one corner and is equal to $3 \cdot 87$ plus $0 \cdot 46$ *i.e.* $4 \cdot 33$ ton/sq ft
The minimum pressure is $1 \cdot 61 - 0 \cdot 46 = 1 \cdot 15$ ton/sq in (compression)
∴ There is no tension in the masonry or concrete faces

Calculations about the lateral axis, span unloaded
In this case the live load is deducted from the gross vertical load.
Let LL $= 96$ ton
∴ Total vertical load $= 255$ ton
Let total longitudinal load due to wind pressure $= 22 \cdot 4$ ton

The maximum and minimum pressures are given by

$$\frac{W}{A} \pm \frac{M}{Z} = \frac{255}{16 \times 8} \pm \frac{22 \cdot 4 \times 20 \times 6}{8 \times 16^2} = 2 \cdot 0 \pm 1 \cdot 31$$

$= 3 \cdot 31$ ton/sq ft compression or $0 \cdot 69$ ton/sq ft compression

Calculations about the longitudinal axis, span unloaded
Total horizontal load due to roller friction $= 3 \cdot 9$ ton
As before the maximum and minimum bearing pressures are given by

$$\frac{W}{A} \pm \frac{M}{Z} = \frac{255}{16 \times 8} \pm \frac{3 \cdot 9 \times 20 \times 6}{16 \times 8^2} = 2 \cdot 0 \pm 0 \cdot 46$$

$= 2 \cdot 46$ ton/sq ft compression or $1 \cdot 54$ ton/sq ft compression

The total maximum pressure $= 3 \cdot 31 + 0 \cdot 46 = 3 \cdot 77$ ton/sq ft compression and the total minimum pressure $= 0 \cdot 69 - 0 \cdot 46 = 0 \cdot 23$ ton/sq ft compression
Example—Design of a similar pier but bearing on a strata where permissible bearing pressure is $1 \cdot 5$ ton/sq ft (*Figure 19*)
Total vertical load $= 351$ ton
Weight of 3 ft thick reinforced concrete $= 450$ lb/sq ft
Weight of earth removed $= 360$ lb/sq ft
∴ additional pressure $= 90$ lb/sq ft $= 0 \cdot 04$ ton/sq ft
∴ effective bearing pressure $= 1 \cdot 50 - 0 \cdot 04 = 1 \cdot 46$ ton/sq ft
By trial select a base 26 ft 0 in × 14 ft 0 in

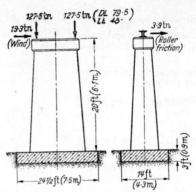

Figure 19. Pier on ground at permissible pressure of 1·5 ton/sq ft (1·6 kg/sq cm) not subject to scour

Calculations about lateral axis, span loaded

$$\frac{W}{A} \pm \frac{M}{Z} = \frac{351}{26 \times 14} \pm \frac{19 \cdot 3 \times 23 \times 6}{14 \times 26^2} = 0 \cdot 96 \pm 0 \cdot 28$$

$= 1 \cdot 24$ ton/sq ft compression or $0 \cdot 68$ ton/sq ft compression

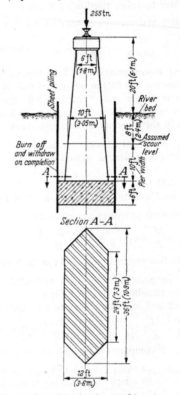

Figure 20. Pier in river subject to scour

Calculations about longitudinal axis, span loaded

$$\frac{W}{A} \pm \frac{M}{Z} = \frac{351}{26 \times 14} \pm \frac{3 \cdot 9 \times 23 \times 6}{26 \times 14^2} = 0 \cdot 96 \pm 0 \cdot 11$$

$= 1 \cdot 07$ ton/sq ft compression or $0 \cdot 85$ ton/sq ft compression

The absolute maximum pressure $= 1 \cdot 24 + 0 \cdot 11 = 1 \cdot 35$ ton/sq ft compression

The absolute minimum pressure $= 0 \cdot 68 - 0 \cdot 11 = 0 \cdot 57$ ton/sq ft compression

Calculations about lateral axis, span unloaded

$$\frac{W}{A} \pm \frac{M}{Z} = \frac{255}{26 \times 14} \pm \frac{22 \cdot 4 \times 23 \times 6}{14 \times 26^2} = 0 \cdot 70 \pm 0 \cdot 33$$

$= 1 \cdot 03$ ton/sq ft compression or $0 \cdot 37$ ton/sq ft compression

Calculations about longitudinal axis, span unloaded

$$\frac{W}{A} \pm \frac{M}{Z} = \frac{255}{26 \times 14} \pm \frac{3 \cdot 9 \times 23 \times 6}{26 \times 14^2} = 0 \cdot 70 \pm 0 \cdot 11$$

$= 0 \cdot 81$ ton/sq ft compression or $0 \cdot 59$ ton/sq ft compression

The absolute maximum pressure $= 1 \cdot 03 + 0 \cdot 11 = 1 \cdot 14$ ton/sq ft compression

The absolute minimum pressure $= 0 \cdot 37 - 0 \cdot 11 = 0 \cdot 26$ ton/sq ft compression

Example—Design of a pier for river with bed subject to scour (*Figure 20*) Assume that calculations of scour give a depth of 8 ft. If the river bed is of soft material then a pad footing would have to be designed as in *Figure 19*. Allowing for extra height of pier assume bearing pressure of $1 \cdot 5$ ton/sq ft

$$\text{Weight of pier} = \frac{38 \times 9 \times 16 \times 140}{2,240} = 343 \text{ ton}$$

$$\text{Total vertical load} = 255 + 343 = 598 \text{ ton}$$

Calculations about lateral axis, span loaded

$$\text{Compression in masonry} = \frac{598}{432} \pm \frac{19 \cdot 3 \times 38 \times 18}{28,083}$$

$$= 1 \cdot 38 \pm 0 \cdot 47 = 1 \cdot 85 \text{ ton/sq ft or } 0 \cdot 91 \text{ ton/sq ft}$$

Calculations about longitudinal axis, span loaded

$$\text{Compression in masonry} = \frac{598}{432} \pm \frac{3 \cdot 9 \times 38 \times 6}{3,888}$$

$$= 1 \cdot 38 \pm 0 \cdot 23 = 1 \cdot 61 \text{ ton/sq ft or } 1 \cdot 15 \text{ ton/sq ft}$$

Absolute maximum compression $= 2 \cdot 08$ ton/sq ft

Absolute minimum compression $= 0 \cdot 68$ ton/sq ft

Calculations about lateral axis, span unloaded

Let live load $= 96$ ton and wind load $22 \cdot 4$ ton

$$\text{Compression in masonry} = \frac{502}{432} \pm \frac{22 \cdot 4 \times 38 \times 18}{28,083}$$

$$= 1 \cdot 16 \pm 0 \cdot 53 = 1 \cdot 69 \text{ ton/sq ft or } 0 \cdot 63 \text{ ton/sq ft}$$

Calculations about longitudinal axis, span unloaded

$$\text{Compression in masonry} = \frac{502}{432} \pm \frac{3 \cdot 9 \times 38 \times 18}{3,888}$$

$$= 1 \cdot 16 \pm 0 \cdot 23 = 1 \cdot 39 \text{ ton/sq ft or } 0 \cdot 93 \text{ ton/sq ft}$$

Absolute maximum compression $= 2 \cdot 02$ ton/sq ft

Absolute minimum compression $= 0 \cdot 40$ ton/sq ft

Assuming $1 \cdot 5$ ton/sq ft allows for weight of base earth removed = effective bearing pressure and that base area is 40×14 ft

Calculations about lateral axis, span loaded

$$\frac{W}{A} \pm \frac{M}{Z} = \frac{598}{560} \pm \frac{19 \cdot 3 \times 44 \times 6}{14 \times 40^2} = 1 \cdot 07 \pm 0 \cdot 23$$

$= 1 \cdot 3$ ton/sq ft compression or $0 \cdot 84$ ton/sq ft compression

Calculations about longitudinal axis, span loaded

$$\frac{W}{A} \pm \frac{M}{Z} = \frac{598}{560} \pm \frac{3\cdot9 \times 44 \times 6}{40 \times 14^2} = 1\cdot07 \pm 0\cdot13$$

$= 1\cdot2$ ton/sq ft compression or $0\cdot94$ ton/sq ft compression

Absolute maximum compression $= 1\cdot43$ ton/sq ft

Absolute minimum compression $= 0\cdot71$ ton/sq ft

Calculations about lateral axis, span unloaded

$$\frac{W}{A} \pm \frac{M}{Z} = \frac{502}{560} \pm \frac{22\cdot4 \times 44 \times 6}{14 \times 40^2} = 0\cdot89 \pm 0\cdot26$$

$= 1\cdot15$ ton/sq ft compression or $0\cdot63$ ton/sq ft compression

Calculations about longitudinal axis, span unloaded

$$\frac{W}{A} \pm \frac{M}{Z} = \frac{502}{560} \pm \frac{3\cdot9 \times 44 \times 6}{40 \times 14^2} = 0\cdot89 \pm 0\cdot13$$

$= 1\cdot02$ ton/sq ft compression or $0\cdot76$ ton/sq ft compression

Absolute maximum compression $= 1\cdot28$ ton/sq ft

Absolute minimum compression $= 0\cdot50$ ton/sq ft

The most economical bridge will result if the cost of the main girders of one span is equal to the cost of one pier. It is usually necessary to prepare several sketch designs with various span lengths and to prepare estimates of cost in respect of each: it will be found that there is a range of span length within which the variation in cost is comparatively small: it is usually wise to select a span length towards the longer end of this range, as the cost of a pier varies little with increase of span and the uncertainties which arise in estimating the cost of a pier greatly exceed those involved in estimating the cost of the superstructure.

TYPES OF DIRECT BEARING FOUNDATION FOR JETTIES AND WHARVES

Direct bearing foundations for jetties and wharves may consist of cylinder piers, large rectangular open caissons usually called 'monoliths', or masses of masonry constructed in coffer dams or in box caissons[4-6]. The design of such piers and monoliths or of the necessary coffer dams and box caissons does not differ from that of the corresponding units as used in the construction of bridge piers, see below, except in wharves subjected to earth pressure, for the design of which see chapter on Harbours and Docks, vol. 3.

CAISSONS

Box caissons

Box caissons are structures essentially similar in form to open topped boxes. They are constructed on shore, launched and floated to the site, where they are sunk on a prepared foundation. This foundation may consist of piles or it may simply have been formed by levelling an area of the bottom. The bottom of the box always forms part of the permanent structure but the sides may or may not: in the latter they really form a coffer dam within which the permanent pier shaft is built. Box caissons may be built of timber, steel or reinforced concrete[4, 7].

Open caissons, cylinder piers and well foundations

The term 'open caisson' is applied to all the types mentioned in the heading and includes three essentially different forms of construction. These are:

a structures similar to box caissons except that they have no bottom if of timber[16], or a removable bottom if of steel or reinforced concrete, and which are sunk in deep water on to, but not deep into, the bottom, and which form permanent or temporary shuttering for the pier shaft[8, 9]

b thin walled cylinders of moderate diameter sunk by water jet, by excavating within either by hand or by air lift pump, by weighting, by driving or rotation, or by combinations of the above methods[5, 10-12]

c thick walled open caissons, or wells, with dredging wells, which are heavy enough to overcome the skin friction of the surrounding earth by their own weight with, or without, the addition of a moderate quantity of kentledge and which have been used for some of the largest and deepest foundations on record. Such caissons may be of timber and concrete, steel and concrete or reinforced concrete and consist of a shaft with one, two, four, six or more dredging wells, shod with a 'well curb' in which the shafts taper out to form the cutting edges.

An example of a steel caisson[13-15] is shown in *Figure 21*.

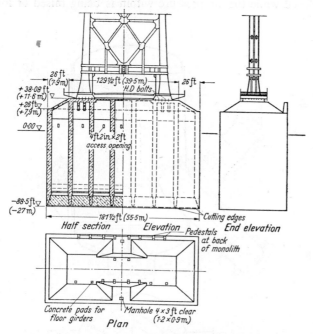

Figure 21. Main pier of Howrah bridge

Well foundations are often sunk in whole or part by the pneumatic process described below. The diameter of the wells is usually a compromise: it is limited by the need to make the caisson as heavy as possible so that it will overcome skin friction but it should, on the other hand, be as great as possible so that large capacity grabs may be used. Air lifts are sometimes used in silt and sand. Skin friction has been found to vary from 0·1 to 0·6 ton/sq ft (0·11 to 0·66 kg/sq cm) and does not appear to bear any direct relation to the shear strength of the soil though it cannot exceed this value. Open caissons are often surmounted by timber coffer dams or steel sheeting within which the pier shaft is constructed between bed level and high water level.

Pneumatic method of sinking caissons

With caissons sunk by the pneumatic process the 'well curb' is designed as a working chamber from which water is excluded by compressed air.

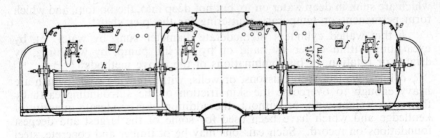

Figure 22. Man lock

Access to the working chamber is secured by means of air locks, small
chambers each provided with two doors of which either the one may be
open to the working chamber or the other may be open to the free air, or
both are closed while the air pressure within is being raised or lowered to

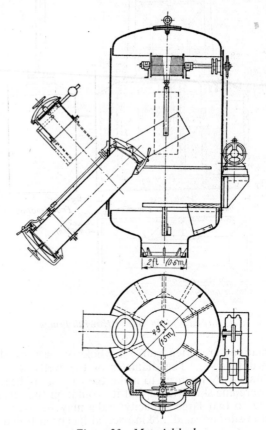

Figure 23. Material lock

the pressure on the side of the door which it is desired to open next. Air
locks may be designed for the passage of men or of materials, or both.
Examples of modern practice are shown in *Figures 22* and *23*. Soft materials
may be expelled from the working chamber by the air pressure itself,
through 'elephant trunks', *Figure 24*.

Pneumatic caissons cannot be used for depths exceeding 115 ft (35 m) below water level as greater depths would require air pressures greater than the maximum in which men can work *i.e.* about 50 lb/sq in (3·5 kg/sq cm). Caissons which it is intended should be sunk by open dredging are often designed so that they can be converted to pneumatic caissons if necessary; advantage can then be taken of the facility afforded by the pneumatic process for the removal of obstructions or for cleaning the foundation bed and placing the sealing plug of concrete. A great advantage of the pneumatic process is that large caissons can be sunk with comparatively little risk of damage to neighbouring structures.

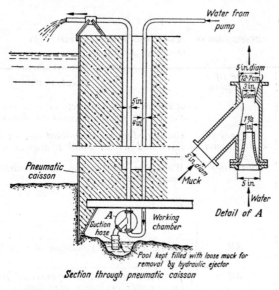

Figure 24. Hydraulic ejector or ' elephant trunk '

The principal differences in construction between caissons to be sunk by open dredging and those in which the pneumatic process may or will be used is that the roof of the working chamber must be designed to resist the maximum air pressure and that the walls of the working chamber may be vertical instead of being sloped to the dredging wells, as is necessary for open dredging. For information on compressed air working see chapter on Works Construction, vol. 4.

COFFER DAMS

Coffer dams are temporary structures designed to exclude water from the working area during the construction of a foundation or other enterprise that must be undertaken below water level. There are various types, some of which are illustrated in *Figure 25*a to d. For examples of double walled sheet pile coffer dam with clay filling see ref. 17 and for a cellular steel sheet pile coffer dam see ref. 18. The overall stability of a coffer dam should be investigated as a dam or as an earth retaining structure.

The strength of a sheet pile coffer dam may be checked with the data given in TABLE 11, but further consideration is necessary in cellular sheet pile coffer dams.

The security of all coffer dams against failure by seepage requires investigation and for further information on this and on other aspects see chapter on Soil Mechanics. When considering seepage it should be remembered that the permeability of soil in a horizontal direction usually exceeds that in a vertical direction: the horizontal permeability should be assumed to be not less than four times the vertical permeability, unless tests have proved otherwise.

INSPECTION AND TESTING OF DIRECT BEARING FOUNDATIONS FOR BRIDGES AND WHARVES

The points to be noted in the inspection of work in progress on direct bearing foundations are set out in TABLE 7.

TABLE 7

INSPECTION OF BRIDGE AND WHARF FOUNDATIONS
(See also p 123)

Stage of construction	Type of foundation	Check that :
Setting out	All	All lines, levels and reference marks are in agreement with approved working drawings
Assembly of well curbs, caissons etc	All types of cylinder and caisson foundation	Cutting edges are assembled and riveted or welded level and within small tolerances of the desired shape Walls are truly plane, or cylindrical, to within small tolerances
Assembly and driving of sheet piles	———	See page 161
Before excavating	All	Check levels and condition of neighbouring structures
Excavation	All	Excavated material is as expected from trial borings: notify engineers immediately of any change
	In coffer dams	Amount of pumping is of expected order and varies steadily and as expected according to depth of excavation Seepage is uniform round periphery Notify engineers immediately if any concentration of seepage is observed, and warn contractors
	In open and pneumatic caissons	Excavation does not proceed too far ahead of sinking Caisson is sunk vertically (or at desired angle). Position of caisson is maintained
		Caisson is sunk without such 'draw' of ground from outside that damage is caused to neighbouring structures
	Pneumatic caissons	All legal requirements or, in the absence of legal requirements, the recommendations of the report of the Institution of Civil Engineers Committee on working in compressed air are complied with
Bottoming up	All	Stratum is as anticipated, or is approved by engineers Bottom of excavation is level or stepped, or sloped, as required
Plugging	Open caissons	No water is seeping into caisson Concrete is of approved mix and placed by approved method e.g. bottom opening skips or tremie and is of sufficient volume to form complete plug. Plug is formed of dense concrete without voids

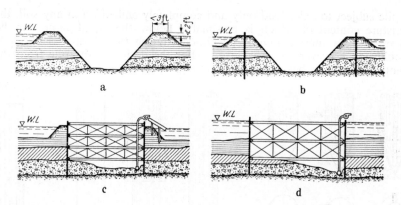

Figure 25. a *earth coffer dam* b *earth coffer dam with sheet pile cut off* c *single wall sheet pile with earth bank* d *single wall sheet pile without earth bank*

PILED FOUNDATIONS

Piles may be classified according to material of construction as timber, steel, steel and concrete, pre-cast concrete, and *in situ* concrete piles, and they may be classified according to method of installation as driven piles, bored piles and screw piles. Most *in situ* concrete piles, some steel and concrete piles, and screw piles are the subject of patents. The most ancient form of foundation in soft ground is the driven timber pile. Pre-cast concrete, *in situ* concrete and steel piles are recent developments which have appeared in about that order.

TIMBER PILES

The advantages of timber piles are *i* they are, in many countries, the cheapest in first cost; *ii* they are easy to cut off.

The disadvantages are *1* they must be capped below ground water level (and prescience concerning future lowering of ground water level must be exercised because of the danger of decay); *2* they are liable to attack by marine borers, such as teredo and other insects; *3* they are easily damaged by overdriving and such damage is almost impossible to detect; *4* in common with other driven piles, driving causes vibrations which may some-times be an impediment to their use: remoulding of sensitive clays due to the volume of displacement of the pile may also give trouble.

The rate of deterioration of timber piles due to exposure to the atmosphere after ground water lowering or to insect attack can be reduced by impregnation with creosote or other preservatives, but timber piles cannot be regarded as other than temporary structures under such conditions. Timber piles are always driven tip down. Except in very soft strata the tip is pointed and the use of a shoe is advisable. A shoe is essential if the pile is to be driven in, or to, stony ground. Suitable pile shoes for timber piles are shown in *Figure 26*a. Timber piles should not be spliced when this can be avoided, as splices are always points of weakness. Suitable types of splice are shown in *Figure 26*b. A steel sheet should always be used to separate the ends of the two parts of a spliced pile in order to prevent splitting. Brooming at the head is prevented by the use of a cap ring as illustrated in *Figure 26*c. Considered as a structural member, a timber pile may be designed to the stresses laid down for timber structures (see chapter on Timber Construction, Vol. 3.

A pile subject to axial load only and completely embedded in any soil, the moisture content of which is reasonably below the liquid limit, can be regarded as a short column. Conditions during the driving of the pile should not, however, be overlooked. For the design of the pile from the point of view of its bearing capacity in a given soil, see p 143.

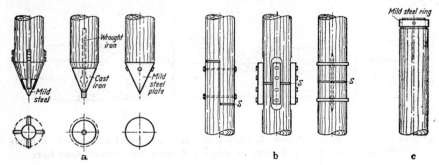

Figure 26. Timber piles a shoes b splices, s=thin steel plate in joint c cap ring for timber pile

PRE-CAST CONCRETE PILES

The advantages of pre-cast concrete piles are *i* permanence (except in certain corrosive soils); *ii* the manufacture of the whole pile can be seen and closely controlled; *iii* high carrying capacity as compared with timber piles.

The disadvantages are: *1* pre-cast piles require great care in handling and pitching, and large piles require tall and heavy rigs; *2* there is a delay in commencing piling until the piles have had time to mature (this delay can sometimes be avoided by purchasing piles from stock); *3* pre-cast piles have to be formed to predetermined lengths; if these are overestimated the wastage is expensive; if they are underestimated, delay is caused whilst extensions are cast on; *4* vibration. Disadvantage *1* may be overcome by pre-stressing.

The ground into which pre-cast (or uncased cast *in situ*) concrete piles are to be driven must always be subjected to tests that will reveal the presence of sulphate and sulphide salts: samples of the ground water should also be subjected to the same tests, see previous chapter.

The structural design of a pre-cast concrete pile requires consideration of the stresses in the pile; *a* during de-moulding and stacking; *b* during transport to the pile driver; *c* during pitching; *d* during driving; and *e* as a part of the completed structure.

TABLES 8A and B have been adapted and amplified from a paper by SAURIN[19]. TABLE 8A shows the bending moments induced in the pile during handling and pitching. Experience shows that piles designed to take a bending moment of $WL/8$ at failure by yield of the steel can be driven satisfactorily. This permits the pile to be lifted without exceeding a concrete stress of 320 lb/sq in (22·5 kg/sq cm), which should be safe at three days, and gives a factor of safety of $2\frac{1}{4}$ at the stage of pitching. TABLES 8A and B are based on the assumption that the yield point of the steel is 38,000 lb/sq in (2,670 kg/sq cm) and the ultimate crushing strength of the concrete (at the time of pitching and driving) is 4,000 lb/sq in (280 kg/sq cm).

Pre-cast piles up to 16 in (0·4 m) diam are usually square, those over 18 in diam are usually octagonal, but triangular, pentagonal and hexagonal piles have also been used. Pre-stressed concrete piles offer advantages in the larger sizes. Square piles are reinforced with four or eight longitudinal

TABLE 8A

STRESSES AND BENDING MOMENTS IN PRE-CAST
CONCRETE PILES

(*Adapted from* SAURIN[19])

Method of lifting or pitching	k	Maximum B.M.	If pile is designed for a B.M. of WL/8 at failure by yield of steel the concrete stress when the pile is lifted as illustrated will be	
			lb/sq in	kg/sq cm
	0·2	$\pm \dfrac{WL}{50}$	340	23·9
	0·25	$-\dfrac{WL}{32}$	530	37·2
	0·3	$\pm \dfrac{WL}{22}$	770	54·1
	0·33	$-\dfrac{WL}{18}$	940	66·1
	0·25	$+\dfrac{WL}{18}$	940	66·1

bars. TABLE 8B indicates suitable bar diameters for both cases for piles from 10 in to 18 in (25 to 45 cm) square and from 25 ft to 75 ft (7·6 to 23 m) long; TABLE 8B also gives normal maximum lengths and loads.

Details of lateral reinforcement are shown in *Figure 27*. A pile shoe should normally be used and an additional spiral reinforcement is sometimes used near the head. *Figure 28* gives typical examples of pile reinforcement and shoe.

Pre-cast concrete piles should be driven with a free falling monkey or single acting hammer. The weight of the falling parts should preferably be about equal to the weight of the pile and should never be less than half the weight of the pile. The drop should be about 3 or 4 ft.

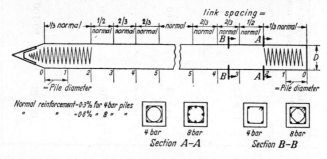

Figure 27. *Details of lateral reinforcement in reinforced concrete piles*
(*adapted from* SAURIN[19])

TABLE 8B

SQUARE PRE-CAST CONCRETE PILES

Pile size in	Normal max load ton	No. of main reinforcement bars	Diameter of reinforcement bar for pile length ft					
			30	40	50	60	70	80
12 × 12	40	4	3/4 in	7/8 in	1 in	1 1/8 in		
		8	3/4 in					
14 × 14	50–60	4	3/4 in	7/8 in	1 in	1 1/4 in	1 3/8 in	
		8	3/4 in	7/8 in	1 in	1 1/8 in		
16 × 16	70–90	4	3/4 in	7/8 in	1 1/8 in	1 1/4 in	1 1/2 in	
		8	3/4 in	7/8 in	1 in	1 1/8 in	1 1/4 in	1 3/8 in
18 × 18	90–100	4	3/4 in	7/8 in	1 in	1 1/8 in	1 1/4 in	2 in
		8	3/4 in	1 in	1 1/8 in	1 1/4 in	1 3/8 in	1 3/4 in

The normal max length is indicated by double line

A driving helmet is placed on top of the pile to take the blow of the hammer and packing is placed between the helmet and the pile. Proper packing and frequent attention to it are necessary to ensure that piles are driven without unnecessary damage to the heads. Care must be taken when driving a pre-cast pile in ground containing obstacles that the pile, if guided at two places in the leads, is not broken by a sudden lateral displacement of the toe.

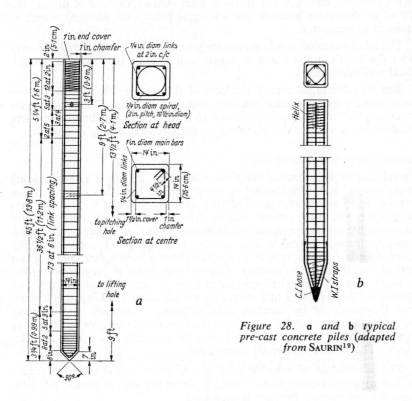

Figure 28. a and b typical pre-cast concrete piles (adapted from SAURIN[19])

STEEL PILES

Steel H section piles from 8 in to 14 in deep have been used to a considerable extent in the U.S.A. (see also chapter on Harbours and Docks, vol. 4); they are useful when they must be subjected to hard driving. Steel bearing piles can be driven at close centres due to their small volume displacement. Welded steel box piles are being used increasingly. Corrosion has not been found to be a serious problem below water level, but for protection above lowest tide or water level concrete casing or cathodic protection should be considered. The compressive stress allowed on the steel section is about 4 to 5 ton/sq in (6 to 8 kg/sq mm).

Concrete filled steel tubular piles

Steel tubular piles, either open ended or closed, have been used in diameters up to about 20 in (50 cm). The earth left in open ended tubes after driving may be blown out with a water jet and compressed air. The tube is filled with concrete but the steel carries most of the load. A type widely used in the U.S.A. is the *Monotube* pile: this is a fluted shell of sheet steel strong enough to be driven and filled with concrete which carries the greater part of the permanent load.

CONCRETE PILES

Cased cast in situ concrete piles

Cased cast *in situ* piles are formed by driving casings which have been threaded on to a mandrel into the ground by means of blows on the mandrel. The mandrel may be of corrugated steel plate *e.g.* the *Raymond* pile or of pre-cast concrete units *e.g.* the *Rotinoff* pile. On completion of driving the mandrel is withdrawn and the pile casing is filled with concrete, which is reinforced as necessary.

The advantages of cased cast *in situ* piles are: *i* it is comparatively easy to vary the length on the site; *ii* it can be seen whether the casing is straight, vertical and undamaged.

The disadvantages are: *1* the cost of the casing which makes them usually more expensive than uncased cast *in situ* piles; *2* driving causes vibration, which may be an impediment to their use; remoulding of sensitive clays due to the volume displacement of the pile may also give trouble.

Uncased cast in situ concrete piles

Uncased cast *in situ* concrete piles are formed by driving a tubular casing into the ground and withdrawing it, either after it has been filled or while it is being filled with concrete. The tube may be provided with a cast iron shoe which is left in the ground, and be driven by a drop hammer or steam hammer acting on its upper end *e.g. Simplex, Vibro*, or it may be driven by a monkey dropped within it and acting on a 'plug' of concrete in the bottom, *Franki*. In this type of pile when driving is complete concrete can be driven out through the bottom of the tube in order to form a bulb foot. The shaft may be formed simply by pouring concrete in at the top and withdrawing the tube at a rate such that an adequate head is always maintained (*Simplex*); or by inserting small charges of concrete and tamping these as the tube is removed, either with the monkey (*Franki*) or by imparting an up and down vibrating motion to the tube, which has a thickened lip (*Vibro*). The shaft is reinforced as required.

The advantages of uncased cast *in situ* piles are: *i* they are cheap; *ii* it is comparatively easy to vary the length on the site; *iii* with a pile with a bulb, the end bearing capacity is increased.

The disadvantages are: *1* particular skill and attention on the part of the piling foreman is essential during the formation of the shaft; *2* vibration. Remoulding of sensitive clays may also cause trouble.

Bored concrete piles

Bored concrete piles are formed by sinking a tube into the ground by excavating within it by means of soil augers, chisels, sand pumps *etc*: the tube may be driven by light blows from a hammer or it may be jacked down. On completion of driving the casing is withdrawn and the shaft is formed as is done in the case of driven uncased cast *in situ* piles. Compressed air may be used to keep the casing dry during concreting, the concrete being placed through an air lock at the top.

The advantages of bored piles are: *i* comparative lack of vibration; *ii* the plant used requires only a low headroom; *iii* a complete record of the strata passed through and in which the pile is founded is available; *iv* it is easy to vary the length on the site.

Extreme care is necessary in sinking the casing through silts and fine sands if disturbance of adjacent structures is to be avoided. Such difficulties can often be avoided by consolidation methods or ground water lowering.

SCREW PILES

Screw piles consist of a helical blade which is caused to penetrate into the ground by a torque applied, either through the permanent shaft or through a withdrawable mandrel, by means of winches or a capstan. Various types of screw pile are illustrated in *Figure 29*.

'Solid' screw piles, *Figure 29a*, have round solid steel shafts 4 in to 8 in (10 to 20 cm) diam provided with cast iron or cast steel screws 3 ft 6 in to 5 ft 6 in (1 to 1·7 m) diam.

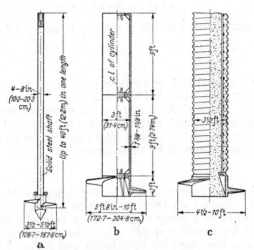

Figure 29. Screw piles

Cast iron cylinder screw piles, *Figure 29b*, have hollow cast iron internally flanged shafts from 36 in to 54 in (0·91 to 1·37 m) diam with bolted joints. The screws of cast iron or cast steel range from 5 ft 8 in to 10 ft 0 in (1·7 to 3·0 m) diam. The screw nose may be either open, in which case the core is extracted with a water jet and air lift pump as the pile is driven, or closed. If the nose is open it is usually plugged with concrete after driving.

The Braithwaite Screwcrete cylinder, *Figure 29c*, consists of a thin corrugated steel or reinforced concrete shell supported and turned by a withdrawable mandrel that also turns the screw. Standard sizes have shafts 19 and 42 in (0·48 to 1·07 m) diam and the screws can be varied from 4 ft 6 in to 10 ft 0 in (1·4 to 3·0 m).

Small screw piles may be driven by an arrangement of winches pulling on ropes wound round a drum secured to the top of the pile, but the Braithwaite patent screwing capstan is a much more convenient means for driving all types of screw pile.

The advantages of screw piles are: *i* the shaft and the screw can each be designed to be efficient for its purpose: the screw to carry the load and the shaft to transmit the vertical load to the screw and to transfer any horizontal forces to the ground; *ii* screw piles can be driven to great depths and can carry very heavy loads if they reach to firm ground; *iii* there is no vibration in driving.

The cost of screw piles is comparatively high but there are many situations in which they can form the most economical foundation.

TYPES OF PILED FOUNDATION FOR BUILDINGS

The selection of the type of pile to be used is a question of economics together with certain technical factors and is considered later on this page. Pile caps are designed as rigid reinforced concrete masses so as to distribute their load as evenly as possible on to the piles supporting them. The design of a piled raft involves consideration of the same factors as enter into the design of a direct bearing raft, see pp 121-122.

TYPES OF PILED FOUNDATIONS FOR BRIDGES AND WHARVES

We may first distinguish between a piled pier and a pile pier in bridge foundations.

Piled pier

A piled pier is a normal pier of masonry or reinforced concrete carried on a group of piles at the lowest level to which it is convenient and economical to carry the pier. Particularly if this level is not below the level of maximum scour, inclined piles may have to be used to carry the horizontal forces acting on the pier, unless the vertical piles used can be reinforced to resist the bending moments induced by these forces[20, 21].

Pile piers

Pile piers consist either of two or more vertical piles capable of resisting the horizontal loads imposed on them and braced together from their top to lower water level or of a group of inclined, or vertical and inclined, piles, joined at the top by a combined pile cap. The estimation of the probable maximum scour is important for both forms and it may be determined as described in ref. 3.

The design and types of wharves and jetties are dealt with in the chapter on Harbours and Docks, vol. 4.

DESIGN OF PILE FOUNDATIONS

The first consideration in the selection of the type of pile to use for a particular job and of the magnitude of load that is suitable is the soil sequence, whether it is *S-H*, involving the use of point bearing piles, or *S-S* or *H-S*, involving the use of friction piles.

In the *S-H* sequence the piles should be driven to the hard stratum and should be capable of deriving the whole of their support from it. With friction piles in an *S-S* sequence it is important first that their length should not be less than twice the least breadth of the building and secondly that an imaginary rigid block foundation, consisting of the piles together with the soil enclosed within their perimeter, should be capable of carrying the load with an adequate factor of safety. The reason for the first requirement is that, if the piles are shorter, the stresses in the soil will be nearly as great as if the building rested on a surface foundation without piles. The second requirement is a safeguard against the fact that a group of piles may not be able to carry a load as great as the safe load on one pile multiplied by the number of piles.

The second consideration arises if the soft material is of a nature that affects the selection of the type of pile to be used. Two such instances arise, the first when the soft material is a clay which is unusually sensitive to remoulding and the second when the 'soft' material is exceptionally pervious to water *e.g.* a loose gravel fill. If piles have to be driven through an extra sensitive clay the remoulding of the material may cause re-consolidation, with the consequence that adhesion between the clay and the piles will tend to add load to them instead of carrying part of their load: in extreme cases the weight of the whole volume of clay enclosed within the periphery of the piles may have to be carried on the piles. This may be of no consequence for point bearing piles provided that the point resistance is sufficiently great, but it will always lead to excessive settlements in friction piles. The criteria for judgement of such clays are given on pp 61 and 63. The remedy is to use bored piles, or to abandon a piled foundation in favour of a floating foundation. If the second case is met with *e.g.* that of a loose gravel fill through which piles must be driven to a firm stratum, uncased cast *in situ* piles should not be used unless it has been proved by actual test that they can be formed successfully.

The third consideration is a general sense of proportion between the magnitude of the loads to be carried and the load on each pile. The number of piles carrying a single stanchion, for example, should not be too many, for the pile cap will then be uneconomical, or too few, when the load might be excessively eccentric due to the piles being, inevitably, slightly out of place. No foundation should consist of less than three piles unless it is connected to other foundations by beams or by a slab capable of absorbing the bending moments due to the possible eccentricity of the piles. It should always be assumed that any pile may be up to 3 in away from its theoretical position and may be inclined as much as one in thirty.

The fourth consideration is whether any horizontal loads have to be resisted, and their magnitude relative to the vertical loads. If the horizontal loads are at all great it is generally advisable to use inclined piles to resist them. Transitory horizontal loads such as wind loads, crane surge *etc* can often be resisted by passive pressure against the pile caps.

When suitable types and sizes of pile have been determined on the basis of these considerations, availability, and preliminary estimates of cost, a trial pile or piles should be driven in positions adjacent to the preliminary borings and test loaded. In extensive foundations requiring many piles it is advisable to drive and test trial piles of various types. In examples of intermediate size a single type of pile may be selected and tested. Test piles should only be dispensed with when the expense of using a relatively high factor of safety exceeds the cost of the tests.

For end bearing driven piles the preliminary estimate of bearing capacity can be made on the basis of a theoretical calculation but must be considered to be subject to a relatively high percentage of error. The bearing capacity of screw piles and other types of cylinder piles can be calculated from the results of soil tests[22].

In friction piles a preliminary estimate of bearing capacity should be made on the assumption that the ultimate bearing capacity is equal to the surface area of the pile, plus nine times the end area, multiplied by the cohesion of the soil; a factor of safety of three should be taken.

A careful record must be made of the driving of each test pile and this should be correlated with the records of the nearest boring: a suitable form for recording the driving of test piles is given in the Code of Practice for Foundations. *Figure 30* shows a suitable form of graphical record.

The test load is best applied as a dead weight, see p 96. It should be imposed in increments each equal to one third of the proposed working load. No increment should be applied until the previous increment has been maintained for twenty four hours without increase in settlement. The test should be continued until the pile continues to sink without the addition of load, or to at least 25 per cent more than the working load.

For limitations on the load to be placed on piles in groups reference should be made to the beginning of this section.

When horizontal loads are significant, horizontal test loads should also be applied to the test piles. If the pile heads are to be fixed in pile caps or a raft, horizontal tests will have to be carried out on pairs of piles with a temporary cap cast on them in order to reproduce the effect of fixity.

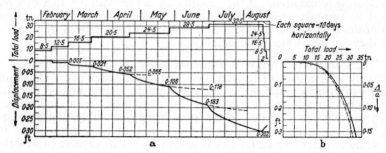

Figure 30.   Graphical record of pile test   a load/time settlement diagram for pile test   b load/ultimate settlement diagram for pile test

Examples of the design of piled foundations

The following examples illustrate the design of piled foundations for a heavy building on friction piles and for a single storey building on bearing piles.

Example—A building 125 ft × 60 ft × 96 ft high founded on friction piles in a deep clay stratum, the cohesion of which is 0·3 ton/sq ft. Weight of building and live loads = 13,000 ton (*Figure 31*)

Design—Average load/sq ft = 13,000/(125 × 60) = 1·733 ton, which exceeds the ultimate bearing capacity *i.e.* 5·5 × 0·3 = 1·65.
Assume piled raft, with piles at 5 ft 0 in c.c. both ways *i.e.* 25 rows of twelve piles = 300 piles.

Average load per pile = 13,000/300 = 43·33 ton.

In order to find the maximum load per pile allowance must be made for the effect of the overturning moment due to the wind and an estimate must be made of the effect of the concentration of stress at the sides and corners, similar to that which occurs under a rigid foundation on clay.

Wind—By Code of Practice (C.P. 3:1952), Chapter V, Loading, the wind velocity for open country, inland up to 300 ft elevation in S.E. England is 70 mph and the corresponding pressure on a building 96 ft high is 21·2 lb/sq ft.

$$\text{Overturning moment} = 21·2 \times 125 \times 96 \times \frac{96}{2} / 2,240$$

$$= 5,450 \text{ ft ton}$$

Moment of resistance of pile group, see *Figure 31*
$$= 25 \times 2 [2·5^2 + 7·5^2 + 12·5^2 + 17·5^2 + 22·5^2 + 27·5^2]$$
$$= 25 \times 2 \times 2·5^2 [1^2 + 3^2 + 5^2 + 7^2 + 9^2 + 11^2]$$
$$= 50 \times 6·25 [1 + 9 + 25 + 49 + 81 + 121]$$
$$= 312·5 \times 286 = 89,375 \text{ (units} \times \text{ft}^2)$$
$$\therefore \text{ Max load on one pile} = \frac{\pm 5,450 \times 27·5}{89,375} = \pm 1·7 \text{ ton}$$

Edge and corner effect—Consider the theoretical distribution of pressure under a rigid strip (see *Figure 31* b). If we take a factor of safety of 2 on the ultimate bearing pressure of 5·4c, the average bearing pressure is 2·7c and the maximum 4·0c, the minimum being 1·35c.

In an analogous way we can assign loads to the piles on the longitudinal and transverse centre lines (see *Figure 31*a) and can scale up the loads on those near the corner. We then have the following total ' pile unit loads ':

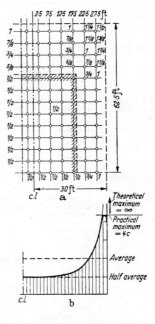

In ¼ raft

$$4 \times 8\tfrac{1}{2} = 34 \text{ at } \tfrac{1}{2} = 17$$
$$4 \times \tfrac{5}{8} \qquad = 2\cdot5$$
$$12\tfrac{1}{2} \times \tfrac{3}{4} \qquad = 9\cdot375$$
$$5 \times \tfrac{7}{8} \qquad = 4\cdot375$$
$$13\tfrac{1}{2} \times 1 \qquad = 13\cdot5$$
$$2 \times 1\tfrac{1}{8} \qquad = 2\cdot25$$
$$2 \times 1\tfrac{1}{4} \qquad = 2\cdot5$$
$$1\tfrac{3}{8} \qquad = 1\cdot375$$
$$1\tfrac{1}{2} \qquad = 1\cdot500$$

$$54\cdot375$$
$$4$$

In whole raft   217·5 *units*

∴ Factor for corner pile $= \dfrac{300}{217\cdot5} = 1\cdot38$

And max pile load $= 1\cdot38 \,(43\cdot3 + 1\cdot7) = 62$ ton.

Figure 31. Pile foundation for heavy building on friction piles   a plan of one quarter of raft distribution of pressure under half of a rigid strip

If minimum factor of safety is to be 2, ultimate bearing capacity of each pile $= 124$ ton.

Assume 16 in sq piles, periphery $= 5\cdot33$ ft, ultimate load $= 5\cdot33 \times 0\cdot3 = 1\cdot6$ ton/ft and required length $= 80$ ft (this length is above the minimum requirement *i.e.* $>$width of building).

Average factor of safety $= 2 \times 1\cdot38 = 2\cdot76$.

Check on piles and included clay as a foundation block. Depth $= Z = 80$ ft, width $= B = 55$ ft.

∴ $\dfrac{Z}{B} = 1\cdot45$ and ultimate bearing capacity (additional to pre-existing load)

$$= 5\cdot5 \,(1 + 0\cdot38 \times 1\cdot45) \times 0\cdot3 = 2\cdot56 \text{ ton p.s.f.}$$

Factor of safety $= 2\cdot56/1\cdot73 = 1\cdot47$, which is sufficient, as a slight increase of cohesion with depth has been neglected.

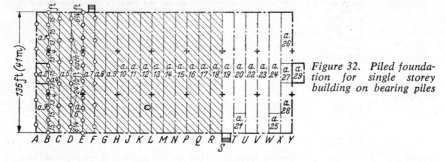

Figure 32. Piled foundation for single storey building on bearing piles

Example—A building 330 ft long × 135 ft wide of single storey construction founded on bearing piles driven through a soft clay stratum to firm underlying strata. Stanchion spacing 45 ft × 45 ft. Ground consists of 1 ft 0 in to 3 ft 6 in of top

TABLE 9

INSPECTION OF PILE FOUNDATIONS

Stage of construction	Type of pile	Check that :
Setting out	All types	All lines, levels and reference marks are in agreement with approved working drawings
Casting piles	Pre-cast concrete	Moulds are to correct dimensions and are properly cleaned, oiled and assembled. Reinforcement, pile shoe and ferrules are correctly assembled and positioned. Concrete materials are to specification. Concrete mix is correct and has correct water-cement ratio and slump. Concrete is carefully placed and thoroughly tamped without displacing reinforcement etc
Demoulding and stacking piles	Pre-cast concrete	Concrete has attained a required crushing strength and pile is carefully lifted by lifting ferrules at 1/5 points. Examine piles for porosity and cracks
Delivery to site and pitching	All piles	Pitched in correct position
	Pre-cast concrete	Concrete has attained a required crushing strength. Pile is lifted by shackle or pitching ferrule. Examine piles for cracks
	Timber or steel and screw piles	Check for size and quality
Driving	Timber, steel and pre-cast concrete and screw piles driven by permanent shaft	Calculated driving resistance will not cause overstress of pile i.e. pile not to be over driven
	Timber and pre-cast concrete	Packings and driving helmet are adequate and in such condition that head of pile is not damaged
	All piles	Pile is maintained within specified limits of vertical and of required position (much closer limits are desirable in the early stages of driving)
	Pre-cast concrete piles	Pile is not cracked by displacement of toe against resistance of guides in leads
	All piles	Continuous check on driving resistance and correlation with driving resistance of piles near boreholes to ensure that desired foundation stratum is reached. In the case of groups of piles check that previously driven piles are not disturbed
	Bored piles	Casing is driven without causing undesired vibration or 'draw' of ground
	Bored piles and open-ended screw piles	Check strata passed through against boreholes to ensure that desired foundation stratum is reached
Plugging	Bored piles and open-ended screw piles	Bottom is plugged so that water can be baled or pumped out and shaft can be formed in the dry (unless shaft is formed under compressed air or by tremie method approved by the engineer)
	All piles	Concrete quality and proportions are as specified
Formation of shaft	Cased cast in situ piles and screwcrete piles	Casing is straight within specified limits of verticality, and free from all but minor dents
	Cased cast in situ and screw-crete piles	Reinforcement is correctly placed and concrete is well compacted in the dry, under compressed air or by tremie (if approved)
	Bored and uncased cast in situ piles	No water enters tube through concrete at bottom. Reinforcement is correctly placed. Quantity of concrete is sufficient
Testing	All types	Piles selected by the engineer are tested and record kept in accordance with p 143
Preparation for capping	Timber	Any brooming of head is cut off (reject split piles)
	Pre-cast concrete	Concrete is carefully stripped to required level, leaving pile reinforcement exposed, and bent if necessary, in accordance with drawings
	In situ concrete and screwcrete	Laitance is removed and reinforcement is correct as above
Capping	All types	Concrete screed of specified thickness is placed to required level. Shuttering or timbering, placing of cap reinforcement, quality and placing of concrete are checked as in reinforced concrete

soil, 3 ft 0 in to 4 ft 0 in. of brown sandy clay (*c*, 0·24 to 0·36 ton/sq ft), and 8 ft 0 in to 10 ft 0 in of blue clay (*c*, 0·12 ton/sq ft) overlying a thick stratum of claystone and gravel (*Figure 32*).

Design—In view of the weakness and compressibility of the blue clay stratum it was decided to carry the structure and ground floor on piles. Cast *in situ* piles were selected and a test pile driven to a depth of 21 ft was tested to a load of 42 ton. A settlement of $\frac{1}{32}$ in was observed at a load of 35 ton and remained constant up to the maximum load. This settlement was found to be elastic as it reduced to zero on removal of the load.

The pile layout is shown in *Figure 32*. The piles were driven in rows at 15 ft 0 in centres and carried beams running across the building, and these beams, in turn, carried the floor slab which spanned longitudinally. It will be noted that the pile arrangement in rows coinciding with stanchion lines was different from that in intermediate rows, as pairs of piles are required to carry the stanchions.

INSPECTION OF WORK IN PROGRESS AND TESTING OF PILE FOUNDATIONS

The points to be noted in the inspection of works in progress are set out in Table 9.

MODIFICATIONS OF FOUNDATION TECHNIQUE UNDER SPECIAL LOCAL CIRCUMSTANCES

MINING SUBSIDENCE

It is necessary to have a clear idea of the mechanics of mining subsidence before designing foundations for structures in mining districts. An excellent description of these phenomena is given in a paper by MAUTNER[23], which also contains a quantity of useful data and examples of foundation design. The following information and data are adapted from that paper by permission.

The magnitude and manner of the subsidence is generally influenced by the following factors: *1* nature of the overlying strata; *2* depth of the worked seam or seams; *3* thickness and slope (dip); *4* method of working of the seams; *5* stowage of filling in the worked areas.

From studies of these factors, from surveys and experience, ideal curves for subsidence, vertical movement and the magnitude and extension of the horizontal strain have been derived by various mining engineers. *Figure 33* shows such ideal curves. The seam in this curve is supposed to be sloping slightly. The chain-dotted curve represents the ideal subsidence curve: the full drawn curve the magnitude of horizontal strain (tension and pressure). From the limits of the worked seam two inclined planes are shown on either side, the inner one representing the 'angle of rupture' and the outer one the 'limiting angle'. This angle of rupture does not, however, coincide with the angle of rupture which is known to structural engineers from the earth pressure theory. The plane inclined with the angle of rupture is an angle determined by the limit of the worked seam and the maximum tensile strain on the surface.

The zero point for the horizontal strain, the point of contraflexure in the subsidence curve, is generally situated vertically just above the limit of the worked seam. This is not quite true in *Figure 33* as the seam has a slight dip but it will be so in a horizontal seam. From this curve it can be derived that in the centre of the subsidence, which for horizontal or slightly inclined seams is in mid-area, the radii of curvature for both curves are rather great, and that the greatest slope angle of both curves is in the vicinity of the points above the border of the worked seam.

With regard to the limiting angle, this is the plane connecting the point of the surface without subsidence and horizontal strain with the limit of the worked seam. The limiting angle is greatly influenced by the strata just below ground: in very soft strata *e.g.* quicksand, there may be a very flat angle, sometimes only 15 or 20°.

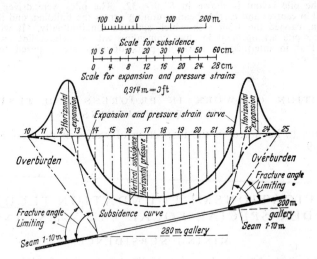

Figure 33. Ideal subsidence and strain (MAUTNER[23])

With regard to the movement itself this consists principally of a truncated cone or pyramid, defined by the angle of rupture, moving vertically downwards into the hollow of the worked seam or seams. Some authors suppose that this vertical movement is accompanied by an inclined sliding movement outside the limit of the worked area, while others assume that the vertical movement of the prismatic part just above the worked seam is accompanied by rotation of the remaining wedges about the edges limiting the worked area. The latter assumption is to some extent corroborated by strain measurements on the roof of the worked seam, which generally showed that the pressure at the roof strongly increased at the limit of the worked area, this being apparently the centre point of this rotating movement.

It is apparent from *Figures 33* and *34* that as excavation of a seam approaches and passes under a structure it will, if designed to bear uniformly on its base, be subject first to hogging and then to sagging bending moments. The length or lengths over which the building is supported at the times of maximum hogging, or sagging, moment will obviously depend upon the ratio of the design bearing pressure on the ultimate bearing pressure of the soil. In calculating these lengths it will be safe to assume a linear variation of bearing pressure, as indicated in the diagrams.

Figure 35 shows how the values of λ/b for the case when the axis of curvature is parallel to one side of a rectangular foundation vary with ratio of the actual ground pressure to the design bearing pressure n and it will be noted that λ increases with n. The value of λ will be clear from *Figure 34*. The axis of curvature may, of course, not be parallel to a side of the foundation and the foundation may not be rectangular. In such instances torsion of the structure may be involved as well as bending.

It should also be noted that the structure may, and probably will, be subjected to horizontal forces from the ground. Such forces will normally tend to stretch the base of a sagging structure and to compress that of a hogging one but, due to the inevitable variations from the necessarily idealized picture that has been given of the process of subsidence, they may well act otherwise and for complete protection structures should be designed to resist the most unfavourable horizontal forces acting in conjunction with the maximum bending moments. The horizontal forces can attain a value equal to the ultimate cohesion over the contact area plus the vertical load multiplied by the tangent of the angle of friction.

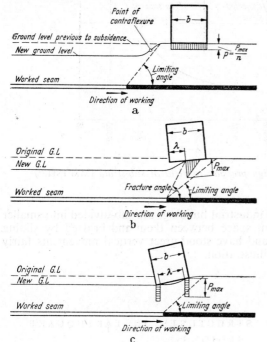

Figure 34. Effect of mining subsidence on *s t r u c t u r e s* a structure outside limiting angle b structure on rim of subsiding area, first or hogging stage c structure on rim of subsiding area, second or sagging stage (adapted from MAUTNER[23])

The above considerations show that the area of foundation in contact with the soil should be kept to a minimum. Illustrations of how this can be done and of the use of a three point support are given by MAUTNER[23].

The foundation methods described above will afford complete protection. It will be clear that such protection is not always possible nor is it always necessary. It is, however, necessary to provide protection against the horizontal forces whenever this is economically feasible.

In small houses on mining estates a strip foundation with tensile reinforcement is generally the minimum of protection. This, however, could be greatly improved if a basement were provided as such a basement with its partition walls acts like a rigid box and is well able to resist the forces in vertical planes. The use of reinforced brickwork for the walls and a naturally rigid plan would help. The adoption of a high design bearing pressure is in any case recommended.

Spacious buildings generally offer the greatest difficulties as the interior usually has no stiffening at all. It is, therefore, generally possible to provide protection only against horizontal forces. It is advisable not to arrange the trusses of steel workshop structures on one side on roller bearings but rather to connect the roof trusses with rocking stanchions incorporated in the walls on one side. Even a distortion in cross section does not then usually do great harm. No 'complete protection' can be reached for multi-storey buildings but the structure may partly be sufficient for the vertical movements if it consists of rigid frames in both directions. In

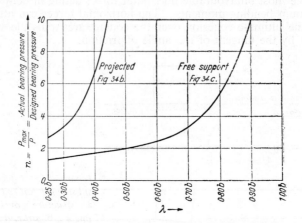

Figure 35. Ratio of design pressure to yield of sub-strata (Mautner[23])

Holland several multi-storey industrial buildings are sub-divided into smaller sectional parts with sufficient space between them and bridged by sliding freely supported structures and have stood great vertical movements fairly well. Mautner[23] gives an illustration.

FOUNDATIONS OF STRUCTURES IN EARTHQUAKE REGIONS

Except close to the epicentre of an earthquake, where appreciable vertical vibrations may occur, the principal phenomenon is a horizontal vibration, shaking the surface of the earth, and everything upon it, sideways. It is usual to specify that a horizontal acceleration *e.g.* $g/10$, be considered in the design of structures.

The main effects of the horizontal vibration on the soil are: *i* cohesion-less soils are compacted and extensive but irregular surface settlement takes place; in fine loosely deposited water bearing sands a quicksand effect may occur, cohesive soils are not thus affected; *ii* banks *e.g.* of rivers, tend to 'spall' off and the widths of river beds and cuttings are decreased.

The precautions to be taken in the case of building foundations are therefore: *a* avoid the neighbourhood of steep slopes and cuttings; *b* if on a cohesive soil, tie the foundations together in such a way that they will resist the greatest horizontal forces that can come upon them: it is quite proper to stress materials up to near the elastic limit in making this provision; *c* if on granular material provision against horizontal forces should be made as in *b* above and, if possible, the structure should be designed to resist appreciable differential settlement, see p 148.

FOUNDATIONS IN PERMAFROST REGIONS

The term 'permafrost' is a recently introduced but convenient abbreviation for 'permanently frozen ground'. Such ground is found at various depths below the surface of regions where the mean annual temperature is below freezing point.

If the natural cover of vegetation, which is a comparatively good heat insulator, is removed and replaced by an earth fill or a road pavement, both comparatively poor heat insulators, or by a structure which may be heated, the permafrost is thawed in the summer to a greater depth than would otherwise be the case, or is permanently melted to an appreciable depth below a heated building. If the permafrost is a type of soil that is liable to frost heave it will, when thawed, expel quantities of excess water which will flow out from under any structure and cause serious settlement. When the ground freezes again in winter renewed frost heave will add to the differential settlement.

The only type of foundation that has so far been found satisfactory is a piled foundation, extending to below the depth where the permafrost never thaws and so devised that the structure is carried on stilts and air can circulate between the base of the structure and the ground. The piles must be so deeply embedded in the permanently frozen ground that they will not be lifted out by frost heave.

The piles are driven into holes formed by steam jets. A pipe about $\frac{3}{4}$ in to 1 in diam is used through which steam is blown at a pressure of 50 to 80 lb/sq in (3·5 to 5·6 kg/sq cm). Piles can be driven up to a week or more after thawing the holes. Steel and timber piles have been used with success. Piles should be driven to twice the maximum depth to which seasonal thawing takes place *i.e.* the embedment in the permanently frozen ground should be equal to the thickness of the 'active layer' above, see papers by CARLSON[24] and HEMSTOCK[25].

FOUNDATIONS FOR MOVING MACHINERY

The design of foundations for moving machinery necessitates particular consideration of the vibratory or impact forces concerned as these can cause excessive settlement of the machine foundations, or neighbouring foundations, or result in troublesome vibration of neighbouring structures.

If a vibrator is placed on the ground and is operated at increasing speeds it will be found that resonance is induced in the ground, as in any other elastic or semi-elastic body, at certain critical frequencies of vibration which are dependent on the characteristics of the machine as well as on those of the ground. Also, as in certain other substances such as rubber and cork, the critical frequencies are not constants of the material alone but depend upon the amplitude induced.

The effect of the vibration on the ground depends very much on the type of ground. It is known that cohesive soils consolidate greatly under steady pressure and that the rate of consolidation is not greatly affected by vibration, whereas cohesionless materials, which only compress slightly under steady pressure, may be compacted to a very considerable extent by vibration. With cohesionless materials it is found that the critical frequencies depend upon the density and, as the static bearing capacity of such materials also depends upon the density there is, as would be expected, a relationship between the critical frequency of sands and gravels and the static bearing capacity. No such relationship exists for clays and other cohesive materials.

If sand or gravel strata are vibrated at a frequency which is close to the critical, excessive settlement of the machine foundation and neighbouring foundations will result. If a machine must be founded on sand or gravel strata the natural frequency of which in combination with the machine foundation is near to that of the machine, the only course is to compact the ground to its maximum density for a considerable distance around the machine by means of piles or sand piles, or to change its nature by chemical consolidation.

It is undesirable, in any ground, that the frequency of the machine should lie between 50 and 200 per cent of the critical frequency of the system comprising the machine and the ground.

TSCHEBOTARIOFF and WARD[26] have shown that there is a fairly definite relationship between what they term 'the reduced natural frequency', which is the natural frequency at an average unit pressure on the ground of 1 ton/sq ft, and the area of the foundation. The natural frequency of the actual combination of ground and machine is then

$$\omega_n = \frac{\omega_{nr}}{\sqrt{q}} \qquad \ldots\ldots\ldots\ldots(4)$$

where ω_n = natural frequency of system, ω_{nr} = reduced natural frequency of system, q = bearing pressure.

Figure 36 (which is adapted from *Figure 3*, ref. 26), shows the range of reduced natural frequencies likely to produce resonance. From this figure it is possible to make an estimate of the size of foundation necessary to avoid resonance in any case. Whenever possible the design should be checked by vibration tests on the site.

Example—A machine weighing 20 ton and having a frequency of 400 c/min rests on a soil which has a maximum safe bearing capacity of 2 ton/sq ft. As the example is one of damped forced vibration, the frequency of the system comprising the machine, its foundation and the soil will also be 400 c/min and the relationship between reduced natural frequency and bearing pressure will be given by the equation: $\omega_{nr} = 400\sqrt{q}$.

At this stage it is necessary to proceed by cut and try methods and TABLE A shows the calculations necessary to find the reduced natural frequency of the system when the machine is carried on solid concrete foundations, one foot of the height of which is above ground and the balance below ground. The bearing pressure q is taken as the net bearing pressure after deduction of the weight of the soil displaced.

A.   FIRST TRIAL—SOLID FOUNDATIONS—1 FT ABOVE GROUND

Fn area sq ft	Fn dimensions length × breadth × depth	Volume cu ft	Wt at 160 lb/ cu ft, ton	Volume of soil displaced	Wt at 112 lb/ cu ft, ton	Net wt of fdn	Total incl machine, ton	q	$\omega_{nr}=$ $400\sqrt{q}$
11	4 × 2·75 × 2·5	27·5	2	16·5	0·8	1·2	21·2	1·93	555
25	6·25 × 4 × 4	100	7·2	75	3·7	3·5	23·5	0·98	396
100	12·5 × 8 × 5	500	36	400	20	16	36	0·36	240
400	25 × 16 × 6	2,400	171	2,000	100	71	91	0·23	191
1,600	50 × 32 × 7	11,200	800	9,600	480	320	340	0·21	184

B.   SECOND TRIAL—FOUNDATION DIMENSIONS AS BEFORE BUT VARYING PERCENTAGE OF VOIDS

Fn area sq ft	Per cent voids	Volume cu ft	Wt at 160 lb/ cu ft, ton	Volume of soil displaced	Wt at 112 lb/ cu ft, ton	Net wt of fdn	Total incl machine, ton	q	$\omega_{nr}=$ $400\sqrt{q}$
100	40	300	22	400	20	2	22	0·22	188
400	50	1,200	85	2,000	100	− 15	5	0·0125	40

These results have been plotted on *Figure 36* as a dotted line and it will be seen that this lies entirely within the danger zone. However it is possible to reduce the bearing pressure q further by hollowing out the foundation, so reducing its weight, as shown in TABLE B, which gives particulars of hollow foundations having areas of 100 and 400 sq ft, and the same dimensions as the corresponding dimensions in TABLE A. These results are plotted on *Figure 36* as a dot and dash line from which it will be seen that a satisfactory foundation will result provided that its area is not less than 250 sq ft and that the net bearing pressure does not exceed 0·043 ton/sq ft.

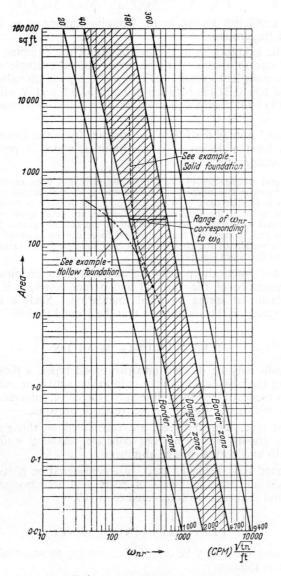

Figure 36. Reduced natural frequency of resonance zone plotted against area of foundation (Adapted from TSCHEBOTARIOFF[26]*)*

It must be remembered that the maximum bearing pressure is that due to the dead weight W plus that due to the inertia force Pa; it is good practice to provide for a sufficient bearing area to give an equivalent dead load equal to $(W + 3Pa)$ and to make W large compared with $3Pa$.

If the periodic impulse due to the machine is given by the equation

$$Q = Q_1 \cdot \sin \omega_n \cdot t \qquad \qquad \dots\dots\dots(5)$$

then

$$Pa = Q_1 N \qquad \qquad \dots\dots\dots(6)$$

where

$$N = 1 \Big/ \sqrt{\left\{ \left[1 - \left(\tfrac{\omega_n}{\omega_0}\right)^2 \right]^2 + \left(\tfrac{2\lambda}{\omega_0}\right)^2 \left(\tfrac{\omega_n}{\omega_0}\right)^2 \right\}} \qquad \dots\dots\dots(7)$$

Here λ is a coefficient known as the damping factor and ω_0 is the natural frequency of the ground.

Very little is known as to the magnitude of the damping factor and it is obviously safe to assume it to be zero. In the example above, if the foundation is made 250 sq ft at 0·043 ton/sq ft, ω_0 will probably lie between 175/0·21 and 630/0·21 *i.e.* between 850 and 3,000, and N will lie between 4/3 and 50/49. Of course ω_0 should be determined experimentally where possible.

TERZAGHI[34] quotes the following abstract from the German Standard Specification for the design of steam turbines, which is pertinent to the selection of an appropriate value for Q_1:

> If the natural frequencies of the foundation have not been computed or if the difference between the number of revolutions n of the turbine and one of the frequencies is smaller than ± 30 per cent of n the designer is required to assume that the members of the support of the turbine are acted upon by a centrifugal force Q_1 equal to twenty times the weight of the rotating parts. For differences between 30 and 50 per cent the centrifugal force can be assumed to be equal to 10 times the weight of the rotating parts, and for differences in excess of 50 per cent equal to five times this weight.

If it is not practically possible to adopt an area of foundation which results in avoidance of the resonant and border zones, it is necessary to adopt an elastic or spring mounted foundation. Such a foundation is normally designed on the assumption that the ground is rigid.

RETAINING WALLS

Retaining walls may be divided into two broad types, *a* those free to tilt slightly about their base and subject only to the active, or minimum, earth pressure, *b* those restrained from tilting and, therefore, subjected to pressures which may considerably exceed the active earth pressure.

The first type, termed 'free', are considered on this page. Typical varieties are gravity and reinforced concrete retaining walls, sheet pile retaining walls and normal bridge abutments.

The second type, termed 'fixed', are considered on p 166. Basement retaining walls and the abutments of portal and arch bridges are typical. Backfilling and drainage are considered on p 167.

'FREE' RETAINING WALLS

'Free' retaining walls may be classified according to material and form of construction as follows:

1 gravity—masonry, brick, mass concrete

2 reinforced concrete—cantilever, counterfort, buttress, shelf

3 crib—timber, pre-cast concrete, pressed metal units

4 sheet pile—timber, steel, reinforced concrete

5 king pile—timber, steel, reinforced concrete

6 'free' bridge abutments (except for arch and portal frame bridges).

These forms of wall are illustrated in *Figures 37* to *44* which indicate when a mass of the earth supported is to be regarded as a part of the wall in the computations for general stability.

The selection of the most appropriate type of wall depends upon several factors and the notes that follow are intended as a general guide to selection. They cannot, however, be valid in all instances.

Height—Up to 6 ft: Gravity or crib wall, R.C. cantilever, king pile walls.
    6 to 30 ft: Gravity, R.C. cantilever, or crib, steel or R.C. sheet pile, king pile.
    Over 30 ft: R.C. counterfort, buttress or shelf, steel sheet pile.

Nature of earth—Cohesionless: any type.
    Cohesive: any type, but when possible use a cohesionless backfill wedge, see *Figure 45.*

Earth containing injurious sulphate and sulphide salts—Masonry or brick (in a resistant cement mortar); reinforced concrete protected by a bituminous layer.

Construction through water—Sheet pile walls or king pile walls.

Availability of materials—When stone, bricks or aggregate are plentiful and cheap, the range of economy of gravity walls encroaches on that of reinforced concrete and steel walls, and *vice versa.*

Appearance is important—Masonry or brick walls, or reinforced concrete walls with a masonry or brick skin applied after structural completion.

The information to be sought in the preliminary exploration of the site is discussed in the previous chapter. The forces acting on free retaining walls are fully stated in the chapter on Soil Mechanics.

Calculation of loads

Points that it is most important to remember when calculating the loads on retaining walls are listed below.

Active pressure—When calculating active pressure, it should be remembered that *i* in cohesionless soils a tilt of $\frac{1}{2}$ per cent of the height of the wall is required to induce the active pressure condition; *ii* some cohesive soils are liable to soften in the course of time and induce increased active pressure; *iii* if steps are not taken to prevent seasonal expansion and contraction of cohesive soils, pressures approaching the passive may be induced near the surface, reducing to the active pressure at the depth where seasonal variation of water content ceases; *iv* rainstorms may temporarily induce a certain amount of water pressure even though drains are provided.

Passive pressure—When calculating passive pressures it must be remembered that *1* a considerable displacement is necessary to induce the full passive pressure. In cohesionless soils this may be about 8 to 10 per cent of the height of face. No more than half the maximum passive pressure should ever be relied upon; *2* if the ground falls away from the toe of the wall the passive resistance will be appreciably reduced.

Other loads—Careful checking is necessary to ensure that consideration has been given to any of the following loads which may act on the wall: *a* surcharge, from distributed loads, tracks, roads or foundations of structures behind the wall; *b* water pressure due to rise and fall of tide, heavy rain *etc*, wave action; *c* pull on mooring ropes, impact of vessels, acceleration and braking forces from traffic on roads and tracks, wind forces on structures founded behind the wall.

Details of design and construction of the various types are dealt with below.

The foundations of gravity, reinforced concrete and crib retaining walls differ from those of ordinary walls only in that the distribution of pressure

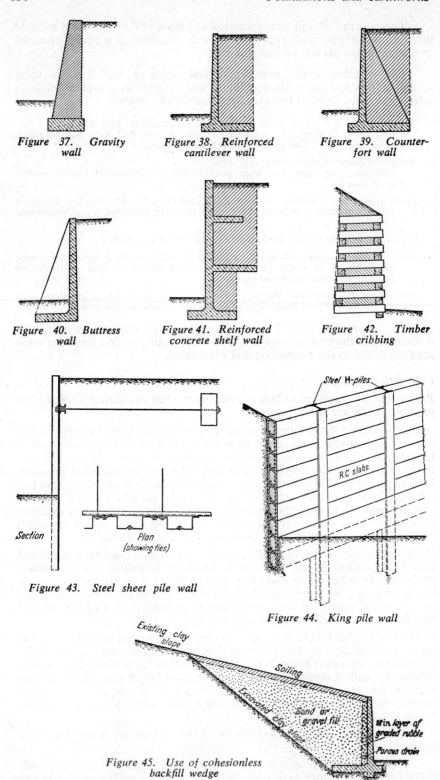

Figure 37. Gravity wall

Figure 38. Reinforced cantilever wall

Figure 39. Counterfort wall

Figure 40. Buttress wall

Figure 41. Reinforced concrete shelf wall

Figure 42. Timber cribbing

Figure 43. Steel sheet pile wall

Figure 44. King pile wall

Figure 45. Use of cohesionless backfill wedge

over the base is normally non-uniform. It is advisable to restrict the maximum, normally the toe, pressure under a retaining wall foundation to the bearing pressure allowable under a normal wall footing. Full uplift water pressure should be assumed to act on the base. The foundation should then be designed in accordance with the recommendations on pp 113-121 and pp 135-147 if the foundation is piled, when it is good practice to use inclined piles to take the thrust.

GRAVITY WALLS

In the design of gravity walls the forces acting on the back of the wall (the extent and inclination of which are determined by the methods described

TABLE 10

MATERIALS AND STRESSES FOR GRAVITY RETAINING WALLS

Material	Stresses				Appropriate Code of Practice	Remarks
	Bending compression lb/sq in	Direct compression lb/sq in	Bending tension lb/sq in	Shear lb/sq in		
Clay bricks	*Not specified in Code but may be taken to be direct compression +30 per cent*	*See chapter on Masonry and Brickwork*	15*	*Not specified in Code but may be taken equal to twice bending tension*	111·101 121·101	*Bricks to comply with Clauses 203/ 205 of Code 121 and to have a minimum crushing strength of 1,500 lb / sq in when tested to B.S. 1257 : 1945*
Sand-lime bricks			15*		111·101 121·101	*Bricks to conform to B.S. 187:1955, and porosity not to exceed 10 per cent by B.S. 1257 : 1945 24 hr immersion test*
Concrete bricks			15*		111·101 121·101	*Bricks to conform to B.S. 1180:1944 and porosity not to exceed 10 per cent by B.S. 1257 : 1945 24 hr immersion test*
Stonework			15		111·101 121·101	
Mass concrete cast in situ 1 : 4 : 8	350	250	15†	30	*B.S. C.P. 111·201*	
Mass concrete cast in situ 1 : 3 : 6	500	350	20†	40		
Mass concrete cast in situ 1 : 2½ : 5	650	500	30	60		
Mass concrete cast in situ 1 : 2 : 4	800	600	40	80		

1 lb/sq in = 0·07 kg/sq cm

*The amount of tension that can be relied upon across the joints in a brick wall depends very greatly upon the brick, the mortar, and the workmanship. No tension should be allowed if *a* pressed bricks, or others with poor adhesion to mortar are used; or *b* the mortar is weaker than 1 part cement to 3 parts sand; or *c* any water pressure can develop at the back of the wall.

†When such weak mixes are used tension may be considered to act only for the dispersal of concentrated loads.

on p 33), the weight of the wall and of any filling that may be included, and the foundation pressures must all balance. The subject is fully dealt with in standard textbooks and will not be repeated here: see chapter on Harbours and Docks, vol. 4.

A wall retaining cohesive materials should not be made less strong than would be necessary if it were required to retain a dry granular material having an angle of friction of 35°: this will be found to be a controlling factor in the case of walls of small height.

TABLE 10, condensed from the C.E. Code of Practice No. 2, Earth Retaining Structures, gives particulars of the allowable stresses in various materials used for the construction of gravity walls and refers to the Codes of Practice governing design in each of these materials. Where the stresses apropriate for the design of gravity walls or the material requirements differ from those specified for general use in the appropriate code, this is noted.

The type of suitable mortar depends, in that order, on the nature of the masonry (*e.g.* the make of brick), the nature of the soil, and upon whether it is desired to take advantage of tension across the joints. The use of a mortar that is unsuitable to the brick or stone used may lead to excessive efflorescence or surface disintegration caused by the migration of salts: combinations of masonry and mortar that have traditionally been found suitable should be used. In general terms a mortar of one part cement, 0 to $\frac{1}{4}$ parts lime, and 2 to 3 parts sand is appropriate for dense stones and engineering bricks: and a mix of 1 part cement to 1 part lime and 5 to 6 parts sand is generally suitable for porous stones and facing and common bricks, though richer mixes, up to 1 cement to 4 sand may sometimes be used for the latter. If the soil contains a high proportion of sulphates and sulphides a mortar of 1 part of aluminous or other resistant cement to 2 or 3 parts of sand should be used and the bricks or stone should be known to be sulphate resistant.

The bricks or stone used for the facing, copings and upper 6 ft (2 m) of the back surface of retaining walls should be highly frost resistant even when saturated.

Figure 46. Stepped foundation for retaining wall

Slip joints should be made right through the wall at all places where there is a sudden change in the section of the wall or the nature of the foundation. Such joints should be at least 1 in wide and should be filled with a bituminous jointing compound and sealed with a U-shaped copper strip, or plastic waterstops should be used. Contraction joints should be formed in mass concrete walls at intervals not exceeding 25 ft. Vertical construction joints should always coincide with the permanent contraction and slip joints. Horizontal construction joints should be made with the utmost care. Steps in the foundation should be overlapped horizontally by at least twice the height of the step, see *Figure 46*.

REINFORCED CONCRETE WALLS

Cantilever, counterfort and buttress walls are designed, as a whole, as reinforced concrete cantilever slabs, T-beams and beams respectively. In the two latter types the slab is assumed to span horizontally between counterforts or buttresses, except for a portion defined by lines rising at 45° from the intersection of the counterforts with the base slab, *Figure 47,* which is assumed to cantilever from the base slab. It must not be forgotten that the slab of a counterfort wall is tending to tear away from the counterforts and that the junction must be reinforced accordingly. In a shelf wall it is assumed, for the design of the slab, that the lateral earth pressure is zero immediately under the slab. For the design of the wall as a whole it is assumed that the wall, shelves and the enclosed earth, *Figure 41,* act as a unit.

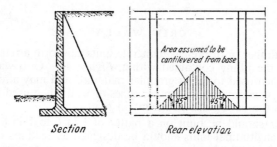

Section   Rear elevation

Figure 47. Reinforced concrete counterfort wall

The width and disposition of the base slab must be chosen so that the safe bearing pressure is not exceeded at the toe, as illustrated in *Figure 48.* The depth to the underside of the base slab is chosen from the same considerations as affect the depth of the base of a normal strip foundation. If the face of earth to the foundation depth is insufficiently deep to develop the passive earth pressure required, an additional depth of face must be provided by a projection below the base, *Figure 49.*

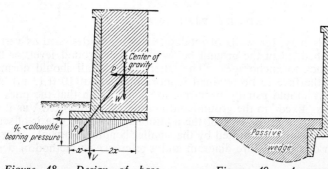

Figure 48. Design of base of reinforced concrete wall. P = total earth pressure, W = total weight of wall and shaded area of soil

Figure 49. Arrangement of key beneath base to provide additional passive resistance

The reinforced concrete should be designed in accordance with normal practice except that it is desirable that the cover should be rather greater than normally specified *i.e.* at least 2 in on faces normally in contact with earth or fresh water and at least $2\frac{1}{2}$ in on faces normally in contact with salt water.

Contraction and slip joints should be provided as with gravity walls, except that the greatest length of wall between such joints should depend upon the design of the horizontal reinforcement. Where there are counterforts or buttresses these should be spaced so as to equalize the maximum bending moments in the slab, *Figure 50.*

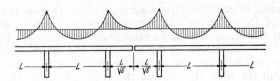

Figure 50. Spacing of buttresses to equalize moments in slab

CRIB WALLS

Crib work of timber or of pre-cast concrete units can form a retaining ' wall' together with the filling contained within, *Figure 42*. Crib walls are most satisfactory when used to retain granular materials and may afford consider-able economy as compared with other types of wall when used for retaining rock filling on the valley side of mountain roads.

Crib walls should be built on a batter of 1 in 6 to 1 in 8, equal back and front. Longitudinal units should be designed as sections of silo walls, transverse units should be designed to act as ties and to carry, as simply supported beams, the maximum weight of earth that can bear upon them; care should be taken that the bearing areas at the ends of all units are adequate to transmit the vertical reactions. Except at the end bearing areas longitudinal units should be recessed so that a slot is formed between each unit and those above and below: these slots will ensure adequate drainage of the fill and proper fitting together of units, even if these are slightly warped.

Timber and reinforced concrete cribs should be designed in accordance with normal practice for each of these materials.

SHEET PILE WALLS

Sheet pile walls may, for walls of moderate height, be designed as vertical cantilevers embedded in the ground below the lower ground level, or they may be tied back to anchorages. The latter type of wall should normally be adopted if the face to be retained is more than about 10 ft (3 m) high. Anchored walls should usually penetrate to such a depth that the piles can be considerd as ' fixed ' in the ground and not merely ' supported ', as it will be found generally that the cost of the additional length of pile is offset by the reduction in section permitted by the smaller bending moment. For the determination of the pressure diagram and a reference to method of design see p 39.

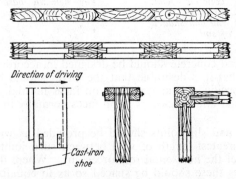

Figure 51. Typical details of timber sheet piles

Timber sheet piles

The stress grades (bending) are 800, 1,000 and 1,200 lb/sq in (56, 70 and 84 kg/sq cm). As the section modulus per ft width is $2d^2$, where d is the thickness in inches, the max B.M. per ft width can readily be found. The max allowable driving resistance per ft width is the stress grade (compression) × area per ft width. Typical details of timber sheet piles are shown in *Figure 51*.

Steel sheet piles

The properties of various types of steel sheet piles are given in TABLE 11. The sections are illustrated in *Figure 52*.

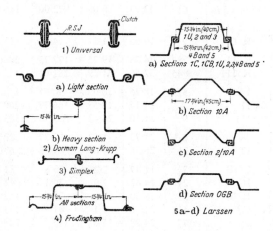

Figure 52.   Steel sheet piles

Reinforced concrete sheet piles

Typical sections and their properties are given in TABLE 12 and typical details are shown in *Figure 53*.

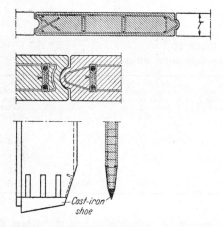

Figure 53.   Typical details of reinforced concrete sheet piles

The section modulus of steel sheet piling having interlocks at the neutral axis has been the subject of considerable discussion. The following extract from the Code of Practice for Foundations gives a sound view on the assumptions which should be made.

Table 11
SHEET STEEL PILES

Type	*Section No.*	*Overall depth in*	*Wt/sq ft of wall lb/sq ft*	*Z per ft width in³*	*Max B.M. per ft width using mild steel (working stress = 9 ton/sq in) ton in*	*Max B.M. per ft width using high tensile steel (working stress = 14.5 ton/sq in) ton in**	*Max allowable driving resistance ton per pile*
Universal	6 *in* × 5 *in*	$6\frac{1}{4}$	76·24	18·86	169·74	273·47	107·46
	8 *in* × 5 *in*	$6\frac{1}{4}$	62·33	14·53	130·77	210·69	115·29
	10 *in* × 5 *in*	$6\frac{1}{4}$	52·63	11·55	103·95	167·48	120·6
	12 *in* × 5 *in*	$6\frac{1}{4}$	46·06	9·68	87·12	140·36	125·91
	13 *in* × 5 *in*	$6\frac{1}{4}$	45·31	9·26	83·34	134·27	133·83
	15 *in* × 5 *in*	$6\frac{1}{4}$	42·93	8·00	72·00	116·0	152·37
Dorman Long-Krupp	K O	$2\frac{9}{32}$	10·65	1·61	14·49	23·35	26·46
	K 11	7·87	24·78	19·75	177·75	286·38	86·31
	K 111	9·45	32·56	31·29	281·61	453·71	112·8
Frodingham	1A	$5\frac{3}{4}$	18·25	10·09	90·81	146·10	63·45
	11	$7\frac{9}{32}$	24·17	18·53	166·77	268·4	84·06
	111	9	31·50	26·42	237·78	383·5	109·62
Simplex	8 *in*	$2\frac{9}{16}$	21·73	1·53	13·77	22·2	38·7
	12 *in*	$3\frac{1}{2}$	26·36	4·64	41·75	67·35	80·2
Larssen	OGB	$2\frac{15}{16}$	11·47	2·2	19·8	31·9	30·33
	1C	$2\frac{1}{2}$	14·47	2·9	26·1	42·1	38·7
	1GB	$5\frac{1}{8}$	18·50	7·8	70·2	113·2	48·96
	1U	$5\frac{1}{8}$	21·70	9·1	81·9	131·8	57·42
	2	$7\frac{7}{8}$	24·98	15·8	142·2	229·0	66·15
	3	$9\frac{3}{4}$	31·74	25·3	227·7	366·5	83·97
	4B	$13\frac{1}{2}$	41·12	42·5	382·5	616·3	108·63
	5	$13\frac{1}{2}$	48·74	55·1	495·9	799·0	129·06
	10A	$7\frac{7}{8}$	27·30	11·7	105·3	169·2	72·27
	2/10A	$4\frac{13}{16}$	26·30	6·9	62·1	100	69·57

* Guaranteed yield point of 23 ton/sq in (36·2 kg/sq mm)

Table 12
TYPICAL REINFORCED CONCRETE SHEET PILES 1 : $1\frac{1}{2}$: 3 MIX

Section	*Longitudinal steel*	*Steel wt/sq ft (normal)*	*Add for additional transverse steel at top and bottom per ft run of wall*	*Max B.M. ft width in ton*	*Max allowable driving resistance per pile, ton*
$4\frac{1}{2}$ *in thick* × 24 *in long*	6 *at* $\frac{5}{8}$ *in*	3·55	4·64	10·1	29·9
6 *in* × 20 *in*	6 *at* $\frac{5}{8}$ *in*	4·24	4·3	17·6	35·9
9 *in* × 21 *in*	6 *at* 1 *in*	9·6	3·3	61·4	70·2
$12\frac{1}{2}$ *in* × 21 *in*	6 *at* 1 *in*	10·4	4·96	97·6	91·3

Sections of steel sheet piling which have their interlocks in the flanges may be considered to develop the full section modulus of an undivided wall of piling. Sections of steel sheet piling with interlocks along the centre line or neutral axis of the sheeting may be assumed to develop the full strength of the undivided section when the piling is driven to normal depths into sand, gravel, clay or other similar material. The shear forces in the interlocks may then be considered as resisted by friction due to the pressure at the walings and the restraint exercised by the soil. If the piling passing through very soft clay or similar material is prevented by rock from penetrating to the normal depth of cut-off, the inner and outer piles of each pair should be connected to one another by welding, pressing or other means to ensure that the interlock common to the pair can develop the necessary shear resistance. If this precaution is not carried out, the section modulus should be reduced below that of the undivided section.

The actual allowable driving resistance will be less than the maximum if the unsupported length of the pile exceeds the critical value: the proportion of the maximum that can safely be taken by various types of pile is given in TABLE 13 for various ratios of length to radius of gyration.

The unsupported length of the pile, during driving, should be taken as the height from the point where it is restrained by being held in the leads of a pile frame to a point either at one tenth of the exposed length below the surface of good ground or at half the penetration into soft clay or silt. In either instance any liquid mud should be neglected.

If the top of the pile is not restrained the unsupported length should be taken as twice the height from the top of the pile to the point indicated above.

Walings, which may be of timber, steel or reinforced concrete, are designed as continuous beams transmitting load from the piles to the anchor ties. Timber or steel walings should be used with timber piles, steel or reinforced concrete walings with steel piles, and reinforced concrete walings with reinforced concrete piles.

Joints in walings should be at the points of minimum bending moment *i.e.* at the one fifth point in the span, and should be staggered. The webs of steel walings may have to be stiffened at the points where the anchor ties are attached. Typical constructional details are shown in *Figures 54* and *55*.

TABLE 13

REDUCTION OF DRIVING RESISTANCE FOR VARIOUS RATIOS OF l/r

(From Code of Practice for Foundations)

Ratio of length to least radius of gyration	Timber	Reinforced concrete	Steel to B.S. 15 : 1948	Steel to B.S. 548 : 1934	Cast iron
0	1·00		1·00	1·00	1·0
10	0·98		0·99	0·99	0·9
20	0·95		0·96	0·96	0·8
30	0·93		0·92	0·92	0·7
40	0·89		0·89	0·88	0·6
50	0·82	1·0	0·84	0·83	0·5
60	0·72	0·9	0·78	0·76	0·4
70	0·61	0·8	0·72	0·67	0·3
80	0·50	0·7	0·65	0·58	0·2
90	0·41	0·6	0·58	0·48	0·1
100	0·34	0·5	0·51	0·40	
110	0·28	0·4	0·45	0·34	
120	0·24	0·3	0·39	0·29	
130	0·21		0·34	0·25	
140	0·18		0·30	0·22	
150	0·16		0·27	0·19	

Tie rods should be of mild steel or wrought iron rounds and the maximum tensile stress should be limited to 7 ton/sq in (11 kg/sq mm), and 5 ton/sq in (8 kg/sq mm) respectively. The ends of the rods may be 'upset' so that the threading does not reduce the cross sectional area.

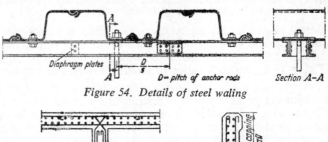

Figure 54. Details of steel waling

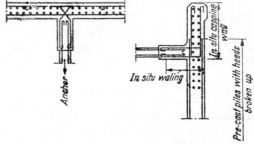

Figure 55. Details of reinforced concrete waling

Anchorages may consist of concrete blocks, reinforced concrete or sheet pile walls, or sets of raker piles. The design of groups of raker piles is dealt with in ref. 21. When designing block anchorages care should be taken that the spacing is such that any 'end resistance' assumed in addition must be placed at such a distance behind the sheet pile wall that the full passive pressure can be developed: the minimum distance is shown in *Figure 56*. For the determination of the passive resistance of these anchorages see p 36. The protection of the piles against corrosion will require consideration. It is often advantageous to connect anchor piles to the sheet pile wall by means of a relieving platform which applies a vertical load to the anchor piles and so relieves the uplift on the tension piles in the group, *Figure 57*. For notes on driving piles, use of taper piles *etc* see chapter on Works Construction, vol. 4.

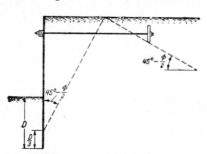

Figure 56. Disposition of anchorage relative to wall

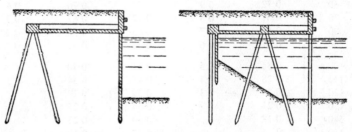

Figure 57. Relieving platforms

KING PILE WALLS

King pile walls consist of horizontal sheeting spanning between 'king' piles. The sheeting is only carried to a depth sufficient to prevent spewing up of the material from behind the wall, whereas the king piles are driven to the penetration that is necessary to provide adequate passive resistance. King pile walls, like sheet pile walls, may be of the cantilever or tied type, and may be of timber, steel or reinforced concrete. Such walls are frequently advantageous, particularly if they are so designed that the sheeting can be slipped into position in the previously driven king piles as excavation proceeds. The king piles are designed as single piles subject to transverse loads. The pressure diagram is determined as described on p 39. The unit passive pressure required on the embedded part of the king pile will normally be fairly high and should be carefully checked.

FREE BRIDGE ABUTMENTS

Bridge abutments may be broadly divided into abutments for girder bridges which carry mainly vertical loads from the superstructure, abutments for arch bridges, and anchorages for suspension bridges.

The most simple type of abutment is the buried pier, *Figure 58*, a normal pier buried in the approach embankment. In addition to the loads from the superstructure the pier is subjected to the difference between the active pressure of the earth on the 'land' side and the amount of passive pressure on the 'air' side which can be developed by the amount of tilt that can occur. The pier, however, should be designed to resist the difference between the active pressures on the two sides.

Figure 58. Bridge with buried pier abutments

The most common type of abutment is the retaining wall type with wing walls. The wing walls may be parallel to the abutment face, inclined, or parallel to the bridge axis. Parallel or inclined wing walls should normally be separated from the abutment by a contraction joint: such wing walls, and the abutment, are designed as retaining walls to resist the full active earth pressure. Wing walls which are parallel to the bridge axis *i.e.* perpendicular to the abutment, may be continuous with the abutment and should be tied across so that the overturning moments are neutralized. If such walls are of masonry they should be founded in the natural ground, but if these, and the abutment, are of reinforced concrete, they may be flying wings, *Figure 59*, and only extend a sufficient depth into the embankment to prevent the soil from spewing out beneath them. A further

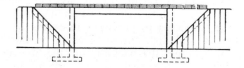

Figure 59. Bridge with flying wing walls

development of this type of abutment is that with flying wings and a relieving slab, known in Germany as a 'knapsack' abutment, *Figures 60* and *61*. In this type the earth pressure is reduced to a minimum. The type illustrated in *Figure 61* is in essence the same as the old arch type abutment or arch type approach.

The foundations of abutments do not differ in essentials from those of other structures.

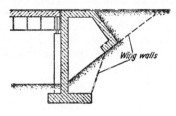

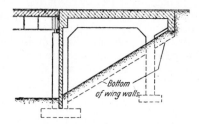

Figure 60. 'Knapsack' abut-
ment

Figure 61. Portal abutment
(Wilson)

In abutments for arch bridges the horizontal thrust from the arch is usually the predominating load, exceeding the earth pressure. The active earth pressure only should be considered in calculations on the stability of the abutment, but earth pressure at rest should be considered in relation to the strength of the abutment structure, and in relation to the strength of the arch when it is greater than the minimum arch thrust. Common types of arch abutment are shown in *Figure 62*a to c.

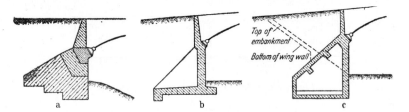

Figure 62. Common types of arch abutment

Suspension bridges are rarely constructed except for great spans. Anchorages for suspension bridges must be constructed so that there is no risk of translation or rotation. Earth pressure at rest should be considered to act on the land side and a high factor of safety should be taken on the passive resistance. The cable passages and anchorages should be accessible for maintenance.

FIXED RETAINING WALLS

'Fixed' retaining walls, such as basement walls and the abutments of arched and portal framed bridges, cannot yield by rotation at the toe and so may, and probably will, be subjected to pressures in excess of the active earth pressure. The intensity and distribution of earth pressure on such walls depends essentially on whether the backfill, and the adjacent soil included within a wedge rising from the heel of the wall at an angle ϕ to the horizontal, is cohesionless or cohesive.

It has been customary to assume that the earth pressure against such walls at any level is the vertical intergranular pressure multiplied by the ' coefficient of earth pressure at rest ', K_0, and to take K_0 as 0·4 to 0·5 in cohesionless materials and 0·8 to 1·0 in cohesive materials. It is not generally realized that K_0 varies with the depth and that the values given above are only applicable at considerable depths. In cohesionless soils K_0 is likely to be 1·0 to 1·5 at the surface and to decrease hyperbolically to 0·4 to 0·5 at a depth of 6 to 8 ft, if the backfill has been compacted in 6 in to 9 in layers, see *Figure 63*. In cohesive soils, which swell after rainy weather and shrink after dry weather, the horizontal pressure at any depth can exceed the vertical pressure by twice the cohesion of the soil *i.e.* we have (after rain):

$$\sigma_h = \sigma_v + 2c$$
$$= \gamma z + 2c \qquad \ldots\ldots\ldots\ldots(8)$$

where σ_h is the horizontal pressure, σ_v the vertical pressure, c the cohesion of soil, γ the unit wt of soil, z the depth below the surface

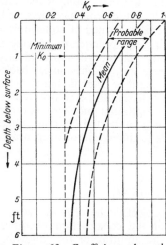

Figure 63. Coefficient of earth pressure at rest in cohesionless fills (Wilson)

and $\quad K_0 = \dfrac{\sigma_h}{\sigma_v} = 1 + \dfrac{2c}{\gamma z} \qquad \ldots\ldots\ldots\ldots(9)$

which tends to unity at considerable depths: c, the cohesion may be taken for design purposes as that of clay with the maximum water content attained in the wet season at a depth of 1 ft below the surface.

Basement walls should always be designed for full water pressure to the maximum level to which the ground water can rise as well as submerged earth pressure, unless absolutely certain means of drainage are provided, when the wall may be designed for drained earth pressure.

BACKFILL AND DRAINAGE

The design and construction of the backfill and drainage must be so arranged that the wall cannot be subjected to a load greater than that for which it was designed.

A large diameter longitudinal drain pipe should be provided at the back of the wall just above the front ground level, or just above low water level if the front of the wall is partly submerged. This longitudinal drain should have branches leading to weepholes through the wall at close centres. Weepholes that may be submerged should be provided with non-return flap valves. The drain should consist of open jointed earthenware, porous concrete or pierced metal pipe: it should be bedded on a layer of impermeable soil and otherwise surrounded with a layer of 1½ to 2 in broken stone such as would be used as coarse aggregate for mass concrete. To ensure minimum pressure on the wall the general backfill should be of clean broken stone, broken brick, gravel, sand or any other pervious material or materials, and the whole must be designed as an inverted filter between the natural ground backing and the layer of coarse aggregate above the longitudinal drain pipe. An example of good practice in backfilling is shown in *Figure 64*.

Cohesive backfill should not be used in such a way that it can exert pressure on the wall unless the wall has been designed to resist such pressure. When cohesive soils have to be retained by a 'free' retaining wall it may be advisable to excavate some of the cohesive bank and substitute a cohesionless filling, see *Figure 45*. Such a course is particularly necessary if the ground rises behind the wall. In general, drainage of the backfill behind basement retaining walls is not possible. Precautions must be taken in placing the backfill behind the abutments of road bridges to avoid settlement which would give rise to a depression in the surface of the road. A temporary surface is often laid adjacent to new abutments and replaced after settlement has occurred.

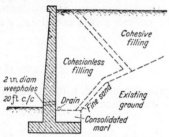

Figure 64. *Typical arrangement of backfill and drainage*

If the bank is formed of cohesionless material, it is good practice to provide a wedge of cohesionless backfill: this, if correctly placed, will taper off any consolidation or swelling of the bank of cohesive soil. Cohesionless backfill should be compacted in layers by vibratory plant or track laying tractors to a density above the critical. Cohesive backfill should be compacted in layers by rollers to maximum dry density at optimum moisture content subject to the proviso that it should not be overcompacted *i.e.* compacted to a void ratio less than that which corresponds to the weight of overburden above it.

INSPECTION AND TESTING

The construction of retaining walls should be subject to the same inspection and testing as is necessary in the course of the construction of other foundations, see pp 123, 134 and 146, with the addition of the following precautions during the placing of the backfill. The following points should be checked: that the weepholes have been constructed at the correct spacing and elevation and are unobstructed; that the bed for the drainpipe is laid and compacted to specific levels; that the drain pipe and branches to weepholes are laid to specified lines and levels and are unobstructed; that grain size distribution of each type of backfill material and of parent soil is satisfactory; and that various layers of backfill are placed with the specified degree of compaction to the specified lines and levels. In the case of large wells it is desirable to keep a check on line and verticality during the period when the load is coming on the wall to find out whether any movement is occurring.

EARTHWORK

FILLING

Filling is usually placed by large capacity pneumatic tyred vehicles, either automotive or pulled by track-laying tractors, which spread the spoil in thin layers; the layers are partly compacted by the vehicles themselves and are further spread by bulldozers and compacted by rollers, smooth wheel, pneumatic tyred, by sheepsfoot or by special vibratory equipment. See also chapters on Soil Mechanics and on Railways, vol. 4 For notes on the use of modern earth moving equipment see chapter on Works Construction, vol. 4.

It has been shown by Proctor that the degree of compaction which can be attained by the use of any particular type of compacting machinery is dependent on the water content of the soil at the time of compaction, that the heavier the machine the greater the degree of compaction obtainable, and moreover that the compaction obtainable in the field can be reproduced in the laboratory.

The Proctor test now known in Great Britain as the British Standard Compaction Test, is described in B.S. 1377.

A study of the subject demonstrates the importance of maintaining the correct water content during the process of compaction. It is apparent that it is easy to add water to material that is too dry, but the ease and cost of removing it from material that is too wet depends upon the warmth, dryness and reliability of the climate. The tolerance in the dry weight of the compacted material must be such that the soil will still be suited to its purpose in the zero air voids (or saturated) condition corresponding to the minimum allowed dry weight. The minimum weight should be representative of an appreciable volume of fill.

Filling, if of suitable material and if properly placed and compacted, can be used without risk of undue settlement as a foundation for even large structures. The old and well based fear of ' made ground ' as a foundation arose from the placing of fills by side and end tipping and the fact that much of the so-called ' ground ' consisted of various kinds of rubbish. Such fill should, of course, be avoided as a foundation. The conditions that are necessary in order that the fill may be satisfactory as a foundation are: *i* that the strata below the fill are of adequate strength and consistency to carry the fill and the superimposed structures without failure or undue settlement; *ii* that the material to be used for filling is *a* suitable and *b* properly placed and compacted. Regarding *i*, reference should be made to pp 108-122, regarding *ii*, available materials should be tested, and, if suitable, compacted as described in TABLE 14 and the following paragraphs.

TABLE 14

SELECTION AND COMPACTION OF MATERIALS FOR FILLING

Type of fill	Tests	Method of compaction
Rock, rubble or shingle, or coarse gravel	Grain size distribution. Finer material should be added, if necessary, so that all voids, down to 1/16 in, are filled	By smooth wheeled roller (preferably vibratory) or track laying tractor in layers which may be up to 18 in deep but should be selected after test fills have been made. Careful control of compaction
Medium gravels and sands, fine sands	As above	By vibratory rollers, plate vibrators or smooth wheeled rollers in layers which may be up to 12 in. Careful control of compacted dry weight
Silts and soft clays	Unlikely to be suitable	
Stiff and medium clays	Proctor compaction tests should be carried out to find optimum moisture content. Specification limits of dry weight should be decided upon and unconfined compression and triaxial tests should be carried out on specimens compacted in this range of dry weight and soaked after compaction. Material having a cohesion less than 1/2 ton/sq ft when soaked should usually be rejected	By smooth wheeled, or rubber tyred, or sheepsfoot roller in 6 to 9 in layers with careful control of moisture content and compacted dry weight

Test fills should be made in connection with any job of considerable magnitude and the results correlated with the Proctor compaction tests. Compaction plant should be chosen that will give the design density with an economic number of passes.

Field control is important. A site laboratory should be set up and dry weight determinations should be carried out systematically in such number that any weak patches can be detected and recompacted without delay to the work.

For an example of the use of fill for the support of the foundations of an important building see ref. 27.

IMPROVEMENT OF POOR GROUND

There are three principal methods by which improvement of poor ground may be effected, each applicable only to one type of ground. These are: *1* accelerated consolidation of clays and silts by vertical drains (this page) or by temporarily loading the surface of the ground. *2* artificial cementing of gravels and sands, p 171; *3* compaction of sands and gravels by vibration, p 171.

In addition, peat may be displaced by other material with the help of explosives, p 171.

For further details of all these methods see chapter on Soil Mechanics.

ACCELERATED CONSOLIDATION OF CLAYS AND SILTS

Clays and silts which are incompletely consolidated under their own weight, or which would take a very long time to consolidate normally under an added load imposed by filling and/or structures, may be caused to consolidate much more rapidly by the installation of vertical drains. The physical reason for this phenomenon is, of course, that the path of the water which is squeezed out during consolidation can be shortened to any desired extent according to the spacing of the drains. KJELLMANN[28] has given diagrams from which the necessary spacing of drains of any diameter can be determined according to the time available for consolidation. Two types of drain have been used successfully, sand wells, about 18 in (45 cm) diameter, in America and cardboard 'wicks' in Sweden. The methods are fully described in papers by STANTON[29] and KJELLMANN[28].

Drains have often to be installed on ground too soft to carry the plant necessary for their installation. A sufficient layer of suitable fill is first placed on the ground: the drains are then constructed by machinery running on this layer. On completion of the drains (sand or wick) a layer of highly permeable material about one foot thick is spread, to collect and discharge the water from the drains, before further fill is placed.

Material for filling sand drains and material for the permeable drainage layer should be as shown in TABLE 15.

TABLE 15

TYPE AND GRADING OF MATERIALS

(*From* STANTON[29])

For filling sand drains clean sand		For permeable layer clean coarse sand or gravel	
Sieve size	Per cent passing sieve	Sieve size	Per cent passing sieve
½ in	90 *to* 100	⅜ in	80 *to* 100
No. 8	25 *to* 100	No. 8	5 *to* 50
No. 30	5 *to* 50	No. 30	0 *to* 20
No. 50	0 *to* 20	No. 50	0 *to* 5
No. 100	0 *to* 3		

ARTIFICIAL CEMENTING OF GRAVELS AND SANDS

Artificial cementing of the ground is often referred to as 'consolidation'; it is not consolidation in the soil mechanics sense and this term should therefore be avoided. Artificial cementing may be by means of cement grout or by means of chemical solutions and emulsions. *Figure 65,* taken from a paper by GLOSSOP and SKEMPTON[30], shows the approximate limits of grading of soil susceptible to treatment by these means. Artificial cementing is still as much an art as a science and is a field in which a few contractors have specialized: such firms' advice should be sought where possible.

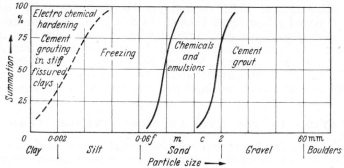

Figure 65. Artificial cementing. Approximate limits of grading of soil for various processes (GLOSSOP and SKEMPTON[30])

COMPACTION OF SANDS AND GRAVELS BY VIBRATION

Sands and gravels, particularly those which are deposited in a loose state, may be compacted by vibration produced by explosives, by driving sand-piles, or by vibratory machinery.

In compaction by explosives buried charges, placed in boreholes, are detonated. The charges should be sufficient to shake the whole mass to be compacted and to fracture the surface of the ground without forming craters. LYMAN[31] has described the first known use of this method.

Compaction by 'sand piles' is carried out by driving a tube, such as is used for the formation of cast *in situ* concrete piles, and then forming the 'shaft' in the normal manner, except that cement is not used, only sand, ballast or other stone aggregate. The vibration due to driving the tube causes compaction of the sand stratum and further compaction is caused if the 'shaft' is formed by ramming.

Vibratory machinery of various types has been used for the compaction of sands and gravels. Deep strata have been successfully compacted by a patented device called a *Vibroflot,* which is similar to, but much larger than, a 'needle' vibrator as used for the compaction of concrete, and is so arranged that water may be forced into the sand at the place where it is being vibrated. STEUERMANN[32, 33] has described the method in two papers.

DISPLACEMENT OF PEAT BY EXPLOSIVES

Roads have been constructed across peat bogs on embankments of sand or gravel constructed by building the banks, oversize, on top of the peat, digging trenches in the peat alongside, and displacing the peat below the banks by detonation of explosive charges placed in the peat in boreholes through the fill. The process has not so far been used for the foundations of structures, but offers interesting possibilities. See also chapter on Railways, vol. 4.

GENERAL EXCAVATION

Notes on modern excavating machinery will be found in the chapter on Works Construction, vol. 4. This section will only deal with points in construction that are of importance to the finished project.

Excavations, particularly in cohesive soils, should be kept free from water, as ponding will lead to swelling which is likely to raise the moisture content above that at which the soil can be compacted. Any unstable ground or tipped refuse found below formation level should be excavated and replaced by good material. Trees standing in areas where there is more than about 2 ft of cut or 4 ft of fill should be felled: elsewhere trees should, where possible, be preserved. Vertical and other temporary faces should be limited to such heights as are suitable to the nature of the soil in order to prevent slips or slides extending beyond the intended limits of excavation.

EXCAVATION IN PIT AND TRENCH: TRENCH TIMBERING

Much excavation in pit and trench is still carried out by hand: the use of machinery, which is increasing, is not without its present dangers as strutting and bracing is an obvious hindrance and it is a temptation to the man on the site to risk the omission of as much as he can get away with. This means that although the timbering of hand dug trenches up to about twenty feet deep is an art based on long experience and can safely be left to the man on the site in normal circumstances, experience of timbering mechanically excavated trenches is of short duration and an insufficient background for use without the aid of engineering knowledge.

The question of pressures on trench timbering is discussed fully on pp 342-353 of the book by TERZAGHI and PECK[34]. The results are generally summarized in *Figures 66* and *67*, which give the pressures recommended for adoption in the design of the timbering of cuts in sand or gravel, above the water table and in inorganic clays of medium plasticity respectively.

In *Figure 66* P_A is the Coulomb active pressure at depth H, $\delta = 0$ if no part of timbering extends below the bottom of the trench, $\delta = \frac{1}{2}\varphi$ if timbering can resist the downward thrust. Average values of φ are:

	Round grains	*Angular grains*
Loose sand	28°	34°
Dense sand	35°	45°

In *Figure 67* γ is the unit weight of clay, c_0 half the unconfined compression strength. In both cases loads in the struts are calculated on the basis of hinged joints at A, A' etc.

There are insufficient measurements of pressures caused by other materials to justify recommendations: no opportunity of taking and reporting such measurements should be missed.

If a trench is to be dug to below the ground water level in a cohesionless soil it is necessary either to lower the ground water to below the trench bottom by means of well points, when the recommendations in *Figure 66* apply, or to drive sheeting to such a depth below the trench bottom that the seepage water will not cause a 'blow' in the bottom, see p 29; the water pressure on the sheeting, as determined from the flow net, will have to be added to the earth pressure.

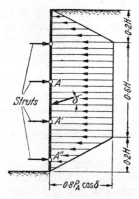

Figure 66. Pressure on trench timbering in sands and gravels (TERZAGHI and PECK[34])

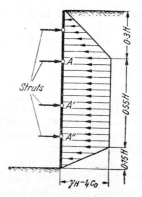

Figure 67. Pressure on trench timbering in inorganic clays of medium plasticity (TERZAGHI and PECK[34])

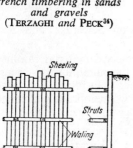

Figure 68. Trench timbering—sheeting, waling and struts

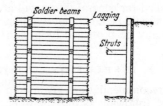

Figure 69. Trench timbering—lagging, soldier beams and struts

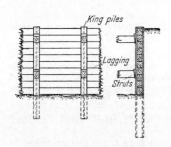

Figure 70. Trench timbering—king piles, lagging and struts

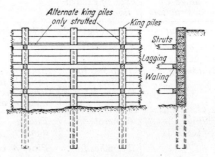

Figure 71. Trench timbering—king piles, lagging, walings and struts

When excavating a trench in clay it is important that the strutting should be so tightly wedged or jacked that no movement of the retained soil can occur, as very high pressures can be built up once any movement starts.

Figures 68 to *71* show common methods of timbering.

When an excavation for a basement is wider than can conveniently be spanned by struts, it is usual first to construct the basement retaining wall in trench round the periphery and then to excavate the remaining dumpling of earth. In very large and deep basements internal stanchion foundations have been constructed in pits in the dumpling and the ground floor constructed to act as strutting to the retaining wall, before the dumpling is excavated. Where there is more than one basement level the dumpling has been excavated in stages, the sub-basement floors being inserted one by one as additional strutting.

If the soil is exceptionally soft or liable to excessive swelling it may be advisable to excavate the dumpling in narrow vertical slices in trenches, instead of horizontal slices as above, in order to expose as small an area of bottom as possible at one time and to keep as large an area as possible under the restraint of the previously superincumbent earth or the completed strips of basement floor.

The treatment of the bottom of trenches and pits depends on whether they have been excavated for the purpose of constructing foundations or laying services. The final 6 in of depth of foundation pits and trenches should not be excavated until immediately before the concrete foundation or screed is placed. If this precaution is not taken the bottom may be seriously weakened by exposure to the weather and to traffic. For notes on trenches for laying services see chapters on Sewerage and Sewage Disposal, vol. 4, and Water Supplies, vol. 4.

The backfilling of trenches should be of selected material rammed in such layers and at such a water content that the minimum dry densities specified for general filling will at least be attained. In foundation trenches care should be taken not to damage any waterproof membrane which should normally be protected by a skin of brick on edge or other suitable means.

INSPECTION AND TESTING OF EARTHWORK

The recommendations given on p 123 should be followed, together with such of the following as may be applicable.

TABLE 16

INSPECTION OF EXCAVATION AND FILLING

Stage of construction	Type of excavation or filling	Check that :
Setting out	General excavation and filling	All important survey points are referenced to points outside the area of cut and fill
Bottoming	Trenches for services	Bottom is true to line and level to receive pipe or conduit, being made up with a layer of soft material where necessary in stony ground; jointing holes are made at all sockets
Filling	General	Filling is being compacted to specified minimum density
	Trenches for services	Pipes or conduits have been tested and approved by engineers before filling is commenced; any haunching specified is carried out before filling is commenced. Filling to 6 in over top of pipe or conduit is placed by hand and rammed in 3 in layers with wooden rammers to specified dry density; filling above this level is compacted to specified dry density

UNDERPINNING

Underpinning may be defined as the construction of foundations for a building that is already in place. It may be necessary for three reasons: *i* if the existing foundation is insufficient; *ii* if excavation for a new structure to be constructed alongside has to be carried close to or below the foundation level of the existing structure; and *iii* if it is necessary to carry a new structure underneath an existing structure.

Because the safety of the existing structure is of paramount importance underpinning must be carried out piecemeal and with great care. In all instances it is advisable to start by making a careful survey of the construction and condition of the existing structure. It is frequently necessary, as a preliminary, to afford temporary support to the existing structure. Many normal foundation methods are used in underpinning; the ramming of piles or sheet piling must generally be avoided, however, because the vibration may be harmful. Certain special methods are employed *viz* excavation in pits with horizontal sheeting and jacking down of tubular piles and caissons. When the new foundation has been constructed load must be transferred to it; this is usually done by a combination of dry packing and ' pre-testing '. The following four sections deal with the survey, the preliminaries, the construction of the new foundation, and the bringing of this foundation into use. PRENTIS and WHITE[35] give much valuable information on the subject.

SURVEY OF EXISTING STRUCTURE

Where possible record plans should be obtained from the local building authority, otherwise the structure should be thoroughly examined so that drawings of all constructional features can be made. A careful joint examination of the structure should then be made by representatives of the owners, of the owners of the new structures, and of the contractors. This examination should include the taking of such levels and measurements as will make it possible to detect any horizontal or vertical movements, and a careful survey of existing cracks or other defects. It is advisable to have photographs taken of all elevations, internal walls and partitions : the extent of cracks should be recorded by a cross mark at each end and by lines ruled across the crack at intervals so that displacements both across and along the crack can be detected, see *Figure 72*.

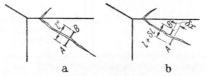

a   b

Figure 72. ' Tell tale ' for crack a at time of measurement b after movement

TEMPORARY SUPPORT

Temporary support is required if a structure is settling rapidly due to an insufficient foundation, if it is necessary to construct a new structure beneath it, or if its base is too small to be underpinned in sections. Temporary support is generally unnecessary if the foundation is stable and so large that about one sixth of its area can be underpinned at one time. Such support may be afforded by the use of shores, needle beams, the strengthening and joining together of footings for mutual support, or by combinations of these methods.

Shores are raking members taking load from a structure at some point, usually a floor level, capable of taking the horizontal component of the thrust, and transferring this load to a temporary foundation at a suitable distance from the structure, *Figure 73*. The foot of the shore is wedged against the temporary foundation: sometimes it is advisable to incorporate a screw jack in the foot of the shore. If the structure cannot resist the horizontal thrust concentrated at the head of the shore this can be distributed by means of a bracket and angle iron steps notched into masonry joints or other slots cut in the face of the structure, *Figure 74*. If the bottom of the wall needs vertical support, a ' figure four ' shore can be used[36].

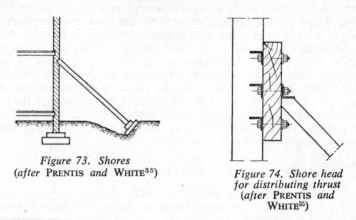

Figure 73. Shores
(after PRENTIS *and* WHITE[35]*)*

Figure 74. Shore head for distributing thrust (after PRENTIS *and* WHITE[35]*)*

Needles, or needle beams, are beams passed through a wall, or attached to two faces of a stanchion, transferring load to temporary foundations on both sides of the part supported[37].

Individual foundations may be joined together so that any one is supported by its neighbour while it is being underpinned. This is commonly done by incorporating a grillage of rolled steel joists into the foundations, *Figure 75*; a very neat application of pre-stressed concrete for this purpose was devised by FREYSSINET[38].

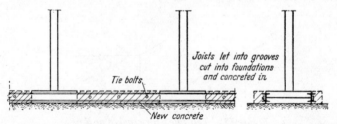

Figure 75. Grillage uniting foundations (after PRENTIS and WHITE[35]*)*

SPECIAL METHODS OF FOUNDATION CONSTRUCTION

Excavation for underpinning is carried out in pits which are often as little as 4 ft square. It is necessary first to construct an approach pit by the side of the foundation to be underpinned and to carry it to such a depth that there is working headroom under the foundation and the actual underpinning pit can be commenced.

The approach pit and the upper portion of the underpinning pit may conveniently be sheeted by the box sheeting method: horizontal boards about 2 in × 6 in to 2 in × 8 in (for a 5 ft pit) opposite pairs of which are side cleated, see *Figure 76*, are placed one by one in trenches dug round the periphery.

This method of sheeting is also used for further deepening of pits in sand or in other cohesionless materials. It is, of course, most important to prevent loss of ground from behind the sheeting. If any ground is lost it should be repacked immediately: this can be done through horizontal slots left between the boards, which may be kept apart by edge cleats at each end, *Figure 76*. Prentice and White recommend salt hay, held at the back of the boards by projecting nails, as being of considerable assistance in retaining ground and they also recommend that the boards be bevelled top and bottom, except at the ends, in order to facilitate re-packing: these recommendations are illustrated in *Figure 77*.

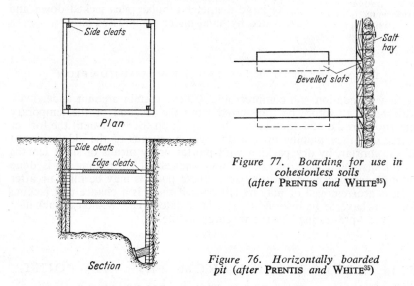

Figure 77. Boarding for use in cohesionless soils (after PRENTIS *and* WHITE[35])

Figure 76. Horizontally boarded pit (after PRENTIS *and* WHITE[35])

If excavation is being carried down through dry sand wetting may help as it gives the sand some virtual cohesion. In clay of medium stiffness the Chicago well method can be used, excavation being carried ahead of the sheeting in steps of two to five ft.

If the desired foundation stratum lies above ground water level, either the natural ground water level or the level to which the ground water can be lowered by well points, the underpinning can be carried out entirely by excavation in pits. If a wall is being underpinned pits should be set out in groups of six and excavated in rotation, *Figure 78*. If the presence of ground water prevents pits being dug to the desired bearing stratum, or where this process is uneconomic, tubular piles may be jacked down in sections. Such piles are usually 12 to 24 in (30 to 60 cm) diam and are made of $\frac{5}{16}$ or $\frac{3}{8}$ in (10 mm) thick steel in sections 2 to 4 ft long. The sections are ended accurately at right angles to the axis and are joined by

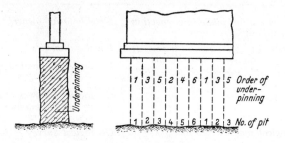

Figure 78. Order of underpinning (after PRENTIS *and* WHITE[35])

Figure 79. Sectional jacked tubular pile (after PRENTIS *and* WHITE[35])

internal sleeves, *Figure 79*. Each section is cleaned out before the following one is put on and sunk, unless soil is 'blowing' into the bottom, when a sufficient 'plug' of soil is left. FREYSSINET[38] attained the same result by the use of a very ingenious pre-stressed concrete tubular pile formed in sections.

Pneumatic caissons from 2 ft 6 in or 3 ft 0 in up to 5 or 6 ft diam have also been used. These are really large diameter tubular piles jacked down and excavated by hand under compressed air.

TRANSFERRING LOAD TO NEW FOUNDATION

The new foundation will compress and settle a certain amount under load. Load should therefore be transferred from the original or the temporary foundations to the new foundations by jacking on the latter until the former are free and then pinning up the structure by means of the old fashioned slates in mortar, by dry packing with mortar or by means of short lengths of steel joists and pairs of steel folding wedges. The building up is done so as to leave pockets round the jacks; these pockets may be filled up after the jacks are removed or may be left open if there is a chance that jacking may again have to be resorted to at a later date. The method of jacking[39] was named ' pre-testing ' by the inventor, White.

SITE EXPLORATION FROM THE VIEWPOINT OF THE DESIGNING ENGINEER

EXTENT AND DEPTH OF EXPLORATION

The extent of exploration that is necessary depends upon the available knowledge of the nature of the soil at the site and upon the magnitude and nature of the proposed structure.

The knowledge of soil conditions that may be available may include any or all of the items tabulated in TABLE 17.

TABLE 17

POSSIBLE SOURCES OF INFORMATION CONCERNING SOIL CONDITIONS

No.	Information available	Probable source in Great Britain
1	Site explorations made in connection with adjoining structures	Neighbouring owners
2	Records of foundation loads of existing structures and details of construction together with examination of present condition	Local authorities Personal examination
3	Borings for wells	Geological Survey, memoirs on county water supplies, well borers, adjoining owners, local authorities
4	Geological maps	Geological Survey
5	No information	

The proposed structure may vary between the pairs of limits given in TABLE 18.

The extent of site exploration necessary will vary from a minimum, or even nil, in the case of a combination of site and structure indicated by a low number in TABLE 17 and small case letters in TABLE 18 to quite an extensive survey that may be necessary in the combination indicated by a high number and capital letters. The extent of site exploration will also depend on the skill and experience of the engineer responsible.

TABLE 18

TYPE OF STRUCTURE PROPOSED

a compact or *A* extensive

b light or *B* heavy, and

c of a type similar in nature and magnitude to structures of which there is local experience, or *C* of a type of which there is no local experience

A site exploration should be planned in two stages: first, a few preliminary borings by quick and cheap methods to indicate the nature and extent of the various strata, and, secondly, a set of final borings laid out and made in such a way as to obtain the test samples that have been found to be required.

The preliminary exploration may be effected by dry sample borings, wash borings, or penetration tests.

The final borings should be such that undisturbed samples can be taken. If no gravel or stony strata are present 2 in diam seamless tube samplers may be used with a $2\frac{1}{2}$ in casing to considerable depths. If coarse grained or stony strata are found, a 6 in casing will be required and will permit the taking of 4 or 5 in diam undisturbed samples. Normal British practice is, however, to require boreholes of 6 in min diam in all cases.

Exploration should extend to the greatest depth at which the soil may be subjected to a dangerous increase of stress or at which the stress may be sufficient to cause undesirable consolidation. The increase of stress to which a sand or a gravel may be subjected with safety increases rapidly with depth. In a uniform bed of cohesive material such as clay or silt however the allowable increase of stress due to a rapidly applied load is sensibly constant whatever the depth: the shear stress should nowhere exceed the cohesion of the material. It is necessary, therefore, to seek to prove the presence or absence of any clay strata within a certain range of depth below the bottom of the foundation and to obtain samples from such strata.

Various criteria for the estimation of this depth are in use. In the United States the ready rule is 'to one and a half times the least width of the building': in Germany the multiple of the building width is made to depend upon the average bearing pressure, taken over the whole area of the base. The 'width of the building' is taken as the overall width of the building and not the width of individual foundations, unless the distance from centre to centre of individual foundations exceeds five times their width, when the most unfavourable condition is found by consideration of an individual base.

The maximum shearing stresses caused by a single strip load at the surface of an elastic material are shown in *Figure 80*. The maximum shear stress at any point P, P' is $\quad \tau_{\text{max}} = \dfrac{q_c}{\pi} \sin 2\alpha = \dfrac{q_c}{\pi} \cdot \dfrac{z/b}{1 + (z/b)^2}$ ....(10)

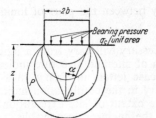

Figure 80. Maximum shearing stresses caused by a single strip load at the surface of an elastic material (Paper No. 15, Instn civ. Engrs., Figure 8, 1946)

This shows, then, that the effect of the American 'rule' is to require exploration to the depth at which the maximum shear stress is 19 per cent of the bearing pressure. If $q_c = 3c$, $z =$ depth at which $\tau = 0.6c$. This is quite logical in a uniform stratum. The German rule for a building the length of which is more than twice its width, and its effects, are given in TABLE 19.

TABLE 19

DEPTH OF EXPLORATION BY GERMAN RULE

Bearing pressure ton/sq ft q_c	Depth of exploration divided by 2b	Maximum shear stress divided by q_c	Maximum shear stress ton/sq ft
1	1	0·255	0·255
2	2	0·150	0·300
3	3	0·103	0·309
5	4	0·063	0·315

In a building the length of which is less than twice its width the German rule requires exploration to eight tenths of the depth given above. This is because the stresses are then rather lower. The German rule is based on the assumption that clay with a shear strength of less than about 0·3 ton/sq ft (4·67 lb/sq in or 0·33 kg/sq cm), plus a factor of safety, will be unlikely to be encountered below the depth in question. It should be remembered that the depth is related to the overall least width of the structure and to the average bearing pressure over this width.

It is worth giving some consideration to these rules. They can be only a general guide to be applied where there is not a more reliable basis. These rules do not give either an upper or a lower limit: if rock is met with at less depth it will rarely be necessary to go deeper while on the other hand if such a depth has been reached and the strata are still alluvial it will be necessary to continue exploration at least to the maximum depth to which piles can be driven. If a hard stratum is found a sufficient number of borings should be sunk to determine the contours of this stratum. If a hard stratum is not found (as happens, for example, in the deltas of great rivers) a floating foundation is probably the best support for a large building and it is sufficient that the properties of the ground should be known to the depth that may be affected during construction, say to a depth below basement level at least equal to the width of the building.

The effect of the German rule which is shown in TABLE 19 leads to inquiry whether a depth from the surface can be assigned below which the cohesion of any clay or silt would always be greater than, say, $\frac{1}{2}$ ton/sq ft (0·55 kg/sq cm). It is probable that strata in the 'solid geology' have at least such a strength below the depth to which weathering extends, and that for alluvial strata no general limit can be set.

SUPERVISION

Boring operations should be closely supervised by the engineer responsible for the design of the building or structure. He should keep in day to day touch with proceedings so that he may order any modifications of the programme that are indicated by new information as it becomes available. The records to be kept are described on p 90.

TESTING OF SAMPLES AND PRESENTATION OF TEST RESULTS

The technique of testing is dealt with on p 1 *et seq*. This section is intended as a rough guide to the tests likely to be necessary in various instances. It will, of course, be realized that it is no more possible to specify what tests should be made in the general case than it is to suggest a definite scheme of exploratory borings. In either instance it is probable that the initial scheme will be modified as a result of what is learnt in the course of the work. A few hints may, however, be of value.

Sands and gravels do not often present problems as foundation materials. When a study of the material is justified the natural density should be determined: a knowledge of the failure characteristics of the material at this density and of the critical density will generally form an adequate basis for design. Cohesionless materials may, however, present problems in the execution of foundation works, especially if they are water bearing. The density and the permeability are then usually the most important factors: the permeability can probably best be determined in the field by the method of pumping into wells. It will also be necessary to determine the grain size distribution if filters will be required to prevent ' blows ' in pump sumps during construction.

In clays and silts the most important factors are natural water content, cohesion and compressibility. Atterberg limits should also be determined on a large proportion of samples as it will often be found that these simple tests, taken with the natural water content, form an index to properties only directly determinable by much more time consuming tests, for example, consolidation tests, and the requisite number of such tests may thereby be considerably reduced.

If the material is such that the use of piles might have to be considered the cohesion should be determined in the remoulded state as well as in the natural state. It is important to remember that soils are very variable and that single results cannot be relied upon. The data should be presented in the manner which permits of the greatest and simplest generalization.

ACKNOWLEDGEMENTS

The author is happy to acknowledge his indebtedness to Drs Terzaghi and Casagrande, who opened his eyes to the new developments in foundation engineering, and to the authors of all the papers and books to which reference is made. His particular thanks are due to the late Dr K. W. Mautner, who kindly gave permission for the use of the material from his paper on mining subsidence, which forms the basis of the section Mining Subsidence, p 147. The author is also indebted to his colleagues who have been so kind as to read the manuscript and make suggestions, and to G. M. J. Williams, M.A., A.M.I.C.E., who prepared many of the illustrations.

REFERENCES

[1] TAYLOR, D. W. *Fundamentals of Soil Mechanics* New York, 1948

[2] JACOBY, H. S. and DAVIS, R. P. *Foundations of Bridges and Buildings Figure 137h,* New York, 1925

[3] LACEY, G. Stable Channels in Alluvium and Uniform Flow in Alluvial Rivers and Canals *J. Instn civ. Engrs* 229 (1930) 259; 237 (1935) 421

[4] GARDNER, A. C. The Construction of Deep-Water Quays *ibid* 14 (1940) 129

[5] CAPPEL, C. G. Steel Caissons support New Orleans Dock *Civil Engineering* 13 (1943) 459

[6] CALLET, P. The Reconstruction of Le Havre Harbour *Société des Ingénieurs Civils de France, British Section,* 1948

[7] JACOBY, H. S. and DAVIS, R. P. *Foundations of Bridges and Buildings, Figures 84a and 86h* New York, 1925

[8] — *ibid, Figure 86a*

[9] KOEFOED, S. M. Four Cofferdams for Forty One Foundations *Engng. News Record, Figure 3* 123 (1939) 47

[10] HAYTER, H. *Proc. Instn civ. Engrs Figure 3* 22 (1863) Plate 17

[11] ANON. *Engng. News Record, Figure* 3 115 (1935) 39

[12] JACOBY, H. S. and DAVIS, R. P. *Foundations of Bridges and Buildings, Figure 27c* New York, 1925

[13] ANON. *Engng. News Record, Figure 4* 138 (1947) 452

[14] HELMERS, N. F. *Civil Engineering* 6 (1936) 444

[15] ENYEDI, BELA. *Oss. Metal, Figure 72* 7 (1948) 53

[16] JACOBY, H. S. and DAVIS, R. P. *Foundations of Bridges and Buildings, Figure 96b* New York, 1925

[17] — *ibid, Figures 86a and 71b*

[18] FOWLER, W. H. *Engng. News Record, Figure 3* 104 (1930) 67

[19] SAURIN, B. F. The design of reinforced concrete piles with special reference to the reinforcement *J. Instn civ. Engrs* 32 (1949) 80

[20] JACOBY, H. S. and DAVIS, R. P. *Foundations of Bridges and Buildings, Figure 145d* New York, 1925

[21] STROYER, R. *Concrete Structures in Marine Work, Figure 162* London

[22] WILSON, G. The Bearing Capacity of Screw Piles and Screwcrete Cylinders *J. Instn civ Engrs* 34 (1950) 4

[23] MAUTNER, K. W. Structures in Areas Subjected to Mining Subsidence *Structural Eng.* 26 (1948) 35

[24] CARLSON, H. Stability of Foundations on Permanently Frozen Ground *Proc. 2nd Internat. Conf. Soil Mech. and Foundation Engng.* Rotterdam 4 (1948) 51

[25] HEMSTOCK, R. A. Engineering in Canada's Mackenzie Valley *ibid* 4 (1948) 62

[26] TSCHEBOTARIOFF, G. P. and WARD, E. R. The Resonance of Machine Foundations and the Soil Coefficients which Affect It *ibid* 1 (1948) 309

[27] WATSON, J. D. and BRADLEY, O. R. *Engng. News Record* 135 (1945) 810

[28] KJELLMANN, W. Accelerated Consolidation of Fine Grained Soils by Means of Cardboard Wicks *Proc. 2nd Internat. Conf. Soil Mech. and Found. Engng.* 2 (1948) 302

[29] STANTON, T. E. Vertical Sand Drains as a Means of Foundation Consolidation and Accelerating Settlements of Embankments over Marsh *ibid* 5 (1948) 273

[30] GLOSSOP, R. and SKEMPTON, A. W. Particle Size in Silts and Sands *J. Instn civ. Engrs* 25 (1945) 81

[31] LYMAN, A. K. E. Compaction of Soils by Explosives *Civil Engng.* 10 (1940) 205

[32] STEUERMANN, S. Silt Consolidation by Vibro Flotation *Proc. 2nd Internat. Conf. Soil Mech. and Found. Engng.* 2 (1948) 297

[33] — A New Soil Compacting Device *Engng. News Record* 123 (1939) 87

[34] TERZAGHI, K. and PECK, R. B. *Soil Mechanics in Engineering Practice* New York, 1948

[35] PRENTIS, E. A. and WHITE, L. *Underpinning* Columbia, 1931

[36] — *ibid plate 14, Figure 1*

[37] — *ibid plate 12*

[38] FREYSSINET, M. *Une révolution dans les technique du Beton (A revolution in concrete techniques)* Paris, 1936

[39] PRENTIS, E. A. and WHITE, L. *Underpinning plate 62* Columbia, 1931

[40] B.S. Code of Practice CP 2001 : 1957 Site Investigations (formerly C.E. Code No. 1 Instn Civil Engineers)

[41] Code No. 4. Foundations (Instn Civil Engineers)

[42] Code No. 2. Earth Retaining Structures (Instn Civil Engineers)

[43] SKEMPTON, A. W. and MACDONALD, D. H. The allowable settlement of buildings *Proc. Instn civ. Engrs* 5, No. 3 (1956) 727

HYDRAULIC POWER PLANTS

CHARLES JAEGER, DR. ES SC. TECH [*]

THIS chapter deals mainly with hydraulic power plants that utilize the power of water flowing under a natural head, with or without storage in reservoirs. Schemes with pumped storage are being developed. Projects to utilize tidal energy are still only on paper, *e.g.* the Severn project in Great Britain and the Rance project in France.

I. THE HYDRO-ELECTRIC INDUSTRY[15-17]

GENERAL

The aim of the hydro-power industry is to produce, transmit and distribute electric energy, generated from hydraulic energy. The exploitation of hydro-power depends largely on natural conditions of climate, rainfall, availability of water all the year round, availability of head. The cost of hydro-power will also depend on the geological conditions.

A hydraulic machine or turbine will produce power N by using a discharge Q over a head H, or better a net head H_0. The general formula which applies is

$$N = w\eta Q H_0$$

where w is the weight of the water (in lb per cu ft or kg per litre or tons per m³); η is an efficiency factor indicating how much electrical energy can be recovered from the hydraulic energy; the quantity $(1 - \eta) Q H_0$ represents the losses in the turbine and generator. In addition, $\Delta H = H - H_0$ is the loss in the tunnels, pipe lines or canals, mainly caused by friction and bends, and $w\eta Q\Delta H$ represents the corresponding loss of energy.

In these formulae all quantities must be expressed in one system of units, *i.e.* foot, pound, second or metre, kilogram, second. The usual units of power are:

1 (British) horse power = 550 ft lb/sec = 0·74570 kW
1 (Metric) horse power = 75 kg m/sec = 0·73550 kW

The electrical unit of power is the watt or kilowatt (kW) and a power of 1 kW used during one hour represents a unit quantity of energy or 1 kWh.

THE PRESENT PRODUCTION OF HYDRO-POWER IN RELATION TO THE MAIN SOURCES OF ENERGY[15, 16]

The production of hydro-power in the world compared with the world production from other main power sources is best shown in TABLES 1 and 2.

TABLE 1   WORLD PRODUCTION OF POWER FROM THE MAIN SOURCES OF SUPPLY

Year	Coal and lignite 10⁶ t	Crude petroleum 10⁶ t	Natural gas 10⁹ m³	Electric power	
				Total 10⁹ kWh	Hydro-electric 10⁹ kWh
1913	1256·1	53·7	18·1	40	40
1938	1300·5	280·7	78·5	460·6	172·9
1946	1290·9	376·8	132·4	644·0	232·0
1952	1608·3	618·1	284·2	1134·0	397·0

*Consulting Engineer, English Electric Company Ltd., Special Lecturer in Engineering Fluid Mechanics, Imperial College of Science and Technology, London.

TABLE 2

WORLD PRODUCTION OF POWER FROM THE MAIN SOURCES, GIVEN IN COAL EQUIVALENTS
IN 10^6 TONS (metric)

Year	Coal and lignite	Crude petroleum	Natural gas	Hydro-electric	Total
1913	1256·1	80·1	27·0	32·0	1395·2
1938	1300·5	418·9	117·2	138·3	1974·9
1946	1290·9	562·4	197·6	185·6	2236·5
1952	1608·3	922·5	425·4	317·1	3273·3

IN PERCENTAGES

1938	65·9	21·2	5·9	7	100
1952	49·1	28·2	13·0	9·7	100

These two tables indicate the economic trends of the world since 1913 as
the demand for power closely follows the rise in economy. In 1958-9 the
gross consumption of electric power in the world rose to 1881×10^9 kWh.

It is seen that the hydro-electric industry represents just under 10 per
cent of the total world production of power, and about 35 per cent of the
total production of electric power.

The growth of the demand for electrical energy is shown in *Figure 1*.
The general trend shows a doubling of the power demand every 10 years,
which corresponds to a yearly increase of about 6 per cent and has been
consistent over a period of 35 years in spite of the economic crisis before

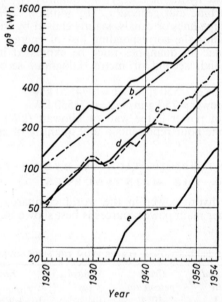

Figure 1. *Demand for electrical energy 1920–54.* (a) *World;* (b) *Trend for
doubling demand every ten years;* (c) *U.S.A.;* (d) *Europe;* (e) *U.S.S.R.*

World War II and during the war itself. In many countries, *e.g.* Canada,
the growth has been far in excess of this figure and many experts suggest
the yearly increase to be about 10 per cent in recent years.

FUTURE OF THE HYDRO-ELECTRIC INDUSTRY[17, 18]

It is estimated that the potential hydraulic energy in the western and central part of the Alps (France, Switzerland, Italy), and in Sweden, will be exhausted in a period of 15 to 20 years' time. Norway, Austria, Yugoslavia will then still possess wide, untapped sources of hydro-power. So will all countries in North, Central and South America, Asia and Africa. TABLE 3 gives the world hydro-power potential, according to the World Power Conference yearly statistics in 1955.

TABLE 3

ESTIMATED POTENTIAL HYDRO-POWER RESERVES IN THE WORLD
(WORLD POWER CONFERENCE, STATISTICAL YEAR BOOK 1955)

1 Continent	2 Potential power in 10^6 h.p.	3 Utilized power in 10^6 h.p.	4 Utilized power in per cent of column 2
Europe	64	48·5	76
North America	90	46·4	52
Asia	156	14·4	9
Australasia	23	1·8	8
South America	62	3·9	6
Africa	250	0·7	0·3
Total	645	115·7	18
(without Africa)	(395)	(115·0)	(29)

Most of these sources will produce hydro-electric energy at a price below that of nuclear power[18], probably for a long time . However, electric power from nuclear energy will not be able to meet the total demand for more power for some time and a wide field of activity is still open to hydro-power.

Hydro-power will remain the preferred source of energy:
(a) when developed in conjunction with irrigation;
(b) as pumped energy using large water storage for producing peak load in conjunction with thermic or nuclear power[18] stations producing base load.

In many other more conventional domains hydro-power is still competitive and its further expansion certain.

II. HYDROLOGY
(See also the chapter on Land Drainage)

RAINFALL

Most rainfall records are obtained by periodic observation of gauges. The usual interval is 24 hours. In hydrological studies, particularly in connection with flood studies, it may be of the utmost importance to know the rate of rainfall at any given time. Automatic recording gauges provide this valuable information and in recent years there has been much discussion and analysis of precipitation[22] in connection with flood hydrographs.

In estimating the run-off of a stream having no discharge records, the recorded run-off of a neighbouring stream is often used, in conjunction with a study of the difference in mean annual rainfall on the two areas. Rainfall records on a given area are also used to determine whether the years of river-discharge records for that area represent high or low periods.

SNOWFALL[35], GLACIERS

In many catchment areas of great importance for the production of hydro-power, snowfall replaces rainfall during the winter period. Snow is of lesser or of no value for hydro-power production, as long as it is not melted. For hydro-power studies snowfall has to be kept apart from rainfall and the year divided into a winter period (October–March in the Alps) and a summer period (April–September in the Alps). TABLE 4 relates snowfall and rainfall in the Austrian Alps.

TABLE 4

| Level above sea-level | Winter | | | Summer | | Yearly total |
| | Rainfall | Water contained in snow | Water available for run-off | Rainfall | Water available | |
m	mm	mm	mm	mm	mm	mm
500	450	7	443	850	857	1300
1000	620	116	564	1080	1196	1700
1500	750	500	250	1280	1780	2030
2000	820	820	—	1460	2280	2280
2500	870	870	—	1640	2510	2510
3000	920	920	—	1790	2710	2710

On higher levels (2300 to 2900 m) the snow density varies between 0·40 and 0·58.

Glaciers play a role similar to snow, and yield water in late spring or early summer.

RUN-OFF

Run-off is that portion of the earth's available water supply that is transmitted through natural surface channels. The hydro-power engineer is interested in two aspects of the run-off: (*a*) the annual run-off; (*b*) the storm run-off.

(a) Annual run-off

Run-off S is equal to the actual rainfall R_a minus a so-called deficit D which represents the losses of water due to evaporation and transpiration, wind effect, absorption of water through the soil: $S = R_a - D$. It is well known that the run-off cannot be expressed as a fixed ratio of the rainfall. This ratio varies from place to place and from year to year for the same place. The water deficit D is not constant and varies less over large areas; it could be determined by analogy with well-studied cases in the same country, under similar climatic and geological conditions.

Methods have been developed to determine the annual run-off relation over small water sheds. These methods are either by direct scientific analysis of all the elements of the problem (evaporation, transpiration, effect of altitude and of main wind direction, absorption by plants and subsoil *etc*)[21, 22] or by statistical analysis of correlations[26, 28]. A method which has been successful for small water sheds could theoretically be extended to larger areas by summation of partial results. This is not done usually because it is too time-absorbing and the detailed information required is usually available for small selected areas only.

For the purpose of establishing the potential hydro-power of a river, direct measurements of discharges over a certain period and the recording of a 'hydrograph curve' covering a certain period is the only correct procedure, even if the number of direct measurements is limited. Short series of measurements covering only a few years can be extended by comparison with neighbouring areas.

These remarks are not valid when the purpose of the enquiry is a rough estimate of the power potential of large areas, or whole countries. Special methods have been developed for such an estimate[34].

(b)   The storm run-off (See chapter on Land Drainage)

The problem to be solved concerns the maximum run-off expected to occur at a certain point of a river, over a short period. This data is required for the design of a spillway or overflow.

(1) *Statistical approach*—When a river has been surveyed over many years and number of floods measured or recorded, a curve can be established relating the flood discharge, Q, to the probability of it occurring over a certain period.

The formulae of Fuller (U.S.A.) or of Gibrat (France and Italy) have been used with good results. In the formula of FULLER[29] the average daily maximum flood Q over a period of n years is given by:

$$Q = a + b \log w, \qquad w = n \times 365 \text{ days}$$

where a and b are constants.

For example for the river Ticino, Swiss Alps, $a = -400$, $b = +400$ and $Q = 1425 \text{ m}^3/\text{day}$ for $n = 100$ years.

The peak flow for the same frequency is then:

$$Q = (1 + \alpha A^{-0.3}) Q$$

For A = drainage area in sq miles, $\alpha = 2$

for A = drainage in sq km, $\alpha = 2.65$

GIBRAT[30] combines the following curve of Gauss:

$$\frac{t}{T} = \frac{1}{\sqrt{\pi}} \int_{-\alpha}^{2} e^{-z^2} dz$$

where t is the number of days during which the discharge is less than q, over a period T, with

$$z = a \log_{10}(q - q_0) + b$$

where a, b and q_0 are constants characterizing the river (*i.e.* for the river Tuyère: $a = 1.828$, $b = 2.713$, $q_0 = 6$).

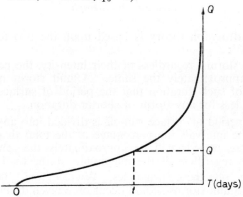

Figure 2. Typical frequency curve showing the discharge occurring t days out of T

Figure 2 shows one of these frequency curves: the discharge, Q, occurs t days out of T. This curve may be established from observations covering a period of 5, 10, 20, 30 ... years and then reduced to a typical yearly

frequency curve. The formula of Gibrat is supposed to give by extrapolation the discharge q occurring 1 in 50 years, 1 in 100 or 1 in 1000
years even if the period recorded is far shorter.

A similar approach was successful in some (European) countries with
mild climate but failed in others, Gibrat's formula giving values which are
too low for prediction over long periods (1000 years probability).

(2) McKay (see chapter on Land Drainage) shows how the direction
of a rainstorm and its distribution over the area finally determines the
flow in the river at the point under investigation. Each river consists of
the main stream fed by numerous tributaries and it is the incidence of the
flood waves in the tributaries on the main stream which determines the
peak discharge there. Assuming a flood wave or flood hydrograph
(discharge against time) at points a, b, c, on the tributaries, the flood in
the main river is calculated as the sum of the partial waves, taking into
account the time lag for the rain to reach different catchment areas and
for the water from the tributaries to reach the main river.

This method has been further developed mainly in the U.S.A. and,
in its more elaborate form, is known as the unit hydrograph method[22, 31].

A *hydrograph* of a stream is a graphical representation of its
fluctuations in flow arranged in chronological order. A complete hydrograph should, if possible, be obtained from a continuous recording gauge.
The analysis of hydrograph curves allows a classification of stream rises.
The curve shows a sharp rise if the rain intensity exceeds the infiltration
capacity: surface run-off occurs. *Figure 3* shows the main branches of a
hydrograph of this type.

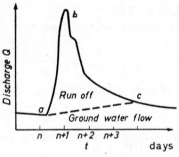

Figure 3. Hydograph

The unit hydrograph theory is based upon the two following fundamental principles[22]:

(1) For all unit storms, regardless of their intensity, the period of surface
run-off is approximately the same. A unit storm may be defined
as a storm of such duration that the period of surface run-off is not
appreciably less for any storm of shorter duration.

(2) If the total period of surface run-off is divided into any given number
of equal time intervals the percentage of the total that occurs during
each of these periods will be approximately the same for all unit
hydrographs regardless of the magnitude of the total run-off.

Commenting on these principles, WISLER and BRATER[22] write:
'Suppose that two unit storms should occur on a given drainage basin, each
of them lasting 24 hours, the first having a total rainfall of 3 in and the
second 5 in. If the time required for the surface run-off to pass a point
at the outlet of this basin is 8 days for the first storm, it will also be
approximately 8 days for the second storm or for any other storm lasting
24 hours or less. Also if the total run-off during the day of peak flow is,

for example, 20 per cent of the total surface run-off for the first storm, it will also be 20 per cent of the total for the second storm or for any other storm of this same duration, regardless of its intensity.'

Factors affecting a hydrograph are: type of precipitation, rainfall intensity, duration of rainfall, distribution of rainfall in basin, direction of storm movement.

The method consists then in making up a 'synthetic storm pattern', in determining the infiltration capacity from available local hydrographs and in constructing the flood hydrograph that should result from this storm.

DETERMINATION BY USE OF EMPIRICAL FORMULAE

The use of empirical formulae should not be discarded off-hand. Some of them have proved to be quite valuable for certain types of river and climatic conditions.

Some of these formulae are of the type:
$$Q=C'A^n$$
or its equivalent
$$q=C'A^{n-1}$$

where $Q=$ the flood in cu ft/sec
 $q=$ the flood in cu ft/sec per sq mile
 $A=$ the drainage in sq miles
 n and C' are characteristic coefficients.

Creager published results showing that
$$n=0.894\,A^{-0.048}$$
and
$$Q=46CA^{\left(0.894A^{-0.048}\right)}$$
$$q=46CA^{\left[\left(0.894A^{-0.048}\right)-1\right]}$$

All storms he analysed are comprised between two enveloping curves traced for $C=100$ and $C=30$. $C=60$ gives good average values for American climatic conditions.

Myers formula is used in the U.S.A.
$$Q=C\sqrt{A}$$

$A=$ area in sq miles, $Q=$ discharge in cu ft/sec.
The constant C has the following values (U.S.A.):

South Atlantic and Gulf of Mexico	6300
Lower Mississippi River basin	6400
Ohio River basin	5800
North Atlantic slope	4800
Pacific slope: Washington and Upper Columbia River basin .	4600
Pacific slope: Oregon and Lower Columbia River basin .	5800

III. ESTIMATE OF AVAILABLE POWER— RESERVOIR DESIGN

POWER

The principle of hydro-power consists in diverting a natural discharge Q through a turbine runner and taking advantage of the natural head H between the intake and the outlet of the system. If ΔH are the hydraulic losses in the system, due to friction in canals, galleries or pipes, intake losses or bend losses *etc*, then the net head is $H_0 = H - \Delta H$ and the power

$$N = w\eta\,(H - \Delta H)\,Q$$

If t is the time during which the power station is running, then the energy or output over a period t is

$$E = \int_0^t N\mathrm{d}t = N_a t$$

if N_a = constant average output.

$$N = \eta\,\frac{1000\,QH_0}{75}\ \text{(metric) h.p. (H_0 in metres, Q in m}^3\text{/sec)}$$

$$N = \eta\,\frac{62{\cdot}4\,QH_0}{550}\ \text{(British) h.p. (H_0 in feet, Q in ft}^3\text{/sec)}$$

For the conversion of power and energy from metric to British units, or vice versa, see Conversion Tables Nos. 14 and 15 (Vol. 1), or use:

$$\text{1 mkg} = 7{\cdot}2331\ \text{ft lb} \qquad \text{1m}^3\text{/sec} = 35{\cdot}317\ \text{cusec}$$

1 h.p. (metric) = 0·9863 h.p. (British)   1 h.p. (British) = 1·0139 h.p. (metric).

THE HEAD

There are several definitions of the head.

The *gross head H* is the simultaneous difference in elevation of the stream surfaces between points of diversion and return. For Pelton wheels (high head turbines) the nozzle level is sometimes taken instead of the water level at the point of return to the stream.

The operating head $H' = H + \dfrac{v_0^2}{2g} - \dfrac{v_n^2}{2g}$ makes allowance for the velocity heads at the diversion and return.

If the water levels vary a maximum head H_{max} and a minimum head H_{min} will be defined (*Figure 4*). The gross head is usually taken as equal to H_{max}, excluding exceptional flood conditions.

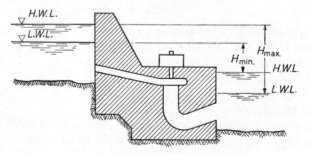

Figure 4.   Head of water

The net head is best defined by the conditions given in *Figure 5*,

where, obviously, $H_0 = H' - \Sigma_1^n \xi_i \dfrac{v_i^2}{2g} = H + \dfrac{v_0^2}{2g} - \dfrac{v_n^2}{2g} - \Sigma_1^n \xi_i \dfrac{v_i^2}{2g}$

The definition of the head is more difficult when the water levels in the head-race canal and in the tail-race canal vary and back-water curves have to be calculated.

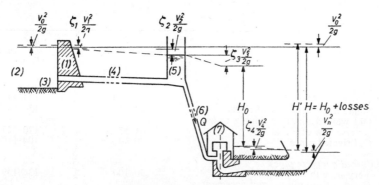

Figure 5. Net head

ESTIMATION OF LOSSES

Friction losses (see chapter on Mechanics of Fluids, Vol. 1, and ref. 10). In order to avoid confusion, most likely to occur with the great number of friction loss formulae to be found in text books, it is suggested that one of the two following formulae be used.

Darcy's formula:

$$i = f \frac{1}{D} \frac{r^2}{2g}$$

where f = Darcy's friction coefficient; or the Manning–Strickler formula:

$$v = k_s m^{\frac{2}{3}} i^{\frac{1}{2}} \text{ (metric units) or}$$
$$v = M m^{\frac{2}{3}} i^{\frac{1}{2}} = 1 \cdot 486 k m^{\frac{2}{3}} i^{\frac{1}{2}} \text{ (foot units)}$$

v = velocity in the conduits, D = pipe diameter, m = hydraulic radius = $D/4$ in the case of circular pipe, i = slope of energy line. For correlating f with k_s or M, use the transformation $k_s = (1/m^{1/6}) \sqrt{8g}/4$.

The Manning–Strickler formula is an improvement on the older well-known formula of Chezy (h = canal depth):

$$v = c h^{\frac{1}{2}} i^{\frac{1}{2}} \cong c m^{\frac{1}{2}} i^{\frac{1}{2}} \ (h \cong m)$$

used for open canals ($c = k m^{1/6}$).

Also $k_s = 1/n$ and $M = 1 \cdot 486/n$, when n is the well-known roughness coefficient of Ganguillet and Kutter.

For very smooth (new welded) pipes or very smooth large tunnels and canals use Nikuradse's formula

$$f_0 = 0 \cdot 0032 + 0 \cdot 221 \, R^{-0 \cdot 237}$$

($R = \dfrac{vd}{\nu}$ = Reynolds' number, ν = kinematic viscosity).

For practical purposes use TABLE 5.

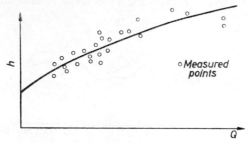

Figure 6. Stage discharge curve

TABLE 5

	Values of k_s	$\dfrac{1 \cdot 486}{n}$ (or *M*)
Steel pipes		
Entirely welded pipes	90–100	134–149
Single transverse row of rivets	88–92	131–137
Old welded pipes or double transverse row of rivets	81–85	120–127
Old riveted pipes	70–80	104–119
Reinforced concrete pipes		
Very smooth	90–100	134–149
Good shuttering and cement rendering	80–90	119–134
Without rendering	65–70	97–104
Rough (old) concrete	60–65	89–97
Wood-stave pipe lines		
New	95	141
In use	85	126
Old	65	97
Tunnels		
Smooth concrete lining	90–95	134–142
Average quality lining	82–85	121–127
Rough rock	23–33	34–49
Canals		
Very smooth	90	134
Lined with bricks or dressed stones	80	119
With granular bed	35–50	49–74
Fine sand	up to 90	134
Rough concrete lining	53–57	79–85
Rivers with rough bed	20–30	30–44

Losses due to discontinuities, hydraulic jump *etc* or at intakes, racks, bends *etc* cannot be dealt with here and reference must be made to a text book such as *Engineering Fluid Mechanics*[10].

ESTIMATE OF POWER ON A RIVER WITH NO STORAGE CAPACITY—RUN-OF-THE-RIVER SCHEMES

(a) *The stage discharge curve* (*Figure 6*) gives the water level *h* in the river against the discharge *Q*. When the river bed is erodible material, this curve may vary over the years and must be checked from time to time and, if so required, corrected. Water depth *h* for flood discharge may be difficult to obtain. On some mountain rivers a solid, masonry sill is sometimes built to stabilize this curve.

(b) *The hydrograph* is the most important curve for showing the characteristics of a river. It gives the water levels against time over a period

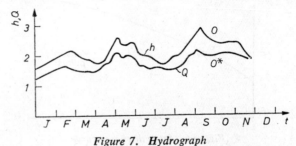

Figure 7. Hydrograph

of at least one year, usually a sequence of 5 to 10 years, sometimes 20 to 30 years. All the hydraulic calculations are based on the hydrograph (curve *O*) on *Figure 7*, or curve *2* on *Figure 9*. If the period for which the hydrograph is available is too short, rainfall curves may be used for extrapolation of the results.

A second curve giving the discharge Q against time t can easily be traced using the stage discharge curve. It yields curve *O** in *Figure 7*.

(c) The depth (and/or the discharge) are classified as shown on *Figure 8*, showing how many days a year a certain depth of water was obtained.

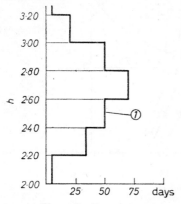

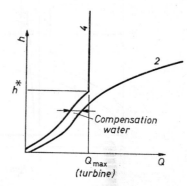

Figure 8. Frequency curve   Figure 9. Corrected stage discharge curve

(d) This classification, which can also be carried out by tabulation, is used to trace a duration curve for the depth h (curve *3* in *Figure 10*) and another for the discharge Q (curve *3a*). A duration curve is a curve of which the abscissa at any point shows the percentage of time during which a level (or discharge) did not exceed, or was equal to, the amount shown by the ordinate of the curve at that point. Usually compensation water is left in the river and the maximum discharge Q_{max} to be absorbed by the turbines is indicated on the diagram. This discharge, Q_{max} is shown to be available during t^* in the year and corresponds to a depth h^*. A corrected duration curve *3b* is traced in *Figure 10* after subtracting the compensation water.

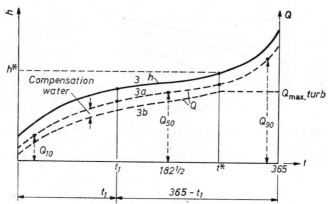

Figure 10. Duration curves

(e) *Figure 9* shows how a stage discharge curve (curve *2*) has been corrected to account for compensation water and for the maximum turbine discharge Q_{max} corresponding to a depth h^* (curve *4* in *Figure 9*).

In *Figure 11*, the upstream water level (curve 5) and the downstream water level (curve 6) are plotted against *h*. If the losses in the head-race canal or conduits and similarly in the tail-race side are calculated, curves 5a and 6a are obtained. If the $v_0^2/2g$ and $v_n^2/2g$ are added, the correct net head H_0 is obtained as the difference between curves 5b and 6b. This estimate of losses will be based on the real conditions in the whole system

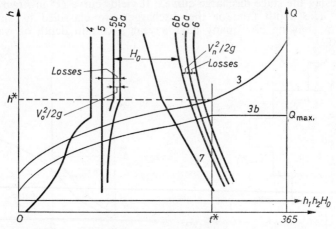

Figure 11. Net head H_0

and they will depend on how the head-race canal is being regulated (regulation through head gates or regulation in the fore bay to the turbines). Curve 7 represents the values of H_0 to a convenient scale.

(*f*) The formula $N = w\eta H_0 Q$ gives the output which in *Figure 12* is plotted once against the depth *h* (curve 8) and once against the time *t*. Curve 9 is roughly a duration curve and could easily be readjusted to give a proper duration curve.

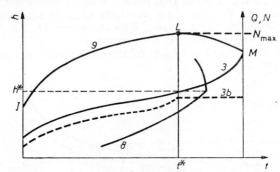

Figure 12. Output against h and t

The output is obviously a maximum ($N = N_{max}$) for $t = t^*$. After that, *N* decreases because usually the net head H_0 decreases with flood conditions in the river, *Q* usually remaining slightly less than Q_{max}, depending on the design of the turbine.

Figure 13 shows how the results of the investigations are summarized on one diagram where the energy production is compared with the energy demand. The duration curve method is suitable for determining the values of Q_{max} and t^* on which depends the capacity to be installed in the power station. With the development of large reservoir schemes there is a tendency to go higher with the t^* and Q_{max} values (higher installed capacity) on associated run-of-river schemes.

For further studies on the economics of the scheme, a diagram similar to *Figure 14*, based on the hydrograph, is of great value: it shows in which part of the year a deficit in energy is likely to occur. This diagram for

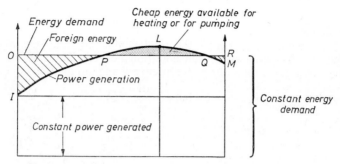

Figure 13. Power production and demand (1)

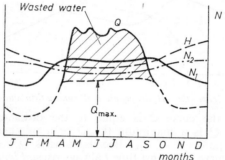

Figure 14. Power production and demand (2)

power generation (N_1) is then compared with the power demand (N_2), as it varies over the year (*Figure 15*). Additional energy from water storage reservoirs or from steam power stations is required to balance production and demand. Some energy may be wasted or sold at a low price at some periods or will have to be bought from other producers at other periods.

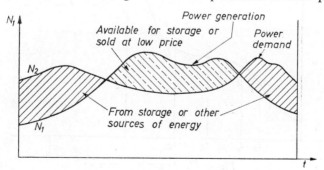

Figure 15. Power production and demand (3)

RESERVOIR DESIGN

Figures 13, 14 and *15* show that it is desirable to supplement the energy produced by run-of-the-river schemes with energy stored as potential energy in large reservoirs.

Curve *1* (*Figure 16*) is a hydrograph curve extended over a period *T* (one day, one week or one year). The second curve (*2*) is a summation curve, such that at any time *t*

$$V = \int_0^t Q \, dt$$

V is a volume and equals the total volume of water passing through the river at the point under consideration between the time, *0* and *t*. From the well-known relations between curves and summation curves, we have

$$\tan \phi = \frac{dV}{dt} = Q$$

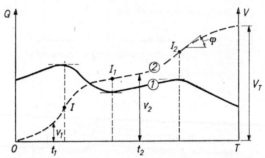

Figure 16. Hydrograph and summation curves

The tangent to the curve *2* is equal to the ordinate of curve *1*. In particular, when *Q* is a maximum (Q_{max}) or a minimum (Q_{min}) curve *2* shows inflection points *I*, I_1, I_2. Because always $Q > 0$, $\tan \phi$ is always positive and the curve *V* against time *t* always rises. *Figure 17* shows one of these summation curves representing the inflow of water in a reservoir. We

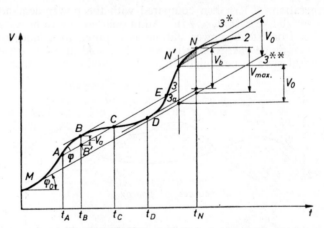

Figure 17. Summation curves

assume that the demand for water is constant and is represented by $Q_0 = \tan \phi_0$, a straight line with constant slope. Let us assume that at the time t_A the reservoir is empty. From time t_A to time t_B the inflow is greater than the demand ($\tan \phi > \tan \phi_0$). Water accumulates in the reservoir and at the time t_B a volume $BB' = V_a$ has been accumulated.

From t_B to t_C, $\tan \phi < \tan \phi_0$ and the reservoir begins to empty. At time t_C, it is empty. From t_C to t_D the inflow is still less than the demand, which cannot be satisfied. The reservoir remains empty and begins to refill after t_D. If all the water betwen t_D and t_N should be retained in the reservoir, then its volume should be at least equal to V_b. If all the water flowing in the reservoir between points M and N should be used at a steady rate $\tan \phi_0$, then the required reservoir volume should be $V_{\max}$ between the parallel lines 3* and 3**, with a slope $\tan \phi_0$. If the actual reservoir volume $V_0 < V_{\max}$ thus some water should overflow between points N' and N (shaded area), until $\tan \phi \leqslant \tan \phi_0$ again.

This diagram shows that the whole discussion on the required volumes for water storage depends on tracing convenient parallel lines with the slope $\tan \phi_0 = Q_0$.

This method has been used for determining the required volume V_q for storing all the water flowing in the reservoir over a period T of 1 year, provided the demand is constant $(Q_0 = \tan \phi_0)$ (*Figure 18*). It can be seen

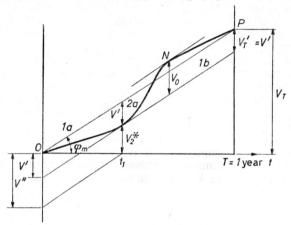

Figure 18. Required storage volume (1)

that at the start $(t=0)$ there must be a volume V' in the reservoir such that $V' =$ outflow $V'' -$ inflow V_2^* during the first t_1 days. At the end of the period of 1 year, the volume of water in the reservoir is again V'. The diagram is based on the assumption of full utilization of the inflow for a constant demand over a period T.

The inflow curve on which the volume estimate is based can be either an 'average' year, obtained by averaging the monthly inflow over a period of 5, 10, 20 years, or a typical dry year, or any other year, depending on the circumstances.

After the reservoir volume V_0 has been determined, the effect of such a reservoir is checked on the real summation curve, over n years. It will

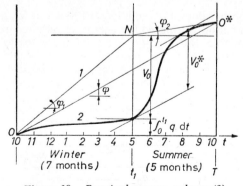

Figure 19. Required storage volume (2)

be found that, after a number of years, the boundary conditions at the point chosen for the beginning of time ($t=0$) are immaterial.

Figure 19 shows the condition on a typical winter storage where the demand for winter power ($\tan \phi_1$) is greater than the demand for summer power ($\tan \phi_2$). The winter inflow is $\int_0^{t_1} Q \, dt$

and the required storage volume V_0 is greater than the volume V_0^* for constant power demand ($\tan \phi$).

PUMPED STORAGE[37]

In recent years pumped storage is developing rapidly either to supplement peak load to an electric grid fed by thermal power stations producing the base load or as a supplement to a system of hydro-power stations.

A true pumped storage scheme is a scheme where the total amount of water passing through the turbines is equal to the total amount of pumped water, the turbine and the pump working under the same head (example: Ffestiniog pumped storage scheme, Wales). A mixed pumped storage scheme is one where either the water passing through the turbines is more than the pumped water, and/or where the turbine gross head is more than the pump gross head (Glen Shira, Clachan, Scotland).

Figure 20 refers to a mixed pumped storage scheme. It shows that if full advantage of the pumped water is to be taken, the volume of the reservoir, estimated without storage of pumped water, must be increased by V_P, where V_P is the amount of water pumped. *Figure 20* assumes

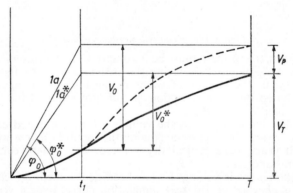

Figure 20. Required storage volume—pumped storage

implicitly that both values V_0^* and $V_0 = V_0^* + V_P$ refer to the same time basis T. If the period during which energy is required remains the same (t_1) then the available discharge $Q_0^* = \tan \phi_0^*$ increases to $Q_0 = \tan \phi_0$.

Another approach to the pumped storage problem is shown in *Figure 21*, when N_b is the base load capacity to be installed and N_T the turbine capacity of the pumped storage scheme. The total load is

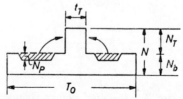

Figure 21. Pumped storage

$N=N_T+N_b$. If T_0 is the base period (say one day) to which the cycle refers and t_r the time during which the turbines are supposed to run at full load, then if θ_0 is the load factor of the system:

$$N_T = \frac{(1-\theta_0)\,T_0}{T_0-t_r}\,N \text{ and } N_b = \frac{\theta_0 T_0 - t_r}{T_0 - t_r}\,N$$

Pumped storage does not create new energy but readjusts the power production to match the demand. It can influence in a favourable way the build-up of a hydro-electric grid. With pumped storage it becomes possible to utilize fully the run-of-the-river stations linked to the system and even to extend them, building-in a higher capacity.

ALLOWANCE FOR EVAPORATION AND FOR ICE ON THE RESERVOIR SURFACE

The diagrams shown in the previous paragraphs must be corrected allowing for evaporation of water and, in cold climates, for the formation of an ice crust.

The United Nations Economic Commission for Europe Technical Committee has published the following figures relating to yearly evaporation[34]:

	mm	in
United States: mean from 17 lakes and reservoirs	1170	46
Southern France and Spain	1500	59
Italy, reservoirs at moderate altitude	200–1200	8–47
Eastern Germany and Poland	450–700	18–28
Tropical countries	2000–3000	78–118

J. Lugeon[21] gives the following rates of evaporation on Alpine lakes:

Height above sea-level		Evaporation	
m	ft	mm	in
500	1640	700	27·5
1500	4920	300	11·8
2000	6560	250	9·8

The volume of water V_{ev} evaporated will depend on the area A of the reservoir surface, the barometric pressure H_B the pressure for saturated vapour F and the actual pressure of the vapour f. F varies from 4·6 mm at 0°C to 92 mm at 50°C. V_{ev} is found to be proportional to $A\,(F-f)/H_B$.

Evaporation varies from month to month. In the Alps evaporation may be 12 times larger in August than in January and December and varies steadily from the minimum to the maximum and vice versa. In a hot, damp country the ratio of the maximum to the minimum monthly evaporation may vary from 3 to 1.

The thickness of the ice crust may vary from 3 to 5 ft (1 to 1·50 m) and freezing and thawing are given by the following table (Alps):

Height		Freezing	Thawing
m	ft		
2500	8200	October	August
2000	6600	November	June
1000	3300	end of December	April

The inflow curve will have to be corrected to take account of evaporation and/or of ice formation.

The maximum size of large reservoirs in tropical areas depends on evaporation. There is a limit to the size of a reservoir when evaporation on the lake surface equals the inflow.

ESTIMATE OF AVAILABLE POWER IN UNDER-DEVELOPED COUNTRIES[34, 38]

It is possible to assess the water-power resources of different regions on a consistent basis if three alternative levels of definition can be used. These levels may be stated as follows[34]:

(a) The gross potential power of the head and flow of water physically available in an average year.

(b) The proportion of this latent power which it is technically possible to harness at a given time.

(c) The proportion which can be exploited economically at a given time.

The estimates under (a), (b) and (c) vary when knowledge of the physical and climatological data involved becomes greater.

The yearly gross hydro-electric potential is given by the expression

$$N = \frac{100}{75} QH \, 0 \cdot 736 = 9 \cdot 81 \, QH \text{ kW or } E = 8584 \, QH \text{ kWh}$$

assuming that the generating stations run during the 8760 hours of the year.

The United Nations' committee which used this method for several European countries arrived at the conclusion that the proportion of power which can be exploited economically represents about 18 to 19·5 per cent of the gross potential power.

A slightly different method has been introduced in Austria, based on tracing elemental rectangles using the actual contour lines and considering the rainfall separately during the winter and the summer periods[35].

Such surveys are of the utmost importance for under-developed countries where detailed studies of all the streams is impossible.

INTEGRATION OF HYDRO POWER IN ELECTRIC SYSTEMS, SYSTEM LOAD ANALYSIS AND LOAD FACTOR

The power demand of any electric system can be represented by a load duration curve (*Figure 21a*). The load factor θ of a generating system with total installed capacity N, producing energy E over a period T, is the ratio

$$\theta = E/NT$$

Any electric power system with a total installed capacity M and a system load factor θ_s can be broken down into system components characterised by their installed capacity $N_1, N_2, \ldots N_i \ldots$ and their load factors $\theta_1, \theta_2 \ldots \theta_i \ldots$ over a period T.

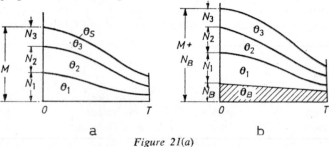

a   b

Figure 21(a)

The following general theorems can be demonstrated using the system duration curve shown in *Figures 21a* and *21b*:

There is a linear relation between θ_s and θ_1, θ_2 . . . depending only on N_1/M, N_2/M . . . . This linear relation does not depend on the shape of the duration curve derived from the load/time curves of the system. *Figure 21a* yields,

$$\theta_s M = \theta_1 N_1 + \theta_2 N_2 + \ldots + \theta_i N_i + \ldots$$

Adding a new source of power (hydro-power) N_B with a load factor θ_B yields (*Figure 21b*):

$$\theta_s (M + N_B) = \theta_1 N_1 + \theta_2 N_2 + \ldots + \theta_i N_i + \ldots + \theta_B N_B$$

Any new source of power (N_B, θ_B) added to an existing system (M, θ_s) may change the load conditions in the system components (N_i, θ_i). The *condition for no change to occur* in the existing system is

$$\theta_B = \theta_s$$

In the more general case

$$\theta_B = \theta_s - \frac{N_i}{N_B} \Delta\theta_i$$

where $\Delta\theta_i$ is the change occurring in the system (N_i, θ_i) owing to the addition of a new source of energy (N_B, θ_B). This fundamenal relation allows us to relate the price analysis of the new system to price changes occurring in the component i. The theorem can obviously be generalized to several components i.

IV. DEBRIS TRANSPORTATION—SILTING UP OF RESERVOIRS AND EROSION

GENERAL DATA ON RIVER TRANSPORT

Most rivers transport debris which often causes serious trouble. Any structure which interferes with the normal flow of the river may increase these troubles.

TABLE 6

River	Country	Area km²	Total transport in m³/km²	Weight %	Per cent of rolled material	References
Several small rivers	Los Angeles Area, U.S.A.	0·7 2·6 2·8 2·6	9750 6500 500 235			W. C. Cassidy New Delhi 1957 Rep. 27
Bureau of Reclamation river survey	U.S.A.			0·01–5	2–8 to 10–20 (max. 50)	Maddock and Borland, L.D.C. New Delhi 1957 Rep. 41
Several Swiss rivers	Switzerland		176 to 513 Average: 365		25–50	H. Dufour
Rhône	Switzerland			0·08– 0·25	44·7–25	L. W. Collet and H. Dufour
Khatima	India			0·38– 1·4		

1 yd³/sq mile = 0·295 m³/km². 1 km² = 0·386 sq mile, 1 sq mile = 2·589 km². 1 kg of material per ton of water = 0·1 percent in weight. The wet density of transported material varies between 1·4 and 1·7 g/cm³ (average 1·5).

Slow flowing rivers (India) transport mainly very fine sand and silt in suspension. Other rivers transport coarse debris and fine sand. The coarse debris is usually rolled along the river bed; the fine sand and silt are maintained in suspension by the natural turbulence of water. TABLE 6 gives some very general data concerning material transported in rivers in different parts of the world.

TABLE 6 shows the considerable variety in the amount of material transported and in the weight and proportion of rolled to suspended material. In fact, the problem has to be subdivided into:

(a) Rivers transporting mainly sand and silt in suspension. This problem is dealt with in the chapter on Hydraulics of Canals and Rivers of Mobile Boundary, and will not be discussed here.

(b) Rivers transporting rolled debris. Many rivers considered for power schemes will be of this kind and the most important problem raised by the rolled debris is in the design of the intake works. This particular aspect of the more general problem of debris transportation is the only one that will be dealt with here.

DEBRIS ROLLED ON THE RIVER BED

The load of rolled debris transported by a river is given by the formula of the Zurich Research Laboratory (MEYER–PETER[41, 42])

$$q^{\frac{2}{3}}i = ad + bq_1^{\frac{2}{3}}$$

all in metric units, where

q = the discharge in litres per second per metre width

q_1 = the dry weight of bed load discharged in kg/sec m width

i = the gradient of the total energy line

d = the mean grain diameter in metres

for q in m³/sec m, q_1 in kg/sec m, and d in m, the constants are

$$a = 0 \cdot 17 \text{ and } b = 0 \cdot 004$$

The transportation of debris begins for a discharge

$$\frac{q_0^{\frac{2}{3}}i}{d} = a \text{ or } q_0 = \left(\frac{ad}{i}\right)^{3/2}$$

The gradient i is given by the formula of Chezy, $v = ch^{\frac{1}{2}}i^{\frac{1}{2}}$ or Mannings, $v = ki^{\frac{1}{2}}h^{\frac{2}{3}}$. The formula has given good results on mountain rivers, like those to be found in the Alps and surrounding plains. A more detailed formula taking into account the meandering shape of rivers was published in 1949 by MEYER–PETER[41] and collaborators. It is important to note that this formula is consistent with the law of similarity of Froude and permits extrapolation to nature of results obtained on models.

SILTING UP OF RESERVOIRS[43, 44, 47]

When a river loaded with silt and debris flows into a reservoir, segregation of the transported material occurs. The debris rolled along the river bed is deposited at the upstream end of the reservoir (*Figure 22*), causing an obstruction of the river bed, which rises continuously. This raising of the bed works itself in the upstream direction, causing a backwater curve to move up the river, disturbing the normal river flow upstream of the reservoir.

The fine silt, in suspension in the water, usually forms a density current[42, 44] which reaches the bottom lower end of the reservoir near the dam forming a 'silt lake'[43]. In some cases the density current is dispersed before reaching the dam. The causes of this early dispersion are not known. Valuable live storage is thus being lost at the upper and at the bottom lower end of the reservoir.

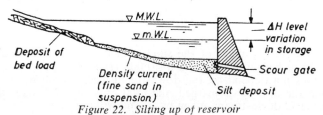

Figure 22. *Silting up of reservoir*

A daily or weekly compensation basin for a peak load station (reservoir capacity about 2,000 to 5,000 m³/km² (7,000 to 1,700 yd³/sq mile) of catchment area) will rapidly be filled, mainly with coarse debris. Flushing of the reservoir during flood periods is essential, possibly lowering the water level during long high-water periods or using two independent intakes for summer (wet period) and for winter months (dry period). Medium-sized seasonal reservoirs (ratio reservoir capacity to catchment area 50,000 to 200,000 m³/km²) are to be treated on similar lines. The deposit of silt may there be as dangerous as the transported debris; hard deposits form steep banks, hard to erode when flushing the reservoir. Opening the reservoir gates of the Nile reservoir upstream of the old Aswan dam during flood periods has saved this reservoir from silting up; the fine sand and silt at Aswan does not form a hardened mass of deposits. Other reservoirs (Algeria) have silted up.

Very large reservoirs (multi-annual) may last several hundred years (*e.g.* Lake Mead, U.S.A.)[48].

EROSION, SCOUR BELOW WEIRS

Erosion and scour below weirs are processes of the same nature as transport of rolled debris. They can be studied on models and the similarity law of FROUDE can be used for interpretation of the results. (See Sect. V.)

The erosion of a meandering river is governed by the debris transportation law. If the bed load entering the upstream end of a river section is more than the q_1 value (extended to the whole river width), the bed level rises owing to the deposit of debris. If the load is less than q_1, the river may erode or not, depending on the type of river bed. Regarding rolled transported debris there are two main types of river:

(*a*) Rivers, the bed material of which has the same granulometric size as that of the transported debris (example: Rhine upstream of Lake Constance). In this case, the load transportation formula gives at any moment the true weight of the transported load q_1 which varies with q. If less or more debris is coming from upstream, the river automatically compensates by eroding its bed or silting up.

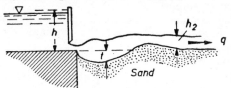

Figure 23. *Erosion when flow is not submerged*

(*b*) Rivers paved with larger pebbles, which can no more be eroded by the river (example: the Rhône downstream of Geneva). In this case the transported load can be less than q_1, or equal to q_1, but never more than q_1 (silting up of the bed).

The nature of the scour below a weir or solid sill depends on the nature of the flow immediately below the weir.

If the flow is not submerged[42] the erosion depth t is given by (*Figure 23*):

$$t = a + b\left(\frac{H}{d_m}\right)^\alpha q^{\frac{2}{3}}$$

For $d_m = 0.2$ cm (diameter of the sand grains) the values of the constants were found to be $\alpha = 1$, $a = 0$ and $b = 0.005$ (H in cm, q in l/sec m). The depth t does not depend on the downstream water depth h_2.

When the flow is submerged, the total erosion depth does depend on the water level downstream, given by h_2 and (*Figure 24*):

$$t + h_2 = C\frac{h^{0.5}q^{0.6}}{(d_{90})^{0.4}} \text{ (width of canal } B = 1 \text{ m)}$$

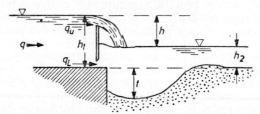

Figure 24. Erosion when flow is submerged

Here t, h_2 and h are in metres, d_{90} in millimetres and q in m^3/sec. d_{90} represents the diameter of the larger particles of sand which make less than 10 per cent of the granulometric distribution curve[42, 45]. The constant c from the results of tests by W. Eggenberger is given by:

$$c = 22.88 - \frac{1}{0.0049\,(q_u/q_L)^3 - 0.0063\,(q_u/q_L)^2 + 0.029\,(q_u/q_L) + 0.064}$$

($q_u = $ overflow, $q_L = $ underflow, *Figure 24*).

V. MODEL TESTS IN HYDRO-POWER ENGINEERING

SIMILARITY IN HYDRAULICS

Whenever a problem of fluid mechanics with a bearing on an important question of design cannot be solved by direct mathematical analysis, hydraulic model tests may bring the required solution. If quantitative measurements are required, the question of the law of similarity to be applied is most important.

To establish mechanical similarity between two motions, it is necessary and sufficient that (theorem):

(*1*) the boundary conditions (boundaries, inlet and outlet conditions for the water, discharge, *etc*) should be mechanically similar in nature and in the model;

(*2*) the forces K_1, K_2 . . ., k_1, k_2 . . . fulfil the following always and at every point, *viz*

$$\mu_r\frac{\lambda}{\tau_r^2} = \frac{K_1}{k_1} = \frac{K_2}{k_2} = \ldots = \kappa$$

In this section; let:

L, l be two corresponding representative lengths, and $\lambda = L/l$;

M, m two corresponding elementary masses, and $\mu_r = M/m$;

$K_1, K_2 \ldots k_1, k_2 \ldots$ the forces acting on the masses, and $\kappa = K/k$;

T, t the corresponding periods of time, and $\tau_r = T/t$;

V, v the velocities of the masses M, m and $\varepsilon = V/v$.

Capital letters refer to motion in a prototype (in nature) and small letters to motion in a model.

From the definition of velocities: $\varepsilon = \lambda/\tau_r$,

Newton's first law: $m \cdot d^2x/dt = k$ gives $\mu_r\lambda/\tau_r^2 = \kappa$.

Two laws of similarity can be applied in hydraulics:

The similarity law of Froude

The only external force to be considered is the weight: $K_1 = Mg$ in nature and $k_1 = mg$ in the model, whence:

$$\mu_r\lambda/\tau_r^2 = Mg/mg = \mu_r \text{ or } \tau_r^2 = \lambda, \ \tau_r = \sqrt{\lambda}$$

As $\varepsilon = \lambda/\tau_r$

$$\frac{V}{(gL)^{\frac{1}{2}}} = \frac{v}{(gl)^{\frac{1}{2}}} = F$$

This means that both for the model and for the prototype flows the Froude number F must be the same.

The similarity law of Reynolds

Let us assume that the viscosity is the only external force. If μ_1 and μ_2 denote the viscosity of two fluids, and ν_1 and ν_2 the corresponding kinematic viscosities, then:

$$\mu_r\frac{\lambda}{\tau_r^2} = \frac{\mu_1\,(\partial V/\partial N)\,A}{\mu_2\,(\partial v/\partial n)\,a}$$

when A and a are corresponding areas N and n the normals to these areas, $\nu = \mu/\rho, \rho = $ mass density of the fluid. This leads to

$$\tau_r = \lambda^2\,(\nu_2/\nu_1) \text{ or } \varepsilon = \frac{1}{\lambda}\,\frac{\nu_1}{\nu_2}$$

and

$$\frac{VL}{\nu_1} = \frac{vl}{\nu_2} = R$$

The similarity of Reynolds requires that the Reynolds' number R must be the same for the model and the prototype.

In the general case, the two laws of Froude and Reynolds are incompatible. Prandtl proved that they are in case of 'fully developed turbulence' (friction losses proportional to the square of the velocity).

Rules

Taking advantage of Prandtl's proof, it can be shown that the following laws apply:

Free surface systems (rivers, canals):
Short structures with negligible frictions: Froude's law.
Short structures with lively turbulence and long structures with fully developed turbulence: Froude's law.

Systems under pressure:
Short structures: in all cases Reynolds' law.
Long structures: Reynolds' law.
For long structures: possibly adjustment of wall roughness required.

Law of similarity for models with movable bed[50, 54]

Use Froude's law and Strickler–Manning's formula for wall roughness, with $k_s = 26/(d_{90})^{1/6}$, d_{90} = diameter of the rougher grains of the granulometric curve. In addition for debris transportation, use the extended formula of Meyer–Peter:

$$\frac{iq^{2/3}}{(w_1')^{10/9}d} = 9 \cdot 57 + 0 \cdot 462 \left[\frac{(q_1')^{2/3}}{(w_1')^{7/9}d} \right]$$

All values in metric units: $w_1' = w_1 - w$ is the rolled material's specific gravity measured under water ($w = 1$), $q_1' = q_1 w_1'/w_1$ in kg/sec m. If the scale of the model is small ($\lambda \geqslant 100$), it is difficult to use sand with the correct granule size in the model. A lighter model material can then be used (specific gravity w_1), but the slope i of the model has to be increased to compensate for the use of lighter material (extended similarity of Froude)[50, 54].

OTHER MODEL TESTS

Photoelasticity is used for measuring strain and stress distribution in hydro-power structures (dams, piers of weirs *etc*). A special technique has been developed for analysing strains and stresses in arch dams (see Sect. IX).

VI. TYPES OF HYDRO-POWER STATION

1. Hydro-power stations can be classified according to head, *e.g.* high, medium and low head. There can be no precise classification but the following, relating head to type of turbine, is suggested.

TABLE 7

CLASSIFICATION OF HYDRO-POWER STATIONS

Type of station	Head		Turbine
	m	ft	
High head	1750–300	5750–1000	Pelton (impulse) wheels
	450–150	1500–500	High head Francis (reaction)
Medium head	150–20	500–65	Low head Francis. Dériaz turbines
Low head	45–3	150–10	Propeller runners and Kaplan turbines

The figures are approximate, as technical progress continually shifts the limits for the different runner types, mostly in the upward direction. Higher head Kaplan turbines tend to displace the ordinary low head Francis type and the high head Francis displaces the conventional Pelton wheel.

2. Another classification relates to the absence or use of storage.

(*a*) Run-of-river plants with no, or negligible reservoir capacity. These stations usually produce base load for an electric system and their load factor is usually high. In recent years the tendency has been to install more capacity in run-of-river stations in order to utilize more of the flood water. This reduces the load factor of the station. Combination with pumped storage may have to be considered in future to increase the over-all efficiency of the station[37a].

(*b*) Storage plants with reservoir capacity, sufficient to adjust the power production to the demand. If the storage capacity is sufficient, these stations will be used as peak load stations, producing power during peak hours. The load factor of storage plants is usually low.

In regions predominantly supplied by hydro-power it is not unusual for the peak power (measured in kWh) to be 2 or 3 times dearer than base power. When hydro-power with storage capacity is connected to a grid predominantly fed with steam power, price comparison is on the basis of the cost of the installed kW, rather than on the produced kWh.

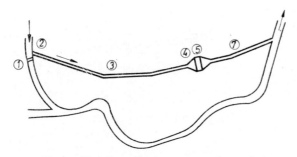

Figure 25. Low head power station—plan

3. Hydro-power stations can also be classified according to the type of flow. In most high head power stations, the water circulates in conduits under pressure. A typical high head scheme is shown in *Figure 5*, where a dam (*1*) creates a storage reservoir (*2*). The water circulates in a pressure tunnel (*4*) from the intake (*3*) to the surge tank (*5*) and then drops through the pressure pipe line (*6*) to the power house (*7*). As shown in *Figure 5*, $H_0 = H - \Sigma\Delta H$. Typical low head power stations (*Figures 25* and *26*) show a weir damming the river (*1*) without creating a large storage reservoir. An intake structure (*2*) regulates the water entering the head race canal (*3*). A forebay (*4*) slows down the water before entering the power house (*5*). After passing through the turbines (*6*), the water is led through the tail water canal (*7*) back to the river. Usually the length of the head race and tail race canals is shorter than the total length of the meandering river. The gradients of the canals are less than the slope of the river bed; losses in the canals are less than the losses in the natural river: all these elements contribute in reducing the head losses $\Sigma\Delta H$, so that a net head H_0 is available for producing energy in the turbines. *Figure 26* shows that $H_0 = H - \Sigma\Delta H$. Alternatives can be worked out where either the head race canal or the tail race canal is suppressed.

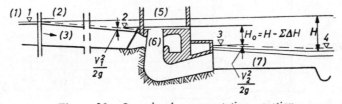

Figure 26. Low head power station—section

Figure 27 shows a much more compact design. The length of head race and tail race is reduced to nothing; the intake is included in the dam. The power house is at the foot of the dam.

There are many alternative designs to these basic types. Power stations can also be above ground (conventional design, *Figure 28*) or underground (*Figure 29*). Underwater power stations, first designed by Arno Fischer (*Figure 30*), and power houses built inside the piers of a weir are special solutions recently developed in Austria and Bavaria.

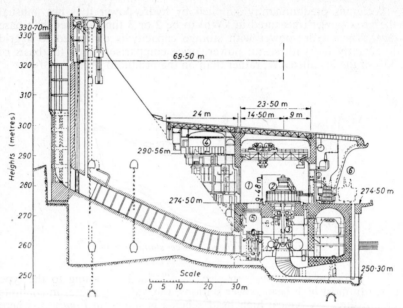

Figure 27. *Génissiat—Cross section of dam and power-house.* 1, *Power-house*:
2, *alternator;* 3, *turbine gallery*: 4, *control room*: 5, *valve chamber*

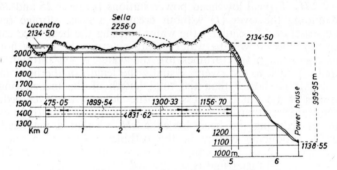

Figure 28. *Lucendro — Longitudinal section*

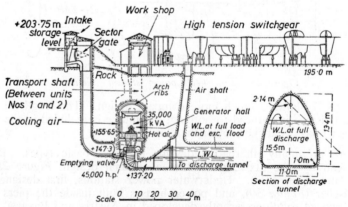

Figure 29. *Underground power station*

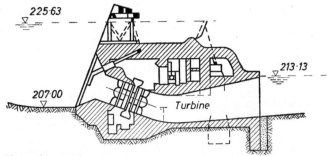

Figure 30. Underwater power station (designed by Arno Fischer)

TABLE 8 summarizes the main design types:

TABLE 8

Head	Conventional design	Underground power station design
High head	(1) Pressure tunnel and open air pressure pipe line.	(1) Pressure tunnel, pressure shaft, tail race tunnel free flow or under pressure.
Medium head	(1) Pressure tunnel and pressure pipe lines. (2) Medium or high head dam, power house at the toe of the dam. (3) Free flow canal, pressure pipe line.	(1) Vertical or inclined shaft, power house, tail race tunnel, free flow or under pressure. (2) Pressure tunnel, surge tank, shaft, power house, tail race tunnel.
Low head	(1) Intake, head race canal power house, tail race canal. (2) Weir or low dam and power house connected. (3) Underwater power station. (4) Power house included in weir or piers.	Same as for medium head.

Pumped storage schemes and tidal schemes are modern developments which are outside the scope of this chapter[37, 38].

4. The linking of low-head run-of-river stations with high head stations provided with some kind of reservoir started very early; *e.g.* Beznau (1902) and Löntsch (1908) in Switzerland both built by Motor. An even earlier example of a run-of-river station connected to a small pumped storage scheme is Letten (1877) near Zurich with day and night time-table for power production and pumping. These methods have been greatly developed in the last 50 years. A modern approach consists in using to the full the best storage basins by drawing water by galleries from tunnels or canals from nearby catchment areas. The number of good sites suitable for large storage is scarce and the price of the stored unit of water is the lower, the larger the reservoir. Typical examples of this concentration of water in a large reservoir (often used as head reservoirs for a series of power stations) are: the Loch Sloy scheme in Scotland, the Snowy Mountain scheme (Australia), the Mauvoisin scheme (*Figures 31(a)* and *31(b)*) and the Grande Dixence in Switzerland; other examples occur in Austria, *etc.*

The modern trend is towards the full development of a whole valley (Maggia, Switzerland) or system of valleys. The Tennessee Valley development in the U.S.A. and the Snowy Mountain scheme in Australia, developed by more or less independent authorities, are typical of the modern approach to hydro-power.

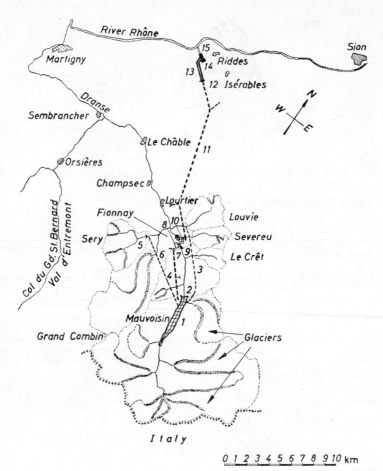

Figure 31(a). Mauvoisin scheme—plan

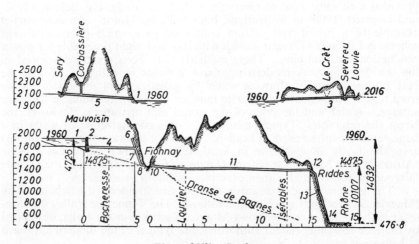

Figure 31(b). Sections

Hydro-power is often linked to steam power. Typical are conditions in Scotland where the Galloway scheme and Loch Sloy storage scheme are linked to the larger steam stations near Glasgow. On a larger scale the power stations in the French Alps and on the Rhône river are directly linked to Paris, surrounded by a series of steam power stations. Steam power stations in the German Ruhr Valley are linked to German and Swiss power stations on the Rhine.

Multipurpose schemes are favoured mainly in countries where irrigation of large areas is of paramount importance (Columbia Basin project, U.S.A., Bhakra dam, India) *etc*. Flood regulation (Fontana dam, U.S.A.) or navigation (Tennessee Valley, U.S.A., St. Laurence River scheme, U.S.A. and Canada) are often combined with hydro-power.

The electrical industry is just beginning to realize the importance of pumped water storage and the great advantages which can be obtained from this most versatile method of converting base load into valuable peak load. Modern examples of pumped storage are the Niagara Falls, the Sir Adam Beck Station No. II, with six reversible Dériaz pump turbines (English Electric Company) in Ontario, Canada, and the Ffestiniog pumped storage scheme in Wales.

Tidal schemes have been discussed for many years. In the Rance tidal scheme, designed to use reversible pump-turbines, a far better utilization of the tidal energy will be possible and the station will produce constant base load.

VII. DAMS

GENERAL

A dam is a structure built across a river or valley in order to store water, to raise the water level of a river or slow down a river flow. Dams are often combined with intake structures, spillways, power houses. In this section dams alone will be considered.

TYPES OF DAM

The principal types of dam are: (*a*) gravity dams, resisting the water pressure by their own weight; (*b*) arch dams resisting the water pressure mainly or partly because of their curved shape; (*c*) hollow gravity and buttress dams, which, compared with the ordinary gravity dam, achieve a better utilization of the bulk concrete and permit cheaper designs (these three types of dam are either of concrete or masonry); (*d*) earth and rock fill dams are in a class apart; (*e*) weirs are dams of limited head, provided with gates or crest gates.

CHOICE OF DAM TYPE

The geology of the site and the shape of the valley are the two main factors to be considered. Availability of suitable materials for concrete or for the clay core and the possibilities of transport of the materials are also most important factors. Then comes the necessity of passing the floods either over the top of the dam or over a lateral spillway, or through a spillway canal or spillway tunnel.

Sometimes several alternatives have to be worked out before a final decision becomes possible. Methods of construction also influence the economics of a dam.

The final safety of a gravity dam, if designed according to well established rules rests on the transmission of shear forces to the rock foundation; arch dams transmit mainly compression forces. The general stratification of the rock and the direction of the main faults and fissures may favour either one type or the other.

Examples—At Picote (Portugal) one fault, plunging downwards in the direction of flow, was discovered on the left abutment: a gravity dam project was therefore abandoned in favour of a gravity arch dam. At Hirfanli (Turkey) fear of possible earthquakes and difficulties concerning the transport of cement to an isolated site were factors in favour of a rock fill dam as against the gravity dam first projected.

The Grib dam (Algeria) is a rock-fill dam because poor rock strata provided unsuitable foundation for a gravity dam and no suitable material was available for an earth dam.

The Serre-Ponçon dam will be a rock-fill dam because of the depth of the alluvium covering the rock bottom of the former deep valley of the Durance (France).

The Trängslet dam (Sweden) is a rock-fill dam built, because it was cheaper, with granite blocks on granite faultless foundation rock.

SITE INVESTIGATION

Careful investigation of (*a*) the whole reservoir area and of (*b*) the possible sites for the dam are essential. In addition it is necessary to determine (*c*) the physical and mechanical properties of the rock or soil; (*d*) whether these properties can be improved, particularly as regards imperviousness; and (*e*) the sources of suitable construction materials.

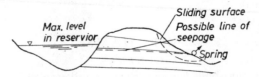

Figure 32.   Inclined strata as cause of water seepage

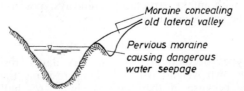

Figure 33.   Lateral valley, covered with moraine causes dangerous seepage

(*a*) The survey of the whole area must be carried out in greater detail than for ordinary geological surveys and by the methods described in the chapter on Site Investigation. The age and quality of rocks and soil, inclination of strata, local and general lines of fault and the position and flow of springs must all be found. The possible effects of inclined strata are shown in *Figure 32* and the risk of dangerous water seepage via a covered lateral valley is illustrated in *Figure 33*.

(*b*) The final site for a dam has to be selected from a number of possible sites, and geophysical exploration methods may be helpful in the preliminary investigations. *Figure 34* shows the rock profile obtained by rod soundings, *Figure 35*, the exploratory shaft and tunnel at Génissiat on the River Rhône and *Figure 36* those at Le Sautet. Exploration of this kind may indicate features not known from the preliminary survey, *e.g.* hidden alluvial deposits as at Mauvoisin, Switzerland, unstable rocks or hot springs as at Serre-Ponçon, France. Detailed maps and sections or a diagrammatic representation of the strata and faults are required before the final location of the dam can be decided. *Figure 37* shows the strata at the Beni-Bahdel dam (Algeria) and a dangerous fault can be seen. The weak layers of marl and clayish schists between harder sandstone strata and the

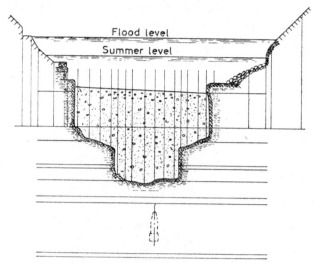

Figure 34. Génissiat: Sounding by rods

dangerous dipping of the strata in the downstream–downwards direction ruled out a gravity dam; a light multiple-arch structure was adopted.

(*c*) The physical and mechanical properties of the rock that have to be determined are:

(*i*) *The rock crushing strength, determined on selected samples*—Values so obtained are likely to be in excess of the rock strength when *in situ*. Rock strength varies so widely that no figures can be given; rely only on results from direct measurements.

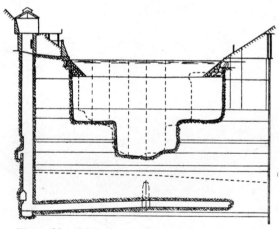

Figure 35. Génissiat: Exploratory tunnel and shaft

(*ii*) *Modulus of elasticity of the rock*—This data must be known if a gravity dam rests on different strata with widely varying elasticities. The modulus of elasticity must be known too for the final design of an arch dam. The modulus of elasticity can be measured in the laboratory on rock samples or by a direct compression test *in situ* or by measuring the velocity of shock waves either on samples (in laboratory) or *in situ*. Measurements *in situ* are by direct compression tests with a hydraulic jack (*Figure 38*), in a trench, or in a gallery (see Sect. XV under 'Geology for tunnels'). It has been found that there is usually some rock plasticity which disappears after several loadings (rock hysteresis), leaving only elastic deformations. The 'modulus of plasticity' is often about one third of the real modulus of elasticity. The elasticity depends on the direction of the force relative to the direction of the strata, as shown in TABLE 9.

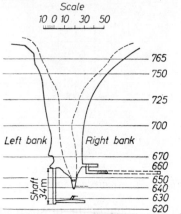

Figure 36. Le Sautet: Exploratory tunnels

Results show the modulus of elasticity to vary from 20,000 kg/cm² (130 ton/sq in) to about 400,000 kg/cm² (2,500 ton/sq in) depending on rock type. The lowest figure is for sandstone. A low value of E does not mean poor rock quality, but elastic rock.

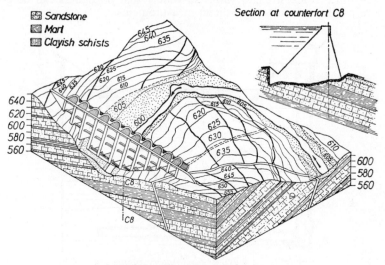

Figure 37. Site of Beni–Bahdel Dam

TABLE 9

MODULUS OF ELASTICITY OF ROCK

	Normal to strata		Parallel to strata	
	kg/cm²	ton/sq in	kg/cm²	ton/sq in
Urseren granite	250,000	1600	400,000	2500
Urseren schists	80,000	500	280,000	1800

For determination of the modulus of elasticity from seismic waves use the following formulae:

$$\mu = \left(\frac{1}{2}\frac{\alpha^2}{\beta^2} - 1\right)\left(\frac{\alpha^2}{\beta^2} - 1\right)$$

$$E = \frac{\gamma\alpha^2\,(1+\mu)\,(1-2\mu)}{144\,g\,(1-\mu)}$$

$$E = \frac{\gamma\beta^2\,(1+\mu)}{72\,g}$$

E in lb/sq in; μ=Poisson's ratio; α=compressional wave velocity; β=shear velocity; γ=density; α, β, γ, g in ft lb/sec units.

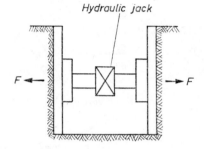

Figure 38. *Measurement of rock proper-*
ties in situ

(*d*) Grouting will improve the modulus of elasticity and of plasticity of hard fissured rock (limestones, *etc*) but not of clayish material, sandstone or marl. The effect of grouting on rock crushing strength has not been investigated. Grouting is used mainly for stopping seepage of water under the dam's foundations or round the abutments of the dam. *Figures 39, 40, 41* and *42* show how grouting is used under different types of dam. A first curtain of deep boreholes (grouted at pressures up to 40 atm) round the periphery of the dam foundations protects the foundations against uplift. This curtain is always on the upstream side of the dam and is supplemented

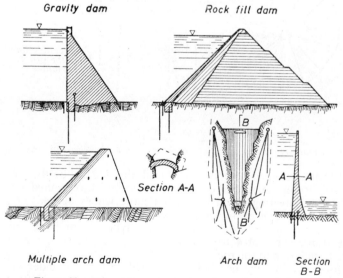

Figure 39. *Schematic arrangement of grouting and drains*

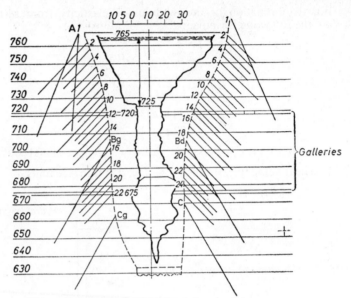

Figure 40. *Le Sautet: Grouting of rock: 1st screen*

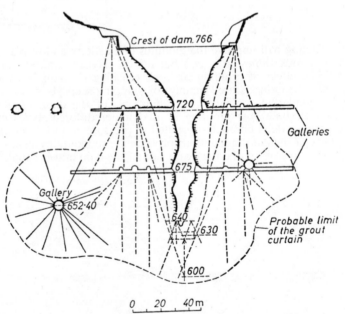

Figure 41. *Le Sautet: Scheme for grouting of rock: 2nd screen*

by a series of ungrouted boreholes used as drains, located on the downstream side of the curtain. A second curtain of boreholes, also grouted at pressures up to 40 atm, covering a wider area but more widely spaced, protects the whole site. Excellent examples of this technique at the dam at Le Sautet are shown in *Figures 40* and *41*. A third type of borehole, shorter and grouted at pressures of 4 to 7 atm, is used to increase the bond of the concrete foundation to the rock.

Before grouting, the boreholes are tested with water under pressure in order to locate the fissures. Grouting proceeds by 5 m (15–17 ft) steps in a downward direction. At Mauvoisin the procedure was: drilling 15 m downwards, grouting by steps from -15 to -10 m (measured from grouting level), from -10 to -5 m, from -5 m to surface, drilling through the first 15 m again and then down another 15 m to level -30 m and grouting upwards from -30 m to -15 m by steps of 5 m. A grouted borehole must then be tested with water under pressure. A rule of thumb states

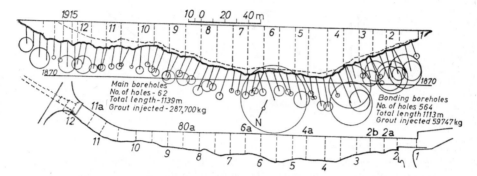

Figure 42. Seeuferegg. Grouting of rock: amount of grout injected

that: the borehole tested under full static pressure (measured from dam crest) plus 40–45 kg/cm² (570–640 lb/in²) additional pressure must not lose more than 5 l./sec per m ($\frac{1}{3}$ gal/sec per ft) length during 5 minutes. This rule may have to be adapted to local conditions. The number and positions of boreholes must be determined on the spot, depending on leakages.

Bitumen, cement/sand mortar, sawdust, ashes have also been used for stopping leakages. Cement mixed with clay and a wetting agent was used in alluvial deposits in the Serre-Ponçon dam foundations. Mortar was used to seal rock fissures in the bottoms of the reservoirs at Monte Jaque, Spain, and at Dokan, Iraq.

Prestressing with cables, anchored at the bottom of boreholes, was used to consolidate rock, in conjunction with grouting, for the foundations of the Castillon dam, France.

(*e*) Good deposits of sand and gravel or a quarry must be found near the site to produce aggregates for concrete if the dam is to be of the arch or gravity type, otherwise the cost may be prohibitive. Similarly for the core of a rock fill or earth dam, a nearby deposit of suitable clay is needed. Spoil from tunnels and underground power stations is often used for the construction of rock fill dams.

FORCES ACTING ON DAMS

Weight of the dam

In the absence of exact information, assume 150 lb/cu ft (2·4 ton/m³) for the density of ordinary concrete, slightly more for vibrated concrete (153 lb/cu ft), cyclopean concrete or granite masonry.

External water pressure (*Figure 43*)

The hydrostatic pressure is always to be taken perpendicular to the masonry surface. If the upstream dam face is inclined the water pressure has two components:

$$H = w\frac{h^2}{2} \quad \text{and} \quad V = w\frac{h^2}{2n}$$

$(1:n = \text{gradient of upstream dam face})$ $w = 62 \cdot 5$ lb/cu ft or 1,000 kg/m³

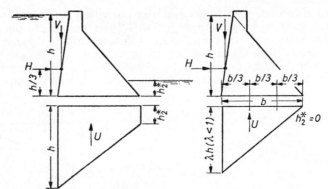

Figure 43. *External water pressures*   Figure 44. *Uplift on dam*

The uplift (*Figure 44*)

Water always penetrates the rock fissures, the pores of the concrete, the working joints of the masonry; the vertical resultant force is called the 'uplift'. Neglect of the uplift force has in the past led to disaster on several occasions. It has been proved that uplift acts on nearly the whole dam base.

The Maurice Lévy rule states that the uplift force (U) is equal to the full water pressure, as shown on *Figure 43*. If the downstream water depth is zero ($h_2^* = 0$) then the uplift is (dam width $= 1$) (*Figure 44*)

$$U = w\lambda \frac{hb}{2}$$

In the rule given above, $\lambda = 1$, but pressure measurements show that usually $\lambda < 1$ and values of $\lambda = 0.7$ to 0.8 (the higher value is the better) are usual for dam design in Europe. American engineers favour slightly higher values. The choice of λ depends on the quality of the rock, the direction of the strata, the efficiency of cut-off, grouting and drainage.

Earth or silt pressure

Use Rankine's formula $P = \dfrac{w_e h'^2}{2} \dfrac{(1 - \sin \rho)}{1 - \sin \rho}$

where P = total horizontal pressure in pounds or kg or tons
  w_e = the density of the silt or earth
  ρ = the angle of internal friction of the material
  h' = the depth of the silt or earth (ft or m)

Ice pressure

It is believed that an allowance of 10,000 lb per linear foot (15,000 kg/m) of dam crest would be ample for ordinary circumstances.

Earthquakes

Add $a = \pm 5$ to ± 20 per cent to all forces of gravity (dam weight, hydrostatic forces) and choose the most dangerous combination of vertical and horizontal forces. The value $a = \pm 10$ is usually taken.

Other forces

Wind forces, waves, weight of a spilling water nappe should be considered in special cases.

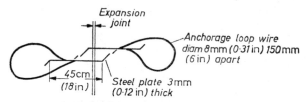

Figure 45. Seal for expansion joint

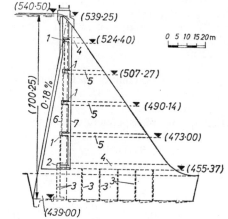

Figure 46. Salto dam. Inspection galleries and drains

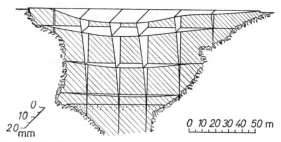

Figure 47. Deformation of the Schräh dam in Switzerland

CONSTRUCTION OF DAMS

Preparation of foundations

The last 2 ft or so should be excavated by pick, without blasting, and all loose rock removed. The rock surface must be thoroughly cleared by the use of high pressure air and water jets. Grease spots on the rock are particularly dangerous and must be cleared. Before placing the concrete the rock surface should be covered with a thin layer of rich mortar.

Concreting

Concreting should follow a pre-arranged programme. Each mass of concrete must be left undisturbed for at least 72 hours, protected by damp sacking against sun and drying winds. Concreting usually proceeds by independent pillars or columns separated by vertical expansion joints. The distance between expansion joints, which used to be 25 to 30 m (80 to 100 ft) has in most modern dams been reduced to about 12 to 15 m

(40 to 50 ft). (Longitudinal expansion joints are used in very large dams only and must be closed as soon as the concrete has cooled.) The columns of a gravity dam may rise independently but the columns of an arch dam must always be at the same level and rise simultaneously, so that the concrete of any horizontal arch is homogeneous and of the same age. The expansion joints are sealed on the upstream face and made water tight. *Figure 45* shows a typical seal.

The expansion joints of an arch dam must be grouted under pressure. This pressure grouting permits, to some extent, an adjustment of the compression stresses in the arches. The grouting usually takes place at the end of the cold (winter) season in order to decrease any danger of tensile stresses in the arches. This technique of grouting the expansion joints is sometimes also used in gravity dams in order to develop a lateral thrust on the abutments of the dam.

Type of concrete to be used. (See chapter on Cements, Vol. 1)

Only the best Portland cements should be used. Because of the cost of the cement, there is a definite tendency to reduce the cement content to a minimum. In particular, the mass concrete mix used for the core of a

TABLE 10

DATA ON LARGE GRAVITY DAMS

Dam	Country	Year	Height m	Volume of concrete cu m	Spacing of joints m	Weight of concrete per cu m kg/cu m		Water/ cement ratio
						Mass con- crete	Faces	
Schräh	Switzerland	1925	110	236,000	32	190	300	0·94-0·63
Barberine	Switzerland	1925	80	22,000	25	200	—	0·75-0·80
Bleiloch	Germany	1931	60	180,000	25	250	350	0·69
Boulder	U.S.A.	1935	220	2,500,000	7·5-20	225	—	0·59
Grand								0·60
Coulee	U.S.A.	1940	160	7,600,000	15	225	—	
Fontana	U.S.A.	1945	146	2,720,000	15	215	280	0·43-0·47
Shasta	U.S.A.	1945	184	5,100,000	—	—	—	0·53-0·57

TABLE 10a

DATA ON LARGE GRAVITY AND ARCH DAMS

Dam	Country	Storage capacity 10⁶ cu m	Volume of concrete 10³ cu m	Total head of scheme‡ m	Energy generated 10⁶ kWh	kWh/ cu m concrete§
Sarrans	France	200	450	430	170	380
Sautet	France	100	100	550	110	1100
Boulder	U.S.A.	18,500	2500	180	7000	2840
Castelo*	Portugal	1070 (875)†	400	95	300	750
Tignes*	France	235	650	982	700	1080
Rossens*	Switzerland	200 (180)†	250	75 and 110	230	920
Grande						
Dixence	Switzerland	350	5890	1814	1365	232
Mauvoisin*	Switzerland	180	2100	1434	564	269
Rätherichs-						
boden	Switzerland	27	2775	1121	65	234

*Arch dams.
†Active storage.
‡Including stations downstream of dam.
§200 kWh/cu m concrete considered to be the lowest acceptable figure for post-war conditions in the Alps.

gravity dam is less rich than the concrete mix used for the faces (see TABLE 10). Low heat cements are often used in the U.S.A. Improved ordinary Portland cement is the rule in Switzerland where climatic conditions rule out the American type of low heat cement. Pozzolanas and pulverized fuel ash as admixtures with cement, and blast furnace cement have been used in the U.S.A., France and Italy.

Cooling of the concrete during the setting period is a major problem; cooling can be by natural or forced circulation of air, *e.g.* Rossens, Switzerland, by water circulating in pipes embedded in the concrete or by cooling the aggregates.

Supervision of existing dams

A dam must be supervised during its whole life. Seepage water must be measured and the amount of lime dissolved by it checked. A system of vertical drains and inspection galleries protecting the dam against water seepage is shown in *Figure 46*. The measurement of temperatures, displacements and strains is a routine procedure in large dams (*Figure 47*). Horizontal displacements of the dam can be checked monthly by an instrument such as the 'Juillard' pendulum or at larger intervals by surveying methods. Various types of gauge suitable for measurement of strains in concrete are described in the chapter on Measuring Appliances, Vol. 1.

Heightening existing dams

The Aswan dam has been heightened twice. Other well-known examples are the Lages dam (Brazil) and the Grande Dixence project (Switzerland). The heightening of the Cheurfas dam in Algeria by Coyne, using stressed steel cables, is a most interesting example of modern techniques (*Figure 48*).

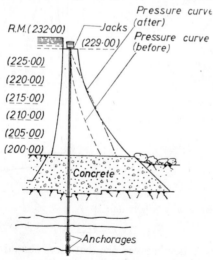

Figure 48. Heightening of Cheurfas dam

VIII. GRAVITY DAMS
Basic rules for calculation and design (TABLE 11)
FUNDAMENTAL APPROACH

It is possible to analyse the strain and stress distribution in a triangular gravity dam, acted on by hydrostatic pressure distribution, using the general

TABLE 11

ACCEPTABLE STRESSES FOR LARGE GRAVITY DAMS IN LB/SQ IN (IN BRACKETS [ ]
IN KG/SQ CM)

	Shasta	Grand Coulee	Bhakra (proposed)
Max. compressive stress	744 [52·3]	767 [53·9]	750 [52·7]
Max. shear stress	349 [24·5]	320 [22·5]	350 [24·6]
Max. sliding factor	0·716	0·833	0·75
Max. shear friction factor	5·0	5·2	5·0
Tensile stresses	None	None	None
Shear stress for shear friction factor estimate	600 [42·2]	700 [49·2]	500 [35·2]

equations of elasticity. The main result is that the distribution of stresses
along any horizontal section at level *y* is nearly linear. This fundamental
result (Pigeaud, France) is used in all the simplified methods dealing with
gravity dam calculation (*Figure 49*).

The relaxation method has also been used (Zienkievicz, London).

SIMPLIFIED APPROACH

Figure 50 shows how the resultant *R* from the horizontal water pressure
and the vertical forces *V*, *G* (own weight) and *U* (uplift) is obtained.

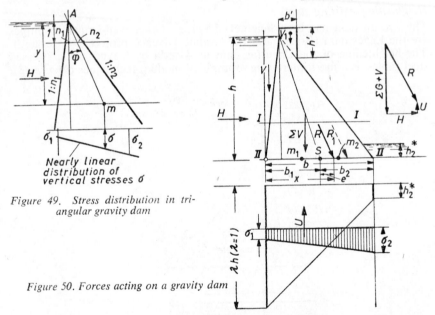

Figure 49. *Stress distribution in triangular gravity dam*

Figure 50. *Forces acting on a gravity dam*

The design rules to be observed are that there should be no overturning
(*R* should be well inside the dam base) and that no tensile stresses should
occur on either face of the dam. When the reservoir is full, tensile stresses
could occur on the upstream face of the dam; when empty, they may occur
on the downstream face. The uplift is usually represented by a triangular
distribution of upward pressure as in *Figure 51* with $\lambda \leqslant 1$.

Condition of no tensile stresses
To avoid tensile stresses, the resultant *R* must be inside the middle third of
the base. In *Figure 50* the base *b* is divided into three equal parts *b*/3 and *R*
is shown inside the middle third. If *e* is the eccentricity of *R* to the centre

of gravity S of the base b, then the stresses σ_1 and σ_2 (vertical stresses) are for a rectangular base $(b_1 = b_2 = b/2)$:

$$\sigma_{1,\,2} = \frac{\Sigma V - U}{b} \pm \frac{M}{I}(b/2)$$

or

$$\sigma_1 = \frac{\Sigma V - U}{b}\left(1 - \frac{6e}{b}\right) \qquad \dots\dots\dots(1)$$

$$\sigma_2 = \frac{\Sigma V - U}{b}\left(1 + \frac{6e}{b}\right) \qquad \dots\dots\dots(1a)$$

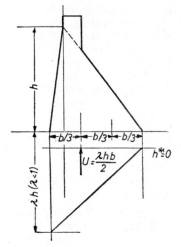

Figure 51. Uplift distribution of pressure

In these formulae $\Sigma V =$ the sum of all vertical forces, $U =$ uplift, $M =$ moment of all forces taken about the centre of gravity, S. If R falls at the limit of the middle third, then the formula yields:

for R at the upstream end m_1

$$\sigma_1 = \frac{2(\Sigma V - U)}{b}$$

$$\sigma_2 = 0$$

for R at the downstream end m_2

$$\sigma_1 = 0$$

$$\sigma_2 = \frac{2(\Sigma V - U)}{b}$$

If the base is not a rectangle, then $(b_1 \neq b_2 \neq b/2)$

$$\sigma_1 = \frac{\Sigma V - U}{A} - \frac{(\Sigma V - U)\,eb_1}{I} \qquad \dots\dots\dots(2)$$

$$\sigma_2 = \frac{\Sigma V - U}{A} + \frac{(\Sigma V - U)\,eb_2}{I} \qquad \dots\dots\dots(2a)$$

where $A =$ area of the base

$I =$ moment of inertia of the base about an axis passing through the centre of gravity S.

N.B.—When the dam has not a triangular section, this calculation must be repeated at different levels I–I, II–II, *etc,* and the resultant R at any level should be inside the middle third.

Shear forces and stresses

The resistance to sliding must be considered with shear neglected and with shear included. With shear strength τ neglected,

$$\frac{\Sigma H}{\Sigma V - U} = \tan \theta < f' \qquad \dots\dots\dots(3)$$

where $\tan \theta$ is the angle of R with the horizontal and f' is the coefficient of static friction in the joint considered; this coefficient is for well dressed surfaces. If a horizontal crack occurs in the dam, the surface will be very rough and the real friction factor f will be at least twice f' ($f \cong 2f'$). After a horizontal crack has occurred in a dam (shear strength $\tau = 0$) the safety factor against sliding is about 2 when conditon (3) is observed.

Note—During the Spanish civil war, one gravity dam near Oviedo was severely damaged by an explosion in galleries that had been cut into the dam. Fissures followed the working joints. These should always be slightly inclined, rising towards the downstream direction, for greater safety. The same rule is to be observed for the dam foundation on rock.

With shear strength τ included,

$$\Sigma H < \frac{f(\Sigma V - U) + r\tau A}{n'} \qquad \dots\dots\dots(4)$$

τ = unit shearing strength of the material (τ is about 350 lb/sq in or 25 kg/cm²)

A = area of the joint or base

r = ratio of average to maximum shearing stress ($r \cong 0.5$)

n' = safety factor. ($n' = 5$ adopted by the U.S. Bureau of Reclamation.)

When all the analyses and calculations have been made it will normally be found that the real safety of a gravity dam depends on this factor, $n' = 5$, against sliding. This is also the case for the stability of the rock foundations of the dam, and the direction of the rock strata is an essential factor for determining the real total safety of the structure. A well designed gravity dam will never fail: the foundations may because rock is often less homogeneous than concrete.

THE TRIANGULAR GRAVITY DAM

Simple formulae can be developed for a triangular dam. Let us assume that the apex of the triangle coincides with the water level. The upstream face is vertical. In addition, the dam crest has a width b' and (*Figure 52*)

$$\eta = \frac{b'}{b} = \frac{h'}{h}$$

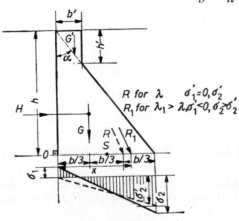

Figure 52. Triangular gravity dam

If w is the density of the water, w_c the density of the concrete, λ the uplift factor, then, the 'no tension condition' or 'middle third condition' yields

$$\tan \alpha = \left(\frac{w}{w_c \left[1 + 2\,(\eta^2 - \eta^3) \right] - \lambda w} \right)^{\frac{1}{2}}$$

$\tan \alpha$ is maximum for $\eta = 0$ or $\eta = 1$, and then

$$\tan \alpha = \left(\frac{w}{w_c - \lambda w} \right)^{\frac{1}{2}}$$

$\tan \alpha$ is minimum for $\eta = 2/3$, and becomes

$$\tan \alpha = \left(\frac{w}{1 \cdot 296\, w_c - \lambda w} \right)^{\frac{1}{2}}$$

These formulae are obtained by writing the overturning moment for all forces about point *O* (*Figure 50*).

If the real uplift factor λ_1 is greater than the assumed value λ, tensile stresses may develop on the upstream dam face. The following group of formulae give the stresses (*Figure 52*) for the case of $\lambda_1 \neq \lambda$

$$\tan \alpha = \left(\frac{w}{w_c \left[1 + 2\,(\eta^2 - \eta^3) \right] - \lambda w} \right)^{\frac{1}{2}}$$

$$\Sigma\, M \cdot w\ \frac{h^3}{6}\ \frac{2 w_c\,(1 + \eta^2) - w\,(\lambda + \lambda_1)}{w_c \left[1 + 2\,(\eta^2 - \eta^3) \right] - \lambda w}$$

$$x = \frac{h}{3} \tan \alpha\ \frac{2 w_c\,(1 + \eta^2) - w\,(\lambda + \lambda_1)}{w_c\,(1 + \eta^2) - \lambda_1 w}$$

$$e = x - b/2$$

$$\sigma_{1,\,2} = \frac{G + G' - U}{b} \left(1 \pm \frac{6e}{b} \right)$$

σ_1 is a tensile stress when $\lambda_1 > \lambda$.

DAM WITH MINIMUM VOLUME

The volume of a dam with vertical upstream face is (for unit width):

$$Vol = \tfrac{1}{2} bh + \tfrac{1}{2} b'h' = \tfrac{1}{2}\,(1 + \eta^2)\, h^2 \tan \alpha$$

Writing $\partial\,(Vol/h^2)/\partial \eta = 0$, yields:

$$\eta^3 - 2\eta^2 - 3\eta + 2\lambda\,\frac{w}{w_c} = 0$$

The root of this equation yields the value $\eta = b'/b$ for which the dam has a minimum volume. For $\lambda = 0 \cdot 8$, the saving in concrete will be about $0 \cdot 7$ per cent as compared with a triangular dam.

More concrete will be saved if the crest (width b') is shifted in the

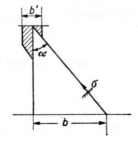

Figure 53. *Crest overhanging upstream face*

upstream direction, as shown on *Figure 53*. When the reservoir is empty, slight tensile stresses may develop on the downstream face. It will be found that they are usually not dangerous. Many reservoirs will never be completely emptied.

OTHER METHODS FOR REDUCING THE DAM VOLUME
(*Figures 54 and 55*)

It is well known that the full strength of the concrete is not used fully in many parts of the dam. Design will be improved if the expansion joints are widened, as indicated in *Figure 54*. This was done for the Rätherichs-boden dam (Switzerland). About 10 per cent concrete can be saved by this method. A further step towards better utilization of the concrete is shown on *Figure 55*. Some work on this type of dam has been done in Germany and the U.S.S.R.

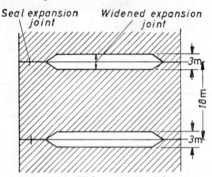

Figure 54. *Wide expansion joints to reduce volume concrete.*

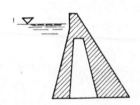

Figure 55. *Design of dam to reduce volume of concrete*

STRESSES ALONG THE DAM FACES AND INSIDE THE DAM

σ vertical, which will now be called σ_x can be calculated assuming linear distribution of stresses along a joint or foundation.

Along the dam faces, the following relations permit other stresses to be calculated (*Figure 56*).

σ_y in the horizontal direction is given by

$$\sigma_y = p - \frac{\tau}{\tan \phi}$$

and

$$\tau = \frac{p - \sigma_x}{\tan \phi}$$

where τ is a shear stress and p is the pressure on the dam face. (On the downstream face $p = 0$.)

From *Figure 57*

$$\sigma_{max} = \sigma_x - \frac{\tau}{\tan \phi} = \frac{\sigma_x}{\sin^2 \phi} - \frac{p}{\tan^2 \phi}$$

On the downstream face, where $p = 0$,

$$\sigma_{max} = \frac{\sigma_x}{\sin^2 \phi}$$

a relation of great importance for the estimate of the greatest compression stress. Thanks to the fact that there are never shear stresses parallel to the dam faces ($\tau=0$) the direction of the principal stresses (σ_{max} and σ_{min}) is known along the dam faces. It is either parallel or perpendicular to the dam face.

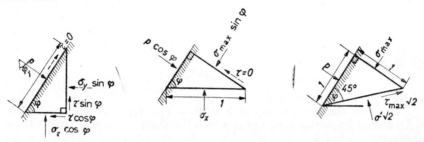

Figure 56. Stresses in dam   Figure 57. Stresses in dam   Figure 58. Stresses in dam

The maximum shear stress τ_{max} forms an angle of 45° with the principal stresses and *Figure 58* shows that

$$\tau_{max} = \frac{\sigma_{max} - p}{2}$$

and

$$\sigma' = \frac{\sigma_{max} + p}{2}$$

σ' being the compression stress in a direction perpendicular to τ_{max}. For $p=0$, $\sigma' = \tau_{max} = \sigma_{max}/2$.

According to Coulomb the shear stress τ at any point of a solid body is partly taken by friction. If $f = \tan \rho$ is the friction factor and σ the normal stress in a direction perpendicular to τ, then

$$\tau = f\sigma + \tau^* \text{ or } \tau^* = \tau - f\sigma$$

τ^* is that part of τ which is taken by shearing only and not by friction. *Figure 59* shows Mohr's circle designed for

$\sigma_{min} = OA$ and $\sigma_{max} = OB$ with a radius equal to $\frac{1}{2}(\sigma_{max} - \sigma_{min})$.

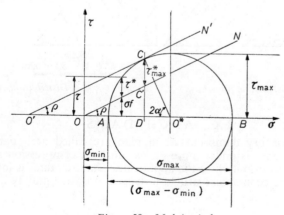

Figure 59. Mohr's circle

If the line ON is traced with an angle ρ to the horizontal, then the relation $\tau = \tau^* + f\sigma$ is as shown on the diagram and the maximum of τ^* is

$$\tau_{max}^* = CC' = CD - C'D$$

It is easy to show, using Mohr's circle, that

$$\tau_{max}* = \frac{\tau_{max}}{\cos\rho} - \frac{\sigma_x+\sigma_y}{2}\frac{\sin\rho}{\cos\rho}$$

or

$$\tau_{max}* = \frac{1}{2\cos\rho}\{[(\sigma_x-\sigma_y)^2+4\tau^2]^{\frac{1}{2}}-(\sigma_x+\sigma_y)\sin\rho\}$$

with

$$\rho+2\alpha=90° \qquad \alpha=45°-\rho/2$$

where α gives the direction of τ_{max}.

In many dams, especially in buttress dams, it is essential to estimate $\tau_{max}*$ and to know the direction in which the shear stress $\tau_{max}*$ is the more dangerous.

It is possible, with Mohr's circle, to calculate σ_x, σ_y, τ, σ_{max}, σ_{min}, τ_{max} and $\tau_{max}*$ at any point M of a dam and also to find the directions of σ_{max}, σ_{min}, τ_{max} and $\tau_{max}*$.

If we trace a continuous line being at any point tangent either to the direction of σ_{max} or to the direction of σ_{min}, we obtain an isostatic line. At any point of the dam, there are obviously always two isostatic lines, normal to each other.

Figure 60(a) shows the isostatic lines in a gravity dam where $\lambda=1$. *Figure 60(b)* shows the distribution curves for maximum compression stresses.

Adhesion between concrete and foundation rock is usually excellent and the dam is a 'built-in' or 'encastre' structure. Near the foundation, the real stress distribution is very different from what would normally be assumed from the usual calculations. The effect of the foundation can be studied in photoelastic models.

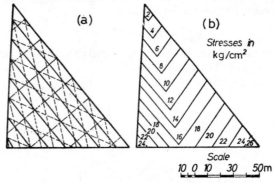

Figure 60(a). Isostatic lines   Figure 60(b). Distribution of stresses

IX. ARCH DAMS

Concrete or masonry dams curved in plan are called arch dams. The concrete or masonry is under more or less uniform compression and some of the loads are transmitted to the abutments. An arch dam is intrinsically a safer and more economical structure than an ordinary gravity dam.

HISTORY AND THEORETICAL APPROACH TO THE DESIGN PROBLEM

The technique of arch dam design and construction has been rapidly developed in the past twenty years, but such dams have been built since the beginning of the century. The 'thin cylinder formula' $\sigma=pr/e$

($\sigma =$ compression stress in arch, $e =$ arch thickness, $r =$ radius of the arch centre line, $p =$ hydrostatic pressure) was then used. Mörsch (Germany, 1908) proposed to calculate independent arches at different levels with the theory of elastic arches commonly used for arch bridge design. H. Ritter (Germany, 1913) assumed the monolithic dam to be composed of a series of horizontal arches and another series of vertical cantilevers. The method is described under the heading 'trial load method', p 232.

F. A. Noetzli (U.S.A., 1921) and A. Stucky (Switzerland, 1922) developed practical methods of calculation based on H. Ritter's recommendation. In 1922 a committee on arch dam investigation was set up in the U.S.A. One of the first tasks of the committee and, undoubtedly, the most important, was the construction of the Stevenson Creek dam, purely for experimental purposes. In close co-operation with the committee, the Bureau of Reclamation built a concrete model of the Stevenson Creek dam on a scale one-twelfth of the prototype, and a concrete model of the Gibson dam. The results of the tests on the Stevenson Creek model were entirely satisfactory and confirmed the usefulness of test models in arch dam analysis.

In 1925, F. Vogt (Norway) stressed the importance of the elastic deformation of the abutments. The ideas of Noetzli were developed further by the Bureau of Reclamation (Denver, U.S.A.), also under the name of 'trial load method', whereas M. Ritter (Switzerland, unpublished works) developed a new simplified method, which included the yielding of the abutment, in a straightforward calculation of the arches and of the cantilevers. J. Lombardi included the torsion effect in arch dam calculation. A mathematically complete solution was given by Allen and Pippard, using Southwell's relaxation method (1956).

Parallel to the analytical approach, methods based on model tests were developed mainly in Italy (Oberti and Semenza), Portugal (Serafim and Xeres) and in other countries.

SHAPE OF DAMS

Basically, arch dams are usually designed with a circular centre line in plan. The circle is well adapted to the concentric water pressure. The circle at the top has obviously the greatest radius. If all the circles have the same central angle, the dam is a 'constant angle' dam, *Figure 61*.

The angle at the centre giving the minimum volume of concrete is 132° if the arch is calculated as a thin cylinder. For practical reasons (cost of shuttering) it is usually less than the most favourable theoretical value, that is about 110° to 125°.

Constant angle dams are not easy to adapt to existing contour lines, so the alternative solution of the 'constant radius' dam, *Figure 62*, is often

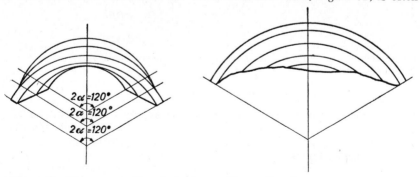

Figure 61. 'Constant angle' arch dam   *Figure 62. 'Constant radius' arch dam, vertical upstream face*

adopted. Sometimes one of the dam faces is a vertical circular cylinder (Rossens, Tignes). Modern dams are often neither constant angle, nor constant radius dams, but thin shells adapted to the shape of the valley.

Some designers prefer arches with constant thickness (Santa Giustina, Italy), possibly with a widened footing (Rossens dam, Switzerland); others favour an arch which thickens towards the abutments (Castelo do Bode, Portugal); the Lumiei dam (Italy) thickens slightly towards the abutments, where a peripheral joint allows for the free expansion of the shell during settling of the concrete (see *Figure 63(c)*). The peripheral joint was concreted before raising the water level in the reservoir.

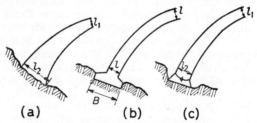

Figure 63. Types of arch dam

Vertical expansion joints are indispensable. They are closed and concreted in cold weather (end of the winter season) before raising the water level in the reservoir. The expansion joints of the Lumiei dam were inclined towards the peripheral joint (*Figure 64*).

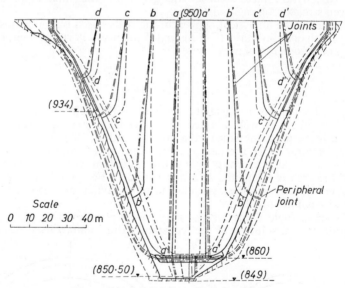

Figure 64. Lumiei dam. Peripheral joint

THE THIN CYLINDER FORMULA

The hydrostatic pressure $wh=p$ acts on the extrados of the circular arch. Let r be the radius of the circular centre line of the arch, e its thickness, $r_e=r+e/2$ the radius of the extrados. Then the pressure p' supposed to act on the centre line is

$$p'=p\frac{r_e}{r}$$

and the uniform circumferential compression stress σ in the thin cylinder, at depth h is

$$\sigma = \frac{p'r}{e} = p\frac{r_e}{e}$$

The formula for thin cylinders yields unreliable results in arch dam calculation and is used only for a rough first estimate.

THE THICK CYLINDER THEORY

Let r_e and r_i be the radii of a thick circular cylinder, p_e and p_i; the pressures, σ_r and σ_t the elastic stresses in the radial and in the circumferential direction (*Figure 65*) and x the position of the fibre considered from the centre. The theory of elasticity gives

$$\sigma_r = \frac{p_i r_i^2 - p_e r_e^2}{r_e^2 - r_i^2} - \frac{p_i - p_e}{x^2}\frac{r_i^2 r_e^2}{r_e^2 - r_i^2}$$

$$\sigma_t = \frac{p_i r_i^2 - p_e r_e^2}{r_e^2 - r_i^2} + \frac{p_i - p_e}{x^2}\frac{r_i^2 r_e^2}{r_e^2 - r_i^2}$$

For dams the external load[86] is $p_i = 0$, $p_e > 0$

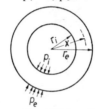

Figure 65. Thick cylinder

For $x = r_i$ (intrados)

$$\sigma_r = -\frac{p_e r_i^2}{r_e^2 - r_i^2}\left(1 - \frac{r_i^2}{r_i^2}\right) = 0$$

$$\sigma_t = -\frac{2 p_e r_e^2}{r_e^2 - r_i^2}\text{(compression)}$$

For $x = r_e$ (extrados)

$$\sigma_r = -\frac{p_e r_e^2}{r_e^2 - r_i^2}\left(1 - \frac{r_i^2}{r_e^2}\right) = -p\text{ (compression)}$$

$$\sigma_t = -\frac{p_e (r_e^2 + r_i^2)}{r_e^2 - r_i^2}\text{(compression)}$$

Because of the axial symmetry of the circular cylinder, the radial deformation of any radius is the same. For a thin cylinder, it is

$$\Delta_r = \frac{\sigma_t r}{E} = \frac{pr^2}{Ee}$$

(E = modulus of elasticity.)

A real arch dam is built in at its ends. If the rock is supposed to be rigid (first approximation) then no radial deflection is possible near the abutments. The arches forming an arch dam may therefore be regarded as encastré arches, to be calculated by the general methods of the theory of elasticity, rather than by the theory of cylinders.

THE TRIAL LOAD METHOD

The dam is assumed to be composed of a series of imaginary horizontal arches and another series of imaginary vertical cantilevers (*Figure 66*). The elastic grid of arch and cantilever elements thus obtained may be treated as a statically highly indeterminate main system by the known rules of statics. The arches and cantilevers are first considered separately and unknown forces X_i are applied to each point of intersection i. The unknown forces X_i are determined by means of the equations of elasticity. Finally the deformations and stresses in the dam are computed. The trial

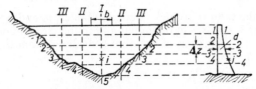

Figure 66. Division of dam into horizontal arches and vertical cantilevers

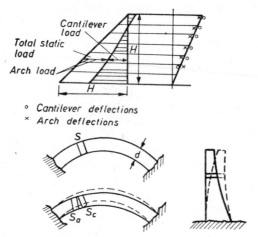

Figure 67. Assumed division of load between arches and cantilevers

load method determines the forces X_i by a tentative division of the hydrostatic load between the arch and cantilever elements in such a way that the deflections of both these elements at their points of intersection become equal. A probable load division for the arches and cantilevers is first assumed (*Figure 67*) and the lines of radial deflection are determined separately for either system. Naturally the first trial does not produce equal deflections at the conjugate points, but the division of load is varied until a sufficiently exact agreement of these deflections is reached. The trial load method is suitable for progressive amplification. Not only the radial deflections but the tangential deflections as well as the twisting of the arch and cantilever elements at their points of intersection are made to agree. Yielding of the abutments should be included.

RITTER'S SIMPLIFIED METHOD

The calculation of an arch dam by the trial load method is extremely complicated and long. Ritter's simplified method considers a symmetrical arch and is concerned only with the deflections of the crown of the arches which are made to agree with the deflection of the central cantilevers. If

n is the number of horizontal arches the problem is finally reduced to the solution of n equations with n unknowns. Radial deflections only are considered.

Calculation of the arches (Figure 68)

Ritter considers a symmetrical arch under uniform normal load p. With such a load, the pressure line of the three-pinned arch ACB is a circle. Let us assume that this pressure line is also the arch centre line. At any

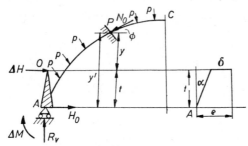

Figure 68. Moments and forces on circular symmetrical arch

point P of the circle, the forces and moments in the real arch are N and M. Ritter introduces two equal and opposite forces H_0 at point A, and so reduces the forces and moments acting on the real arch to:

$$\Delta H = H - H_0 \text{ acting at point } 0,$$
$$H_0 \text{ acting in } A,$$

the vertical reaction R_v in the simply supported beam and the residual moment ΔM, equal to the external moment in the abutment minus $H_0 t$ in A. (With $M_0 =$ moment of external loads, $H_0 =$ thrust at the abutment A of a three-pinned arch, and $M_0 - y'H_0 = 0$ and $N_0 =$ const. in a three-pinned arch 'pressure line'):

$$M = M_0 - y'H_0 + \Delta M - \Delta Hy = \Delta M - \Delta Hy$$
$$N = N_0 + \Delta H \cos \phi$$
$$Q = -\Delta H \sin \phi$$

The thin cylinder formula yields $N_0 = pr = $ const.
($r =$ radius of the circular centre line)
At the abutment A, we shall have for $\phi = \psi$

$$M_a = \Delta M + \Delta Ht$$
$$N_a = N_0 + \Delta H \cos \psi$$
$$Q_a = -\Delta H \sin \psi$$

Let α be the angular rotation of the abutment, δ the horizontal component of the lengthening of the arch due to elasticity, the crown C being supposed fixed (because of the symmetry of the arch) and $e =$ the horizontal displacement of the point A (abutment) then:

$$\alpha = \int_0^\psi \frac{Mds}{EI}$$

$$\delta = \int_0^\psi \frac{Myds}{EI} - \int_0^\psi \frac{N \cos \phi ds}{EA} + \int_0^\psi \frac{Q \sin \phi ds}{GA'}$$

$$e = \alpha t + \delta$$

where A = arch cross section, I = moment of inertia of the arch, E = modulus of elasticity of the concrete, $G = E/2(1+1/m)$, $A' = Am/(1+m)$, m = Poisson's ratio ($m \cong 5$ for concrete). On the other hand, considering the rock abutment with modulus of elasticity E_f and A_f, I_f = the foundation area and moment of inertia, d = arch thickness near abutment:

$$\alpha = -\varepsilon Ma + \varepsilon' Qa, \qquad \varepsilon \cong \frac{0 \cdot 6 d}{E_f I_f}, \qquad \varepsilon' \cong \frac{0 \cdot 6}{E_f A_f}$$

$$\delta = e - \alpha t, \qquad e = \delta_n \cos \psi + \delta_x \sin \psi \quad (Figure\ 69)$$

ΔM and ΔH are unknown quantities, t can be chosen freely.
   It can be shown that, if

$$t = \frac{\displaystyle\int_0^{\psi} \frac{y' ds}{EI} - \varepsilon' \sin \psi}{\displaystyle\int_0^{\psi} \frac{ds}{EI} + \varepsilon} \qquad \text{then } \Delta M = 0,$$

and $\Delta H = \dfrac{-N_0 \left(\displaystyle\int_0^{\psi} \frac{\cos \phi ds}{EA} + \delta_N' \right)}{\displaystyle\int_0^{\psi} \frac{y^2 ds}{EI} + \int_0^{\psi} \frac{\cos^2 \phi ds}{EA} + \int_0^{\psi} \frac{\sin^2 \phi ds}{GA'} + \delta' + \varepsilon t^2 + \varepsilon' t \sin \psi}$

where, according to Ritter:

$$\delta_N' = \delta_N \cos \psi$$

$$\delta' = (\delta_N \cos^2 \psi + \delta_M t \sin \psi + \delta_q \sin^2 \psi)$$

$$\delta_N = \frac{2d}{E_f A_f}, \qquad \delta_M = \frac{0 \cdot 06 d^2}{E_f I_f}, \qquad \delta_q = \delta_N$$

If the elasticity of the rock is neglected (first approximation) then $\delta_N' = 0$, $\delta_N = 0$, $\varepsilon = 0$, $\varepsilon' = 0$.

With this method, the correct choice of t permits the elimination of ΔM and it can be seen that $\Delta H = -C N_0$, where C = constant. This important end result justifies the intricate basic assumptions of the method.

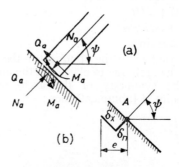

Figure 69.   *Moments and thrust at abutment*

Calculation of the cantilevers (Figure 70)
The calculation of the cantilever deflections is a straightforward one. Let us suppose that a force $P_i = 1$ is acting at point i. We want to know the

deflection produced at point j by this force $P_i=1$ at i. Let us suppose that the element ds alone is elastic. The angular deflection of this element is (*Figure 70*):

$$d\phi = \frac{Mds}{EI}$$

where

$M=$ moment at point ds due to $P_i=1$; $M=z_i$
$E=$ modulus of elasticity of the concrete
$I=$ moment of inertia of the cantilever considered at point ds.

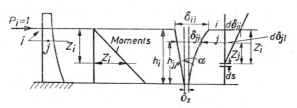

Figure 70. Cantilever deflections

Owing to $d\phi$ the elastic displacement of point j is:

$$d\delta_{ji} = z_j d\phi = \frac{z_i z_j ds}{EI}$$

The total displacement of point j, owing to $P_i=1$ at i is obtained when considering that all elements ds between the foundation level and the level of j are elastic. We, therefore, obtain for this displacement:

$$\int \frac{z_i z_j ds}{EI}$$

To this elastic displacement we have to add the tangential displacement δ_x of the foundations and the displacement αh_j due to the angular rotation α of the foundation, so that

$$\delta_{ji} = \int \frac{z_i z_j ds}{EI} + \delta_x + \alpha h_j$$

All the values δ_{ji} have to be calculated for the cantilever.

Total elastic deformation of the dam. Equations of elasticity

Let us consider the deflections of the dam crown only. The dam is assumed to be composed of n 'arch slices' in the usual manner, the height of any slice being Δz_i. The width of the cantilever at the crown is b. The arches are loaded with uniform water pressure. The total water loads are:

$$W_1, W_2 \ldots W_i \ldots W_n$$

Part of these loads are taken by the cantilevers, which are under the action of the forces:

$$P_1, P_2, \ldots P_i \ldots P_n$$

so that the loads on the n arches are:

$$(W_1-P_1), (W_2-P_2), \ldots (W_i-P_i) \ldots (W_n-P_n)$$

The δ_{ji} value is the elastic deflection of point j of the central cantilever produced by a force $P_i=1$ acting at point i. Furthermore, let δ_{si} be the deflection of the crown of arch i due to the uniform load$=1$ acting on arch i. The crown deflection is a linear function of the load, so the final deflection is

$$(W_i-P_i) \delta_{si}$$

The equations of elasticity are obviously:

$$P_1\delta_{11} + P_2\delta_{12} + P_3\delta_{13} + \ldots = (W_1 - P_1)\,\delta_{s1}$$
$$P_1\delta_{21} + P_2\delta_{22} + P_3\delta_{23} + \ldots = (W_2 - P_2)\,\delta_{s2}$$
$$P_1\delta_{31} + P_2\delta_{32} + P_3\delta_{33} + \ldots = (W_3 - P_3)\,\delta_{s3}$$

All the factors δ_{s1}, δ_{s2}, δ_{s3} ... and δ_{11}, δ_{12}, δ_{13} ... δ_{ji} are calculated in advance. The n forces $P_1, P_2, P_3 \ldots P_n$ are obtained from the solution of the n linear equations of elastic deformation. The yielding of the abutment can easily be included in this calculation, as shown previously.

THE EXTENDED METHOD OF LOMBARDI

Lombardi uses the equations of thin shells, published in 1934 by Flügge, which he simplifies and adapts to the problem of arch dams. The treatment is in line with the approach by M. Ritter. The most important achievement of this method is to include in the analysis the torsion of the dam. This was found to take a substantial part of the load, even in the case of symmetric arch dams. The thin shell theory explains the bending of the line of principal stresses towards the abutments (*Figure 71*) which is obtained by direct measurements on arch dams or on models.

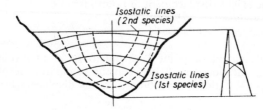

Figure 71. Lines of principal stresses (from measurements)

DIRECT ANALYSIS BY THE RELAXATION METHOD

The relaxation method of R. V. Southwell is obviously the proper tool for a further advance in arch-dam analysis. The method has been used by Allen, Chitty, Pippard and Severn in an investigation of the design for the Dokan dam[87].

MODEL TESTS ON ARCH DAMS

In the design of modern arch dams full advantage is taken of the technique of model testing.

To express the similarity relations, the following notations are used.

E_m = modulus of elasticity of dam model material
E_d = modulus of elasticity of prototype material
λ = scale ratio of prototype to model (about 1 to 50 to 1 to 100)
δ^* = specific gravity of model liquid (mercury 13·6) or equivalent pressure by hydraulic jacks.

The relation between deflections measured on the prototype and the model will be:

$$\rho = \frac{E_m\lambda^2}{E_d\delta^*}$$

The similarity relation between the unit deformation is:

$$\rho_1 = \frac{E_m\lambda}{E_d\delta^*}$$

The similarity relation between stresses is:

$$\rho_2 = \lambda / \delta*$$

Suppose that μ is the ratio of the crushing strength of the concrete to the crushing strength of the model; the load on the model when crushing occurs is produced by a system of hydrostatic jacks, representing an ideal liquid with a specific density of $\delta_{cr}*$ by which the model is supposed to be ruptured. The similarity relation in this case is:

$$\rho_{cr} = \frac{\lambda}{\delta_{cr}*}$$

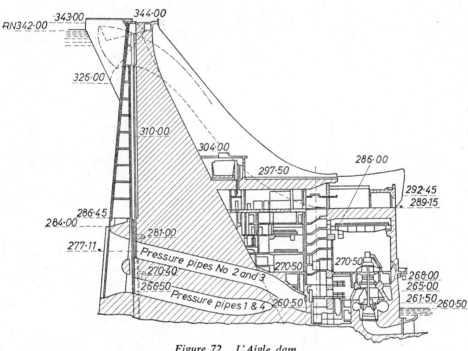

Figure 72. L'Aigle dam

and the safety factor ε against rupture of the dam itself:

$$\varepsilon = \frac{\mu}{\rho_{cr}}$$

Plaster of Paris (Castelo do Bode, *etc*), light concrete (Pieve di Cadore), rubber (Dokan) *etc*, have been used for dam models. Strains and stresses are measured on the model which can be used not only for checking a design, but for the design itself (Oberti, Serafim)[91, 92].

ARCH DAM DESIGN AND CONSTRUCTION
(*Examples: Figures 72 to 77*)

The general shape of arch dams has been discussed in Sect. IX, 2, of this chapter. Modern dams are seldom constant angle dams. They usually are more or less constant radius dams, adapted to the contour lines; departure from the constant radius is noticeable mainly at the dam bottom (Rossens, Tignes). One of the modern dams with varying radius is the Enchanet dam in France.

When designing a new dam, it is recommended that a start be made from the known data of existing dams, conveniently interpreted (law of similarity for stresses and strains). This first design will be checked by model tests and calculations. Later on, direct measurements may be made on the prototype. For example, the existing designs of the Rossens and Tignes dams were found to be most useful when designing the Dokan dam.

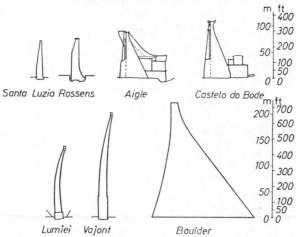

Figure 73.   Cross sections of some large arch dams

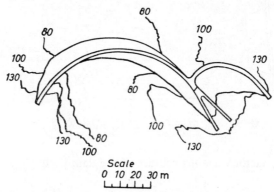

Figure 74.   Plan of Santa Luzia dam,   Portugal

The first design was then tested on a rubber model and re-calculated by Southwell's relaxation method.   Special attention should be given to the shaping of the abutments, to joints, temperature stresses, cooling of the concrete and the progress of the work.   Radial expansion joints are always used, being closed at the end of the cold season.   Circumferential expansion or working joints are used only in very large dams (Boulder dam, Mauvoisin).   For actual examples see TABLE 12 and *Figures 72–77*.

X.   BUTTRESS DAMS—HOLLOW GRAVITY DAMS[95-100]

In ordinary gravity dams, the properties of the concrete are not used to the full.   In the central part of the dam, the high-strength concrete is not stressed as it could be.   The basic idea of hollow gravity dams and buttress

TABLE 12

DATA ON SOME RECENT ARCH DAMS

Name of dam	Country	Year	Height H, m	Crest length L, m	L/H	Radius at crest level, m	Radius at the base, m	Angle at crest level, deg.	Thickness of arch crest, m	Thickness of arch base, m	Thickness at foundation level, m	B/H	I volume of impounded water 10⁶ m³	V volume of concrete 10³ m³	I/V	Remarks
Rossens	Switzerland	1945-48	83	320	3·85	165	105	111°	5	14	28	0·169	180	250	720	Downstream face a cylinder. Enlargement at the dam base
Clark Dam	Tasmania		59	254	4·3	118	45·7	120°*	5·2	24	24	0·41				U-shaped valley. Upstream face a cylinder
Santa Luzia	Portugal	1943	70	115	1·64	57·5		110°	2·5	12	13·5	0·171				Downstream face non-concentric circles. Two arches with intermediary buttress
Castelo do Bode	Portugal	1947-50	115	255	2·2	150	21	114°	6	52	52	0·475	875	400	2180	Main arch twisted. Upstream face vertical cylinder
Marèges	France		90	247	2·7	100			3·0	19·10	35	0·212	35	185	190	Overhanging upstream face; thick abutments
Aigle	France	1949-53	90	290	3·2	150	46·25†	111°	5·5	45·5	56·2	0·505	160	240	668	Downstream face is a conoid
Tignes	France		180	295·5	1·64	ext. rad.	125‡		10	43·6	43·6	0·243	235	650	360	Upstream face a cylinder
Pieve di Cadore	Italy	1947-49	110 / 55*	410	3·7 / 7·4*		11·50	146°	5	35·8	35·8		64	737	170	Valley unsymmetrical. Arch and arch gravity dam combined
Osiglia	Italy	1939	75	225	3·0								13	75	174	
Val Gallina	Italy	1950	86	225	2·6			97°					59	80	740	
Lumiei	Italy	1941-47	136·5	138·4	1·0	128	73·96	104°	3·15	14·3	15·6	0·1048	75	100	750	Cupola-arch dam with peripheral joint
Santa Giustina	Italy	1946-50	152·5	90	0·59	74			3·5	16·5	16·5	0·106	172	130	1433	Downstream face a cylinder; V-shaped valley
Vajont†	Italy	design	207	130	0·63			100°	3·5	16	17·5	0·077	58	190	306	Project (provisional values only) cupola-arch dam; V-shaped valley
Cabril	Portugal	1951-54	132	300	2·3	155	79	110°	5	20·6		0·16	600	280	2100	Cupola-arch dam
Gage	France	1953	38	143	3·75	65	65	126°	1·3	2·57	2·57	0·0676	3·3	6·5	500	Thin vertical circular cylinder
Dokan	Iraq	1956-60	116·5	240	2·06	120	120	115°	6·2	32·45	54	0·333	6800	364	18700	U-shaped valley; upstream face is a vertical cylinder
Lienne	Switzerland	1955-58	160	246	1·54	140	90	101°	7	25	25	0·156	50			V-shaped asymmetrical valley
Mauvoisin	Switzerland	1951-59	237	520	2·19	2734	69	109°	14	53·5	53·5	0·225	180	2030	89	V-shaped valley

*Average height on Pian dell Ere neglecting plug in narrow gorge.

†Downstream face of Aigle dam given by $\rho = 1.5z \cos\varphi + 2(75 - z)$; gradient of generatrix $J = -\dfrac{d\rho}{dz} = 2 - 1.5\cos\varphi$, with ρ = radius, z = depth from dam crest and $\varphi = \frac{1}{4}$ angle in the centre.

‡Downstream face of Tignes dam given by $\rho = 140 - z^2(360 - z)\,\dfrac{1 - 0.66\cos\varphi}{35000}$.

dams is to reduce the total volume of concrete by concentrating the material where the stresses are higher. Various types have been developed, from the Rätherichsboden type (enlarged expansion joints saving about 10 per cent in concrete) to the thin buttress dams.

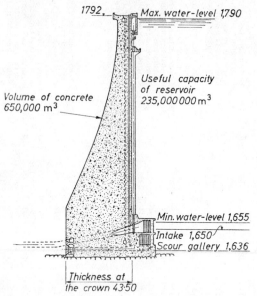

Figure 75. Tignes dam

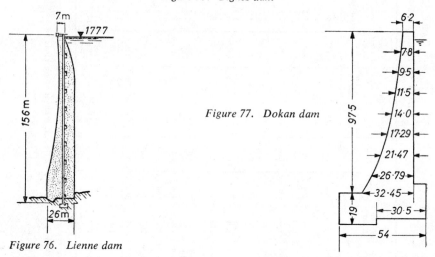

Figure 76. Lienne dam

Figure 77. Dokan dam

TYPICAL EXAMPLES

(a) The gravity dam with enlarged expansion joints, *e.g.* Rätherichsboden, Switzerland (*Figure 54*), Konar dam (Damodar Valley, India).

(b) The hollow gravity dam. *Ex.*: Krangede, Sweden (*Figure 78*).

(c) The Armbusten type with plane upstream face. *Ex.*: the Storglomm-vann dam, Norway (*Figure 79*).

(d) The multiple arch dam, where the upstream face is formed by a succession of cylindrical arches. The classical example is the Beni-Bahdel dam, Algeria (see *Figure 37*).

(e) The Noetzli type dam with diamond-headed buttresses.
(f) The Dixence type, cellular buttress dam (*Figure 80*).
(g) The modern alpine type, developed simultaneously by Italian and
or an improvement on the Noetzli type (e). *Ex.*: The Lucendro dam,
Switzerland (*Figure 81*); the Bau Muggeris and Sabbione dams (Italy).
The upstream face is inclined.

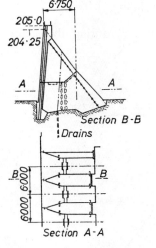

Figure 78. *Krangede dam, Sweden*

Switzerland (*Figure 81*); the Bau Muggeris dam (Italy). The upstream
face is inclined.
(h) The light buttress dam, the most striking examples being the Faux-
la-Montagne dam, France, and some Norwegian dams.
(i) Buttresses anchored in foundation rock: Saint Michel dam in Brittany,
France.

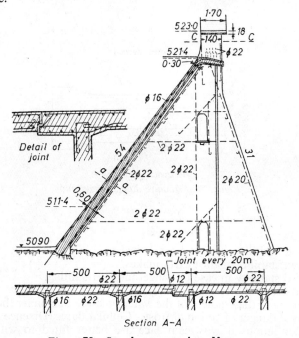

Section A–A

Figure 79. **Storglommvann dam, Norway**

ADVANTAGES AND DISADVANTAGES OF BUTTRESS DAMS

The main advantages are:

(*a*) Economy in volume: about 30 per cent for the Lucendro type, representing an economy of 10–25 per cent in price (depending mainly on cost of shutters) and even more for very light buttress dams.
(*b*) Better distribution of the compression stresses on the foundation.
(*c*) Better conditions for stability against sliding.
(*d*) Suppression or decrease of the uplift.
(*e*) Better dissipation of the heat generated during the setting of the cement.

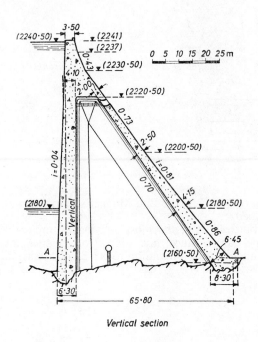

Vertical section

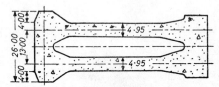

Horizontal section A-A

Figure 80.   Dixence dam, Switzerland

Disadvantages:

(*a*) Reduced stability against lateral thrust.
(*b*) Reduced stability against earthquakes.
(*c*) Reduced stability in case of dangerous over-spilling.
(*d*) More difficult shuttering work.
(*e*) Steepening of the gradient of the water pressure line under the dam.
(*f*) Increased danger of action of frost. Cellular dams (Dixence, Lucendro) with continuous downstream face are better fitted to withstand the action of frost.

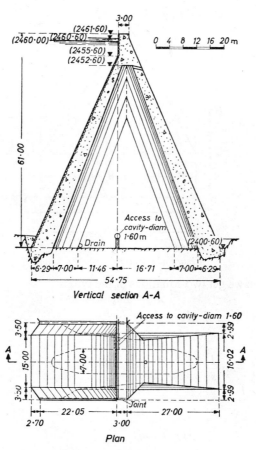

Figure 81. Sabbione dam, Italy

METHODS OF CALCULATION

General stability conditions. (*Method of Contessin.*) (*Figure 82*)

A buttress dam depends on the following main free parameters:

The ratio of the buttress thickness s to the distance l between the axis of two buttresses:

The slope of the upstream face cot $\phi_w = \theta_w$

The slope of the downstream face cot $\phi_a = \theta_a$

According to *Figure 82*, $b = (\theta_w + \theta_a) y$, ($y$ = height of dam).

The position of the resultant R is given by $\alpha = r/b$.

The horizontal water load is $H = \frac{1}{2}wy^2l$, the vertical water load is $V = \frac{1}{2}w\theta_wy^2l$, the uplift is $U = \frac{1}{2}w\lambda y \cdot nb \cdot l$.

The own weight of the buttress is: $P_1 = (w_c/2) y^2\theta_a s$, and $P_2 = (w_c/2) y^2\theta_w s$. If f is the friction factor ($f = 0.65$ to 0.75 are usual values), the condition for 'no sliding' is given by:

$$P_1 + P_2 + V - U - H/f \geqslant 0$$

Similarly, taking moments about point 0 yields an equation of the type:

$$P_1p_1 + P_2p_2 + Vv - Hh - Uu = \alpha b (P_1 + P_2 + V - U)$$

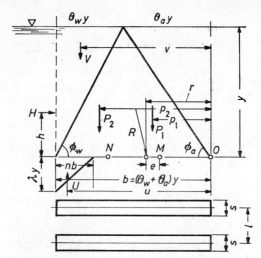

Figure 82. Forces on buttress dam

By substitution we get two equations of the type:

$$A\theta_w + B\theta_a - C = 0$$

where

$$A = \frac{w_c}{w} + \frac{l}{s} - \lambda n \frac{l}{s}$$

$$B = \frac{w_c}{w} - \lambda n \frac{l}{s}$$

$$C = \frac{1}{f}\frac{l}{s}$$

and

$$D\theta_w^2 + E\theta_a^2 + F\theta_w\theta_a - G = 0$$

when

$$D = \frac{w_c}{w}(\tfrac{1}{3} - \alpha) + \lambda n \frac{l}{s}(\alpha + \tfrac{1}{3}n - 1) + \frac{l}{s}(\tfrac{2}{3} - \alpha)$$

$$E = \frac{w_c}{w}(\tfrac{2}{3} - \alpha) + \lambda n \frac{l}{s}(\alpha + \tfrac{1}{3}n - 1)$$

$$F = \frac{w_c}{w}(1 - 2\alpha) + 2\lambda n \frac{l}{s}(\alpha + \tfrac{1}{3}n - 1) + \frac{l}{s}(1 - \alpha)$$

$$G = \tfrac{1}{3}\frac{l}{s}$$

A first approach to the problem consists in determining beforehand a certain value $\alpha \geqslant 0\cdot333$ and finding suitable values for l/s, θ_a and θ_w.

Another approach is to consider the condition for no tensile stresses on the upstream face of the dam (*Figure 83*), *i.e.*

$$\sigma_{\mathrm{II}} = \sigma_{x_1}(1 + \theta_w^2) - wy\frac{l}{s}\theta_w^2 = 0$$

which gives

$$\sigma = \frac{wy(l/s)\theta_w^2}{1 + \theta_w^2}$$

On the other hand

$$\sigma_{x_1} = \frac{6\Sigma(V)e}{sb^2}$$

where $\Sigma(V)=$ sum of all vertical forces. Replacing $\Sigma(V)$ and b by their values yields a value $\alpha=\alpha^*$ for which $\sigma_{II}=0$. If the chosen value is $\alpha>\alpha^*$ then σ_{II} is always positive.

This approach is most helpful for a first estimate.

Figure 83. *Condition for no tensile stresses on upstream face*

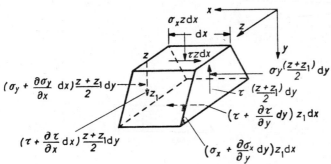

Figure 84. *Equilibrium forces in a buttress dam*

Direct calculation

It is assumed that the thickness z of the buttress varies linearly with the depth y but does not vary with x (*see Figure 84*). The equations of equilibrium for an elemental volume $zdxdy$ are:

$$\frac{\partial \tau}{\partial x} = \frac{\sigma_x}{z}\frac{\partial z}{\partial y} + \frac{\partial \sigma_x}{\partial y} - w_c$$

$$\frac{\partial \sigma_y}{\partial x} = \frac{\tau}{z}\frac{\partial z}{\partial y} + \frac{\partial \tau}{\partial y}$$

($w_c=$ density of concrete)

σ_x is known through direct calculation, as explained in the general section on gravity dams and in the previous section. At any point x (*Figure 85*)

$$\sigma_x = \sigma_{x_2} - x\frac{\sigma_{x_2} - \sigma_{x_1}}{b}$$

In addition, according to our assumption, $(1/z)(\partial z/\partial y)$ has a constant value. The second term $\partial \sigma_x/\partial y$ represents the variation of σ_x along a vertical ($x=$const). To calculate this value, the σ_x will be calculated at the depth $y-\Delta y$, y and $y+\Delta y$ and the average value $\partial \sigma_x/\partial y$ calculated (graphically) for a number of vertical sections $x=x_1, x=x_2, x=x_3, \ldots$ This calculation yields $\partial \tau/\partial x$ and finally (*Figure 86*)

$$\tau = \tau_2 + \int \frac{\partial \tau}{\partial x} dx$$

when τ_2 is the value of τ (horizontal) at the downstream face ($x=0$), and at the depth y. The calculation is repeated for the whole dam, y varying from top to bottom.

In order to check this calculation the relation

$$H = z\int_0^1 \tau dx$$

can be used.

Small discrepancies may occur, owing to the fact that τ values in multiple arches are negative.

After calculating the τ values at levels $y-\Delta y$, y, $y+\Delta y$, the $\partial\tau/\partial y$ values are derived, and the second equation is used for calculating $\partial\sigma_y/\partial x$.

σ_x, σ_y and τ being known, Mohr's circle yields σ_{max} and σ_{min}, τ_{max} and $\tau^*=\tau-f\sigma$ and its maximum value τ^*_{max} (*Figure 59*).

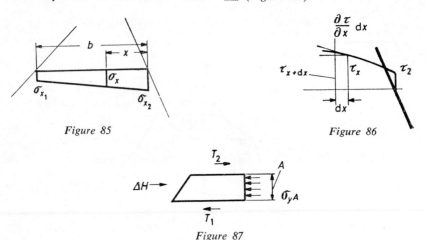

Figure 85   Figure 86

Figure 87

If z varies with x, use the following formulae and methods:

$$\frac{\partial\tau}{\partial x} = \frac{\sigma_x}{z}\frac{\partial z}{\partial y} + \frac{\partial\sigma_x}{\partial y} - \frac{\tau\partial z}{z\partial x} - w_c$$

The calculation is more difficult than when $\partial z/\partial x=0$.

The second equation

$$\frac{\partial\sigma_y}{\partial x} = \frac{\tau}{z}\frac{\partial z}{\partial y} + \frac{\partial\tau}{\partial y} - \frac{\sigma_y}{z}\frac{\partial z}{\partial x}$$

is difficult to manage and it is easier to write the bulk equilibrium of part of the buttress as shown on *Figure 87*, where $T=\int_0^x z\tau dx$, $A=$ vertical area of the element considered and $\Delta H=$ water load:

$$\sigma_y A = \Delta H + T_2 - T_1$$

All calculations should be made with great accuracy (6 to 7 figures).

XI. EARTH DAMS AND ROCK-FILL DAMS[101-117]

Many of the best sites for gravity or arch dams have been used, and in the further development of hydro-electric potentialities it may be necessary to consider less favourable sites where the ground conditions are not suitable for these types of dam. Earth or rock-fill dams may then be chosen. The continued increase in prices and wages favour the earth or rock-fill types because less skilled labour is needed and heavy mechanical equipment can be used to advantage. For example, many of the dams recently built in Sweden have excellent rock foundations, but the rock-fill type was chosen. Other factors that may influence the decision in favour of the earth or rock-fill type are difficulties in obtaining or transporting cement and aggregates or the higher resistance to earthquake damage, *e.g.* the Hirfanli dam in Turkey.

FOUNDATIONS

No special comments are required for foundations on rock. The only problem is the sealing-off of possible faults. An inspection gallery running underneath the dam is recommended and grouting can proceed from this gallery after the completion of the dam, if the water seepage is more than expected. Any seepage of water has a certain value which can be estimated in kWh and in money, against which the cost of more grouting may be balanced. This calculation shows when further grouting would become uneconomical. Grouting of the foundations of a rock-fill dam for a medium-head plant in Sweden would be stopped earlier than the grouting of a similar dam for a high-head scheme in the Alps, because of the higher potential value of the unit volume of water in the latter case.

Foundations on gravel or on gravel and sand are secure, but the seepage of water underneath the dam through the pervious material has to be stopped or reduced, either by carrying the impervious core of the dam down to the rock strata, or by using steel sheet or concrete piling or by grouting.

Foundations on clayey material are impervious, but clayey alluvium of recent geological formation may not be compact and may move under the weight of a dam.

GROUTING OF FOUNDATIONS

The foundations of the Serre-Ponçon dam[114] presented many difficult problems. Much geological investigation by means of shafts, galleries, vertical and inclined boreholes had to be undertaken. Hot springs with considerable amounts of mineral salts were encountered during the investigation. A test cutting was carried out in 1955 to test, on the site, the possibility of sealing the pervious alluvium under the dam. It consisted of a series of boreholes, drilled in successive rows down to the hard rock foundation. A mixture of very fine clay and slag cement was used for grouting, which was carried out from borings equipped with tubes and rubber valves. The pressures reached in the deeper zones were of the order of 50 to 60 kg/cm^2 (700 to 850 lb/in^2). The consumption of dry injection material of clay and slag was 500 kg/cu m (31 lb/cu ft) during the tests; this will be reduced to 350 kg/cu m (22 lb/cu ft) for the final grout curtain. The permeability of the alluvium was reduced from about 2×10^{-2} cm/sec in the natural state to about 10^{-4} or 10^{-5} cm/sec in the grouted area. The upper layer of 7 m (23 ft) depth could not be grouted because it would have been lifted by the grout pressure. It was removed before building the core of the dam. The efficiency of the grout curtain was duly tested by test pits before the final decision to proceed with the dam construction was taken. The latest project for the Sadd-el-Ali dam (High Aswan dam), Egypt (1956), is based on the same principles as the Serre-Ponçon dam which are typical of modern grouting techniques in alluvium.

TYPES OF DAM

Depending on the type of material available near the site, either earth or blocks of rock are used for the bulk of the dam. With rock filling a core of fine clay or a concrete wall or an inclined concrete slab may be used to form an impervious layer.

Figure 88 represents a dam built with homogeneous pervious materials, with a vertical clay core in the middle of the dam. In *Figure 89* this clay core has been replaced by a vertical concrete wall. *Figure 92* shows the clay core to be inclined. This reduces the total volume of the dam and/or increases its stability. The inclined clay core can be built only after the bulk

pervious material on which it rests has settled and when no further major
settlement is to be feared. This may slow down the construction of the
dam or even make it too expensive for this solution to be adopted, depending
on climatic conditions.

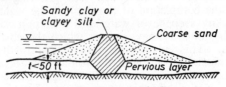

Figure 88. *Earth dam with clay core*

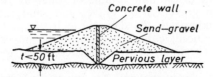

Figure 89. *Earth dam with concrete core wall*

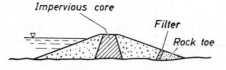

Figure 90. *Dam on impervious foundation*

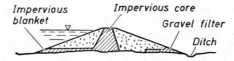

Figure 91. *Dam on pervious foundation of great depth*

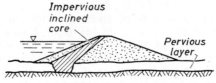

Figure 92. *Dam with inclined clay core reaching down to impervious foundation*

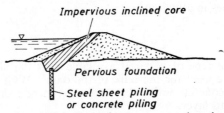

Figure 93. *Dam with inclined clay core on pervious foundation*

Figures 90, 91, 92 and *93* show how the dam design is adapted to
the different types of underlying strata (pervious or impervious). Sometimes the foot of the clay core is consolidated by a concrete footing;

sometimes it is completed by a cutting filled with concrete. The slope of the dam faces depends mainly on the quality of the material and the methods of construction. TABLE 13 contains data referring to different types of dam.

TABLE 13.   EARTH AND ROCK-FILL DAMS

Dam	Country	Year	Volume		Height		Crest width		Slopes (1 vertical)		Membrane
			10³ cu yd	10³ cu m	ft.	m	ft.	m	Upstream	Downstream	
American and Canadian											
Dix	U.S.A.	1925	1747	1336	275	83·8	20	6·1	1 & 1·2	1 & 1.4	Reinf. concrete
Salt Spring	U.S.A.	1931	3200	2448	328	100	15	4·6	1·3	1·4	Reinf. concrete
San Gabriel 2	U.S.A.	1935	1200	918	280	85·3	18	5·5	1·2 & 1·3	1·5	Reinf. concrete
Bersimis I	Canada	1959	3671	2808	225	68·6	30	9·1	2 & 2·35	1·38	Inclined upstream core
European and Algerian											
Bakkadda	Algeria	1933	419	320	148	45	16·4	5	0·86 & 1	1·25	Reinf. concrete
Bou Hanifia	Algeria	—	876	670	180	55	16·4	5	0·8 & 1	1·33	Bitumen concrete
Ghrib	Algeria	1936	876	670	236	72	16·4	5	0·67 & 1	1·25	Bitumen concrete
Serre-Ponçon	France	Under constr.	18300	14000	400	122	32·8	10	2·5	2 & 3	Vertical core (compacted alluvium)

PERMEABILITY OF DAMS.   SEEPAGE OF WATER

The line of saturation must first be determined. This can be done by calculation, by tests on models or by using electrical analogues. The following figures refer to typical cases.

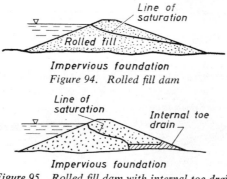

Figure 94. Rolled fill dam

Figure 95. Rolled fill dam with internal toe drain

(a)   Rolled fill dam, *Figure 94*.
(b)   Rolled fill dam with internal toe drains, *Figure 95*.
(c)   Wide impermeable core (with upstream impervious blanket and downstream gravel filter) on pervious strata, *Figure 91*, or without, *Figure 94*.
(d)   The Serre-Ponçon dam with vertical, impervious core.
(e)   Dam on pervious layer on impervious strata, *Figure 96*.

As soon as the line of saturation has been established the flow net and stream lines can be determined by the usual well-known methods. The stream lines are essential for determining the stability of the slopes of the dam faces.

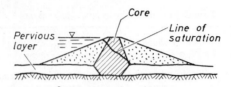

Figure 96. Dam on previous layer on impervious strata

FAILURE OF EARTH AND ROCK-FILL DAMS

TABLE 14 has been prepared from the detailed study by MALLET and PACQUANT[111] into the causes of failure of a large number of earth and rock-fill dams.

TABLE 14

CAUSES OF FAILURE OF EARTH AND ROCK-FILL DAMS

Causes of failure	*Number*	*Per cent*
Insufficient spillway capacity for discharges	32	39
Uplift	15	18
Infiltration along the intake galleries	14	17
Other causes	21	21
Total	82	100

Insufficient spillway capacity for flood discharges is the largest single item in this list.

Figures 97(a) and *(b)* illustrate how the destruction of a dam by uplift may occur. *Figure 97(a)* shows the sliding of the downstream dam face;

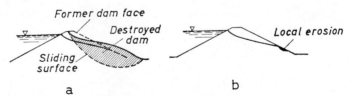

Figure 97. Causes of failure

the weight of the dam material plus the dynamic water pressed into the pores of the dam material overcome the shear strength of the material. Sliding may also occur on the upstream side of the dam, when the reservoir level is suddenly lowered. In *Figure 97(b)* localized damage caused by leakage of water will finally result in a major slide. Local damage inside the dam by water filtering through it may cause similar slides and ultimate failure of the dam.

REQUIREMENTS FOR THE SAFETY OF EARTH DAMS

The practical criteria for the design of earth dams may be stated briefly as follows:

(a) There should be no danger of overtopping, *i.e.* sufficient spillway capacity and sufficient freeboard to contain waves set up by wind should be provided.

(b) The seepage line should be well within the downstream face. Drainage through a rock-fill toe or a filter blanket of coarse material are recommended to keep the saturation line well inside the dam. *Figure 98* shows how the seepage line can be traced roughly, when the dam is not drained, by a method described by CREAGER and JUSTIN, ref. 103, p 412.

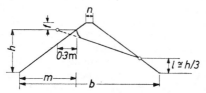

Figure 98. Rough estimate of line of saturation

(c) The upstream face slope should be safe against sudden draw down. An inverted filter and coarse material must protect any inclined core.

(d) The upstream and downstream slopes must be flat enough in relation to the material need to ensure stability and a satisfactory factor of safety.

The methods to be used for investigating points (b) and (d) are basically the same as those described in the chapter on Soil Mechanics.

(e) The upstream and downstream slopes of the earth dam must be flat enough so that the shear stress induced in the (horizontal) foundation is acceptable, *i.e.* less than the shear strength of the material in the foundation to ensure a suitable factor of safety. For this calculation, only the 'downstream portion' of the dam should be considered (this means the dam portion downstream of the core or of the dam axis). This analysis should be extended to the underlying layers of foundation material.

(f) There must be no opportunity for free passage of water from the upstream to the downstream face. Many designers would disapprove of intake galleries through the mass of the earth dam.

If these are unavoidable, special care must be taken for stopping any seepage of water and suitable drains must be provided. Water which percolates through and under the dam when it reaches the discharge surface should have a pressure and velocity so small as to be incapable of moving the material of which the dam or its foundation is composed. This is one of the major problems of earth dam design. A filter at the downstream dam toe may be useful.

(h) The upstream face must be properly protected against wave action and the downstream face must be protected against the rain.

Conditions on the dam during construction should also be considered when the dam is rising rapidly and pressure on the underlaying wet material increases.

ADVANTAGES OF ROCK-FILL DAMS

The downstream and the upstream slopes are usually made the natural slope of rock dumped from cars or trucks or about 1 in 1·3 to 1 in 1·4. Dams exceeding 100 ft (30 m) in height should have a crest width of not less than 15 ft (4·5 m). The safety against sliding along the horizontal foundation is usually high, depending on the slopes and on the position of the impervious core. When the upstream face is impervious, and the ratios of dam height to dam base are $1 : 2\cdot25$ to $1 : 2\cdot5$, the safety factor is as high as $4\cdot5$ to $6\cdot45$ (Galloway)[113].

In recent years much progress has been made in the mathematical analysis of earth and rock-fill dams, which cannot be summarized here (see MALLET and PACQUANT[111]).

XII. BARRAGES AND LOW-HEAD DAMS[118-125]
TYPES OF BARRAGE OR WEIR

The dams described in the previous section are of considerable height. In most cases they were built to create storage reservoirs of large capacity. In this section are considered low dams built on rivers to gain the head necessary for power production in run-of-river stations with little or no storage of water. The free discharge of flood water through adequate openings is a main condition of the scheme and the gates occupy a large part of the dammed river section. These requirements lead to a type of dam often called a barrage or weir.

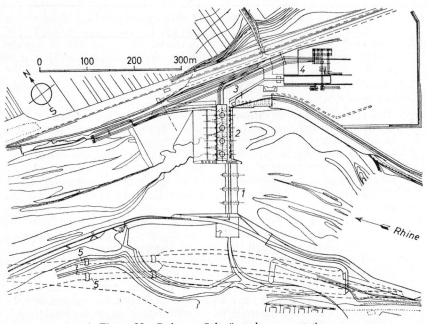

Figure 99. Rybourg–Schwörstadt power station

Figures 99 and *100* show a typical barrage at a low-head power station (Rybourg-Schwörstadt). It consists of independent piers founded, if possible, on rock with a concrete sill at river-bed level. Gates of various kinds close the openings. The sill is designed to protect the foundations against erosion and to destroy the energy of the water. The power house in these river power stations (Flusskraftwerke) is usually built on one side of the river. *Figure 101* shows various arrangements of barrages and power houses, that at (*d*) being common because of the better flow conditions.

The design problems include investigations into:

(*a*)   the stability of the piers;

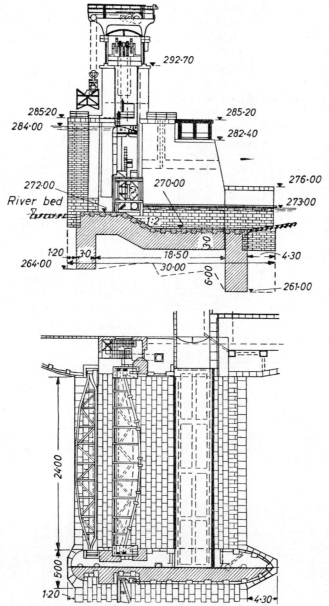

Figure 100. Rybourg–Schwörstadt power station. Details of barrage

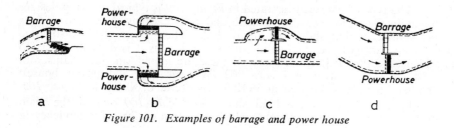

Figure 101. Examples of barrage and power house

(*b*)   the flow of water between piers, the formation of a backwater curve upstream of the barrage and possibly the formation of a free hydraulic jump or a drowned hydraulic jump on the downstream side of the sill;

(*c*)   the destruction of the energy of the water;

(*d*)   the transport of debris and the danger of erosion or of silting up of the river bed;

(*e*)   the foundations of the piers and sills.

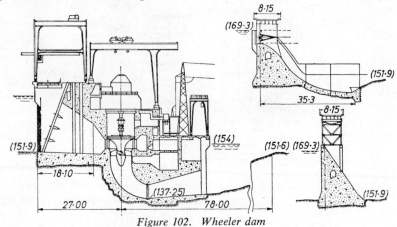

Figure 102.   Wheeler dam

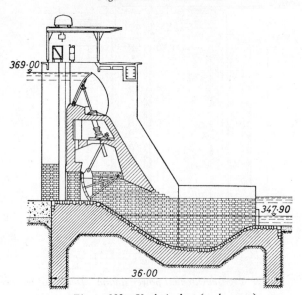

Figure 103.   Verbois dam (or barrage)

The type of barrage illustrated in *Figure 100* is typical of many designs found in Germany, Austria, France and Italy.   Many American designs are similar to that shown in *Figure 102*.   There is no sharp distinction between barrages and dams and with some designs it is difficult to say to which class they belong.   Typical of these are many American dams with crest gates, as shown in *Figure 102* (Wheeler dam and power house); another example is the weir at Verbois, Switzerland, shown in *Figure 103*.

In a structure of the kind shown in *Figure 100* one of the main problems is the pier foundations, which are often costly.   The tendency in

Europe has been, therefore, to reduce the number of piers and to use wider gates. On the other hand, if the American solution of a continuous dam with crest gates (*Figure 102*) is adopted, no separate foundations are needed for the piers and the gates are designed as cheaply as possible; they will usually be more or less square. This solution requires a greater number of smaller gates.

As can be seen from this discussion there are two different types of low-head dam which could be denominated 'barrages' and 'low dams with crest gates'.

Another classification would distinguish barrages or low dams which are isolated structures, damming a river (example: Rupperswil) or which are part of a larger structure, including intake and power house. These are sometimes called river power stations (see Sect. XIV).

STABILITY OF PIERS

Piers are calculated like dams. The vertical weight G of the masonry has to withstand the horizontal thrust H of the water on the pier upstream face and on the gates. The resultant $\vec{R} = \vec{H} + \vec{G}$ should if possible remain in the middle third of the horizontal cross section of the pier. Two cases are to be considered:

(a) All the gates are lowered and all the forces on the pier are symmetrical: The resultant R lies on the axis of the pier (*Figure 104*).

(b) The gates on one side of the pier are raised and the water passes through the free opening, whereas the stop logs on the other side of the pier are lowered (for repair of a gate) and the water between stop logs has been pumped out (*Figure 105*). There is a lateral

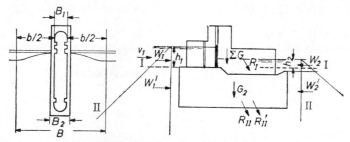

Figure 104. Symmetrical forces on pier

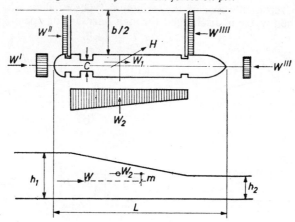

Figure 105. Unsymmetrical forces on pier

unbalanced water thrust on the pier, caused by the hydrostatic load of the water flowing by the pier. The resultant R no longer passes through the axis of symmetry of the pier. In addition, bending moments and torques act on the pier. In this case tensile stresses may occur and steel reinforcing bars have to be added.

Figure 104 shows the forces acting on the pier in case (*a*) where h_1 is the water depth upstream of the closed gates, h_2 the depth downstream of the pier. The horizontal hydrostatic thrust on the upstream side is

$$W_1 = B \frac{h_1^2}{2}$$

and

$$W_2 = B \frac{h_2^2}{2}$$

on the downstream side. ΣG is the sum of all the vertical weights of masonry, gates and hoisting machinery. If the gates rest on the sill, their weight is to be neglected. Combining W_1, W_2, ΣG and the uplift U yields the resultant R_I at level *I–I*. The same procedure yields the reaction R_{II} at level *II–II*. In this case the forces W_1' and W_2' affect only the width B_2 of the foundation of the pier. R_{II} can be calculated neglecting the uplift, and R_{II}' is the same resultant when the uplift is taken into account.

Case (*b*) is illustrated in *Figure 105*. The water level upstream of the pier is h_1 and downstream of the pier h_2. Between these two points the water surface describes a draw-down curve, which, for simpler calculation, is assumed to be a straight line. The lateral thrust W_2 is then

$$W_2 = \tfrac{1}{6}(h_1^2 + h_2^2 + h_1 h_2)$$

The forces W', W'', W''' and W'''' have a resultant $W_1 = W' + W'' + W''' + W''''$ which does not lie in the axis of the pier but is parallel to it. (The loads W'' and W'''' are being transmitted from the gates to the grooves in the piers.) W_2 is perpendicular to this axis and in a horizontal plan different from that containing W_1. The two forces W_1 and W_2 have a common resultant H plus a torque $M = m\,W_2$ which has to be considered in the calculations as it causes bending stresses.

The piers are usually heavily reinforced because of these bending stresses. In addition, reinforcing bars are needed to distribute the heavy load transmitted from the gate rollers or wheels to the pier. Further reinforcement is required to strengthen the pier at the gate grooves.

HYDRAULICS OF FLOW THROUGH WEIRS

Figure 106 represents five of the principal types of flow which are likely to occur when water is discharged through barrages or openings.

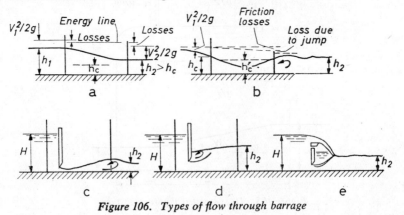

Figure 106. *Types of flow through barrage*

Case a: Gates fully open.   The flow remains tranquil everywhere ($h > h_c$ everywhere).

Case b: Depending on the conditions downstream (h_2), the flow between the piers is sometimes shooting or supercritical.   The critical depth (h_c) usually occurs at the upper end of the piers, or very near to it. As the flow in the river is supposed to be tranquil ($h_2 > h_c'$ in the river) a hydraulic jump must occur somewhere, usually near the downstream end of the pier.   The losses at the pier ends and the loss caused by the hydraulic jump are calculated by the equation of momentum[120].   *Figure 106(c)*, (*d*) and (*e*) represents the flow with the gates in different positions. In *case c*, the flow is shooting and the hydraulic jump is free.   In *case d*, the hydraulic jump is submerged, owing to the higher depth h_2.   In *case e*, the flow passes above and below a gate which is supposed to consist of two independent leaves.

By another approach, which can and should be combined with the previous one, the weir discharge coefficients, using values obtained on model tests, can be found.   According to the U.S. Bureau of Reclamation 'Dam and Control Works', if l_n is the net or effective length of weir crest, l_t the total clear length (total length–thickness of piers) then (*Figure 107*)

$$l_t = l_n + H\,(n_a k_a + n_b k_b \ldots)$$

H = head = water depth at crest + $v^2/2g$.

k_a, k_b ... are contraction coefficients and n_a, n_b ... the numbers of contractions having the coefficients k_a, k_b ....   The values of k_a are given in *Figure 107* and example *107(b)* is calculated as follows:

$n_a = 4$ (2 piers, 4 faces), $k_a = 0 \cdot 025$.

$n_b = 2$ (2 abutment faces), $k_b = 0 \cdot 1$.

$l_n = 67 \cdot 5$ ft. $H = 9$ ft.

$l_t = 67 \cdot 5 + 9 \quad (4 \times 0 \cdot 025 + 2 \times 0 \cdot 1) = 67 \cdot 5 + 9 \times 0 \cdot 3 = 70 \cdot 2$, which is the required weir length to be considered.

DESTRUCTION OF THE ENERGY OF THE WATER AND PROTECTION OF THE RIVER BED

It is highly desirable for the flow always to remain tranquil (*Figure 106, case a*).   But this will occur only exceptionally.   In most cases the flow will accelerate somewhere to supercritical velocities and a hydraulic jump will be formed.   Both supercritical velocities and the turbulence of the hydraulic jump may cause severe erosion of the river bed which must be protected.

The conventional method is to protect the river bed with a heavy concrete slab or sill, the surface of which is usually bucket-shaped to accelerate the destruction of the energy of the water jet by causing stable vortices, with horizontal axes, to develop and absorb energy.

Typical examples are given in *Figures 103* and *108* where the bucket ends in an inclined plane which lifts the jet clear of the downstream end of the concrete sill.   Erosion will occur at some distance from the sill edge and the vortex at the bottom of the jet tends to consolidate the edge of sill.   An alternative design is shown on *Figure 100* where a series of alternate vertical and inclined teeth (introduced first by Rehbock) lifts the jet, destroying part of its energy.

It is usual to check the design of a sill by model tests for different discharges Q, heads H and downstream water depths h_2.   There are several types of flow on which the shape and depth t of the erosion depend.   The flow can be free (with free jump) or submerged, with drowned hydraulic jump[120].

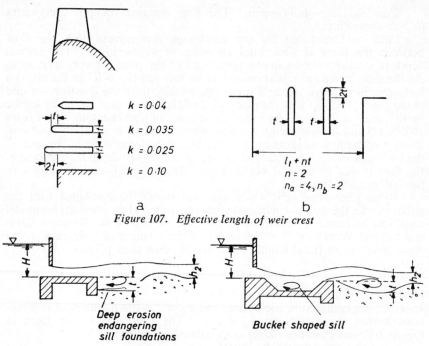

k = 0·04
k = 0·035
k = 0·025
k = 0·10
a
$l_t + nt$
n = 2
$n_a = 4, n_b = 2$
b

Figure 107. Effective length of weir crest

Deep erosion
endangering
sill foundations
Bucket shaped sill

Figure 108. Protection of river bed

When the river is transporting debris, the sill must be located at the level of the natural river bed. If located higher, the river bed will rise steadily, which may be detrimental to other permanent structures (bridges, power stations) established in the upstream reach of the backwater created by the weir.

WEIR FOUNDATIONS. OTHER DETAILS

If possible, the foundations of the piers and sills should be on solid rock as has been done, for example, at Rybourg-Schwörstadt (*Figure 99, 100*), Wheeler (*Figure 102*) and Verbois (*Figure 103*). In some cases the sound rock surface is at a great depth and caissons have to be used, as at Rupperswil (*Figure 109*).

361·10
361·10
359·60
356·30
351·60
350·10
351·10
347·10
2·50
4·80
3·60
3·60
3·90
14·90
22·10
338·50
333·00
34·00

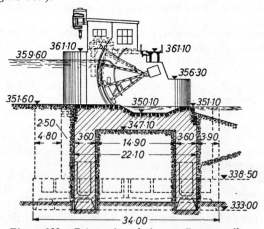

Figure 109. Caisson foundations at Rupperswil

Very difficult foundations on clay had to be carried out on the River Svir (U.S.S.R.). Because of the very low friction factor f between concrete and clay ($f=0\cdot2$ measured, $f=0\cdot1$ used for stability calculations) the width of the structure had to be increased. Special care had to be taken to avoid uplift. Two cross sections of this barrage are shown in *Figure 110*.

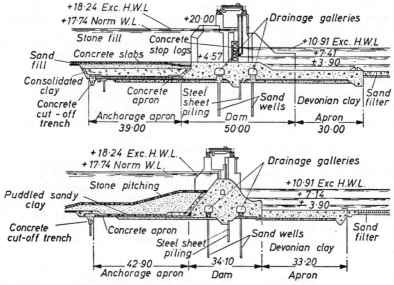

Figure 110. Foundations of barrage on River Svir

Differential settlement must be avoided when a barrage is built on silt or soft alluvium because of the danger of jamming the gates. In one case a continuous heavily reinforced concrete slab was built under the whole barrage foundation. In another, the continuous concrete slab was in 'Prepakt' concrete (*i.e.* concrete made by first placing the coarse aggregate in position and pouring on the cement–sand mix containing additives) poured continuously without transverse construction joints.

In conventional designs heavy service bridges are built on top of the piers to carry the machinery controlling the heavy gates. In more recent designs, the hoisting machinery is on top of, or inside, the piers and the service bridges are reduced in size or omitted altogether to improve the aesthetic appearance of the weir. (Examples: Donzère-Mondragon in France, Birsfelden in Switzerland.)

XIII. GATES[126-134]

Gates are used to control the flow of water, *e.g.* at barrages, over dams (crest gates) and at intakes where the pressure is medium or low. The designs vary according to the use, width of gate and the pressures to be sustained. There is no uniformity in nomenclature. The main types of gate are: (1) sluice gates and stop logs, (2) Tainter or radial gates, (3) sector or drum gates, (4) rolling gates, (5) bear trap weirs and (6) tilting or Aubert gates.

SLUICE GATES

Figure 111, taken from a publication by Stambach, shows the evolution of sluice gates from the early types to the more modern designs. The first gates consisted of independent horizontal girders, which, later on, were stiffened at their ends with stiff vertical main girders. Later, large sluice gates were divided into two leaves moving independently. The main advantage of this type is the reduction in weight of the gate, the power and cost of the hoisting machinery and the total height of the pier, determined by the gate in the raised position. When the upper leaf is in the lowered position, small floods, floating debris or ice can pass over the upper gate without raising the heavy lower leaf. Another factor in the evolution of the design of large sluice gates is the number of horizontal girders. The oldest type of gates had a large number of horizontal girders. When such a structure is stiffened by stiff vertical end girders, it becomes highly indeterminate. In most European designs the tendency has been towards a limited number of horizontal girders, two for each leaf, so that the structure is statically determinate. There are two wheels for each horizontal girder on each side, or eight wheels for each leaf. Each leaf rolls on its own rails which complicates the design of the grooves and sealings.

This evolution in the design of sluice gates led to the so-called 'hook gate', where the upper leaf has the shape of a hook. The advantages of the hook gate are: reduced total height in raised position; compact design; skin located on the upstream side of the gate, all parts of which are protected against water; easy maintenance; correct discharge of the water nappe on top of the correctly shaped upper leaf or hook gate. The rollers of the hook gate roll on the same rail as do those of the main leaf, which simplifies the design of the gate grooves. The most recent development has been the extension of the hook gate design to Tainter gates. (See below.)

In the U.S.A. the evolution of the design of sluice gates has been quite different. American designers have retained the one-leaf sluice gate type with multiple horizontal girders, stiffened by heavy vertical end girders with numerous wheels. This solution has also been adopted for large intake gates to turbine spiral casings. The Tennessee Valley Authority (T.V.A.) have developed an intermediate solution consisting of two independent leaves (with multiple horizontal girders and number of wheels), but the wheels are all rolling on the same rail. A gate lifting extension is required (*Figure 112*).

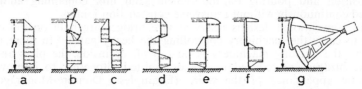

Figure 111.   Evolution of sluice gates

For design and calculation the gate is assumed to consist of the skin plate, the main and secondary horizontal and vertical girders, and vertical end girders.

The hydrostatic load is supposed to be transmitted from the skin plate to the secondary girders forming a grid and from those to the main girders (*see Figure 100; Figure 113* shows pressure test results on a rolling gate). If s is the thickness of the rectangular skin plate, $2a$ and $2b$ the side of the rectangle $ABCD$, then the bending stresses σ perpendicular to a diagonal AC or BD is by the formula of Föppl-Bach:

$$\sigma = \frac{c^2}{2\phi s^2} p$$

where p = hydrostatic load on the plate (average value), c = height of triangle ABC or CDA, ϕ a factor which, according to Bach, is $\phi \cong 1 \cdot 1$ (see *Figure 114*). The girders are calculated according to the usual rules of statics.

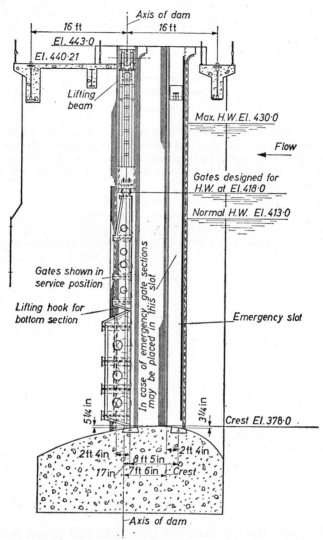

Figure 112. *Tennessee Valley Authority gate*

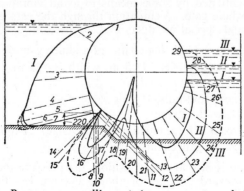

Figure 113. *Pressures on a rolling gate (measurements made in Germany)*

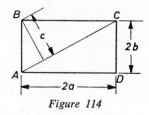

Figure 114

It is essential to design the gate correctly to obtain a smooth flow of water over the top of the gate and below its lower edges. A faulty hydraulic design will lead to increased vertical reactions on the lifting chains and possibly to vibrations. Model tests will help to find the correct solution for both conditions.

The following points have to be watched.

(*a*)   The water nappe flowing on top of the upper gate leaf should cause neither high positive nor dangerous negative pressures. Typical for the correct design of a hook gate are pressure distribution tests. Similar tests are shown in *Figure 115* for a tilting gate.

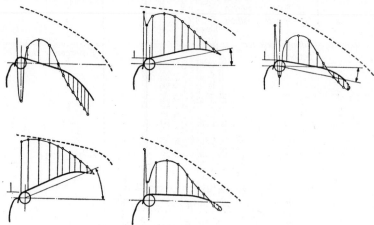

Figure 115. Pressure distributions on tilting gate (according to Charmilles)

(*b*)   The water flowing underneath the lower leaf should not cause any suction on the edge of the lower gate leaf.

(*c*)   If the water depth downstream of the gate is low, the water nappe should be ventilated by some means to avoid vibration of the nappe and of the whole gate. Ventilation through the gate grooves is often insufficient and special air ducts may be necessary.

Example of forces on the hoisting chains of a sluice gate:

Gate dimensions: depth H=11·5 m; width B=25 m.

Gate weight, 198 tons.

Friction on wheels and rails, 31 tons.

Friction on side walls, 30 tons.

Negative hydrostatic force (suction on gate edge), 21 tons.

Total=280 tons on gate chains.

When the gate is in a lowered position, the pressure on the sill should be a positive downward pressure of about, and not less than, 0·5 ton/m (0·15 ton/ft) of sill.

Stop logs—Stop logs are horizontal beams, piled up to shut a gate opening (for repair or maintenance of a gate). They must be strongly built as they have to be lowered against the full force of the water nappe. Vertical or slightly inclined stop logs have been used in a few cases (Donzère-Mondragon weir).

TAINTER GATES OR RADIAL GATES

Figure 116 represents a typical Tainter or radial gate. The basic idea of this design is to put the main struts supporting the gate frame into compression; the hydrostatic forces acting on the gate skin-plate have a radial resultant which, in the simplest gate design, passes through the gate trunnion (*Figure 117*).

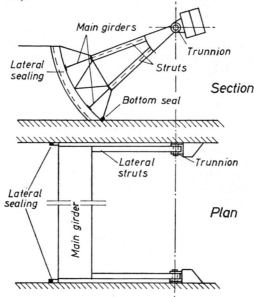

Figure 116. *Tainter or radial gate*

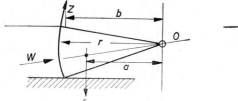

Figure 117. *Resultant force passing through trunnion of Tainter or radial gate*

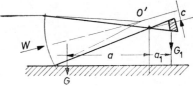

Figure 118. *Resultant force not passing through the trunnion*

Tainter gates are used as crest gates for dams, barrage gates, intake gates, lock gates. They can also be designed for high pressure conditions. Comparative studies indicate that Tainter gates are often the cheapest type of gate.

Figure 117 shows how the forces acting on a Tainter gate can be calculated. Assuming that the gate skin plate is a circular cylinder with centre at O and that the hydrostatic force W (perpendicular to the skin plate) passes through the trunnion O, the lifting force is $Z = Ga/b$, where $G =$ the weight of the gate. If friction forces are included then

$$Z = \frac{Ga + M_f + F_r}{b}$$

where $M_f =$ friction in the trunnion (torque) and $F_r =$ the friction torque caused by the lateral sealing. The lifting force Z can be reduced by using a counterweight or by arranging that the resultant hydrostatic pressure W does not pass through the trunnion O (*Figure 118*) but through a point O', so that there is an eccentricity, c. In *Figure 118* the torques $W.c$ and $G_1 a_1$ tend to lift the gate.

The design and construction of Tainter gates follow the lines discussed for sluice gates. The hydrostatic pressure transmitted to the skin plate is taken by the secondary horizontal and vertical girders and transmitted to horizontal girders and the radial struts and finally to the trunnion.

The anchorage of the trunnion in the mass of concrete is a difficult problem which can be solved by a step-by-step calculation, or by the relaxation method. Photoelastic model tests have proved useful in estimating the stress distribution caused in a pier by the concentrated load transmitted by the trunnion gate. Tainter gates can be combined with hook gates (Rupperswil) as shown in *Figure 109* or with tilting gates (Donzère).

SECTOR OR DRUM GATES

Sector or drum gates are often used as crest gates, regulating the flow over the top of a dam or weir. *Figures 119* and *120* show two examples of gates of this type. The position of the gate can be regulated by the pressure of the water under the gate. Sector gates and drum gates require deep foundations and are not used for low barrages with flat sills.

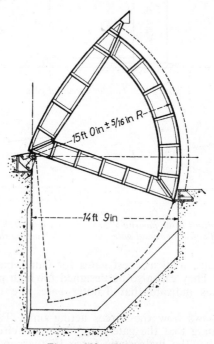

Figure 119. Drum gate

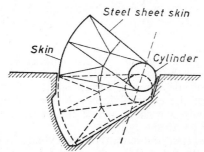

Figure 120. Drum gate. Modern German (M.A.N.) design

ROLLING GATES

A rolling gate is a horizontal cylinder used for closing a gate opening. One end of the cylinder is provided with a hoisting chain or cable. The cylinder gate rolls on an inclined plane. Rolling gates were first developed in Germany and used on large rivers with widths of 35 to 40 m (115 to 130 ft) and for heights from 2 to 4 m (7 to 13 ft). They are stiff structures, designed to withstand bending moments and torques, and are used on rivers with heavy debris transportation and in cold climates where there is a danger of the gate bottom sealing getting frozen or when the gate has to withstand the pressure of floating ice. They have also been used in the U.S.A. and Canada.

An early rolling gate at Poppenweiler (Germany) collapsed in 1912. The cause of the accident was traced to negative pressure under the gate, downward suction of the gate and vibration (see *Figure 113*). To avoid these troubles it is suggested that the gate diameter should not be more than 3/4 *h*, if *h* is the height of the gate. A plate closes the bottom part of the opening as indicated in *Figure 121*. When this skin plate is extended over the whole gate height the circular cylinder then acts merely as a stiffener and

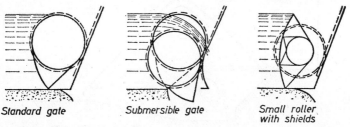

Standard gate   Submersible gate   Small roller with shields

Figure 121. Types of rolling gates. German and American designs

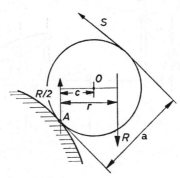

Figure 122. Forces on a roller gate

roller. By suitable design of the sill the gate can be lowered to allow flood water, floating debris or ice to pass over the top of the gate. There is no need to raise the gate to allow the passage of water under it unless a major flood has to be dealt with, when the whole gate is lifted. Partial raising may result in high and dangerous velocities under the gate.

Figure 122 shows the forces acting on the cylinder of a rolling gate. R is the resultant of the external forces. The roller rests in A and B. Rr is the moment of the external forces, S is the force in the chain and $Sa = Rr$. There is only one chain at one end of the roller, which causes a torque to be transmitted to the cylinder.

The average load (per unit length) on the cylinder is $p = R/l$ ($l =$ cylinder length), and a reaction force $R/2$ acts at each end of the cylinder.

The maximum bending moment on the cylinder is $M_{max} = pl^2/8 = Rl/8$.

The torque at end A of the cylinder (where the chain force S is acting) is

$$M_{T_A} = R\,(c/2 - r)$$

At the end B $(S = 0)$

$$M_{T_B} = \frac{R}{2}\,c$$

At a distance x from B,

$$M_{T_x} = M_{T_B} + px\,(r - c) = \frac{R}{2}\,c + \frac{R}{l}\,x\,(r - c)$$

The shear stresses in the cylinder, caused by the torque, are

$$\tau = \frac{2M_T}{D^2\pi e} \qquad (e = \text{steel plate thickness})$$

BEAR TRAP GATES

Bear trap gates, *Figure 123*, require a deep foundation and are, therefore, expensive. They do not require a heavy service bridge and are used mainly where appearance is important and it is desired not to spoil a view, *e.g.* in a town.

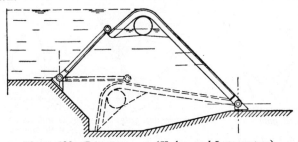

Figure 123. Bear trap gate (Huber and Lutz system)

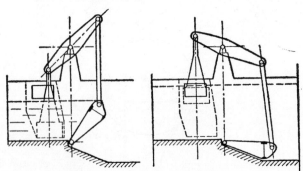

Figure 124. Tilting gate with float

TILTING GATES. AUBERT GATES

Tilting gates (*Figure 124*) are used as crest gates. A typical example is the crest gate of Verbois (*Figure 103*). On French rivers, a special type of tilting weir has been known for many years as Chanoine gates. This type has recently been modernized by Aubert, *Figure 125*, who used it successfully at Seyssel (France). Aubert claims that these gates are very cheap.

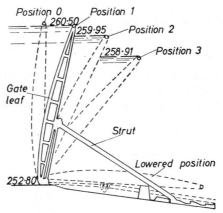

Figure 125. Aubert gate

SUSPENSION OF GATES

Gates are usually suspended at both ends. It is essential for the lifting or lowering movements at both gate ends to be absolutely synchronous, in order to avoid twisting or jamming. Roller gates and bear trap gates have only one hoisting chain on one side, whereas tilting gates, sector and drum gates are evenly supported over their full length.

SEALING OF GATES

Correct sealing of gates is a difficult problem, mainly because of gate deflections (when two gates have to be sealed one against the other) and because of the friction forces the seal causes. The rubber seal (or music note seal) as shown in *Figure 126* is commonly used today with few examples of other types. Some gates are designed so that, before lifting and when lowering, the seal is released to avoid high friction forces.

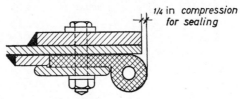

Figure 126. Rubber seal for gates

AUTOMATIC GATE REGULATION

Some gates (crest gates) are automatically regulated, a float upstream of the gate controlling the gear regulating the gate level. To avoid 'hunting' of the gate, modern designs (*e.g.* Verbois) provide the regulating gear with a 'return motion' or 'feed back', based on the return motion used in turbine governors.

XIV. INTAKES AND GENERAL ARRANGEMENT OF WORKS. FLOOD DISCHARGE, SAND ELIMINATORS[135-146b]

The design of the intake works is not a problem which can be solved by itself, without taking into consideration the general layout of the whole scheme: type of dam or weir, type of spillway, location of the power house. Decisions concerning the intake have often to be postponed until other more difficult questions are settled. Furthermore the design of intake works on schemes with a storage reservoir is very much different from the intakes on rivers and from the design of run-of-river stations.

INTAKES ON STORAGE RESERVOIRS

(*a*) The intake can be part of the dam as at Génissiat, Castelo do Bode, Hiwassee, Fontana, *etc.* This solution is often adopted when the power house is located at the toe of the dam. Alternatively the intake can be a tower just in front of the dam (Cabril), or can be independent of the dam as an intake tower (Boulder dam intake towers) standing apart from the dam or as inclined intakes (Wäggital). For typical examples see *Figures 27* and *127* to *130*, also *Figure 72* (Aigle dam).

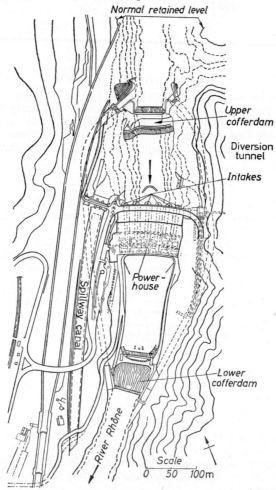

Figure 127. Génissiat: plan of dam and power-house. (For section see Figure 27)

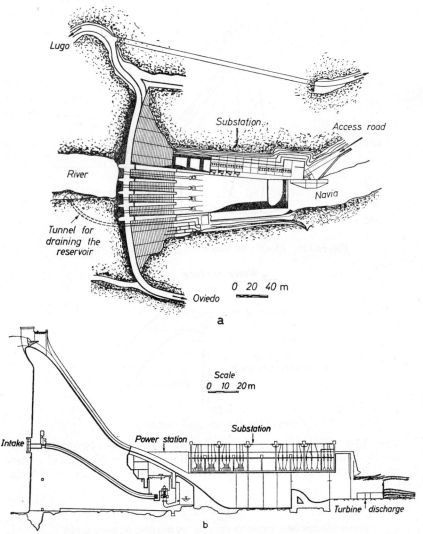

Figure 128. Salime: plan and section. (a) Plan of dam and spillway. (b) Vertical
section through dam, power house and spillway

These intakes are usually, if not always, provided with screens and
emergency gates or covers or stop logs.

(b) *General arrangement of works*—The major decision usually
depends on the arrangements for discharging floods.

According to expert opinion the best position for a spillway overtopping a dam is in the axis of the river. This opinion is correct, but the
power house also should be located in this preferred position. There are
few cases where the valley is large enough for both the spillway and the
power house to be conveniently located in this position (*e.g.* Grand Coulee
dam). More often, there is a conflict between the requirements for flood
discharge and for location of the power intake and power house.

Floods up to 2,000 m³/sec to 4,000 m³/sec (70,000 to 140,000 cusecs)
often by-pass the power house by using a lateral spillway (Castelo do
Bode), a lateral spillway canal (Génissiat) or a lateral spillway tunnel
(Fontana dam).

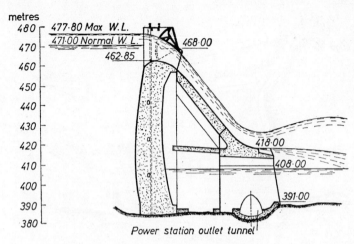

Figure 129. *Picote: Section through dam and spillway*

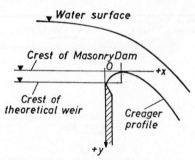

Figure 130. *Creager spillway profile*

Very high floods, up to more than 10,000 m³/sec (350,000 cusecs), are usually kept in the river axis: the station will then be located underground (Bhakra dam, Picote) or under the spillway itself (Salime, l'Aigle, Bort).

TABLE 15

CO-ORDINATES OF A 'CREAGER-PROFILE' IN DIMENSIONLESS VALUES

Head $H = 1$

x (horizontal)	y (vertical)	
	Lower nappe	*Upper nappe*
0·0	0·126	− 0·831
0·1	0·036	− 0·803
0·2	0·007	− 0·772
0·3	0·000	− 0·740
0·4	0·007	− 0·702
0·6	0·063	− 0·620
0·8	0·153	− 0·511
1·0	0·267	− 0·380
1·4	0·59	− 0·030
2·0	1·31	0·693
3·0	3·11	2·50
4·0	5·61	5·00

(*c*) *Spillway*—The length profile of any spillway has to be established so that the hydrodynamic pressures are always and everywhere positive ($p > 0$) but never too high. For the upper part of the spillway, the so-called 'Creager-profile', *Figure 130*, is often adopted, as given in dimensionless (relative) values in Table 15.

There are rare exceptions to this rule, where slightly negative pressures have been allowed (at the top of spillways on thin arch dams).

The pressures along the whole spillway are usually checked on an appropriate model.

The downstream end of the spillway is sometimes spoon-shaped so that the jet of water is lifted in the air, in order to have its kinetic energy braked by friction. These are the so-called *ski-jump* spillways (*e.g.* l'Aigle, Bort).

The axis of these spillways is straight in plan view. Some spillways are curved in plan view (Castelo do Bode) in order to direct the jet towards the centre of the valley. Such spillways require careful checking on models as it is difficult to divert water flowing at high, supercritical velocities.

The principles established for open spillways and spillway canals are also valid for spillway tunnels. With the high velocities of water obtained on spillway or spillway tunnels ($v = [2g(H - \Delta H)]^{\frac{1}{2}}$ where H = dam height, ΔH = friction losses) only slight curvatures of the spillway axis is permissible. Owing to these very high velocities, there is a danger of cavitation. It is essential to make sure that there is always enough positive pressure on the concrete surface, which must be absolutely smooth if cavitation is to be avoided. Any misalignment of the surface, any hump is to be avoided.

SPECIAL CASES

The classical arrangement with power house at the toe of the dam is well known and requires no special comment. Two interesting alternatives may be described.

(*a*) *Salime*—The dam is located in the steep narrow valley of the Navia (Spain). The spillway passes on top of the power house. Because of poor rock conditions and dangerously steep river banks, a ski-jump spillway similar to Aigle or Bort could not be considered. The spillway designed for 2,000 ton/sec is continuous down to the dam toe, and the spilling nappe does not leave the concrete surface. The energy of the water has to be destroyed in a deep stilling basin, the water level of which is controlled by a counter-dam. This basin is 40 m (131 ft) long and 11 m (36 ft) deep.

If the turbine draft tube had discharged into this stilling basin, there would have been a permanent loss of head, about equal to the counter-dam height It was therefore decided that the tail race at the end of the turbine draft tube line should be a pressure tunnel by-passing the stilling basin. Because of its length, this tail race pressure tunnel is provided with a surge chamber, located under the spillway, immediately downstream of the power house.

(*b*) *Picote*—The 'Douro' (Spanish 'Duero') is, at that place, forming a very narrow valley, with steep banks. The rock is excellent granite and a ski-jump spillway has been designed. The power house is not located under the spillway, partly because of lack of space, but even more because of the works schedule during the concreting of the dam. During the construction period floods were passing over the partially built dam and a power house site located at its toe would have slowed down the progress of the work.

The power house is therefore located underground, in sound rock. The tail race tunnel is under pressure. Its length is kept short so that no surge tank is required. The tail race discharges under the spillway. This arrangement has two advantages:

(*i*) The water underneath the spillway is quieter than in the river itself where the flow is highly turbulent, during flood periods, owing to the discharge from the spillway. (*ii*) During the flood period the spilling jet of water creates a suction effect, which depresses the water level at the tunnel outlet and increases the head on the turbines by several metres.

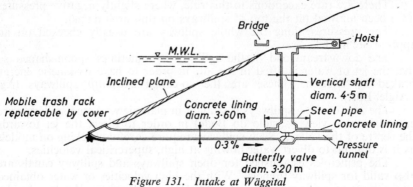

Figure 131. Intake at Wäggital

(*c*) *Intake works*—Intakes directly connected to the dam can be seen in *Figures 27, 127* and *72* (Génissiat and Aigle). An independent spillway is shown on *Figure 131* (Wäggital).

INTAKES ON RUN-OF-RIVER STATIONS WITH NO OR SMALL RESERVOIR CAPACITY

(*a*) *Case 1*—The power house and its intake are on the main river and form part of the weir (French: usines-barrages; German: Flusskraftwerke; suggested English translation 'power house barrage', see *Figures 99* and *100* (Ryburg) and *132* (Birsfelden)). This is the most common and most popular arrangement for run-of-river stations. It is also probably the cheapest one, given convenient topographical and geological conditions.

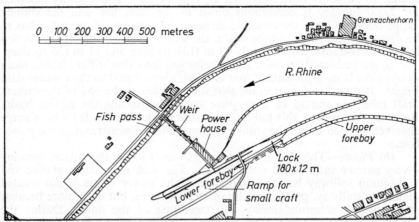

Figure 132. Birsfelden: General plan

The main problems are: geology of the river bed, foundations; flood discharge, erosion; transported debris, floating debris, ice.

For the barrage see Sect. XII; for the powerhouse design see Sect. XXI.

(*b*) *Case 2.* (*Power stations with independent intake*)—*Figure 133* (Mörel power intake, Switzerland) shows how a low-head barrage dams the river. The intake is on the left-hand bank, with two separate channels leading to two sand eliminators. The intake channels are provided with coarse and fine trash-racks and with scour galleries to eliminate as much floating and transported debris as possible, before the water enters the sand eliminators.

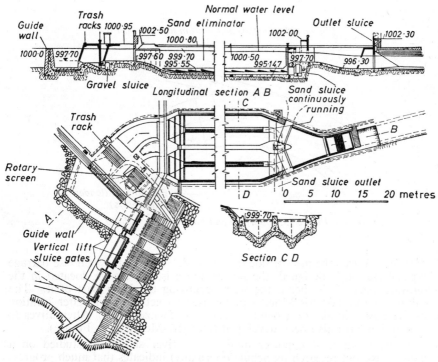

Figure 133. Mörel: Intake and sand eliminator

Note the partition wall, parallel to the river axis, in front of the intake, which serves to protect the intake from transported debris. Under normal conditions, the gate nearest to the intake is closed. The partition wall favours the formation of secondary flow lines and of vortices which divert the transported debris from the intake. When heavy floods have to be dealt with, the gate is opened and the canal in front of the intake works as a scour canal.

FLOW PATTERN

The remarks at the end of the last paragraph stress the fact that the correct design of river power stations of any type is based on a correct knowledge of the flow patterns which may occur under different running conditions.

There is a tendency for transported debris to be sucked through turbine inlets or into power canals. This is shown in *Figure 134*. The clear water at the river surface passes the open barrage, whereas the debris-loaded water at the river bottom is sucked into the power intake, especially when the canal discharge is great compared to the discharge passing the barrage. The example of Mörel shows how to avoid or mitigate such conditions.

When the river describes a bend, *Figure 135*, the flow takes a spiral movement, the clean surface water moving towards the outer side of the bend, and the heavier, debris-loaded stream tubes at the river bottom being

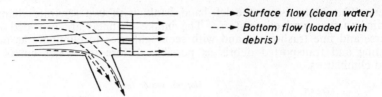

Figure 134. Surface and bottom flows at barrage

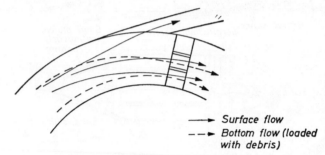

Figure 135. Surface and bottom flows at bend

directed towards the inward side of the bend. When a power house barrage type of station is designed, the power house is, if possible, located in the outward part of the bend, the weir occupying the inner part of it. The solution developed for Mörel can be used to get an even better location of the power intake in a bend (*Ex.*: Lavey, Switzerland). Alternatives to this design have also been developed (Donzère-Mondragon, France).

The location of a power intake on a river should be studied on a model. Recent research by Schulz (Germany) indicates that much progress can be made in the design of power intakes and barrages[135].

The Dufour sand eliminator

In spite of careful design, sand and gravel, which may be entrained in the power intake, will have to be eliminated, because of possible damage to the turbines (erosion of turbine blades and hood).

Sand eliminators designed to accumulate debris, which should be flushed periodically, do not work properly. During the flood period, when a heavy load of debris is being transported by the river, the sand eliminators should be flushed continuously. This requires about 8–10 per cent of the total water discharge to be absorbed by the sand eliminator and to pass through the scour galleries. This percentage has to be looked on as a loss. As this occurs mainly during the flood period, this loss is immaterial.

Dufour was the first to design sand eliminators on this principle. The Dufour sand eliminator consists of a silting chamber; the reduced velocity of the water permits the sand particles to settle slowly, while the dirt concentrates at the bottom of the chamber, which is conveniently shaped and provided with guide vanes. The dirty water is then eliminated. For the design of a sand eliminator the maximum permissible sand diameter d, the vertical settling velocity V and the horizontal water velocity v are the main variables to be considered (see *Figure 133*).

In recent times, more compact sand eliminators have been designed for Innertkirchen[146b].

XV. HYDRO-POWER TUNNELS AND TUNNELLING [147-162]

GENERAL REMARKS

The modern technique of tunnelling was developed during the expansion period of the railways, mainly at the end of the last century and at the beginning of the twentieth century. Tunnelling for hydro-power schemes brought new requirements, mainly concerning the speed of tunnelling, the water tightness and rock strength and finally the cost. This section is to be considered as a specialized supplement to the more general chapters on Tunnelling Practice, p 366, and Tunnels and Tunnelling in Switzerland, p 383.

TYPES OF HYDRO-POWER TUNNELS AND EXCAVATIONS

Hydro-power tunnels can be either free flow or pressure tunnels, power or discharge tunnels. They can be lined or unlined.

Power tunnels

Most of the power tunnels are pressure tunnels. Free flow power tunnels are the exception, as it is more difficult to accelerate or decelerate water in an open flume (translatory waves) than in a pressure vessel (water hammer and surges). Power tunnels are either unlined, or concrete lined or steel lined, depending on rock conditions and on hydrostatic pressure.

The velocity $v_0 = Q_0/A$ in pressure tunnels is usually greater than 2 m/sec (6·5 ft/sec) but not more than 5·5 to 6 m/sec (18 to 19·5 ft/sec). The gradient of a pressure tunnel is immaterial and is not directly linked to the velocity. It may depend on the surge tank height, the quality of the rock, the maximum hydrostatic pressure the rock is allowed to stand and finally on the tunnelling methods to be used. Inclined shafts (steel lined) are often built as an alternative to pressure pipe lines. The gradient of free tunnels depends on the velocity v_0 for maximum discharge Q_0. It is determined so that the tunnel gradient is parallel to the energy line of the uniform flow for $Q = Q_0$.

Diversion tunnels and spillway tunnels

In diversion and spillway tunnels the water may reach high velocities; far higher than in power tunnels. They are therefore usually concrete lined (not steel lined) and sharp bends have to be avoided. They should be tested on models in order to check the behaviour of the flow.

Tail race tunnels

Recently large tail race tunnels have been built mainly in connection with underground power stations (Sweden, Scotland). They are usually unlined. The water velocity in these tunnels is about the same or slightly less than the velocity at the draft-tube outlet of the turbines. The Storrnorfors tail race tunnel (Sweden) with a height of 29 m (95 ft) is, for the time being, the largest in the world.

Power house excavation

With the development of large underground power stations, the excavation of large caverns for locating the power house inside solid rock has become a new branch of tunnelling technique (see Sect. XVII).

GEOLOGY FOR HYDRO-POWER TUNNELS

There is a marked difference between tunnelling geology in general and geology for hydro-power tunnels. Because of the inside water pressure to be supported by hydro-power tunnels, they must be located in reasonably good rock. This is also required from a financial point of view, as difficult tunnelling slows down work in the tunnel and increases costs. In general there is more freedom in the choice of the tunnel location when dealing with hydro-power tunnels than with railway tunnels. A very detailed geological survey of the region where a hydro-power tunnel has to be built is required.

The general remarks and rules developed in Sect. VII apply here. This mainly concerns the geological survey and the dipping of strata and rock quality along the tunnel axis.

Measurement of the modulus of elasticity of the rock in a tunnel

Such measurements can be carried out either in specially excavated galleries or in parts of the gallery, which can be lined or unlined. The method consists of closing a certain length of tunnel with a concrete plug provided with a steel cover and with pipes passing through the concrete plug for pumping water into the closed tunnel section and taking manometer readings. A pipe at the bottom of the plug is used for emptying the test section. Water is pumped into the test section and pressure on this water rises during the tests. The elastic deformation of three or four diameters is measured in several cross-sections, taking the necessary precautions to eliminate the effect of temperature variations (cold water in warmer tunnel).

The natural prestressing of the rock

It has been noted during the construction of the large alpine tunnels (mainly St. Gothard and Simplon) that the rock is strained or 'prestressed' in a natural state. When a tunnel is excavated, some of these stresses are released. It is essential to determine if the natural prestressing of the rock is less or higher than its elastic limit or its crushing strength. For hydro-power tunnels the amount of natural prestressing of the rock is even more important and should be determined by measurements. It is also essential to know the direction of the prestressing.

To measure the amount of prestressing of the rock, the following methods can be used.

(*i*) An extensometer or strain gauge is sealed to the face of the rock and a cylindrical hole is bored round the gauge, leaving a rock core to which the gauge is attached. When boring the hole the natural strains in the rock are relieved and the readings on the apparatus give the amount of strain which existed in the rock before stress relieving the core. If this measurement is repeated on these strain gauges, placed at correct angles (90° and 45°) the 'prestressing' of the rock can be calculated, provided the modulus of elasticity of the rock is known.

(*ii*) By using flat hydraulic jacks (Freyssinet type) and strain gauges, the stresses can be measured direct, without knowing the modulus of elasticity of the rock. Extensometers are disposed on the rock surface at convenient angles so that zero readings correspond to the conditions before cutting out the horizontal channel. After excavation the pressure inside the jack can be read directly when the readings on the extensometers are readjusted to zero.

Measurements have shown the rock to be always 'prestressed' at a certain depth. Very often the prestressing of the rock is of the so-called 'hydrostatic pressure distribution type', which means that the stresses round any point are more or less the same in any direction (theory of Heim).

Sometimes the distribution of the prestressing depends on the modulus of elasticity of the rock and Poisson's ratio for rock (theory of Terzaghi).

BRIEF SUMMARY OF THE THEORY OF STRESSES IN UNLINED AND LINED HYDRO-POWER TUNNELS

Prestressing of the rock. Stresses caused by excavating a circular tunnel or gallery in homogeneous rock

If the rock pressure p^* produced by the rock's own weight is acting on the circular contour of the tunnel in one direction (vertical) only, the stresses at the tunnel wall on the horizontal axis Oy are $\sigma_r=0$ (in the radial direction) and $\sigma_t=3p^*$ (in a circumferential and tangential direction). On a vertical axis Ox they are $\sigma_r=0$ and $\sigma_t=-p^*$ (tensile stress) (*Figure 136(a)*).

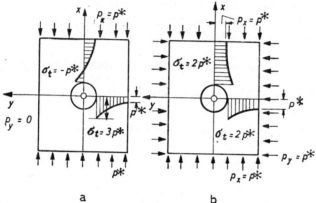

a   b

Figure 136. Stresses in circular tunnel in homogeneous rock

The recent theory of Terzaghi and Richart, introducing a component in a direction normal to p^* (due to Poisson's ratio), shows that the stresses are: $\sigma_t<3p^*$ on a horizontal diameter, $\sigma_t>-p^*$ on a vertical diameter.

If the pressure p^* has the character of a hydrostatic pressure ($p_x=p_y=p^*$) (Heim) the stresses on the axis Oy are, as shown on *Figure 136(b)*, $\sigma_r=0$, $\sigma_t=2p^*$. They are the same for any diameter (because of symmetry).

Denoting the limit of elasticity of the rock by σ_{el} and its crushing strength by σ_{cr}, then if $\sigma_{el}>\sigma_t$ the tunnel is stable. If the local pressure σ_t is greater than the limit of elasticity, plastic deformation of the rock will occur. Crushing of the rock will occur if $\sigma_{max}-\sigma_{min}>\sigma_{cr}$.

Effects of hydrostatic water pressure inside the tunnel

The theory of strains and stresses developing inside the wall of a conduit or round an excavated tunnel when water pressure is applied is based on the theory of the thick cylinder. A tunnel can be regarded as a pipe with infinitely thick walls.

The theory can be extended to lined and steel-lined tunnels or shafts (as those used for underground power stations). A steel-lined shaft can be considered as being formed by a thin steel sheet, a thick concrete cylinder and a rock tunnel. A certain amount of pressure is transmitted from the thin steel shell to the concrete cylinder and from the concrete cylinder to the rock wall (*Figure 137*). The amount of pressure so transmitted depends on the relative elasticity of the shell, or cylinder, and of the rock. The boundary condition which allows a solution of the equations is that the deformation of the steel shell is identical with that of the inner radius of the concrete cylinder and that the elastic deformation of the outer radius of the concrete is identical with that of the rock wall.

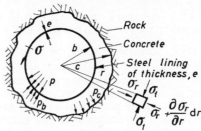

Figure 137. Transmission of pressure in steel-lined shaft

The main results of the theory are as follows:

(*i*) *Ordinary unlined tunnel*—The circumferential stress σ_t in the rock near the wall is a tensile stress $\sigma_t = -p$ and the radial stress σ_r is $\sigma_r = +p$ $= -\sigma_t$.

The stresses decrease rapidly inside the rock and at any point in the rock $\sigma_r = -\sigma_t < p$.

(*ii*) *For a steel-lined tunnel or shaft, the boundary conditions yield* (*Figure 137*):

In the steel plate $\sigma = \dfrac{(p-p_b)\,b}{e} = p\,\dfrac{(1-\lambda_1)\,b}{e}$

where

$$\lambda_1 = \frac{p_b}{p}$$

$$\lambda_1 = \frac{b^2/Ee}{b^2/Ee + \dfrac{b}{m_1 E_1\,(c^2-b^2)}\,[(m_1-1)\,(b^2-\lambda_2 c^2)+(m_1+1)\,(1-\lambda_2)\,c^2]}$$

$$\lambda_2 = \frac{p_c}{p_b} = \frac{2b^2/E_1\,(c^2-b^2)}{(m_2+1)/m_2 E_2 - \dfrac{(m_1-1)\,c^2+(m_1+1)\,b^2}{m_1 E_1\,(c^2-b^2)}}$$

In these formulae (see *Figure 137*)

p_b is the pressure transmitted from the steel lining to the concrete

p_c the pressure transmitted from the concrete to the rock

b and c are the radii of the concrete lining ($c > b$)

E is Young's modulus of the steel plate, e its thickness

E_1, m_1 Young's modulus and Poisson's ratio for concrete

E_2, m_2 the same for the rock.

Similar formulae can be developed for fissured concrete and rock.

If the hydrostatic pressure is $p = p^*$ and if the prestressing of rock p^* is of the type described by Heim, then the conditions round the perimeter of the gallery would be identical to those prevailing before the construction of the tunnel and the rock would return to the original state of uniform stress distribution: $p^* = $ a constant. Such conditions will not occur, as always, for reasons of security, $p < p^*$ is a well-accepted rule. This remark shows how prestressing relieves the rock stresses caused by the hydrostatic water pressure inside the tunnel and how this hydrostatic pressure partially relieves stresses from rock prestressing.

ROCK OVERBURDEN ABOVE THE TUNNEL

The accepted rule is that p (water pressure) should be not more than the rock overburden h. If $p < h$, and if $w_r = 2 \cdot 50$ t/m³ is the (metric) density of the rock, then the safety factor against the rock being lifted by the water pressure is $n \geqslant 2 \cdot 5$. h is supposed to be measured in the direction of the shortest distance to the surface.

Recently, shallower overburden had been admitted (mainly in granite or equal). This raises the question of what really is a 'safe' limit for the overburden. The 'accepted rule', as given above, does not take into account the spread and decrease of normal stresses at a distance from the tunnel, nor the shearing stresses. It is suggested that this problem could be tackled on lines similar to the theory of Boussinesq for loading of foundations.

CONSTRUCTION OF HYDRO-POWER TUNNELS

The need of rapid daily progress and low costs in hydro-power tunnelling has led to important developments in tunnelling methods.

Excavation technique

New drilling equipment has been developed mainly in U.S.A. and Sweden. Swedish engineers have introduced hard metal bits (Swedish coromant steel or tungsten carbide steel) and light or medium equipment. The Americans use heavy equipment.

Weight of drills or machines

Light equipment: to less than 18 kg
Medium equipment: 18–27 kg
Heavy equipment: 27–60 kg (mostly 36–40 kg)

Other characteristics and data

Number of blows: 2,000 to 2,500 per minute
Duration of coromant and hard metal bits: 150–250 m
Drilling speed of drills: light or medium equipment, 35–40 cm/min; heavy equipment, 70–90 cm/min, 3 m (10 ft) usual borehole length.
Force on the drill: about 90–140 kg
Air pressure used: 6 atmospheres.

All these equipments are fixed on columns, 'jumbos', or frames. In large tunnels part of the work is done automatically (*Ex.*: Storrnorfors tunnel).

Reinforcement of tunnels (*Provisional during construction*)

According to TERZAGHI[148] the rock pressure can be estimated as follows:

TABLE 16

ROCK PRESSURE[147]

(B = tunnel width, H = tunnel height)

		Pressure on roof*
Hard rock	dry	0
Hard rock, moderately fractured	dry	0–$0 \cdot 12$ B
Hard rock, moderately fractured	wet	0–$0 \cdot 25$ B
Slightly plastic rock	wet	$0 \cdot 25$–$0 \cdot 35$ $(B+H)$
Hard rock, widely fractured	wet	$0 \cdot 25$–$0 \cdot 35$ $(B+H)$
Very fractured	wet	$0 \cdot 35$–$1 \cdot 1$ $(B+H)$
Marl, clayish material	wet	$1 \cdot 1$–$4 \cdot 5$ $(B+H)$

*The pressure is given in t/m² if H and B are in metres.

This pressure has to be withstood either by timbering or steel frames or rings, alternatively, by roof bolts.

(*i*) *Roof bolting or pinning (Figure 138)*—The following example is given by TALOBRE[147] (see also RABCEWICZ[158] and FREY BÄR[159]):

The rock pressure is estimated at $p = 3$ t/m²

Tunnel radius 2·5 m

Bolt length 2·5 m.

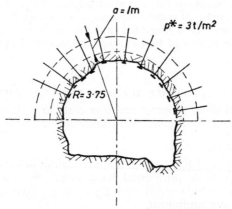

Figure 138.   Roof bolting or pinning

A reinforcing ring has to be created in the rock, with a radius of $R = 3·75$ m and 1 m thickness. The circular compression force on this ring is $N = pR = 3 \times 3·75 = 11·25$ tons.

Let us assume that tests made on the rock show that for a tangential stress of 11·25 t/m², a radial stress of 2 t/m² is required for rock stability. Bolts capable of taking 4·5 tons, spaced 1·5 m would just be sufficient. For safety calculate the bolts for $2 \times 4·5 = 9$ tons.

In coherent rock, similar estimates can be derived direct from the theory of Heim.

(*ii*) *Lining*—Hydro-power tunnelling has developed the concrete lining technique inherited from railway tunnelling. A concrete lining is capable of standing outside pressure from the rock but not the inside water pressure. Most concrete linings in tunnels carrying water under pressure are slightly cracked and are never entirely watertight. The principal function of a concrete lining is to reduce the friction losses as compared to an unlined tunnel, but water-tightness is not less important.

Reinforcement bars do not improve substantially the quality of concrete linings. The modern technique consists rather in compressing the lining by rock grouting or other methods of prestressing. These techniques have been further developed and real prestressing of the concrete lining has been used (Austria, Germany) in tunnel sections traversing poor rock sections. The aim of rock grouting and of concrete prestressing methods is to induce in the concrete shell a radial compression force p' larger than the hydrostatic inside water pressure p ($p' = 1·5$ to $2 \times p$).

The concrete lining is usually concreted behind movable shutters. Concrete pumps are often used, or alternatively the concrete is moved continuously in pipes by constant air pressure from a compressor. 'Prepakt' concrete (*i.e.* the coarse aggregate is first placed then grouted in place) has been used in several cases, especially behind steel liners (Kemano pressure shaft).

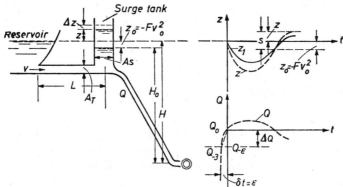

Figure 139. Surge tank analysis

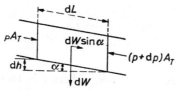

Figure 140.   Forces on element in pressure tunnel

XVI.   SURGE TANKS [163-172d]

Let us consider the elementary hydraulic system, represented in *Figure 140*,
consisting of: reservoir, pressure tunnel, surge tank, pressure pipe-line or
penstock and control valve or turbine gates.   When the demand for power
on the electric grid varies, the turbine governor automatically opens or
closes the control valve or turbine wicket gates, disturbing the steady flow
of water in the hydraulic pressure system.   Masses of water have to be
suddenly accelerated or decelerated, which causes considerable forces to
develop.   Elastic pressure waves, called water hammer, develop in the
pipe-line or penstock.   The pressure tunnel is sensitive to pressure variations
and the purpose of the surge tank is to protect the tunnel from sudden high
pressure variations.

The water in the tunnel too has to be accelerated or decelerated.   This
causes surges to develop in surge tanks, which can be compared to mass
oscillation in communicating vessels.

The period of the water hammer waves is short: a fraction of a second
to a maximum of a few seconds.   The surge oscillations are slower, the
period ranging from 100 to 400 or 500 seconds.   Recording manometers
placed at the bottom of the pipe-line and at the bottom of the surge tank
will record the water hammer and the surges and show the different periods.
The theory of surges in surge tanks considers mass displacements of water
in the pressure tunnel and in the surge tank, assuming the water not to be
elastic.   Friction losses in the tunnel are the main damping force.

Notation (see *Figure 139*)

H = gross head, H_0 = net head available at surge tank, in steady state,
losses in the pipe-line being neglected

$\pm Fv^2$ = head loss in tunnel, positive where $v > 0$

$Z_0 = -Fv_0^2$ = head loss in tunnel in steady state: $H_0 = H - Fv_0^2$

L = lenth of tunnel

A_T = area of cross-section of tunnel, $A_T = \dfrac{\pi D_T^2}{4}$

A_s = horizontal area of cross-section of surge tank
v = velocity of flow in tunnel, positive for flow from reservoir
Q = instantaneous flow required by turbines
z = water level in surge tank above reservoir level
τ = closing or opening time of valve or wicket gate
w = density of water

THE BASIC EQUATIONS OF MASS OSCILLATIONS IN THE SIMPLE SURGE TANK

We define the 'simple' surge tank as a tank or shaft of constant horizontal cross-sectional area A_s.

The dynamic equation

The forces acting on an element of length dL of the pressure tunnel in the direction of the tunnel axis are (*Figure 140*):

The component of the weight $= dW \sin \alpha = wA_T dL \sin \alpha = wA_T dh$, because $dh = dL \sin \alpha$.

The pressure $= -A_T dp$.

The frictional resistance $= -wA_T i dL$, where i is the energy gradient. As the mass of the element of water in the tunnel is $(w/g) A_T dL$, the dynamic equation for this element is

$$(w/g) A_T dL \partial v / \partial t = wA_T dh - A_T dp - wA_T i dL.$$

In order to allow the integration of these equations from 0 to L, the following assumptions are necessary:

(a) Both the tunnel and the water are incompressible.

(b) As a first approximation the velocity head $v^2/2g$ is negligible.

(c) The value for the frictional resistance substituted in the equations is the value for steady flow at any one time t when, instantaneously, the energy gradient i obtains. The head loss iL is proportional to v^2, or $iL = Fv^2$.

(d) The mass of the water in the surge shaft, in a first approximation, is negligible.

The dynamic equation can then be integrated and becomes (see *Figure 139*):

$$\frac{1}{g} \cdot \frac{dv}{dt} \int_0^L dL = \int_{H_s}^{H_a} dh - \int_{H_i}^{H_a+z} \frac{dp}{w} - i \int_0^L dL$$

or, after simplification:

$$\frac{L}{g} \cdot \frac{dv}{dt} + z \pm Fv^2 = 0 \qquad \ldots\ldots\ldots\ldots(1)$$

The positive sign is to be used when the direction of flow is from the reservoir to the surge tank.

Equation of continuity

Using the nomenclature of *Figure 139* we obtain:

$$vA_T = A_s \frac{dz}{dt} + Q \qquad \ldots\ldots\ldots\ldots(2)$$

Direct integration of equations (1) and (2) is possible in a limited number of cases. Step-by-step integration or graphical methods are used in others.

SOLUTION OF EQUATIONS (1) AND (2), NEGLECTING TUNNEL FRICTION

Sudden closure of turbine valve

The case of sudden rejection of load (sudden closure of the turbine valve) can be solved by direct integration, when friction losses in the tunnel are neglected. At the time $t=0-\varepsilon$, $Q=Q_0$ and at the time $t=0$, $Q=0$. Also: $A_T v = A_s$, dz/dt, and $dv/dt = (A_s/A_T)(d^2z/dt^2)$. As:

$$F=0, \quad (L/g)(dv/dt)+z=0$$

or

$$\frac{L}{g}\frac{A_s}{A_T}\frac{d^2z}{dt^2}+z=0$$

as $z=0$ for $t=0$.

The solution of the equation is:

$$z=Z_* \sin\frac{2\pi t}{T} \text{ and } v=v_0 \cos\frac{2\pi t}{T} \qquad \ldots\ldots\ldots\ldots(3)$$

It can be shown that:

$$Z_* = v_0 \left(\frac{L}{g}\frac{A_T}{A_s}\right)^{\frac{1}{2}} \text{ and } T=2\pi \left(\frac{L}{g}\frac{A_s}{A_T}\right)^{\frac{1}{2}}$$

In the case of partial closure reducing the flow from Q_0 to Q_1,

$$z=(v_0-v_1)\left(\frac{L}{g}\frac{A_T}{A_s}\right)^{\frac{1}{2}} \sin\frac{2\pi t}{T}$$

Sudden opening of turbine valve or sudden increase in load

If the flow Q_1 is suddenly increased to Q_0 with corresponding steady tunnel velocities v_1 and v_0, we obtain the equation:

$$z=(v_1-v_0)\left(\frac{L}{g}\frac{A_T}{A_s}\right)^{\frac{1}{2}} \sin\frac{2\pi t}{T}$$

where $v_1 < v_0$.

CALCULATION OF WATER-LEVEL OSCILLATIONS INCLUDING TUNNEL FRICTION

Sudden complete closure of turbine valve. (See below)

Step-by-step integration

The differential equations (1) and (2) can be replaced by difference equations, wherein the infinitesimally small time interval dt is replaced by a small, but finite, interval Δt. The difference equations

$$\frac{L}{g}\frac{\Delta v}{\Delta t}+z_m \pm F v_m^2 = 0 \qquad \ldots\ldots\ldots\ldots(5)$$

$$v_m A_T = Q_m + A_{sm}\frac{\Delta z}{\Delta t} \qquad \ldots\ldots\ldots\ldots(5a)$$

where

$$t_{i+1}=t_i+\Delta t, \quad z_m=z_i+\frac{\Delta z}{2}, \quad Q_m=\tfrac{1}{2}(Q_i+Q_{i+1})$$

$$v_m=\tfrac{1}{2}(v_i+v_{i+1})=v_i+\frac{\Delta v}{2},$$

can then be integrated step by step. Δv can be calculated from the equation:

$$\pm \tfrac{1}{4} F (\Delta v)^2 + \left[\frac{L}{g \Delta t} + \frac{A_T}{4 A^s{}_m} \Delta t \pm F v_i \right] \Delta v + z_i + \frac{A_T}{2 A^s{}_m} v_i \Delta t - \frac{Q_m}{2 A^s{}_m} \Delta t \pm F v_i{}^2 = 0$$

where $A^s{}_m$ = mean horizontal cross-sectional area of the surge tank.

In recent years difference equations have been used for extensive surge-tank investigations carried out on digital computers.

INTRODUCTION OF RATIOS INTO THE CALCULATION OF SURGE TANKS

Dimensionless parameters of great significance may be introduced into the discussion of surge-tank problems because of the existence of categories of surge tanks with similar oscillations: if the oscillations of one surge tank are known, the behaviour of all other tanks belonging to the same category can be predicted. The parameters to be used here are those introduced by Calame and Gaden, where

$$Z_* = v_0 \left(\frac{L A_T}{g A_s} \right)^{\frac{1}{2}} = Q_0 \left(\frac{L}{g A_T A_s} \right)^{\frac{1}{2}} \text{ and } T = 2\pi \left(\frac{L A_s}{g A_T} \right)^{\frac{1}{2}}$$

are the units of surges and of time respectively, so that

$$z_r = \frac{z}{Z_*}, \; F_r = \frac{F v^2}{Z_*}, \; F_{r0} = \frac{F v_0{}^2}{Z_*}, \; F_r = F_{r0} \left(\frac{v}{v_0} \right)^2, \; t' = t/T.$$

In addition (Q = discharge through turbine):

$$w = \frac{Q}{A_s}, \; w_0 = \frac{Q_0}{A_s}, \; v_0 = \frac{Q_0}{A_T}, \; u_0 = \frac{Q_0}{A_s} = w_0$$

If w_r is a relative value of the discharge through the pipe-lines and u_r is a relative velocity in the surge tank, then:

$$v_r = \frac{v}{v_0}, \; w_r = \frac{w}{w_0}, \; u_r = \frac{u}{u_0}$$

By substitution the continuity equation may be re-written in the form

$$\frac{A_T v}{Q_0} = \frac{A_s u}{Q_0} + \frac{Q}{Q_0} \text{ or } \frac{v}{v_0} = \frac{u}{u_0} + \frac{w}{w_0}$$

or

$$v_r = u_r + w_r \qquad \qquad \dots\dots\dots(6)$$

Similarly, substituting

$$\frac{dv}{dt} = \frac{A_s}{A_T} \frac{du}{dz} \frac{dz}{dt} + \frac{A_s}{A_T} \frac{dw}{dt}$$

into the dynamic equation, and using the ratios as defined:

$$u_r \frac{du_r}{dz_r} + \frac{1}{2\pi} \frac{dw_r}{dt'} + z_r \pm F_r = 0 \qquad \qquad \dots\dots\dots(7)$$

Application to the calculation of instantaneous total closure (instantaneous rejection of load)—In the case of total instantaneous rejection of load

$$w_r = 0, \; \frac{dw_r}{dt'} = 0 \text{ and } v_r = u_r$$

which leads to

$$F_r = F_{r0} v_r{}^2 = F_{r0} u_r{}^2$$

The dynamic equation may be re-written in the form

$$\frac{d\,(u_r{}^2)}{dz_r} + 2F_{r0}u_r{}^2 = -2z_r$$

the general integral of which becomes

$$(u_r=1 \text{ and } z_r=-F_{r0} \text{ for } t_r=0)$$

$$u_r{}^2 = \frac{1}{2F_{r0}{}^2}\left[1 - 2F_{r0}z_r - e^{-2F_{r0}\,(z_r+F_{r0})}\right] \qquad \dots\dots\dots\dots(8)$$

The highest level is reached when $dz/dt=0$ or when $u_r=0$, therefore

$$1 - 2F_{r0}z_r - e^{-2F_{r0}\,(z_r+F_{r0})} = 0 \qquad \dots\dots\dots\dots(9)$$

gives the first maximum surge z_{r1} in relative values.
Numerically, equation (9) yields the following:

F_{r0}	0	0·1	0·2	0·4	0·6	0·8	0·9	1
z_{r1}	1	0·933	0·875	0·76	0·65	0·555	0·512	0·475

The most important conclusion of this discussion is that the ratio z_{r1} is solely a function of $F_{r0}=Fv_0{}^2/Z_*$. A *single curve*, instead of the family of curves required for dimensional variables, connects the two dimensionless numbers z_{r1} and F_{r0}. All surge tanks whose parameters F_{r0} are equal have similar surges.

Other important results—The first draw-down after closure is given by

$$z_{r2} \cong -1 + 2F_{r0} \qquad \dots\dots\dots\dots(10)$$

The first down surge after sudden opening from rest is equal to

$$2_r' \cong -1 - 0\cdot125F_{r0} \text{ for } F_{r0} < 0\cdot8 \qquad \dots\dots\dots\dots(11)$$

SPECIAL SURGE TANKS

The simple cylindrical surge tank or surge shaft which we have considered up to now often has very large dimensions. In order to save volume, a

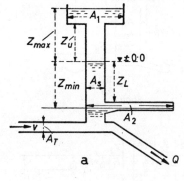

a

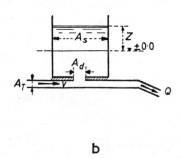

b

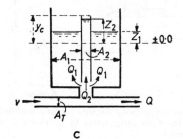

c

Figure 141. Special surge tanks. (a) Surge tank with expansion chamber. (b) Throttled surge tank. (c) Differential surge tank

number of types of surge shafts or tanks have been invented which are all based on the same idea: the flow in the tunnel will be retarded, or accelerated, more speedily the quicker the rise, or fall, of the pressure at junction of tunnel and surge shaft. Either a suitable shape of shaft, or the provision of a throttle at the inlet to the shaft, speed up as much as possible the pressure change in the tunnel at its junction with the surge shaft.

The surge shaft with expansion chambers (*Figure 141(a)*), the throttled surge tank (*Figure 141(b)*) and the differential surge tank (*Figure 141(c)*) are modern volume-saving designs.

MULTIPLE SURGE TANKS
(*Figures 142(a) and 142(b)*)

Multiple surge tank is a term used to denote a system in which two or more tanks rise from the pressure tunnels. Fundamentally we may distinguish between two kinds of multiple surge tanks. In the first of them the turbine (reaction wheel) is situated between the tanks, a design now frequently used for underground hydro-power stations. In the second, the two tanks are situated upstream of the turbine.

The treatment consists in writing two dynamic equations one for each tank and the corresponding tunnel length. Two equations of continuity provide the necessary link between the two former dynamic equations, the result being two equations of the fourth order.

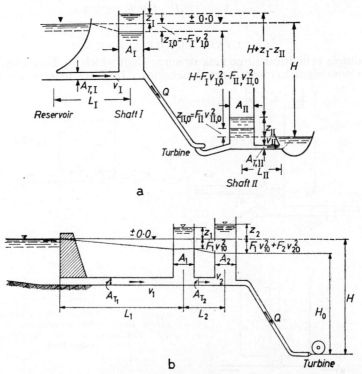

Figure 142. *Multiple surge tanks.* (a) *Two surge tanks located on one upstream, the other downstream of a reaction turbine.* (b) *Two surge tanks in series on a pressure tunnel*

THE GRAPHICAL METHOD OF SCHOKLITSCH

The graphical method, the very simple principles of which are due to Schoklitsch, may be adapted to the analysis of a great variety of surge system types. The main graph consists of a curve relating z to v. The time t is treated as a variable parameter so that the curve relating z to t follows simply.

On the main diagram, with v as abscissa and z as ordinate, two auxiliary curves are plotted first to suitable scales (see *Figure 143*): Curve (1), the curve of head losses $\Delta H_e = \pm F v^2$ with v as abscissa and ΔH_e as ordinate, where ΔH_e is plotted downwards if $v > 0$. Curve (2), the straight line representing the equation $\Delta v = -(g/L)\Delta tz$, which also passes through the origin. It is here assumed that the time increment Δt, on the choice of which there is no restriction, is constant.

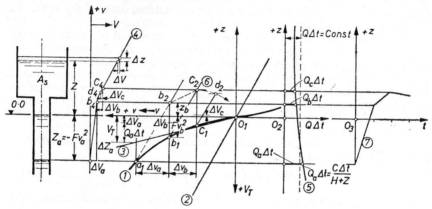

Figure 143. Graphical method of Schoklitsch

Two further auxiliary curves are required, of cubic content and quantity of water, and for these too, suitable scales have to be chosen. Line (3) connects v as abscissa with V_T as ordinate, where $V_T = vA_T\Delta t$ is the volume of water flowing through the tunnel in the time Δt. This equation is represented by a straight line, also passing through the origin. It is convenient to plot V_T positive downwards, for $v > 0$. The fourth auxiliary curve (4) relates the cubic content V of the surge tank to z; the elevation z is plotted as ordinate and V as abscissa. The origin of curve (4) which represents the equation $\Delta V = A_s\Delta z$, may be chosen anywhere.

The dynamic equation may be written in the form

$$\Delta v = -(g/L)\Delta t\,(z + Fv^2) \qquad \ldots\ldots\ldots\ldots(12)$$

where z is positive upwards. Equation (12) represents a straight line parallel to the auxiliary line (2). The values $z = -Fv^2$ and $\Delta v = 0$ will always satisfy equation (12), and the lines representing it will pass through points a_1, b_1, c_1 on curve (1), whose co-ordinates are $v = v_a, v_b, v_c \ldots$ and $z = -Fv_a^2, -Fv_b^2, -Fv_c^2 \ldots$

The equation of continuity is

$$V_T = vA_T\Delta t = Q\Delta t \pm \Delta V \qquad \ldots\ldots\ldots\ldots(13)$$

where $\Delta V = A_s\Delta z$ is the increase in storage volume in the surge tank due to a rise Δz in water level. On curve (4) ΔV is measured horizontally. $V_T = vA_T\Delta t$ is the ordinate of line (3).

$Q\Delta t$ represents the quantity of water flowing to the turbine during the time interval Δt. $Q\Delta t$ is plotted against z on auxiliary curve (5). If, for example, $Q\Delta t = \eta_0 Q_0 H_0\Delta t/\eta\,(H + z)$ (governing equation), the corresponding curve will be a hyperbola.

At time $t=t_a$, point a_1 on the curve (1), is known ($V=V_a$ and $z=z_a=-Fv_a{}^2$), the straight line a_1b_2 is drawn through point a_1 on curve (1), parallel to line (2). $Q_a \Delta t$ and V_{Ta} are known. Graphical subtraction yields ΔV_a which is plotted as abscissa on curve (4), giving b_4, and, on a horizontal line, the point b_2. The curve representing the oscillation may be drawn through points $a_1b_2c_2d_2$.

THE STABILITY OF SINGLE AND MULTIPLE SURGE TANKS

Some surge tanks have proved to be 'unstable'. Under certain circumstances the surges are of the 'forced oscillation type'. Thoma was the first to show that, with an automatically governed turbine, the surge tanks will only be (hydraulically) stable if the horizontal cross-sectional area of the tank, A_s, exceeds a certain minimum value A_{Th} (Thoma's area).

Referring to *Figure 139*, the possibility of this kind of instability may be deduced from simple physical considerations. At the instant $t=-\varepsilon$ the flow through the pressure tunnel and pipe-line is at the uniform rate $Q_{-\varepsilon}$. In the short interval of time ε the rate of flow $Q_{-\varepsilon}$ to the turbine is increased by an amount ΔQ to $Q_0=Q_{-\varepsilon}+\Delta Q$. It is now possible to calculate the surges that would result if the governor ensured a *constant discharge* Q_0. The resultant oscillation in the surge tank has been plotted on *Figure 139*, (z_1).

In practice, the governor of a turbine does not ensure constant discharge but *constant power*, or

$$N=\eta_0 H_0 Q_0 w=\eta Q (H+z) w \qquad \text{............(14)}$$

If $H+z$ varies with z, Q will also vary, but in the opposite direction. As shown in *Figure 139*, the graph of Q plotted against time t is a curve which oscillates approximately in symmetry (about a horizontal axis) with the graph of z_1 against t. A more precise calculation will now show a new curve for z showing increased oscillations. Oscillations of this type may under certain circumstances become unstable. There must be a limiting value (A_{Th}) for A_s, which will depend on the ratio z_{max}/H_0. The analytical treatment of the problem leads to the condition

$$A_s \geqslant \frac{v_0{}^2}{2g} \frac{LA_T}{Fv_0{}^2 H_0} = A_{Th} \text{ or } A_s=nA_{Th}, \text{ with } n \geqslant 1$$

This is *Thoma's condition for stability of single surge tanks, assuming oscillations of small amplitude and* A_{Th} *is Thoma's least area of cross-section of a surge tank.* The theory can be extended to restricted orifice tanks, to differential surge tanks and to systems of surge tanks[172, 172c].

DIMENSIONS OF SURGE TANKS
(*Figure 144*) [172d]

Two formulae can be developed giving the proper dimensions of surge tanks ($Vol=$volume of tank):

(a) $\quad Vol_{I} = 1 \cdot 3 \dfrac{L}{H_0} (v_0 D)^2$

(b) $\quad Vol_{II} = \dfrac{\pi}{g} \dfrac{k \sqrt{n}}{7 \cdot 1} v_0 \left(\dfrac{L}{H_0}\right)^{\frac{1}{4}} D^{8/3}$ ($k=$Manning–Strickler friction factor)

The first formula is based on a limiting value of the surge ($\lambda = Z_* / H_0 \cong 0 \cdot 12$) acceptable for the turbine gate openings, the second on the formula of Thoma (equation 14).

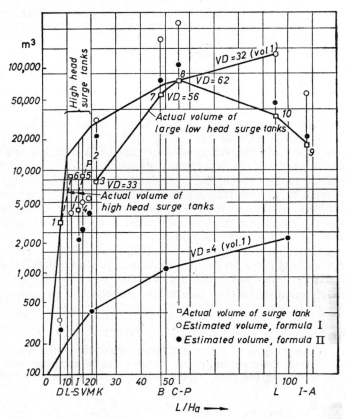

Figure 144. Surge tank volumes. D, Dixence; L-S, Loch Sloy; I, Innertkirchen; V, Verbano; M, Malgovert; K, Kemano; B, Bersimis; C-P, Chute des Passes (Project); L, Lavey; I-A, Isère-Arc

Figure 144 shows that high head surge tanks are often larger than the largest value of *Vol*, whereas others are, if possible, kept smaller than the smallest value of *Vol*.

CHOICE OF A SURGE TANK

The choice of the type of surge tank to be adopted and of its dimensions depends mainly on the head H_0, on the ratio L/H_0 and the discharge Q_0. In addition the conditions on the electric network to be fed by the station are of paramount importance for the final choice.

These questions are fully discussed in specialized text books and papers (refs. 171, 172-172d).

XVII. UNDERGROUND HYDRO-ELECTRIC POWER STATIONS[173-181]

A substantial proportion of the hydro-electric schemes built since 1940 have underground power stations.

1. The first underground power station to be built was that of Snoqualmie (10,000 hp) in the State of Washington, U.S.A., in 1898. Brechbergmuehle (Germany), followed in 1907 and Porjus (Sweden) in 1914. Later on the technique developed in Sweden (Krangede). Brommat (1928–

31) was for many years the only station of this type in France. Then came a series of power stations, north and south of the Alps (Switzerland and Italy): the now well established technique spread all over the world to Scotland, Canada, Portugal, Spain, Algeria, *etc.*

REASONS IN FAVOUR OF THE NEW TYPE OF STATION DESIGN

(*a*)   In some cases an underground development is better suited to contour lines or to geological conditions.

(*b*)   Considerations of climatic conditions and of avalanches may be decisive in choosing the underground alternative.

(*c*)   Thanks to modern tunnelling techniques, an underground power station may be cheaper than a conventional alternative. Comparable cost estimates are usually the deciding factor.

(*d*)   A pipe-line entirely in rock is safer than a conventional pipe-line, provided the rock is reasonably sound.

(*e*)   The technique of underground power stations allows a very high concentration of power in one power station. Kemano, Bersimis I and Chute des Passes, all in Canada, are designed for 1,000,000 hp or over.

(*f*)   An underground station does not spoil the scenery.

TYPES OF UNDERGROUND POWER STATION

Depending on the position of the power house relatively to the intake and outlet of the system, underground power stations can be arranged with long head race, or with long tail race. Intermediate solutions are also possible (*Figure 145*).

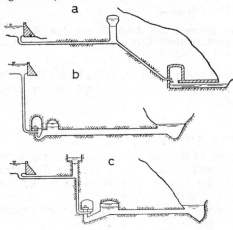

Figure 145. Types of Underground power station. (a) Head-race arrangement. (b) tail-race arrangement. (c) intermediate solution

Another well-known classification of underground power stations is based on the hydrodynamic characteristics of different schemes, especially with regard to governing conditions. In this classification there are the following five types (*Figure 146*):

(*1*)   The tail race tunnel is a free flow tunnel, without a surge tank downsream of the power house (*ex.:* Innertkirchen, Clachan, Krangede, Isère–Arc).

(*2*)   The tail race tunnel is a pressure tunnel with a conventional surge tank on the tail race; there is no surge tank on the upstream side (*ex.:* Harspranget, Stornorrfors).

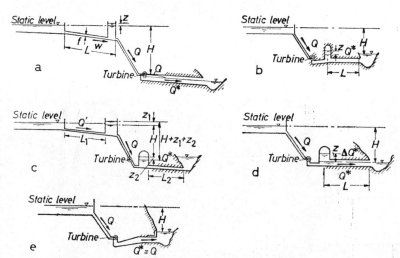

Figure 146.   Five principal hydro-dynamic types of underground hydro-electric power station

(3)   The whole system is under pressure, with surge tanks on both sides of the turbine.   In this case, the behaviour of the system will depend on whether the turbine is of the reaction or impulse type (*ex.:* Chute des Passes).   Interference of the oscillations in the two surge shafts occurs and must be analysed[172a, 172b].

(4)   Free flow exists in the tail race tunnel during normal steady conditions but the tunnel will fill up during major disturbances in the flow. In such a case, the tank is called a 'partial working' surge tank (Wettingen type).

(5)   Finally the whole system, if very short, can be fully under pressure without any surge tank (*ex.:* Picote).

The choice between these different systems depends mainly on local geological and topographical conditions.   When a solution has been chosen, water hammer and surge conditions must be checked carefully, together with the turbine regulation.   The surge stability condition formula of Thoma often causes difficult problems for large low-head underground schemes.   For excavation and lining of tunnels and shafts see Sect. XV.

EXCAVATION FOR GENERATOR HALLS

Light drills have been successfully applied to cavern excavation, and in one recent case (Kemano turbine hall) diamond drilling has been used in conjunction with rock blasting.   The technique of excavating the power house will depend on the rock, its stability and strength, and the main direction of the strata.   There is a definite tendency everywhere, even where labour is cheap, to adopt Swedish or American machinery and methods of excavation.

Excavation work starts with one or more galleries being excavated parallel to the power house axis.   Normally the excavation and the concreting of the arched roof of the power house will be given first priority and then the excavations work will proceed downwards on the whole width of the power house (as at Lavey), or in trenches along the walls, leaving a central core to be excavated later (as at Innertkirchen).   An entirely new technique has been used at Kemano[176].

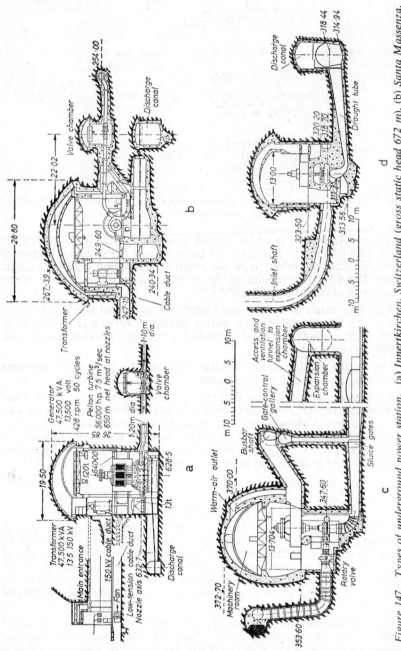

Figure 147. Types of underground power station. (a) *Innertkirchen, Switzerland (gross static head 672 m).* (b) *Santa Massenza, Italy (gross static head 590/460 m).* (c) *Santa Giustina, Italy (gross static head 183/95 m).* (d) *Isère-Arc, France (gross static head 152 m)*

TABLE 17

DATA ON UNDERGROUND POWER HOUSES

Date of commission	Power station	Country	Capacity kW	Gross head ft	Turbines h = horizontal v = vertical	Volume cu yds	Excavation for transformer or valve house, etc. cu yds	Volume of power house per kW installed cu yds
1910	Porius	Sweden	60,000	183	8 Francis, h	35,000	6,000	0·58
1932	Brommat	France	186,000	855	6 Francis, v	60,000	16,000	0·32
1942	Innertkirchen	Switzerland	210,000	2,200	5 Pelton, v	59,000	20,000	0·28
1947	Lumiei (Ampezzo)	Italy	58,500	1,465	3 Pelton, h	33,000	—	0·565
1948	San Giacomo	Italy	200,000	2,140	3 double Pelton, h	37,000	5,000	0·19
1948	Soverzene	Italy	220,000	870	4 Francis, v	85,500(a) / 102,000(b)	16,500(a)	0·390(a) / 0·465(b)
1949	Mar	Norway	180,000	—	Francis, v	60,000	—	0·334
?	Vinstra	Norway	180,000	838	3 Francis, h	30,000	8,170	0·167
1949	Provvidenza	Italy	150,000	133·5	3 Kaplan, v	44,000	3,000	0·29
1950	Lavey	Switzerland	76,000	1,520	4 Pelton, v	54,500	7,200	0·715
1952	Handeck II	Switzerland	114,000	560	3 Francis, v	39,000	—	0·34
1951	Santa Giustina	Italy	108,000	353	3 Francis, v	40,000	—	0·37
1951	Harspranget	Sweden	288,000(c) / 380,000(d)	—	4 Francis, v / 2 40,000 h.p. Pelton, v	63,300 / 79,000	30,000(e)	0·22(c) / 0·206(d)
1951	Ahrzerouftis	Algeria	66,500	1,125	1 7,500 h.p. Pelton, v / Francis, v	44,000(f) / 80,000(g)	—	0·66 / 1·20
1951	Santa Massenza I	Italy	302,000	1,940 to 1,505	6 Pelton, h	203,000	10,900(h)	0·92
1952	Santa Massenza II	Italy	25,500(k)		2 Francis, v	21,000	8,000	0·32
?	Monte Argenta	Italy	66,000	164	3 Francis, v	29,000	1,000	0·29
1952	Montorio	Italy	100,000	845	3 Francis, v	33,000	—	0·33
1953	Verbano	Switzerland	100,000	973	4 Francis, v	68,000	—	0·50
1954	Isère-Arc	France	135,000	500	4 Francis, v	26,300	—	0·226
1954	Montpezat	France	116,000	2,080	2 double overhang Pelton, v			
1954	Kemano	Canada	835,000(f) / 1,670,000(k)	2,597	8 Pelton, v / 16 Pelton, v	278,000 / 473,000	21,000	0·333 / 0·284
1953-4	Nilo Pecanha	Brazil	355,000	1,122	6 Francis, v	98,000	—	0·28
1955	Ceannacroc	Scotland	20,000	299	1 Francis, v	9,800	—	0·49
1957	Glen Moriston	Scotland	30,000	311	2 Francis, v	12,700	—	0·40
Constr.	Cubatao	Brazil	465,000	2,365	6 Francis, v	123,000	7,900	0·29
Constr.	Fionnay	Switzerland	127,500	1,555	3 Francis, v	27,000	1,800(a)	0·21(a)

NOTES. (a) *Without transformer house.* (b) *Including transformer house.* (c) *First stage.*

(d) *Second stage.* (e) *For transformer house.* (f) *Useful excavation.*

(g) *Including 10 ft thick walls and roof.* (h) *For valve house.* (j) *First stage.*

(k) *Second stage.*

TABLE 18

DIMENSIONS OF SOME LARGE UNDERGROUND POWER STATIONS

Power house	Head m	Total height* m	Total width m	Total length m	Crane span m	Crane capacity tons	Turbine horse-power	Distance between turbine centres m	Position of transformers	Valves
Kemano, 1st stage	790	41	25·5	214	—	2×225	8×140,000	—	Inside main excavation	Special excavation
Kemano, 2nd stage		42·4	24·8	344	15·25	—	16×140,000	18·3	Inside main excavation	Special excavation
Innertkirchen	672	26·85	19·5	96·70	10·8	120	5×56,000	14·50	Inside main excavation	Special excavation (28-ton crane)
Montpezat	634	23·2	16·1	50	13·5	2×135	2×81,000	—	Outside	?
Santa Massenza I and II	590/460	28·0	28·8	192·7	14·2	—	4×80,000 2×40,000 1×25,000	18·0	Inside main excavation	Special excavation
Cavergno (Maggia)	590	21·5	28	—	11·6	—	2×25,500	—	Inside main excavation	Inside main excavation
Lumiei	480·6	24·2	15·4	71	12·0	—	3×25,500	—	Outside	Special excavation upstream of main excavation
Handeck II	463	25·55	16·8	79·25	10·70	—	4×41,000 2×23,500	14·0	Inside main excavation	Special excavation
Peccia (Maggia)	426	21·5	28	—	11·6	—	2×11,600	—	Inside main excavation	Inside main excavation
Ahrzerouftis I and II	345	22·4	20	67	—	120	2×40,000 1×7,500	—	Outside	Inside main excavation
Vinstra	?	27	13	73	11	—	4×60,000	11	Inside special excavation	Straight flow valves, inside
Bersimis	336	28·5	19·4	171	18·4	2×200	8×175,000 (8×200,000)	16·8	Inside main excavation	Inside main excavation
Snowy Mountain T1	334	28	17	92	14·5	—	4×134,500	12·8	Inside special excavation	Straight flow valves, inside
Soverzene	265	35·1	25·5	73	17	140	4×72,500	14	Inside special excavation	Inside main excavation
Brommat	260	31·4	21·8	?	11·5	—	6×40,000	—	Outside	Inside main excavation
Santa Giustina	183/95	29·5	17	61·3	13·7	—	3×47,500	12·8	Inside prolonged main excavation	Inside main excavation
Isère-Arc	152	31·6	16·8	56·25	13	—	3×45,000	10	Inside special excavation	Inside main excavation
Harspranget, 1st stage	108	33 43‡	18·3	100 109†	—	2 cranes	4×127,000	20		—
Lavey	40·6	31	21	64	14·5	2×60	3×33,500	14	Outside	Separate excavation

*Not including draught-tube height.   †Including transformers and workshop.   ‡Including draught-tube height.

The power house walls will usually be lined with concrete, the concrete adhering directly to the rock. Norwegian engineers prefer to leave the rock without direct lining, the concrete walls and the concrete roof being at some distance (0·50 to 1·0 m) from the rock. Thorough drainage and ventilation are necessary to keep the rock dry. In solid granite the walls, and sometimes the roof, may be without any lining, and the bare rock is directly visible (Swedish stations).

In a few cases the valves in front of the turbines are located in a separate valve chamber excavated parallel to the main power house excavation. The transformers are either above ground (Lavey), inside the main power house excavation (Innertkirchen, Kemano), in the prolongation of it (Isère–Arc), or in a specially excavated cavern (Harspranget, Soverzene).

Figures 147 to *149* show sketches of some of the principal designs which have been worked and TABLES 17 and 18 contain data on under-ground power houses and their dimensions.

Underground stations are most suitable for the high concentration of power, which is a trend of all modern power developments. This is one reason why they attract the attention of modern designers.

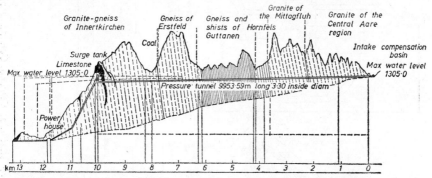

Figure 148. *Underground power station (Innertkirchen)*

COST OF UNDERGROUND POWER STATIONS

The final decision between underground power design or conventional design is usually taken by comparison of detailed cost estimates. The great number of underground power stations built in the last 10 or 15 years proves that the balance of costs is often in favour of this alternative. This is mainly due to the improved tunnelling technique and progress in large excavations.

Even if the excavation of the power house is expensive substantial economies may be made on the weight of steel required by the pressure pipe.

Good rock quality is essential for the technical and financial success of an underground power scheme.

XVIII. PRESSURE PIPE-LINES, PRESSURE SHAFTS AND ANCHOR BLOCKS—VALVES[182-8]

Pipe-lines are used for bringing the water from the reservoir, the intake or the surge chamber to the turbines (or pumps), and sometimes instead of, or in conjunction with, pressure tunnels. Principal types of pipe-lines are:

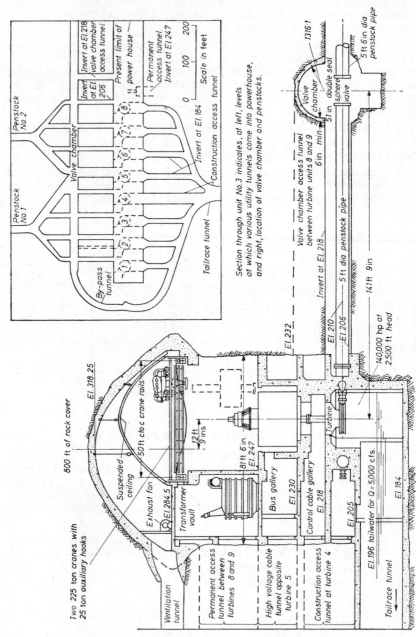

Figure 149. Underground power station at Kemano, Canada (gross static head 790 m)

Steel pipe-lines
Banded steel pipe-lines
Prestressed steel pipe-lines (French design)
Steel-lined pressure shafts and galleries
Reinforced (also prestressed) concrete pipes
Wood-stave pipes.
Pipe-lines have been designed for heads up to 1,700 m (5,600 ft).

THIN PIPES—THICK PIPES

Thin pipes, *Figure 150*, are calculated by the formula

$$\sigma = \frac{pr}{t}$$

when t is the thickness of the pipe wall
  p the design pressure
  r the radius of the pipe
  σ the permissible working stress in the shell (taking into account the efficiency of the longitudinal joint if the shell is of steel plates).

σ and p are expressed in kg/cm² or in lb per sq in. r and t in metres or in inches.

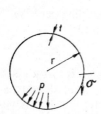

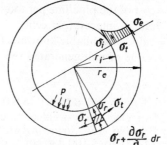

Figure 150. *Thin pipe*   Figure 151. *Thick pipe*

For thick pipes the formula is (*Figure 151*)

$$\sigma_e = \frac{2pr_i^2}{r_e^2 - r_i^2} \qquad \sigma_i = \frac{p(r_e^2 + r_i^2)}{r_e^2 - r_i^2}$$

where r_i is the inner radius
  r_e the external radius of the thick shell
  σ_e the external stress
  σ_i the stress at the internal side of the thick pipe.

The design pressure p is equal to the static pressure, plus the surge, plus the water hammer, the worst possible combination of pressures being assumed.

Sometimes the design pressure is prescribed (say 15 or 20 per cent above the static pressure) and the surge and water hammer pressures have to be adjusted to this prescribed value, which then determines the closing time of the turbine gates or valves or of the relief valve (reaction wheels) or jet deflector (impulse turbines).

BUCKLING OF A PIPE DUE TO OUTSIDE PRESSURE

According to Allievi, buckling occurs for an outside pressure

$$p = \frac{24\,IE}{D^3}$$

where I is the moment of inertia of the pipe. For a pipe not reinforced by collars $I = t^3/12$ and $p = 2Et^3/D^3$.

OTHER USEFUL FORMULAE—FRICTION LOSSES

The losses in pressure pipe-lines are usually estimated by the Manning–Strickler formula

$$S = \frac{V^2}{k^2 R^{4/3}} \text{ (metric) or } S = \frac{V^2}{M^2 R^{4/3}} \text{ foot units}$$

where S = the hydraulic gradient (head loss per unit of pipe length)

V = the velocity of flow

R = the hydraulic mean radius obtained by dividing the cross-sectional area of the pipe by the wetted perimeter.

M or k, the coefficients of roughness*, are given on p 192. By balancing the income losses due to friction and the capital charges of a steel pipe, the economical diameter of a pipe is obtained by the formula

$$D = \left[(1104\,K + 210\,U\theta)\, \frac{Q^3}{I.C.H.} \right]^{1/7\cdot33}$$

where D = economic diameter of the pipe-line (feet)

Q = quantity of water at full load (cusecs)

H = design head for the pipe-line (feet)

θ = load factor of station

C = cost of the pipe-line per ton of steel (pounds sterling)

I = rate of interest (per cent)

K = value of available kilowatts (pounds sterling per kW)

U = value of unit generated (pence per unit)†.

QUALITY OF STEEL AND WORKING STRESSES

For riveted or electrically-welded pipe-lines the steel should be in accordance with B.S. No. 15: *Structural steel* (ultimate tensile strength of 28–33 ton/sq in (4,300 to 5,100 kg/cm²), or B.S. No. 14: *Marine boiler plate* (ultimate strength of 28–32 ton/sq in). For water–gas lap-welded pipes, the steel should be to B.S. No. 534: *Steel* (ultimate strength 24–28 ton/sq in) 3,700 to 4,300 kg/cm²). A working tensile stress of 6 ton/sq in (930 kg/cm²) is usually adopted for the 28–33 quality steel.

There is a tendency on the Continent to use steel of better quality and to work to higher stresses. An aluminium steel has been used in Austria for high head penstocks (ultimate strength 5,400 to 5,800 kg/cm²). For bands (banded pipes) an even better steel quality is required. The French 'prestressed pipes' are cold stressed beyond the yield point. The test pressure (in the workshop) is 2·5 times the working (dynamic) pressure. Electricité de France relate the safety factor to the yield point, disregarding the ultimate strength, whereas in other countries much attention is directed to the latter.

TYPE OF JOINT

A pipe-line may be constructed with either riveted, electrically welded or water–gas lap-welded joints. Welding has made rapid progress in recent years and improving of welded pipes as compared with riveted pipes will continue. Welding permits a substantial reduction in the over-all weight of the pipe, as compared to a riveted pipe; there are fewer transverse welded joints than riveted joints and pipe sections are usually longer. Friction losses are lower in welded pipes than in riveted pipes.

*Detailed tables for practical values k and M are given in ref. 191.

†J. GUTHRIE BROWN[197]: A similar formula was first developed by A. Schoklitsch.

ELECTRICALLY WELDED JOINTS

The following British Standard specifications give general information on electrically welded joints

(a) B.S. 538: *Metal arc welding as applied to steel structures;*

(b) B.S. 1500: *Fusion welded pressure vessels;*

(c) B.S. 639: *Covered electrodes for metal arc welding wrought iron and mild steel.*

'Single V' welds are permissible for plate thicknesses up to $\frac{1}{2}$ in. 'Double V' welds should be used whenever possible, and for plates of greater thickness. For exceptionally thick plates the double 'U'-type of joint should be considered.

RIVETED JOINTS

It is not possible to deal with the design of riveted pipe joints here.

TEMPERATURE STRESSES IN PIPES

Figure 152 shows pipes with and without expansion joints. In the former case, due to a temperature variation Δt, the pipe length varies by Δl proportionally to Δt and to the pipe length l:

$$\pm \Delta l = \pm \alpha \Delta t l$$

where $\alpha = 0\cdot000012$ if the temperature is measured in °C, and $\alpha = 0\cdot0000065$ if Δt is in °F.

Ex.: $l = 100$ m, $\Delta t = \pm 1°C$, $\Delta l = \pm 1\cdot2$ mm.

If the pipe is not free to expand, stresses σ_t develop in the steel sheet. As $\Delta l/l = \sigma_t/E$,

$$\sigma_t = \alpha E \Delta t$$

The temperature stresses do not depend on the length of the pipe. With $E = 2\cdot15 \times 10^6$ kg/cm², $\alpha E = 26$ kg/cm² for 1°C and $\sigma_t = 26\Delta t$.

Ex.: For $\Delta t = \pm 20°C$, $\sigma_t = \pm 520$ kg/cm².

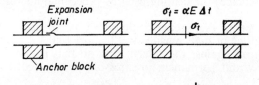

a　　　　　　　　　b

Figure 152. Pipes with and without expansion joints

OTHER LONGITUDINAL STRESSES IN PIPES

(a) Suppose the circumferential tensile stress in the pipe wall is $\sigma = p(R/t)$. If the pipe is free to expand, this tensile stress causes a shortening of the pipe

$$\Delta l_{tr} = \frac{\sigma l}{mE} \quad \text{where } m = \text{Poisson's ratio}$$

If the pipe is not free to expand this corresponds to a longitudinal stress $\sigma' = \sigma/m \cong 0\cdot3 \sigma$ ($m \cong 3\cdot33$).

(b) If the pipe $(D = 2R)$ is closed by a valve or cover and there is no expansion joint, the hydrostatic pressure p causes a longitudinal stress in the pipe wall (*Figure 153*)

$$\sigma'' = \frac{(\pi D^2/4)\,p}{\pi Dt} = \frac{pD}{4t} = \frac{\sigma}{2}$$

The 'closing temperature' of pipes should be chosen to reduce the temperature stresses.

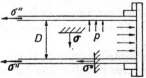

Figure 153.   Longitudinal stress σ'' in pipe wall

BANDED PIPES

In a banded pipe external shell rings or bands reinforce the inner shell or sleeve.   The bands are weldless rings, of high tensile steel (ultimate strength $\sigma = 5,300$ to $6,500$ kg/cm²).   They are heated before being put into position on the steel sleeve.   When cooling down they shrink on the sleeve.   When the pipe is put under hydraulic pressure from the inside, stresses are distributed between the steel shell and the bands.

This type of pipe is used for very high heads only.   *Ex.:* The old Dixence pipe-line, $h = 456$ to $1,748$ m ($1,495$ to $5,733$ ft), and the lower section of the two Malgovert pipe-lines, $H = 750$ m ($2,460$ ft), $200,000$ hp per pipe.

FRENCH PRESTRESSED PIPES

Instead of heating the bands, the inner shell can be pressed against the bands.   The method consists in closing the pipe at both ends with covers and filling it with water, which is then put under pressure.   The French specialists recommend a pressure as high as $2 \cdot 5$ times the working pressure (static plus hydrodynamic = working pressure).   The circumferential stresses in the pipe exceed the yield point of the steel plate so that permanent plastic (non-reversible) deformation of the shell takes place.   This method of prestressing replaces the heating used by other manufacturers to prestress the bands.

The next step in the French technique was to replace the solid steel rings by wire hoops of high tensile steel ($\sigma_{\text{yield}} = 15,000$ kg/cm²).   The steel shell is then forced against the steel hoops, so that it expands beyond the limit of elasticity and permanent prestressing is obtained.

STEEL PIPES WITH DRESSER COUPLING (*Figure 154*)

Most pipes are fixed by anchor blocks.   An anchor block is required at every bend of the pipe.   The Bridge River pipe-line (British Columbia) has, however, been built without any anchor block.   It is laid in a trench and the 40 ft sections of the steel pipe forming the penstock (outside diam. $75\frac{5}{8}$ in ($1 \cdot 9$ m) $H = 1,200$ ft (365 m)) are joined by Dresser flexible couplings.

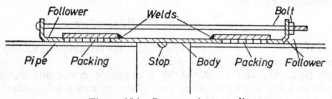

Figure 154.   Dresser pipe coupling

These simplified the erection of the pipe. They have the effect of providing an expansion joint for small movements at the end of each 40 ft pipe section. There are no special expansion joints, but the number of saddles is double (two saddles for each pipe length).

UNDERGROUND PIPES

Underground pipes are constructed in open cuttings, which are afterwards filled in. The pipe is thus protected against extreme temperature variations and expansion joints are not needed. The Malgovert pipe-line is underground, but this pipe is provided with proper anchor blocks at each pipe bend or change of direction. A few old pipes have been built without anchor blocks and without expansion joints.

It is essential for the underground pipes to be properly protected with bitumen layers against rusting and against damage by stones falling on the pipe during the backfilling of the trench.

CONCRETE PIPE-LINES

For low heads, reinforced concrete pipes have been used. Small cracks in the concrete should be avoided. This requires maintaining the tensile stresses in the reinforcement bars at a low figure, and this makes the pipes expensive. Modern designers think rather in terms of prestressed concrete. The concrete is always under compression and high tensile stresses are allowed for the steel reinforcement hoops. Similar techniques have been used to prestress the concrete lining for hydro-power pressure tunnels.

STEEL-LINED SHAFTS — PIPES EMBEDDED IN CONCRETE — PRESTRESSED CONCRETE TUNNELS

When conventional lining of a pressure tunnel or shaft with concrete (reinforced or not) is considered not to be safe, a steel lining may be added. The hydrostatic pressure forces this steel lining against the concrete lining and strains and stresses are transmitted from the steel shell to the concrete lining and from there to the rock (see also Sect. XV).

STRESS ANALYSIS

Inside water pressure

Strain–stress equations are written for the thin steel shell, the concrete lining and the rock being considered as thick cylinders, the latter with infinite outside radius. Two equations for equal elastic deformations are written, one for the steel shell and the inner radius of the concrete cylinder and a second for the concrete outer radius and the rock inner radius; both must be identical.

It can be shown that a high proportion of the hydrostatic pressure is thus transmitted to the rock; hence the thickness of the steel shell can be substantially reduced as compared to a standard pipe-line for the same head and diameter, but without support from the rock.

Outside water pressure—resistance to buckling

Buckling due to outside water pressure (water under pressure contained in rock fissures or outside grout pressure caused by rock grouting) is a more likely cause of rupture of the steel shell than inside water pressure.

According to Knapp, the critical outside radial pressure p_{cr} which might cause buckling of a steel shell with radius r and wall thickness t is given by:

$$p_{cr} = \frac{E}{12} \left(\frac{t}{r}\right)^2 \left[\left(1 + 24 \frac{\sigma_y}{E} \frac{r}{t}\right)^{\frac{1}{2}} - 1 \right]$$

when $E =$ modulus of elasticity of the steel and $\sigma_y =$ yield point.

PRESSURE DUE TO ROCK OVERBURDEN

For normal rock conditions the stresses developing along the tunnel profile owing to the rock overburden are relieved as soon as the steel lining is forced (by inside water pressure or grout pressure) against the rock; there is no radial component of pressure acting towards the steel lining but a sharply increased circumferential stress in the rock (see Sect. XV). Hydrostatic pressure in the tunnel will partly relieve these stresses in the rock.

PIPES EMBEDDED IN CONCRETE (PIPES PASSING THROUGH DAMS)

Stress and strain conditions can more or less be assimilated to what has been said on steel lining in tunnels.

PRESTRESSED CONCRETE TUNNELS
(See Sect. XV)

STEEL PIPE SPECIALS AND VALVES

Among the specials required in steel pipe-lines are Y-branches or bifurcations, *Figure 155*, manholes, *Figure 156*, and expansion or movement joints, *Figure 157*. A Straightflow valve (English Electric Co. Ltd.) is shown in *Figure 158(a)* and (*b*) and a diffusing relief valve (English Electric Co. Ltd.) in *Figure 159*.

There are many other types of valve and relief valve and for full details the manufacturers should be consulted.

ANCHOR BLOCKS AND SADDLES

The forces acting on an anchor block are represented in *Figure 160*. They are:

(*1*) Forces due to the weight of the steel pipe:

$$P_1' = g_r' L_i' \sin \alpha_i \quad \text{and} \quad P_1'' = g_r'' L_i'' \sin \alpha_{i+1}$$

where g_r' and g_r'' are weights per unit length of pipe.

(2) Weight of the water column ($w =$ specific weight of water)

$$P_2' = w \frac{\pi}{4} D_i^2 L_i' \sin \alpha_i \quad \text{and} \quad P_2'' = w \frac{\pi}{4} D_i^2 L_i'' \sin \alpha_{i+1}$$
$$= g_w L_i' \sin \alpha_i \qquad\qquad = g_w L_i'' \sin \alpha_{i+1}$$

where $g_w =$ weight of water per unit length of pipe.

(3) Water pressure acting down the pipe

$$P_3 = w \frac{\pi}{4} D_i^2 h_i'$$

(4) Water pressure acting up the pipe

$$P_4 = -w \frac{\pi}{4} D_i^2 h'_{i+1}$$

(5) Friction on saddles or intermediate supports when pipe length varies with temperature ($L_i = L_i' + L_i''$):

$$P_5 \cong (g_r + g_w) L_i \mu \cos \alpha_i$$

$\mu =$ friction factor, values of which are:

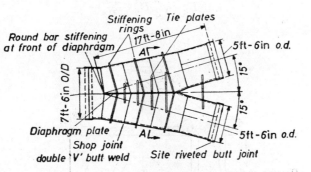

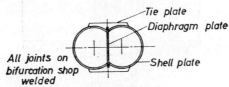

Figure 155. Steel pipe bifurcation

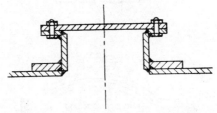

Figure 156. Pipe manhole

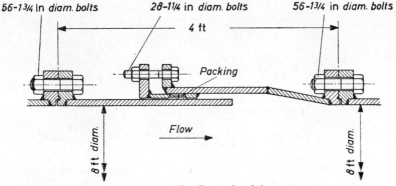

Figure 157. Expansion joint

Steel on phosphor bronze, well lubricated $\mu = 0.15$
Steel on phosphor bronze, unlubricated $\mu = 0.25 - 0.30$
Pendulum $\mu = 0.05$
Roller bearings $\mu = 0.01$

(6) Friction forces in sealings of expansion joints: P_6 (usually negligible).

(7) Friction forces developing between pipe wall and water (using Manning–Strickler formula)

$$P_7 = w \frac{\pi}{4} D_i^2 \frac{v_i^2 L_i}{k^2 R_i^{4/3}}$$

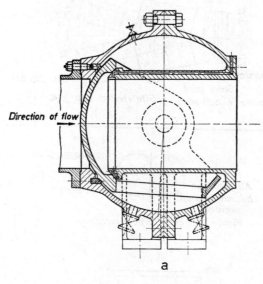

a

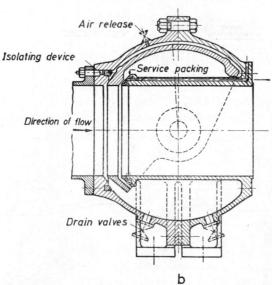

b

Figure 158. Straight flow valve. (a) *Valve closed.* (b) *Valve open*

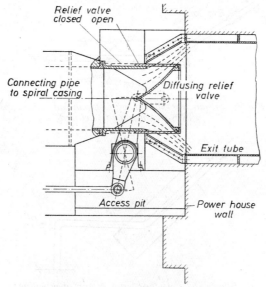

Figure 159. *Diffusing relief valve*

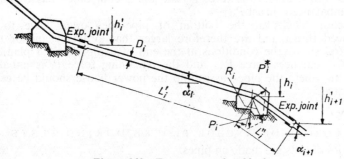

Figure 160. *Forces on anchor block*

(*8*) Forces on any taper section and taper shell of expansion joint, P_8 (usually negligible).

(*9*) Forces due to the momentum of the water

$$P_9 = \frac{w}{g} Q v_i \text{ upstream of bend}$$

$$P_9' = \frac{w}{g} Q v_{i+1} \text{ downstream of bend.}$$

These forces P_1 to P_9' should be added as vectors and their resultant P_i^* added to the anchor block weight P_i to a general resultant R_i which should be inside the middle third of the base of the anchor block. For high head penstocks, the forces caused by water pressure P_3 and P_4 are the more important ones. In large low pressure pipes the momentum forces P_9 and P_9' may become the more important and should not be neglected.

SPECIAL CASES

In *Figure 161* there is an expansion joint upstream of the anchor block but none downstream; the valve is closed as shown. The force $P'/2 + P'/2 = P'$ in

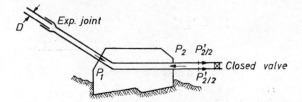

Figure 161. Forces on anchor block with expansion joint upstream but none downstream and valve closed

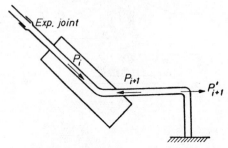

Figure 162. Anchor block at end of pipe line

the pipe wall balances the force P_2 and the anchor block has to stand the whole unbalanced thrust P_1.

Anchor blocks at the bottom of pipe-lines often have to stand unbalanced thrust and are therefore larger than ordinary anchor blocks. *Figure 162* shows the conditions at the end of a pipe-line (in plan). The force P'_{i+1} balances force P_{i+1} and the remaining force P_i is unbalanced. Conditions where the pipe passes into the power house should be carefully investigated.

FORCES ON ANCHOR BLOCKS DURING TESTS

Two series of tests are made on pipes.

(*a*) *Figure 163* shows a short piece of pipe being tested on an anchor block before being concreted in. Covers are bolted on both ends. On one side an expansion joint is shown included in the pressure test. This causes forces on the anchor block to be unbalanced. Depending on the position of the expansion joint the turning moment on either side of the anchor block caused by unbalanced forces may or may not be dangerous.

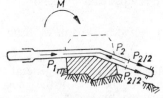

Figure 163. Pressure test at anchor block

(*b*) General pressure tests on the whole pipe-line when *in situ*. Sometimes pressure tests are made on the whole pipe-line. The test pressure p_t at any point is often chosen so that it should be larger than 1·5 times the local dynamic pressure p_s but less than 1·75 times p_s ($1·5\,p_s < p_t < 1·75 p_s$). The pipe-line is divided into convenient sections for these tests and the anchor blocks will be checked for the forces occurring in this case.

SADDLES

When Dresser couplings are used, saddles have to be designed for the
resulting forces. (See *Figure 164* showing a conventional saddle.)

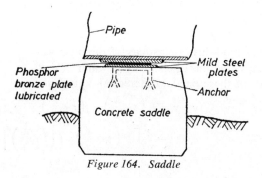

Figure 164. Saddle

XIX. THEORY OF WATER HAMMER[189-197]

The sudden variation of the power demand on the electric network causes
the turbine gates to open or to close automatically to vary the water
discharge. The sudden acceleration or deceleration of the mass of water
flowing in the pipeline requires or creates forces of considerable magnitude
which set up elastic waves travelling up and down the pipe-line. These
waves produce what is called water hammer.

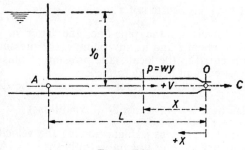

Figure 165

Notation (*Figure 165*)

$D = 2r =$ diameter of pipe-line

$A =$ area of internal cross-section of pipe-line

$e =$ thickness of wall of pipe-line

$L =$ length of pipe-line

$Q =$ discharge in pipe-line

$v = Q/(\frac{1}{4}\pi D^2) =$ mean velocity of flow in pipe-line which depends on x and t

$c = (2gh)^{\frac{1}{2}} =$ exit velocity from nozzle at downstream end

$wh =$ pressure at downstream end at time t

$p = wy =$ pressure at any point at a distance x from outlet, at time t

GENERAL EQUATIONS FOR WATER HAMMER

Allievi has demonstrated that water hammer is governed by the two
partial differential equations:

$$\frac{\partial v}{\partial t} = g \frac{\partial y}{\partial x} \qquad \dotsb(1)$$

$$\frac{\partial v}{\partial x} = \frac{g}{a^2} \frac{\partial y}{\partial t} \qquad \dotsb(1a)$$

where $\quad a = \left(\dfrac{g/w}{1/E_w + D/Ee}\right)^{\frac{1}{2}}$

where E = Young's modulus of elasticity of the pipe wall

$\quad E_w$ = Young's modulus of elasticity of water

The integrals of these partial differential equations are:

$$y = y_0 + F\left(t - \frac{x}{a}\right) + f\left(t + \frac{x}{a}\right) \qquad \dotsb(2)$$

$$v = v_0 - \frac{g}{a}\left[F\left(t - \frac{x}{a}\right) - f\left(t + \frac{x}{a}\right)\right] \dotsb(2a)$$

PHYSICAL INTERPRETATION OF THE FORMULAE (2) AND (2a)

The quantity a has the dimensions of velocity and represents the velocity

of two pressure waves $F\left(t - \frac{x}{a}\right)$ and $f\left(t + \frac{x}{a}\right)$.

$F\left(t - \frac{x}{a}\right)$ is constant if $x - at$ is constant,

and $f\left(t + \frac{x}{a}\right)$ is constant if $x + at$ is constant.

The former wave travels up the pipe-line, the latter in the downward direction. At any moment t and at any point x, the pressure y (measured in head of water) is equal to the local static pressure y_0 plus the two waves F and f, which travel without being deformed.

Similarly, the velocity of the water v is equal to the difference of v_0,

the velocity at the time $t = 0$ (steady flow conditions) $-\dfrac{g}{a} F$ and $+\dfrac{g}{a} f$.

The velocity a of the waves is high, nearing the velocity of sound in water. For preliminary designs the table published by Allievi contains values of sufficient accuracy.

y_0	m	10	30	60	100	140	300	600	1000
	ft	33	99	198	330	462	990	1980	3300
a	m/sec	665	717	777	837	883	1000	1110	1184
	ft/sec	2200	2360	2560	2760	2925	3300	3660	3910

ALLIEVI'S INTERLOCKED SERIES OF EQUATIONS

It can be shown that the boundary conditions at the upper end A of the pipe-line (reservoir or large surge tank) are such that the pressure there remains constant and that

$$y = y_0 + F\left(t - \frac{L}{a}\right) + f\left(t + \frac{L}{a}\right) = y_0$$

which yields

$$F\left(t - \frac{L}{a}\right) = -f\left(t + \frac{L}{a}\right)$$

Replacing t by $t = t_1 - L/a$

$$f(t) = -F(t-T) \qquad \ldots\ldots\ldots (3)$$

where $T = \dfrac{2L}{a}$ = period of the pipe-line.

This equation, valid only if *total reflection occurs at the upper end A* of the pipe, is the key to the analysis of water hammer in *simple* pipe-lines. Considering the pressure waves occurring at the times

$$0, \; T, \; 2T, \; \ldots \; nT,$$

the integral equations (2) may be set down *for point* 0 at the downstream end where $x=0$ [where F_i and f_i represent, more briefly $F(t_i)$ and $f(t_i)$]:

$$h_1 = h_0 + F_1 + f_1$$
$$h_2 = h_0 + F_2 + f_2$$

and

$$v_1 = v_0 - \frac{g}{a}(F_1 - f_1)$$

$$v_2 = v_0 - \frac{g}{a}(F_2 - f_2)$$

Equation (3) may be re-written in the form

$$f_i = -F_{i-1}$$

and finally

$$\left. \begin{aligned} h_1 - h_0 &= \frac{a}{g}(v_0 - v_1) \\[1em] h_1 + h_2 - 2h_0 &= \frac{a}{g}(v_1 - v_2) \\[1em] h_2 + h_3 - 2h_0 &= \frac{a}{g}(v_2 - v_3) \end{aligned} \right\} \qquad \ldots\ldots\ldots (4)$$

These are Allievi's interlocked series of equations. They relate the dynamic pressure head h_i at point 0 and the velocity v_i at the downstream end of a simple pipe-line.

Further treatment of the problem requires the introduction of a second boundary condition relating h_i to v_i. Allievi assumes the Bernoulli equation to be valid at the downstream end even if the outflow is unsteady or variable. If c_i is the exit velocity, and $A_i = \eta_i A_0$ the effective area of the downstream valve or gate at the time t_i (where the relative gate opening is η_i) the velocity close to the gate is:

$$v_i = c_i \frac{A_i}{A} = \eta_i \frac{A_0}{A}(2gh_i)^{\frac{1}{2}} = \eta_i v_0 \left(\frac{h_i}{h_0}\right)^{\frac{1}{2}} \qquad \ldots\ldots\ldots (5)$$

Allievi introduces the following ratios:

$\zeta_i^2 = \dfrac{h_i}{h_0}$, the pressure ratio or relative pressure

$\zeta_i^2 - 1$, the ratio of excess to steady pressure and

$\rho = \dfrac{av_0}{2gh_0}$, pipe-line characteristic.

If τ is the time required to close (or open) the valve, then the relative time $\theta = \tau/T$ is used.

Allievi's equations may now be expressed in their classical form:

$$\left. \begin{aligned} \zeta_1^2 - 1 &= 2\rho(\eta_0 \zeta_0 - \eta_1 \zeta_1) \\ \zeta_1^2 + \zeta_2^2 - 2 &= 2\rho(\eta_1 \zeta_1 - \eta_2 \zeta_2) \\ \zeta_2^2 + \zeta_3^2 - 2 &= 2\rho(\eta_2 \zeta_2 - \eta_3 \zeta_3) \end{aligned} \right\} \qquad \ldots\ldots\ldots (6)$$

SOME PARTICULAR PROBLEMS OF IMPORTANCE AND THEIR SOLUTION

Allievi proved that the values ζ_{i-1}, ζ_i, ζ_{i+1}, are converging towards a final value $\zeta_m{}^2$. This remark is true for linear closure and linear opening. If ζ_1 is the pressure at the time $t_{1l} = T$ and ζ_m the pressure at the end of the closing or opening movement of the valve, then:

For linear closure:

$$\zeta_1 = -\rho\eta_1 + (\rho^2\eta_1{}^2 + 1 + 2\rho)^{\frac{1}{2}} \qquad \ldots\ldots\ldots\ldots(7)$$

with $\eta_1 = 1 - 1/\theta$

and

$$\zeta_m = \frac{\rho}{2\theta} + \left[\left(\frac{\rho}{2\theta}\right)^2 + 1\right]^{\frac{1}{2}} \qquad \ldots\ldots\ldots\ldots(8)$$

Figure 166 gives some typical pressure rise curves caused by linear closure.

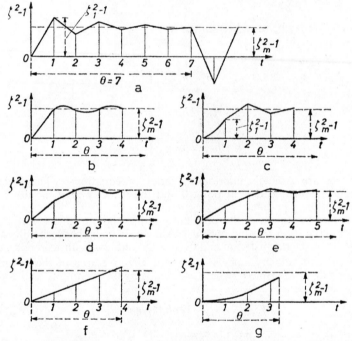

Figure 166. Ratio of excess pressure $(\zeta^2 - 1)$ plotted against time t. Water hammer curves of greater importance

For linear opening:

$$\zeta_1 = -\frac{\rho}{\theta} + \left[\left(\frac{\rho}{\theta}\right)^2 + 1\right]^{\frac{1}{2}} \qquad \ldots\ldots\ldots\ldots(9)$$

and

$$\zeta_m = -\frac{\rho}{2\theta} + \left[\left(\frac{\rho}{2\theta}\right)^2 + 1\right]^{\frac{1}{2}} \qquad \ldots\ldots\ldots\ldots(10)$$

After complete closure, we always have

$$\zeta_{m+i}{}^2 - 1 = -(\zeta_{m+i+1}{}^2 - 1) \qquad \ldots\ldots\ldots\ldots(11)$$

WATER HAMMER IN PIPES WITH REVERSED FLOW (PUMPS)

The basic equations are then

$$y_{i-1} + y_i - 2y_0 = \frac{a}{g}(-v_{i-1} + v_i)$$

or in terms of ratios

$$\zeta_{i-1}^2 + \zeta_i^2 - 2 = 2\rho(-\eta_{i-1}\zeta_{i-1} + \eta_i\zeta_i) \qquad \dots\dots\dots\dots(12)$$

GENERAL THEORY OF WATER HAMMER IN A SYSTEM OF PIPE-LINES [190]

The theory of Allievi can be extended to any system of pipe-lines like the one represented on *Figure 167.*

The extended theory is based on the fact that, at any bifurcation *A*, at any time t_i, the reflected wave f_i is related to the primary wave F_i in a form expressed by the equation

$$f_i = -\alpha_i F_i \qquad \dots\dots\dots\dots(13)$$

α_i is a function which will depend on the pressure waves set up in pipe-lines I, II and III.

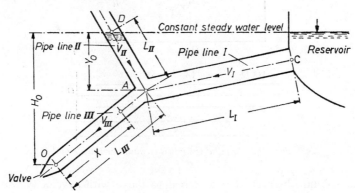

Figure 167. Sketch of basic supply system with cylindrical surge tank

For the very first wave, *F*, arriving at *A*, the function α_1 is a constant:

$$\alpha_1 = r_{\mathrm{III}} = \frac{1/\rho_{\mathrm{I}} + 1/\rho_{\mathrm{II}} - 1/\rho_{\mathrm{III}}}{1/\rho_{\mathrm{I}} + 1/\rho_{\mathrm{II}} + 1/\rho_{\mathrm{III}}} \qquad \dots\dots\dots\dots(14)$$

where ρ_{I}, ρ_{II}, ρ_{III} are the characteristics of the pipes I, II, III.

For successive waves, the deflection factor α_i can be shown to be represented by a series, usually converging towards a final value.

This theory has been extended to the theory of water hammer in surge tanks and to cases of resonance. It can be shown that resonance usually causes the doubling of the pressure at the pipe end:

$$h_n = 2h_0$$

THE GRAPHICAL METHOD OF SCHNYDER AND BERGERON

Let us suppose that the pressure $y_{x.T}$ and the discharge $q_{x.T}$ at point X and time T are known. It can be shown that for an imaginary observer

moving with the velocity $+a$ from X in the direction of $-v$, the function F
is constant and that the pressure $y_{x,\,t}$ and the discharge $q_{x,\,t}$ are given by

$$y_{x,\,t} - y_{X,\,T} = \frac{a}{gA}(q_{x,\,t} - q_{X,\,T}) \qquad \dots\dots\dots(15)$$

the equation correlating x, t to T, X is

$$x = X + (t-T)\,a$$

(equation of the 'observer'). Equation (15) *represents the water hammer
line of the pipe-line for observer I.* It is a straight line passing through
points $q_{X,\,T}$ and $y_{X,\,T}$.

Its slope is $\tan \alpha_1 = \dfrac{a}{gA}$ *(Figure 168).*

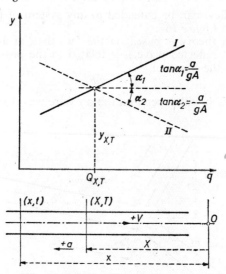

Figure 168. (a) and (b). Water hammer lines I and II

A second observer II is assumed to move with a velocity $-a$ in the
direction $+v$ along the pipe-line. His equation is:

$$x = X - (t-T)\,a$$

and the water hammer line of the pipe for observer II is

$$y_{x,\,t} - y_{X,\,T} = -\frac{a}{gA}(q_{x,\,t} - q_{X,\,T}) \qquad \dots\dots\dots(16)$$

with $\tan \alpha_2 = -a/gA$.

Provided always that the equation $x = X \pm (t-T)\,a$ is valid, the two
water-hammer lines enable the pressure head $y_{x,\,t}$ at point (x, t) to be found
from a known pressure head $y_{X,\,T}$ at a point (X, T). $q_{x,\,t}$ is similarly derived
from $q_{X,\,T}$. The derivation is valid if the velocity a is constant.

For turbines the $+x$ direction coincides with the $-v$ direction. For
pumps the $+x$ and $+v$ directions coincide. Equation (15) is valid for the
$-v$ direction and equation (16) for the $+v$ direction[196].

FUNDAMENTAL PROBLEMS

(i) y and q, at time T, at points x_1 and x_2 distant l are assumed to be
known *(Figure 169).* The pressure is required at point x_3, half-way between
x_1 and x_2 at time $T + l/(2a)$.

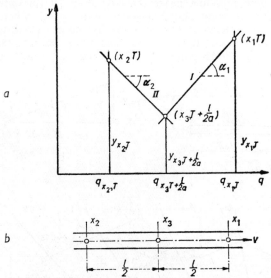

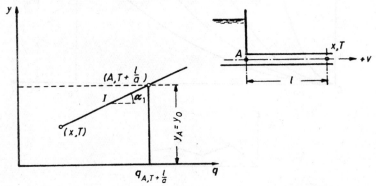

Figure 169 (a) and (b). Determination of pressure at point x_3 along the pipe-line $x_1 x_2$

Figure 170. Pressure head y and discharge q at point A at the instant $T + (l/a)$

Observer I leaves x_1 and observer II leaves x_2, both at the same instant T. They meet at point X_3 at time $T + l/2a$. The pressure head is given graphically by the point of intersection $(X_3, T + l/2a)$ of the lines I and II, and is $y_{x_2, T+l/2c}$. The corresponding flow is $q_{x_3, T+l/2a}$

This method may be generalized for any point P between X_1 and X_2 $(AP = l_A, BP = l_B)$ provided the observers are chosen so that they arrive at P simultaneously.

(*ii*) A pipe-line is connected, at point A, to a large reservoir (*Figure 170*). Given, at time T, the values of y and q at point X, distant l from A, it is desired to find y and q at point A at time $T + (l/a)$.

The pressure head at A is always constant and equal to y_0. The horizontal line $y = y_0$ is, therefore, one locus of the solution, and the point $(X + l, T + l/a)$ is at the intersection of the horizontal line $y = y_0$ and line I.

LINEAR SLOW CLOSURE (*Figure 171*)

The unit of time is $T = 2l/a$. A family of parabolas ψ_i represents the boundary conditions at $t = 0, 1, 2, 3$ (relative time values). Up to $t = 0$

the flow in the whole pipe-line is steady. At point B this condition is changed at $t=0$, but at point A it continues until $t=0·5$, when the first pressure wave from B reaches A (point $A_{0·5}$). At point C, half-way along the pipe-line, steady conditions are maintained until $t=0·25$, point $C_{0·25}$ on the diagram. The three points B_0, $C_{0·25}$ and $A_{0·5}$ must, therefore, coincide.

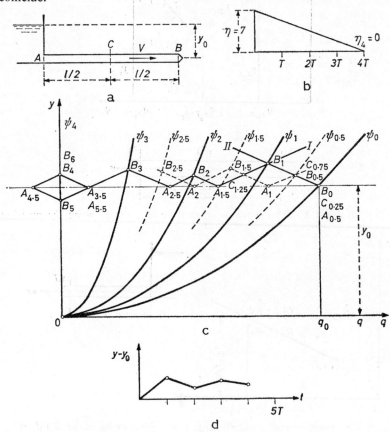

Figure 171 (a), (b), (c) and (d). *Graphical analysis of water hammer due to slow linear closure of valve in time* $\tau=4T$

An imaginary observer II is assumed to leave point A, at $t=0·5$, in the downstream $(+v)$ direction. This observer arrives at point B at the instant $t=0·5+0·5=1·0$. At this instant the boundary condition of the needle valve B is represented by parabola ψ_1 (degree of valve opening η_1). Point B is given by the intersection of water-hammer line II and parabola ψ_1.

The observer may now leave point B_1 in the $(-v)$-direction towards A where he arrives at $t=1·5$. A line I cuts the horizontal line $y=y_0$ at point $A_{1·5}$.

Observers working in both directions will yield the points B_2, $A_{2·5}$, B_3.

ABRUPT CLOSURE

The case of abrupt closure $(0<\tau<T)$ is represented in *Figure 172*, where $0<t<\tau$.

LINEAR SLOW OPENING

Linear slow opening is similarly represented in *Figure 173*.

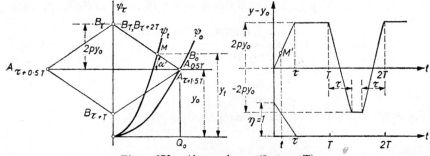

Figure 172. Abrupt closure $(0 < \tau < T)$

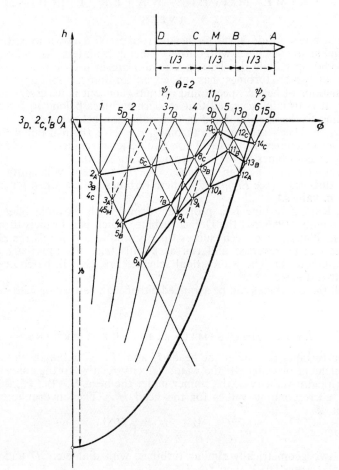

Figure 173. Linear opening in $\theta = 2$. *Water hammer at points A, B and C*

FINAL REMARKS ON WATER HAMMER

The closing time τ of the gates or valves is usually calculated so that the pressure rise is not more than 10 to 25 per cent.

In some cases this value τ is too long for proper governing of the turbines. The turbine is then provided with a jet deflector (Pelton wheels) or relief valve (reaction wheels). The flow to the turbine is then cut rapidly but the flow in the pipe is slowed down slowly in order to limit the water hammer.

Resonance oscillations (*e.g.* hunting of the governor) may cause doubling of the pressure. It can be shown that the worst pressure variation on a pipe, at a distance L_1 from the top of the pipe is given by the formula of Michaud–Marchetti:

$$\frac{\Delta p}{w} = \pm \frac{2L_1 v_{max}}{g\tau}$$

For conditions at the bottom of the pipe, take $L=L_1$.

XX. PRIME MOVERS—WATER TURBINES [198-209]

TYPES

Water turbines are designed for heads from 5,800 ft down to 3 ft (1,760 to 1 m) and single machines with outputs ranging from less than a horse power to 250,000 hp (Chute des Passes, Canada) are in use or being built. The design of water turbines has to cover an almost infinite number of combinations of heads, speeds and outputs, hence it is necessary to classify them. It is usually accepted that modern turbines belong to three groups, according to the specific speed n_s (see definition below).

Pelton wheels are impulse turbines, $n_s = 2-8$ (British units) for single-jet machines, n_s up to 11 for double-jet machines.

Francis turbines ($n_s = 14$–90) (reaction turbines).

Propeller and Kaplan turbines ($n_s = 70$ to 220) which are reaction turbines. (See *Figure 174* where turbines are classified for increasing n_s values.)

A Kaplan turbine is a propeller turbine with movable blades.

Recently (1956/57) the Dériaz turbine, which is a Francis turbine with movable blades, has been successfully introduced. Kaplan and Dériaz turbines can be reversed and run as pumps (*e.g.* Niagara Falls pumping station, Ontario). The Rance tidal scheme, France, will be equipped with 'tubular turbines'.

All these turbines can be arranged either with vertical or with horizontal shaft.

HYDRAULIC SIMILARITY FOR TURBINES

Let two turbines run under the heads H and H'. C is the absolute velocity of an element of water, W the water velocity relative to the runner, and U the peripheral velocity of the runner under the head H. Let C', W' and U' be the corresponding values for the head H'. Then hydraulic similarity prevails if

$$\frac{C}{C'} = \frac{W}{W'} = \frac{U}{U'} = \left(\frac{H}{H'}\right)^{\frac{1}{2}}$$

If two geometrically similar turbines, with diameters D and D^*, run under the same head, then $U=U^*$ and

$$U = \frac{\pi D n}{60} = U^* = \frac{\pi D^* n^*}{60} \quad \text{or} \quad \frac{n}{n^*} = \frac{D^*}{D}$$

where n and n^* are the speeds of the turbines (in rev/min).

Hydraulic similarity leads to the definition of the specific speed. The specific speed n_s is defined as the speed in revolutions per minute at which a turbine would run at the best efficiency for full guide-vane opening under a head of one foot, its dimensions having been adjusted to produce one horse power.

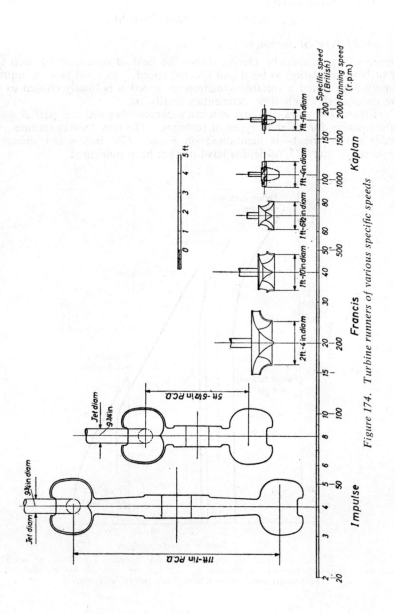

Figure 174. *Turbine runners of various specific speeds*

It can be shown that

$$n_s = \frac{n}{H}\left(\frac{N}{\sqrt{H}}\right)^{\frac{1}{4}} \quad \text{or} \quad = n\frac{\sqrt{N}}{H^{5/4}}$$

where *H* is in feet and *N* in British horse power.

In the metric system

$$n_s \text{ (metric)} = 4\cdot45\, n_s \text{ (British)}$$

Choice of type of turbines

Figure 175 published by Dériaz shows the field of operation of each type of turbine in relation to head and specific speed. As soon as n_s is approximately determined a suitable synchronous speed *n* is finally chosen to suit the generator; which then determines finally n_s.

Figure 176 shows typical efficiency curves obtained for partial guide-vane opening for different types of turbines. The new Déviaz turbine—still under development—is mentioned on *Figure 176*, but is not shown on *Figures 174* and *175*, as details have not yet been published.

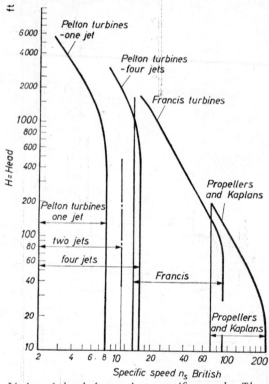

Figure 175. Limits of head for various specific speeds. The field of operation for each type of turbine is limited by its highest and lowest n_s and by the maximum head under which it can safely be operated

Setting of turbine

The setting of Francis and Kaplan turbines (elevation of runner axis) is determined in order to avoid cavitation. The danger point for incipient cavitation is determined by model tests on the 'cavitation plant' and the elevation of the actual turbine is calculated using the similarity law for cavitation

$$H_s \leqslant H_B - \sigma H$$

where H_s = elevation of runner vane upper edge

H_B = barometric pressure measured in water column

H = head and σ 'critical sigma' for cavitation (obtained from model tests).

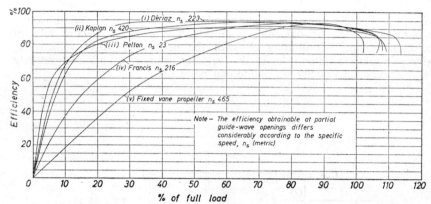

Figure 176. *Load efficiency curves of the various types of water turbines*

Pelton wheel

Figure 177 shows how a Pelton wheel is designed, the proportions of jet (*d*) bucket and pitch circle. The number of buckets depends mainly on the specific speed, n_s, per jet. Usually the forces on a Pelton wheel are calculated from the formulae

$$\text{Jet force on the runner} = \frac{w}{g} Q (v - u)(1 - \cos \alpha) \quad \text{lb}$$

$$\text{Jet force on the bucket} = \frac{w}{g} Q \frac{(v - u)^2}{v} (1 - \cos \alpha) \quad \text{lb}$$

where w is the weight of a cubic foot of water in lb, Q the flow in the jet in cubic feet per second, $(v - u)$ is the difference between the velocities of jet (v)

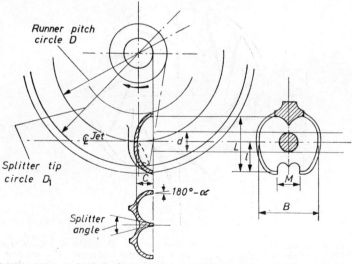

Figure 177. *Pelton wheel design. B=3·0 to 3·5d; L=0·8 to 0·9B; C=0·27 to 0·3B; l=0·5 to 0·6L; M=1·0 to 1·25d*

and pitch circle (u) in ft/sec and α is the angle of deviation, measured from the tangential direction of motion to the relative direction of discharge from the bucket in a tangential plane. α is a little less than $180°$ and $(1 - \cos \alpha)$ is nearly 2.

Francis wheel

A typical Francis runner is shown in *Figures 178* and *179*. The absolute water velocity C_1 at the inlet point (1) has a radial inward velocity component C_{m1}. Combining C_1 with the peripheral wheel velocity u_1 gives the relative water velocity W_1 (velocity triangle). This inlet velocity W_1 becomes the velocity W_2 at the exit point (2).

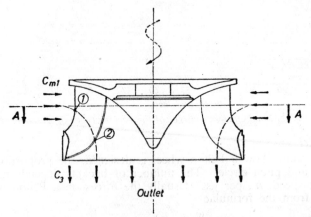

Figure 178. *Typical Francis turbine runner. The water at inlet has a radial inward component of velocity C_{m1}. The outlet velocity is substantially axial at C_3 and at the near optimum efficiency*

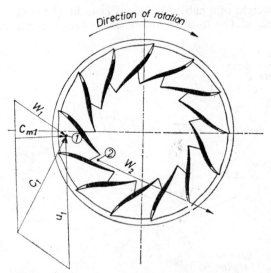

Figure 179. *Sectional plan of Francis turbine runner. Diagram of velocities at inlet point (1): u_1=peripheral velocity; C_1=absolute water velocity; W_1=relative water velocity; C_{m1}=radial component of velocity C_1. Because the channel between adjacent vanes is tapered, the velocity W_1 is increased to W_2 at exit point (2)*

The runner exit diameter D_2 is given by

$$D_2{}^3 \cong \frac{90Q}{n}$$

(Q=discharge at full load). The other dimensions D_1 exterior, D_1 interior and D_2 interior are calculated from *Figure 180* where the peripheral velocity

$$\phi = \frac{\pi D n}{60 \, (2gH)^{\frac{1}{2}}}$$

is plotted against the specific speed, n_s. The different D values are then calculated from the values for D_{1ex}, D_{1in}, D_{2in}.

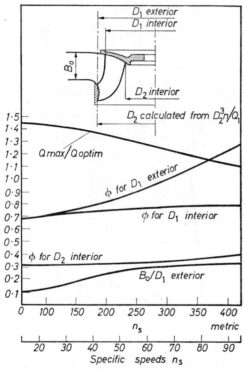

Figure 180. *The coefficient of peripheral velocity* $\phi = \pi \, Dn/60 \, (2gH)^{\frac{1}{2}}$ *is plotted against specific speed.* Q_{max}=*discharge when the maximum power is obtained.* $Q_{optimum}$=*discharge at highest efficiency*

Kaplan turbine

A typical Kaplan turbine is shown in *Figure 181*. The Kaplan blades are mobile and flatter than the Francis blades.

Dériaz turbine

The principle of the Dériaz turbine is shown in *Figure 182*. (See also *Figure 184*.) In some cases the Kaplan turbine and the Dériaz turbine can be reversed and used as pumps.

Acknowledgment—Figures 174 to 181 are taken from J. Guthrie Brown, *Hydro-Electric Engineering Practice*, Vol. II.

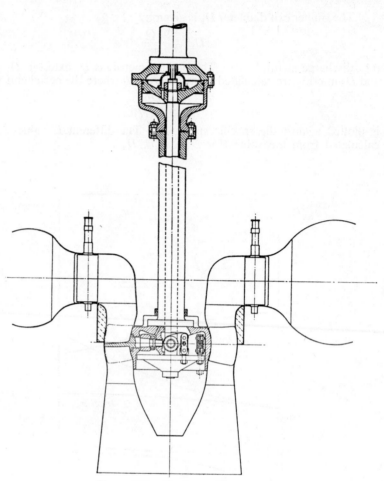

Figure 181. Kaplan turbine

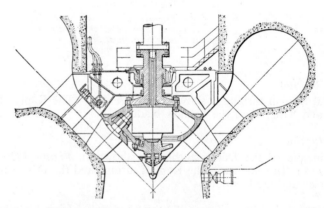

Figure 182. Dériaz turbine

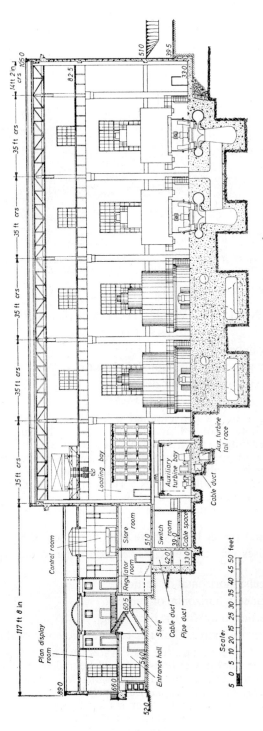

Figure 183. Loch Sloy. General arrangement of power house

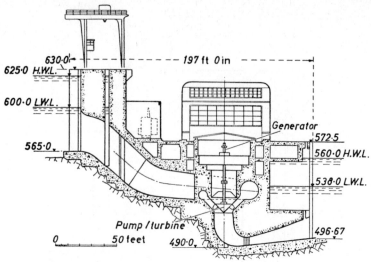

Figure 184. Section through the Niagara pumped-storage station showing the extremely compact layout obtained with a reversible Dériaz pump-turbine

XXI. POWER HOUSE DESIGN
CLASSIFICATION

Power houses can be either

- (*a*) above ground, conventional design; or
- (*b*) above ground, open air design; or
- (*c*) underground, excavated in rock[209].

Figure 183 shows a conventional power house (Loch Sloy, Scotland) located at the bottom of a long pressure pipe. The building houses the turbines and generators; the transformers are outside.

Above ground open air designs, where there is no general roof on top of the machines but only a travelling gantry crane, were first developed in countries with warm or mild climates. The Vargön power station in Sweden was for a long time an exception. Now open air power stations are being built in any type of climate; *e.g.* the Niagara Falls pumping station, Canada (*Figure 184*).

Underground power houses have been described in Sect. XVII.

Power houses may also be classified according to the type of turbines they house:

Pelton wheels: horizontal or vertical.

Francis runners: horizontal or vertical.

Dériaz: vertical only (for the time being).

Kaplan: vertical only. (Tubular turbines are horizontal or inclined.)

In addition to these types, the underwater turbine houses (Arno Fischer type, *etc*) and the tidal power houses should be added for completeness.

Innertkirchen with a vertical Pelton, Santa Massenza with a horizontal Pelton, and Lavey (vertical Kaplan) are well-known examples of classical arrangements for underground power stations.

Loch Sloy (*Figure 183*) is located at the bottom of a high head penstock, Génissiat is at the toe of a high dam, so are l'Aigle and Bort, where the flood water is discharging on top of the power house roof which is used as a spill-

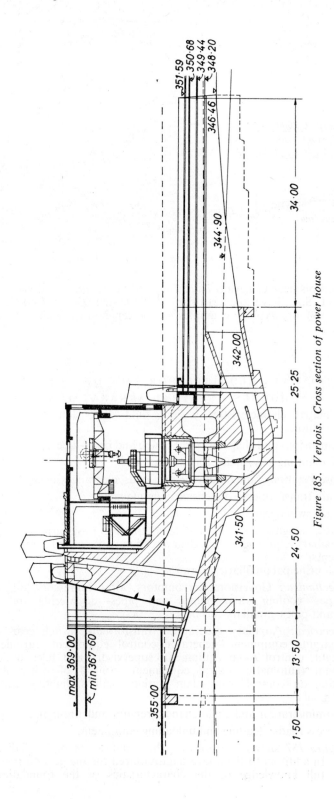

Figure 185. Verbois. Cross section of power house

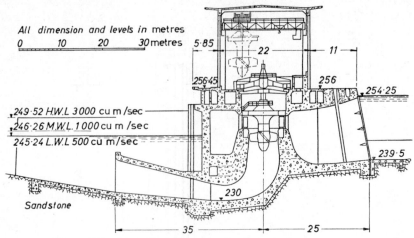

All dimension and levels in metres

Figure 186. Birsfelden. Cross section through the power house

way. Verbois near Geneva (*Figure 185*) and many other stations in Scotland and the U.S.A., have low head dams. Birsfelden (*Figure 186*) and Ryburg (*Figure 99*) are typical examples of power houses built for low head barrages.

GENERAL DATA REQUIRED FOR THE DESIGN OF POWER
HOUSES—GENERAL ARRANGEMENT

(*a*) Principal characteristics, weights and dimension of turbines and generator.

(*b*) Dimensions and shape of spiral casing and draft-tube.

(*c*) Dismantling bay, space for maintenance.

(*d*) Power station crane requirements: loads, clearances, access.

(*e*) Main transformers: dimensions, maintenance.

(*f*) Main switchgear.

(*g*) Sizes, weights and permissible alternative positions of all items of auxiliary equipment and their erection, access and support requirements.

The principal auxiliaries comprise:

Mechanical: Governors, servomotors, air compressors, oil reservoirs and pipes—cooling water pumps and pipes—dewatering and drainage pumps and pipes, auxiliary turbines.

Electrical: Auxiliary generators, transformers, switch gear—batteries and charging equipment—generator control equipment, turbine control equipment, control room equipment, supervisory and telecommunication equipment (automatic control equipment, control of other stations if depending on control from main station), cables, lighting and heating arrangements.

(*h*) Administration and maintenance, repairs and fire-fighting equipment.

(*j*) Access roads: loading and unloading equipment.

Figure 187 shows in plan view the arrangement of the Salime power house. In addition to the above data required for the general power house design, full knowledge of the characteristics of the foundations (rock

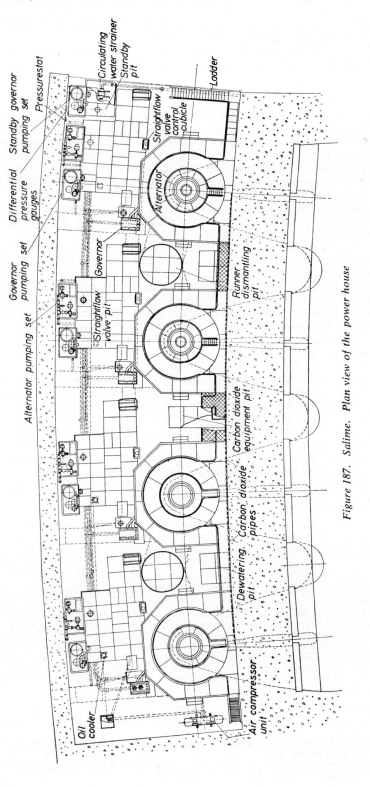

Standby governor pumping set
Pressurestat
Circulating water strainer
Standby pit
Differential pressure gauges
Ladder
Governor pumping set
Straightflow valve control cubicle
Alternator pumping set
Governor
Alternator
Straightflow valve pit
Runner dismantling pit
Carbon dioxide equipment pit
Carbon dioxide pipes
Dewatering pit
Oil cooler
Air compressor unit

Figure 187. Salime. Plan view of the power house

strength, or resistance of the soil, water table, possible subsidence, settlements, differential settlements) is required.

Lowering the water table and dealing with ground water are major problems during the construction period.

STATICAL CALCULATION OF POWER HOUSES

The conditions of equilibrium of the power house as a whole have to be investigated on the same principles as for a gravity dam. The oblique resultant from full horizontal water thrust and vertical weights has to be well inside the middle third and conditions against the danger of sliding must be investigated. These investigations will include the different construction stages as the power house may have to bear the full horizontal water thrust before the full value of the vertical weights and loads is reached.

Safety margins must be specially ample as measurements under existing power houses have shown the stress distribution to be far off the linear stress distribution usually assumed.

Possible subsidence of the foundation, uplift pressure, *etc*, will have to be carefully analysed. Special problems occur when the power house is not on solid rock but either on weak foundations or even on a floating raft on poor alluvium (Katima power house in India, Swir power house in U.S.S.R.). In the case of the Swir power station a friction factor of only 0·1 was assumed between concrete and clayish soil, which caused the foundation width of the whole barrage and power house to be increased in order to get the necessary safety factor against sliding.

The second step comprises the analysis of each element of the power house for all the possible load conditions, assuming normal running conditions, or water-hammer conditions, or assuming some parts of the spiral and casings to be empty on one side, *etc*. The turbine cover will be calculated for full uplift pressure in the turbine. The stay vanes will be analysed for full normal uplift (sometimes assuming the generator to be removed and uplift from the downstream side); then the same stay vanes will be calculated, assuming there is no water in the turbine ducts (turbine not running or removed, generator removed) in order to get the maximum upthrust and the maximum downpull for the stay vanes.

An unlined spiral casing may have to be considered as a vertical concrete cylinder, with horizontal reinforcement loops[208]. If the spiral casing is steel lined, it will be considered as a self-supporting steel structure. Each wall, each girder or floor will be considered for all possible load conditions.

The torque caused by braking the generator is an important element of the calculations of the steel reinforcement in the generator floor.

BIBLIOGRAPHY

Periodicals

Water Power (London), *La Houille Blanche* (Grenoble, France), *Revue générale de l'Hydraulique* (Paris), *Wasserwirtschaft* (Germany), *L'Energia Elettrica* (Milan, Italy), *Schweizerische Energie and Wasserwirtschaft* (Zürich, Switzerland), *Schweizerische Bauzeitung* (Zürich, Switzerland), *Engineering* (London), *The Engineer* (London), *English Electric Journal* (London and Stafford), *Charmilles—Informations Techniques* (Geneva, Switzerland), *Escher Wyss Mitteilungen* (Zürich, Switzerland), *Brown Boveri and Co. Bulletin* (Baden, Switzerland), *Indian Journal of Power and River Valley Development* (Calcutta).

Congresses

Congress on Large Dams, Stockholm 1948, New Delhi 1951, Paris 1955, New York 1958

International Conference on Soil Mechanics and Foundation Engineering, Zürich 1953, London 1957

World Power Conference, London 1950, New Delhi 1952, Rio de Janerio 1954, Vienna 1956, Montreal 1958, Madrid 1960.

REFERENCES

General

[4] SCHOKLITSCH, A. *Hydraulic Structures* 1st ed. New York and 2nd ed. Vienna, 1952
[2] CREAGER, W. P. and JUSTIN, J. D. *Hydroelectric Handbook* 2nd ed. New York and London, 1950
[3] DAVIES, C. V. *Handbook of Applied Hydraulics* 2nd ed. New York and London, 1952
[4] GUTHRIE BROWN, J. (Ed.) *Hydro-electric Engineering Practice* Glasgow, 1958
[5] U.S. Bureau of Reclamation *Treatise on Dams*
[6] U.S. Army *Engineering Manual for Civil Works*
[7] PRESS, H. *Talsperren, Wehre, Wasserkraftanlagen,* 3 vols, Berlin, 1953–4, 2nd ed., 1958–9
[8] GOMEZ NAVARRO, J. and ARRACIL, J. J. *Saltos de Agua y Presas de Embalse* 2nd ed., 2 vols, Madrid, 1952–3
[9] MOSONYI, E. *Wasserkraftwerke* Hung. Acad. Sci., Budapest, 1956
[10] JAEGER, C. *Engineering Fluid Mechanics* Glasgow, 1956; New York, 1957; Berlin, 1949; Paris, 1954
[11] ROUSE, H. *Engineering Hydraulics* New York and London, 1950
[12] SCHLEICHER, *Taschenbuch für Bauingenieure* vol. 2, 2nd ed., Berlin, 1955
[13] ROUSSELIER, L'orientation des études des nouveaux projets hydrauliques *Travaux* Paris, 1957
—, Hydro-electric projects from the point of view of the best use of natural sites *Travaux* No. 247, *Int. Congr. on Large Dams* Paris, 1955
[14] GRZYWIENSKI, A. Wasserkraftanlagen der Gegenwart und Zukunft *Öst. Bauzeitschr.* 11, No. 5-6 (1956)

I. *The Hydro-electric industry*

[15] United Nations Economic Commission for Europe (U.N.E.C.E.) *Hydro-electric potential in Europe* E./ECE/E.P/131, Geneva, 1953
[16] JAEGER, C. The Hydro-electric industry. *Engl. Elect. J.* 13, No. 8 (1954). *Indian J. Power River Valley Development* 5, No. 5 (1955)
[17] U.N.E.C.E. E./ECE/E.P./173, Geneva, Nov. 1955
[18] JAEGER, C. The economics of pumped storage *Water Power* 9, Nos. 2 and 3 (1957)
[18a] JAEGER, C. The correlation of nuclear, thermal and pumped-storage capacity *Water Power* 10, Nos. 6, 7 and 8 (1958) pp 206, 260, 292
[19] JUKES, G. A. *Information Conference on Nuclear Energy for Management* O.E.E.C., Paris, 1957 and *Engineering,* June 14 1957
[20] *Statistical Year Book of the World Power Conference* No. 8, London, 1956

II. *Hydrology*

[21] LUGEON, J. *Le cycle des précipitations atmosphériques* Neuchâtel, 1928
[22] WISLER, C. O. and BRATER, E. F. *Hydrology* New York and London, 1949
[23] HUNTER ROUSE. *Engineering Hydraulics* (chap. IV, Hydrology; chap. III, Flow Measurement) New York, 1950
[24] LINSLEY, R. K., KOHLER, M. A. and PAULHUS, J. L. H. *Applied Hydrology* New York and London
[25] CREAGER, W. P., JUSTIN, J. D. and HINDS. J. *Engineering for Dams* Chap. by Hathaway, G. A. and Cochran, A. L., Flood Hydrographs, New York, 1944
[26] COUTAGNE, A. L'étude statistique des débits de crue *Rev. gén. Hydraul.* Vol. III, Nos. 16 and 18, Nov. 1937
— Meteorologie et Hydrologie *Houille blanche* 3, No. 3 (1948)
[27] LINSLEY, R. K. and ACKERMANN, W. C. A method of predicting the run-off from rainfall *Trans. Amer. Soc. civ. Engrs* 107 (1942) 825
[28] Société Hydrotechnique de France. Pluie, evaporation, filtration et ecoulement (Apr. 1954) *Houille blanche* (1954)
[29] FULLER, W. E. Flood flows *Trans. Amer. Soc. civ. Engrs* 77 (1914) 565
[30] GIBRAT. *Rev. gén. Hydraul,* No. 11, Oct. 1936
[31] SHERMAN, L. K. Stream flow from rainfall by Unit-Graph method *Engng News Rec.* (1932) 501
[32] HATHAWAY, G. A. Military Airfields *Trans. Amer. Soc. civ. Engrs* 110 (1945) 697
[33] GUMBEL, E. J. *The statistical forecast of floods* Ohio Water Resources Board, Columbus, 1948

III. *Estimate of available power—Reservoir design*

[34] U.N.E.C.E. *Hydro-electric potential in Europe* E./ECE/E.P./131, Geneva, May 1953
[35] Austrian Federal Ministry for Trade and Reconstruction *Energiepotential des Niederschlages im Oesterreichischen Bundesgebiet* Vienna, 1956 laso *Water Power* (1957) 150-51

36 FENTZLOFF, H. E. Systematik der Wasserkraftnutzung *V.D.I.-Forschungsheft* 453, B/22 (1956)
37 JAEGER, C. The economics of pumped storage *Water Power* 9, Nos. 2 and 3 (1957)
38 JAEGER, C. The Hydro-electric Industry *Engl. Elect. J.* 13, No. 8 (1954)
38a JAEGER, C. The correlation of nuclear, thermal and pumped-storage capacity *Water Power* 10 (1958) 206, 260, 292
38b JAEGER, C. Pumped storage capacity correlated to base load electric energy generation. A simplified mathematical approach *Proc. Instn civ. Engrs* 14 (1959) 291-318

IV.   *Debris transportation, silting of reservoirs and erosion*
39 DUFOUR, H. Le Dessableur de l'Usine de Lavey *Bull. tech. Suisse rom.* 1 (1951)
40 DROUHIN, G. Silting of reservoirs and related problems *4th Congress on Large Dams* Vol. IV, pp. 1-14, New Delhi, 1951. See also Reports by Cassidy, W. C., Maddock and Borland, Rao, Duquennois
41 MEYER-PETER, E. and MÜLLER, R. Formulas for bed-load transport *Proc. Int. Ass. Hydraulic Res., Stockholm,* 1948, Pap. No. 2 and *Schweiz. Bauztg* 105, Nos. 9 and 10 (1935) 67; No. 3 (1949)
42 JAEGER, C. *Engineering Fluid Mechanics* pp. 492–510. Glasgow, 1956, New York, 1957
43 REMENIERAS, G. and BRAUDEAU, G. Quelques observations sur l'alluvionnement dans les reservoirs Français *4th Congr. on Large Dams* vol. IV, p 197. New Delhi, 1951
44 JAEGER, C. Discussion *4th Congr. on Large Dams* vol. IV, pp 6–8. New Delhi, 1951
45 MÜLLER, R. and EGGENBERGER, W. Mitteilung Versuchsanstalt Wasserbau *E.T.H.* No. 5. Zürich, 1944
46 Société Hydrotechnique de France, Transport hydraulique et décantation des matériaux solids *Houille blanche* (1952)
47 KHOSLA, A. N. *Silting of reservoirs* Simla, 1953
48 GROVER, N. C. and HOWARD, C. S. The passage of turbid water through Lake Mead *Trans. Amer. Soc. civ. Engrs* 103 (1938) 720
49 DUQUENNOIS, H. Lutte contre la sedimentation des barrages réservoirs, No. 2 and 3 *Élect. Gaz d'Algérie* (1955) (1956)

V.   *Model tests*
50 JAEGER, C. *Engineering Fluid Mechanics* pp 5-12 and 492–506, Glasgow, 1956
51 *Proc. int. Ass. Hydraulic Res.* (I.A.H.R.) Bombay, 1951; Minneapolis, 1953; The Hague, 1955; Lisbon, 1956
52 Tennessee Valley Authority *Fontana Project, Hydraulic Model Studies, Pub. No. 68*
53 *Proc. int. Ass. Hydraulic Res.* Minneapolis, 1953
54 EINSTEIN, H. A. and MÜLLER, R. *Schweiz. Archiv.* 5, No. 8 (1939)

VI.   *Types of hydro-power station*
55 GUTHRIE BROWN, J. (ed.) *Hydro-electric Engineering Practice* Glasgow, 1958
56 GRZYWIENSKI, A. Wasserkraftanlagen, Theorie, Konstruktion, Ausführung und Betrieb *General Report H, 5th World Power Conf.* Vienna, 1956 and *Ost. Bauztg.* 11, Nos. 5–6 (1956)
57 JAEGER, C. The new technique of underground power stations *Engl. Elect. J.* 14, No. 2 (1955)
58 FENTZLOFF, H. E. Principe fondamentaux de la construction des Centrales submersibles *Houille blanche* (1949) 560-5 and 598–621
59 JAEGER, C. The economics of pumped storage *Water Power* 9, Nos. 2 and 3 (1957)
60 GIBRAT. L'Energie des Marées *Bull. Soc. franc. Élect.* 7/III, No. 29 (1953) and *5th World Power Conf.* Vienna, 1956. Pap. iii H/22

VII.   *Geology for dams and dam construction*
61 CREAGER, W. P., JUSTIN, J. D. and HINDS, J. *Engineering for Dams* New York, 1944
62 LUDIN, A. (Ed.) *Wasserkraftanlangen—Talsperren* by Tölke. Berlin, 1938
63 PRESS, H. *Wasserkraftwerke* (vol. I *Talsperren*) Berlin, 1953
64 LUGEON, M. *Barrages et Géologie* Lausanne, 1933
65 GIGNOUX and BARBIER. *Géologie des Barrages et Aménagements Hydrauliques* Paris, 1955
66 LEGGETT, R. F. *Geology and Engineering* New York, 1939
67 Commission Suisse des Grands Barrages *Mesures, Observations, Essais* Berne, 1946
68 TERZAGHI, K. and PECK, R. B. *Soil Mechanics in Engineering Practice* New York,
69 HEILAND, C. A. *Geophysical Exploration* New York, 1946
70 — *Erdbaukurs der Eidg. Technischen Hochschule* (E.T.H.), Zürich, 1938. (A Collection of papers on Foundation Engineering)

[71] JAEGER, C. Present trends in the design of pressure tunnels and shafts for underground hydro-electric power stations *Proc. Instn civ. Engrs* (1955)

[72] BLYTH, F. G. H. *Geology for Engineers* 1943

[73] BOUSSINESQ, J. *Application des Potentiels à l'Etude de l'Equilibre et du mouvement des solides élastiques* Paris, 1885

[74] EVISON, F. F. The seismic determination of Young's Modulus and Poisson's ratio for rocks *in situ. Géotechnique* VI, No. 3 (1956)

[75] MAYER, A. Les propriétés mécaniques des roches. *Géotechnique* No. 3 (1953)

[76] KRYNINE, D. P. and SUDD, W. R. *Principles of Engineering Geology and Geotechnics* New York and London, 1957

[77] *Congr. on Large Dams* Stockholm, 1948; New Delhi, 1951; Paris, 1955

[78] Heightening the Lages Dam, Rio de Janeiro *Engineering* (1949)

VIII. *Gravity dams*

[79] Compagnie Nationale du Rhône, Génissiat *Houille blanche* (Special issue) 1949-50

[80] Tennessee Valley Authority, Technical Reports on Hiwassee, Fontana, *etc.*

[81] HOLMES, W. H. How do U.S.-Swiss designs compare *Engng News Rec.* (1957)

IX. *Arch dams*

[82] RITTER, H. *Die Berechnung von bogenförmigen Staumauern Karlsruhe*, 1913

[83] NOETZLI, F. A. Gravity and arch action in curved dams *Trans. Amer. Soc. civ. Engrs* (1921) 1

[84] U.S. Department of the Interior. Bureau of Reclamation *Treatise on Dams* 1950

[85] JAEGER, C. modern trends in arch dam construction and design *Civ. Engng, London* (1950); *Engl. Elect. J.* 12, No. 4 (1951)

[86] BOURGIN, A. *The Design of Dams* transl. F. F. Fergusson, Pitman, London, 1953

[87] ALLEN, D. N. and PIPPARD, A. J. S. The experimental and mathematical analysis of arch dams. with special reference to Dokan *Proc. Instn civ. Engrs* Part I, 5 (1956) 198-275

[88] LOMBARDI, J. *Les barrages en voûtes minces* Lausanne, 1955

[89] FLÜGGE, W. *Statik und Dynamik der Schalen* Berlin, 1934

[90] GUTHRIE BROWN, J. (ed.) *Hydro-electric Engineering Practice* chap. 10, C. Jaeger, Arch Dams, Glasgow, 1958

[91] ROCHA. R. and SERAFIM, L. Analysis of concrete dams by model tests, Rep. C. 36 *5th Congr. on Large Dams* Paris, 1955

[92] OBERTI, G. Risultati di studi sperimentali eseguiti sopra un modello di digha ad arco *Energia elett.* (1940)

[93] Società Adriatica di Elettricità *Impianto Idroelettrico Piave-Boite-Mae-Vajont* Venezia, 1956

[94] *Congress on Large Dams* Stockholm, 1948; New Delhi, 1951; Paris, 1955; New York, 1958

X. *Buttress dams*

[95] SCHORER. H. The buttressed dam of uniform strength *Trans. Amer. Soc. civ. Engrs* 96 (1932) 666

[96] NOETZLI, F. A. Round-head buttress dam *J. Amer. Concr. Inst.* 4 (1932) 161

[97] CONTESSINI, F. Dighe a speroni, allegerite e piene *Energia Elett.* 25, No. 7 (1948)

[98] FREY BAER, O. Die Berechnung der Pfeiler aufgelöster Staumauern *Schweiz. Bauztg.* 123, No. 9 ,1944)

[99] STUCKY, A. Le Barrage d'accumulation de BEN-METIR en Tunisie *Bull. Tech. Suisse Rom.* 81, No. 21-2 (1955)

[100] JAEGER, C. Faux la Montagne Dam *Water Power* (April, 1952)

XI. *Earth dams and rock-fill dams*

[101] PROCTOR, R. R. Fundamental principles of soil compaction *Engng News Rec.* (1933)

[102] TERZAGHI, K. *Theoretical Soil Mechanics* New York, 1943

[103] CREAGER, JUSTIN and HINDS. *Engineering for Dams* Vol. III, New York, 1944

[104] TERZAGHI, K. and PECK, R. B. *Soil Mechanics in Engineering Practice* New York, 1948

[105] WILLIAMS, F. H. P. Compaction of soils *J. Instn civ. Engrs* 33 (1949)

[106] GLOSSOP, R. The principles and applications of soil mechanics *J. Instn civ. Engrs* (1946)

[107] CASAGRANDE, A. Seepage through dams. Boston Soc. Civil Engrs *Contributions to Soil Mechanics, 1925-40* (1940)

[108] KRYNINE, D. P. *Soil Mechanics* New York, 1947

[109] RICE, O. L. and ARTHUR. H. G. The most recent methods developed to avoid piping or blowouts in dams *3rd Congress on Large Dams, R.49* Stockholm, 1948

[110] KEIL, K. *Der Dammbau* 2nd Ed., Berlin, 1954

[111] MALLET, C. and PACQUANT, J. *Les Barrages en Terre* Paris, 1951

[112] POST, G. and LONDE, P. *Les barrages en Terre compactée. Pratiques Americaines* Paris, 1953

[113] GALLOWAY, J. D. The design of rock-fill dams *Trans. Amer. Soc. civ. Engrs* 104 (1939)
[114] *The Serre Ponçon Dam. 5th Congr. on Large Dams* Special publication of *Travaux* Paris, 1955. See also P. O. Wolf *Water Power* 9, No. 4–8 (1947)
[115] TOMINI, H. The Kennedy Dan *Engng J.* Montreal 37, No. 11 (1954) 1386–97
[116] JAEGER, C. *Engineering Fluid Mechanics* Glasgow, 1956; New York, 1957
[117] KRYNINE, D. P. L. and JUDD, W. R. *Principles of Engineering Geology and Geotechnics*

XII. *Barrages and low-head dams*

[118] MOSONYI, E. *Wasserkraftwerke* Budapest, 1956
[119] SCHULZ, A. B. *Die Strömungstechnische Gestaltung der Wehre und Flusskraftwerke Mitteil No. 42* Institut für Wasserbau, Berlin–Charlottenburg, 1954
[120] JAEGER, C. *Engineering Fluid Mechanics* Glasgow, 1956
[121] GRZYWIENSKI. *Das Donauwerk Ybbs-Persenbeug* Springer, Vienna, 1949
[122] GRZYWIENSKI. *Flusskraftwerke und Stromwerke* Springer, Vienna, 1948
[123] Donzère-Mondragon, *Houille blanche* special issue, 1953
[124] JAEGER, C. The Rhône development *Water Power* 5, No. 1 (1953)
[125] JAEGER, C. Birsfelden power station *Water Power* 7, No. 2 (1955)

XIII. *Gates*

[126] CREAGER and JUSTIN. *Hydro-electric Handbook* New York, 1950
[127] U.S. Bureau of Reclamation *Dam and control works*
[128] BUZZELL, D. A. Recent trends in hydraulic gate design *Proc. Amer. Soc. civ. Engrs* 80, No. 517 (1954)
[129] ACKERMANN, H. *Aus der Entwicklung der beweglichen Wehrverschlüsse* Verlag Mensch und Arbeit, Zürich
[130] GÉRODOLLE, H. and MUSSARD, F. *Les Vannes de Génissiat, Houille Blanche,* special issue, Grenoble, 1950
[131] BUSS and KLUS. *Schweiz. Bauztg* 74 (1956)
[132] ESCHLER, H. *Schweiz. Bauztg* 75, No. 27 (1957)
[133] AUBERT, J. *Barrages et Canalisation* Paris, 1949
[134] *Informations techniques Charmilles* No. 1 (1945)

XIV. *Intakes and general arrangement*

[135] SCHULZ, A. B. Thesis No. 42, Institut für Wasserbau. Berlin–Charlottenburg, 1954
[136] PRESS, H. *Stauanlagen und Wasserkraftwerke* Vol. II, Wehre, Berlin, 1954 and 1959
[137] MÜLLER, R. *Theoretische Grundlagen der Flussverbauungen* Zürich, 1943
[138] MOSONYI, E. *Water Power Development* Vol. I, Budapest, 1957
[139] GRZYWIENSKI *Das Donauwerk* Ybbs-Persenbeug, Vienna, 1949
[140] AEGGERTER and BOSSHARDT. Das Kraftwerk Birsfelden *Schweiz. Bauztg* 67 No. 37 (1949) and *Water Power* 1955
[141] GÉNISSIAT. *Houille blanche* 1950
[142] BORT. *Houille blanche* 1953
[143] DONZÈRE-MONDRAGON. *Houille blanche* 1955
[144] POUND-CORNER. Salime hydro-electric power station in Spain *Engl. Elect. J.* 15, No. 1 (1957)
[145] GUTHRIE BROWN, J., et al. *Hydro-electric Engineering Practice* Vol. 1, Glasgow, 1958
[146] CREAGER and JUSTIN. *Hydro-electric Handbook* 2nd Ed., New York, 1950
[146a] MAITRE, R. *Houille Blanche* 13, No. 1 (1958)
[146b] GARIEL, P. *Houille Blanche* 13 (1957)

XV. *Tunnels*

[147] TALOBRE, J. *La Mécanique des Roches* Paris, Dunod, 1957
[148] TERZAGHI, K. Introduction to tunnel geology, *in Rock Tunnelling with Steel Supports* by R. V. Proctor and T. L. White, Youngstown, Ohio, 1946
[149] JAEGER, C. Present trends in the design of pressure tunnels and shafts for underground power stations *Proc. Instn civ. Engrs* I, 4, No. 2 (1955) with discussion by many contributors. See also *Water Power* Feb., March, April and May (1955)
[150] JAEGER, C. Tunnels for hydro-electric power, in *Tunnels and Tunnelling* edited by C. A. Péquignot, Hutchinson, London, 1960
[151] JAEGER, C. *Theorie générale du coup de bélier* Dunod, Paris, 1933
[152] LUGEON, M. *Barrages et Géologie* Lausanne, Paris, 1933
[153] GIGNOUX and BARBIER. *Géologie des Barrages et des Aménagements Hydrauliques* Chap. V, pp. 224–61, Masson, Paris, 1955
[154] SHEPHERD, R. Physical properties and drillability of rocks *Water Power* March, July (1951)
[155] MATTHIAS, F. T. Kemano underground *Engng J. Can.* 37, No. 11 (1954) 1398–1412
[156] HUBER, W. G. Kemano penstocks *Engng J. Can.* 37, No. 11 (1954) 1413–20

[157] OLIVIER-MARTIN, D. and KOBILINSKY. L'execution d'un grand Souterrain pour l'aménagement hydro-électrique d'Isère-Arc *Tech. d. Tran.* April (1955) 145–56

[158] RABCEWICZ, L. Bolted supports for tunnels *Water Power* April (1954). See also *Schweiz Bauztg* 70, No. 17, 18, 19 (1952)

[159] FREY BÄR, O. Sicherung des Stollenvortriebes *Schweiz. Bauztg* 74, No. 38 (1956). See also *Schweiz. Bauztg* Sept., Oct. (1944), Oct. (1947) and April (1955)

[160] *Third Conference on Soil Mechanics* Zürich, 1953 (2 vols)

[161] DILLON, E. C. The Mullardoch-Fasnakyle-Affric tunnels *Works constr. Paper No. 16. Instn civ. Engrs* 1952

[162] GRUNDY, C. F. The Cunie tunnel on the Tummel Gary hydro-electric project *Works constr. Paper No. 15. Instn civ. Engrs,* 1950

XVI. *Surge tanks*

[163] JOHNSON, R. D. The surge tank in water power plants *Trans. Amer. Soc. mech. Engrs* 30 (1908) 443

[164] PRASIL, F. Wasserschlossprobleme *Schweiz. Bauztg* 52 (1908-II)

[165] SCHOKLITSCH, A. Spiegelbewegung im Wasserschlössern *Schweiz. Bauztg* 79 (1923–I)

[166] THOMA, D. *Beiträge zur Theorie des Wasserschlosses bei selbsttätig geregelten Turbinen anlagen* Munich, 1910

[167] CALAME and GADEN. *Theorie des Chambres d'équilibre* Paris and Lausanne, 1926

[168] HUNTER ROUSE, et al. *Engineering Hydraulics* New York, 1950, chap. VII by J. S. McNown: Surges and Water Hammer

[169] JAEGER, C. *Engineering Fluid Mechanics* Glasgow and New York, 1956

[170] GARDEL, A. *Chambres d'équilibre* Lausanne, 1956

[171] JAEGER, C. Present trends in surge tank design *Proc. Inst. mech. Engrs* 168, No. 2 (1954)

[172] JAEGER, C. De la stabilité des chambres d'equilibre *Schweiz, Bauztg.* 122, Nos. 21, 24, 25, 26 (1943)

[172a] JAEGER, C. The double surge tank system. General discussion on the stability problem *Water Power* 9, No. 718 (1957)

[172b] JAEGER, C. Contribution to the stability theory of systems of surge tanks *Trans. Amer. Soc. mech. Engrs* 80, No. 7 (1958)

[172c] JAEGER, C. A review of surge tank stability criteria *A.S.M.E. pap.* 59-A-270, A.S.M.E. meeting Nov./Dec. 1959

[172d] JAEGER, C. The economics of large surge tanks *Water Power* 10, No. 5 (1958)

XVII. *Underground hydro-electric power station*

[173] JAEGER, C. Underground hydro-electric power stations *Civ. Engng Publ. Wk Rev.* 43 (1948) 620 and 44 (1949) 38

[174] JAEGER, C. Present trends in the design of pressure tunnels and shafts for underground hydro-electric power stations *Proc. Instn civ. Engrs* Pt. I (March 1955). See also: *Engl. Elect. J.* 14, No. 2 (1955) and *Water Power* Feb., March, April and May 1955

[175] WESTERBERG, G. and HELLSTROM, B. Swedish practice in water power development. Paper No. 2, Sect. H.I. *Fourth World Power Conference* 1950, vol. 4, 2071

[176] KEMANO-KITIMAT. *Engng J.* Montreal 37, No. 11 (1954) contains several papers on this station. See also *Engineer* 195, May, June (1953)

[177] RABCEWICZ, L. The Forçacaba hydro-electric scheme *Water Power* 5, Nos. 9, 10 and 11 (Sept., Oct., Nov. 1953)

[178] LAVEY. Publication of Ville de Lausanne, 1951

[179] HEGGSTAD, R. Norwegian hydro-electric power stations built into rock, Paper No. 1, Sect. H.2. *Fourth World Power Conference* London, 1950

[180] TALOBRE, J. *La Mécanique des Roches* Dunod, Paris, 1957

[181] JAEGER, C. Chap. 22, Underground power stations *Hydro-electric Engineering Practice* (Guthrie Brown, ed.), Glasgow, 1958

XVIII. *Pipe-lines, etc.*

[182] GUTHRIE BROWN, J., et al. *Hydro-electric Engineering Practice* vol. I, chap. 19, Glasgow, 1957

[183] CHAPMAN, E. J. K. Pressure pipelines for hydro-electric works *Civ. Engng Publ. Wks Rev., Lond.* Oct. 1950, Feb. 1951

[184] FERRAND. Over-pressured and self-hooped penstocks *Water Power* 4, No. 10 (1952); Nos. 3 and 4 (1950). See also FERRAND *Houille blanche* No. 4 (July 1946)

[185] JAEGER, C. Present trends in the design of pressure tunnels and shafts for underground power stations *Proc. Instn civ. Engrs.* Pt. I (March 1955) and F. H. KNAPP, Correspondence on the paper (July 1955)

[186] JAEGER, C. *Theorie générale du coup de bélier* Paris, 1953. See also: Water hammer effects in power conduits *Civ. Engng. Lond.* (Feb./May. 1948)

[187] Canadian Power Plant has 1200 ft. Head *Engng News Rec.* (Feb. 1949)

[188] *La Houille blanche* No. 4 (July 1946)

XIX. *Theory of water hammer*

[189] ALLIEVI, L. *Teoria del colpo d'ariete* Milan, 1903, 1913. English translation by
E. E. Halmos as *The Theory of Water Hammer,* Amer. Soc. Mech. Engrs 1929
[190] JAEGER, C. *Theorie générale du coup de bélier* Paris, 1933
[191] JAEGER, C. *Engineering Fluid Mechanics* Glasgow, 1956; New York, 1957
[192] ANGUS, R. W. Water hammer in pipes, including those supplied by centrifugal
pumps; graphical treatment *Proc. Instn mech. Engrs* 136, 245 (1937) and *Trans.
Amer. Soc. civ. Engrs* 340 (1939)
[193] BERGERON, L. *Rev. gén. Hydraul.* 1, 2 (1935) and *Tech. mod.* 2, 3 (1936)
[194] SCHNYDER, O. *Wasserkraft, Munich* 27, No. 5, 6 (1932). *Schweiz. Bauztg* 94,
No. 22-3 (1929)
[195] JAEGER, C. Water hammer effects in power conducts. Accidents due to water
hammer *Civ. Engng* (Feb., May 1948)
[196] JAEGER, C. Water hammer caused by pumps *Water Power* 11, No. 7 (1959), see
also GUTHRIE BROWN, J. (ed.) *Hydro-electric Engineering Practice,* vol. I, chap.
20
[197] GUTHRIE BROWN, J. (ed.) *Hydro-electric Engineering Practice* Glasgow, 1958

XX. *Prime movers—water turbines*

[198] GUTHRIE BROWN, J. *Hydro-electric Engineering Practice* vol. II, Glasgow, 1958
[199] DÉRIAZ, P. and WARNOCK, J. G. Economic advantages of variable pitch runners,
World Power Conf., Montreal, 1958, Pap. No. 130, A2/5

XXI. *Power house design*

[200] SCHULZ, A. B. Neuzeitliche Staukraftwerke *Die Wasserwirtschaft* No. 3 (Dec. 1950).
See also SCHULZ: Thesis at Technical University Berlin-Charlottenburg, 1954
[201] FENTZLOFF, H. E. Principles fondamentaux de la construction des centrales submersibles *Houille blanche* (Sept./Oct. 1949)
[202] GÉNISSIAT. *Houille blanche* (1950)
[203] BORT. *Houille blanche* (1953)
[204] DONZÈRE-MONDRAGON. *Houille blanche* (1955)
[205] POUND-CORNER: Salime hydro-electric power in Spain *Engl. Elect. J.* 15, No. 1
(March 1957)
[206] BOVET, G. and TH. *Inform. Tech. Charmilles* No. 1 (May 1945
[207] GUTHRIE BROWN, J., *et al.* *Hydro-electric Engineering Practice* vol. I, Glasgow,
1958
[208] JAEGER, C. Design of unlined spiral casings *Water Power* 4 (Feb./Mar. 1952)
[209] JAEGER, C. The new technique of underground hydro-electric power stations.
Engl. Elec. J. 14, No. 2 (1955)

OVERHEAD TRANSMISSION LINES

N. G. Simpson, M.I.C.E., M.I.E.E. and B. C. Edwards

1. INTRODUCTION

Two basic methods are available for the transmission and distribution of electric power: insulated cables laid below ground and overhead lines with bare conductors suspended at a safe height above ground and insulated from the supporting structures.

Buried cables are usually confined to areas with high load density whilst overhead lines are used exclusively for extra high voltage long-distance transmission and to a very large extent for distribution of supplies in rural areas. The latter are normally cheaper than the corresponding buried cables and the disparity becomes more significant as the circuit voltage increases. The present extent of electricity supplies in rural areas would not have been possible but for the availability of overhead lines for this purpose.

This chapter deals with the technique of overhead line construction which is predominantly structural and mechanical in character, subject to the briefly outlined initial electrical requirements.

2. ASPECTS OF ELECTRICAL DESIGN

Modern electric power systems may consist of a number of elements as shown typically in *Figure 1*.

Overhead lines interconnect power systems, convey power from generating stations or bulk supply points to centres of load, distribute power from load centres to secondary substations and from these to domestic and other consumers.

Alternating current (a.c.) has exclusively superseded the early use of direct current (d.c.) for several reasons, *e.g.* the simplicity of the generators and the ease of voltage transformation by static transformers and of the interruption of power at all voltages by circuit breakers. Economic and operational considerations have led to the widespread adoption of three phase a.c. systems, although single phase lines are occasionally used. There has been renewed interest in d.c. systems for high voltage bulk supplies but its use is likely to be restricted to transmission of loads over 200 MW and distances greater than 250 miles for some years except for special cases, *e.g.* submarine cables. Generation and utilization of power will remain a.c.

System voltages (3 phase, 50 c/s) in accordance with British practice are as follows (preferred voltages are in bold type):

TABLE 1

Low voltage distribution lines	415 V (voltage to neutral 240 **V**, the domestic utilization voltage)
High voltage distribution lines	3·3 kV, 6·6 kV, **11** kV, 22 kV, **33** kV
High voltage transmission lines	66 kV, 88 kV, 110 kV, **132** kV
Extra high voltage transmission lines	220 kV, **275** kV, 330 kV, **380** kV

335

Overhead line costs depend largely on conductor size and voltage and the initial object is to select the most economical combination of the two, ensuring that reliability and operational requirements are obtained. Investigations may involve: (*i*) selection of conductor size and line voltage; (*ii*) selection of insulation, clearances and protection against lightning.

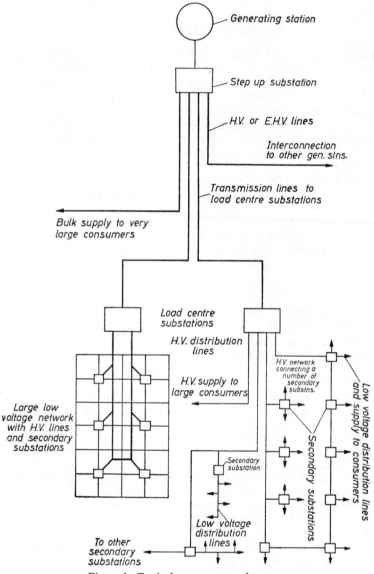

Figure 1. Typical power system layout

2.1. *Conductor size and line voltage*

When the load and transmission distance are known the following aspects are considered:

(*a*) *Thermal rating*—The currents corresponding to a range of line voltages are evaluated and from these the smallest conductor sizes which will convey the currents without exceeding the specified temperature limit are found. These should be such that the conductor temperature does not rise above the annealing point of the conductor material (*i.e.* approximately 75°C for hard drawn copper and aluminium).

(*b*) *Corona*—The electrical breakdown of air on conductor surface is termed 'corona' and is dependent mainly on conductor diameter, phase spacing and voltage. Corona causes radio interference and an increase in power loss. A corona loss of 0·5–1 kW per three phase mile in fair weather gives acceptable interference level. Up to 33 kV corona is not likely to occur. At voltages above 220 kV the diameter of single conductors from corona aspects becomes too large to be economical and hollow or 'bundled' conductors are used, the latter especially in recent years. Typical minimum steel cored aluminium conductor (copper equivalent) sizes from corona considerations are 0·035 sq in at 66 kV, 0·125 sq in at 132 kV, 0·25 sq in at 220 kV, twin 0·175 sq in at 275 kV and twin 0·4 sq in at 385 kV. The last two 'bundled' conductor arrangements were selected for the British 275 kV and 380 kV lines on corona loss basis.

(*c*) *Voltage drop and power loss*—Depending on whether a single or double circuit line is to be employed (related to the degree of supply reliability) and on the type of structure, an estimate can be made of conductor spacing. By using standard electrical analysis procedure the 'equivalent' phase spacing and circuit constants (resistance, reactance and capacitance *etc*) can be determined. The voltage drop and power loss are then calculated for a number of conductor sizes and line voltages such that:

(*i*)   Voltage drop is within 5–6 per cent for low voltage lines, 6–10 per cent for high voltage distribution lines and 10–15 per cent for extra high voltage transmission lines.

(*ii*) Power loss should be approximately 5–7 per cent, bearing in mind the minimum conductor sizes previously set by thermal and corona considerations.

For line voltages up to 66 kV and lengths up to 60 miles, line capacitance can be neglected and the calculations are made by the 'short line' formula. Above either of these limits, treatment becomes more complex and more exact methods must be used.

(*d*) *Stability limit*—From fundamental considerations, the rotating machines in an a.c. system must run in synchronism. Steady overloads beyond machine capacity and transient disturbances such as switching, faults, *etc*, tend to destroy synchronism and the system becomes 'unstable.' The power that can be transmitted by an EHV line during and after such disturbances without loss of synchronism is called the 'stability limit' and depends on the reactance of the line, machines and equipment, machine and circuit breaker characteristics and line voltage. For voltages above 66 kV and lines greater than 100 miles long, the stability limit often determines line voltage and conductor size, and related calculations become very complex.

Analogue computers (a.c. or d.c. analysers) and sometimes digital computers are frequently used both for this and for (*c*) above, and, with complicated networks, this is the only practicable way of carrying out the electrical analysis.

(*e*) *Range of conductor sizes*—The range of conductor sizes normally used is given in TABLE 2.

TABLE 2

Voltage limit	Conductor size (equivalent copper area)	
	sq in	sq cm
LV lines	0·025–0·2	0·161–1·29
Lines up to 33 kV	0·025–0·25	0·161–1·61
66 kV	0·035–0·15	0·226–0·97
132 kV	0·125–0·4	0·81 –2·58
220 kV	0·25 –0·4	1·61 –2·58
275 kV	Twin 0·175–Twin 0·4	Twin 1·13–Twin 2·58
380 kV	Twin 0·4	Twin 2·58

2.2. Insulation, clearances and lightning protection

The selection of line insulation and the air gap clearance between conductor phases and phase to earthed metal-work is governed by the following.

(a) *Internal overvoltages*—These arise from switching operations and faults and are alternating in character. Their magnitude depends on the type of protective gear and system of neutral earthing (fuses produce higher overvoltages than circuit breakers, effectively direct earthed neutral systems produce lower overvoltages than other types of neutral earthing), and may be 3–7 times the line voltage in the lower voltage range up to 33 kV and 2·5–3·5 times for 132 kV and higher line voltages with a duration from a few thousandths to several seconds. The magnitude of the overvoltage is estimated from previous experience on similar lines combined with laboratory and mathematical investigations. The line insulation and clearances are then selected to withstand this overvoltage, taking into account the lowering effects on the insulation characteristics of pollution, rain and swing of conductors. The power frequency voltage (*e.g.* 50 cycles a.c.) withstand or flashover values of insulators and air gaps are used as the basis of insulator selection.

(b) *External overvoltages*—These are produced by lightning strokes on or near the line. Lightning overvoltages are in the form of uni-directional impulse waves of very large magnitudes but with a duration of the order of 100–1,000 microsecs. Line protection against lightning is obtained by:

(*1*) Shielding the line conductors with overhead earthwires suitably earthed at the structures and designed to intercept direct lightning strokes and drain them to earth. The preferred shielding angle (ψ) should not be greater than 30° although angles up to 45° have been used in relatively low lightning intensity areas (see *Figure 6*). Single earthwires are normally used but double earthwires are necessary on certain types of structure and in regions of very high lightning intensity.

(2) Providing insulation of adequate impulse voltage value between line conductors and the earthed portion of the structure. During the draining of lightning current, the earthed structure is raised to a high potential, and the line insulation normally provided, sometimes in combination with the wood insulation of structures and crossarms, prevents back flashover from structures to conductors for the majority of lightning strokes. It is impracticable to design a fully lightning-proof line as the amount of insulation and the clearances required would be excessive. Methods are available for estimating the amount of insulation required to give a pre-determined lightning performance.

Normally, high voltage distribution lines are designed for an outage rate not greater than 20–30 per 100 miles per year, and an outage rate not greater than 2–10 per 100 miles per year for important EHV transmission lines. The electrical behaviour of insulators and air gaps under impulse voltages differs from that under power frequency voltages. Impulse withstand or flashover values of insulators and air gaps are used as a basis for the selection of insulator and clearance from lightning considerations.

(*3*) Providing low structure footing resistance such that the magnitude of the back potential (lightning current × tower footing resistance) is reduced as far as possible. Suitable values of structure footing resistances are 5–7 ohms for 33 kv, 10–12 ohms for 132 kV and 20–30 ohms for higher voltage lines. Earth plates, driven rods, continuous counterpoises (wire or tapes) buried in earth are normally used for earthing. Low values of earth resistance are also necessary on all metal structure lines to provide a low resistance path for the fault currents, both from safety considerations and for the operation of protective gear.

(*4*) Providing quick acting circuit breakers at the source of supply which prevent damage due to power follow current in the event of flashover initiated by lightning (lightning flashovers themselves seldom cause damage). The heating effect of power frequency arcs which follow lightning flashover is mostly responsible for insulator breakage and conductor burning. If circuit breakers clear the power follow current within 2–3 cycles damage is avoided in most cases. Arcing horns on insulators is a common form of protection against arc damage.

The amount of impulse insulation to be provided must be a compromise between the degree of operational reliability required and cost. Insulation levels for lines in moderate lightning intensity area (*e.g.* Great Britain and Europe) and the corresponding air gap clearances for typical line voltages are shown in TABLE 3. At voltages greater than 220 kV, the internal over-voltage generally determines the insulation level.

TABLE 3

System voltage kV	Impulse insulation flashover voltage kV	Power frequency flashover voltage kV	Minimum live metal to earth clearance (*x*) in	Typical insulators
11	75	32	4	Pin insulator B.S. rating No. 30
33	170	74	7	Pin insulator B.S. rating No. 70
66	325	165	20	5 discs 10 in diam. × 5½ in spacing
132	650	350	42	10 discs 10 in diam. × 5½ in spacing
275	1300	710	80	18 discs 11 in diam. × 6¾ in spacing
380	1700	910	110	25 discs 11 in diam. × 6¾ in spacing

Higher insulation levels than those given in TABLE 3 are often adopted in areas of severe lightning intensity and/or of severe atmospheric pollution.

Inexpensive lines on wood poles without earthwires, *e.g.* B.S. 1320 type of construction, are used extensively in Great Britain. The insulation value of the wood pole prevents line-to-earth faults in the event of lightning stroke but not flashover between conductors, and such lines must rely on protective gear for protection against such damage.

3. REGULATIONS

The design and construction of overhead lines in all countries must conform to statutory regulations which prescribe certain minimum safety requirements. In some countries these regulations or accompanying codes of practice are detailed in character but this is not the case in Great Britain. British regulations are the responsibility of the Ministry of Power and apart from the following summary of the main requirements for high voltage lines relating to conductors, supports and ground clearance, they cover such matters as access to live conductors, earthing, unauthorised climbing, special crossings, *etc.*

(*i*)   *Conductors*—Minimum factor of safety=2 (on breaking load) when at 22°F (-5.5°C) they have a $\frac{3}{8}$ in (9·5 mm) radial thickness of ice and are subjected to a 50 m.p.h. (80 k.p.h.) wind on the full projected area of the ice coated conductor, equivalent to 8 lb/sq ft (0·004 kg/sq cm).

(*ii*) *Supports*—To withstand the longitudinal, transverse and vertical forces imposed by the conductors under the above conditions of loading without damage and without movement in the ground. Wind pressure on supports=8 lb/sq ft on projected area and with compound structures such as steel towers, the pressure on the lee side members may be taken as one half that on the windward side. Minimum factors of safety under these maximum working loads, calculated on the crippling load of struts and the elastic limit of tension members, are as folows:

Material	Factor of safety
Iron or steel	2·5
Wood	3·5
Reinforced concrete	3·5

(*iii*) *Minimum height of conductors*

Maximum a.c. voltage	Ground clearance at 122°F
66 kV	20 ft (6·1 m)
110 kV	21 ft (6·4 m)
165 kV	22 ft (6·7 m)
Exceeding 165 kV	23 ft (7·0 m)

Relaxations of these regulations are permitted for lines on wood poles up to 11 kV constructed in accordance with B.S. 1320. The principal variations are the adoption of a minimum factor of safety on conductors of 2·5 at 22°F with a wind pressure of 16 lb/sq ft (no ice) and a factor of safety on imported red fir poles of 2·5. A reduced normal ground clearance is permitted of 17 ft and 20 ft across roads. This particular construction is limited to conductor sizes of 0·025 and 0·05 sq in (max) hard drawn copper and other conductor materials of 0·04 sq in copper equivalent.

4. CONDUCTORS, INSULATORS AND FITTINGS

4.1. *Conductors*

The three main conductor types now in universal use are steel cored aluminium (SCA, or ACSR according to American terminology) hard drawn copper (h.d. copper) and hard drawn aluminium (h.d. aluminium). To these can be added galvanised steel, which has a very restricted use as a conductor but is commonly employed for overhead earthwires, and also aluminium alloy.

SCA is used for the majority of extra high voltage transmission lines, fulfilling the economic requirements of long span construction with high strength conductors. Comparable alternatives in strength such as cadmium copper alloy, copper covered steel and steel cored copper have almost entirely disappeared. On high voltage distribution lines, the issue between the three main types varies to some extent with the relative cost of the basic metals, as with low voltage lines where the choice is between h.d. copper and h.d. aluminium.

Conductor corrosion is often a critical problem, particularly in intense industrial and marine atmospheres. Grease is used for the protection of the SCA conductors, varying from standard treatment of the core to total impregnation for the worst situations. Special precautions are not normally necessary with h.d. copper conductors although they are vulnerable to attack by sulphur compounds present in industrial atmospheres.

Conductors consist of three or more individual wires stranded together and the standard method of nomenclature is on the basis of equivalent copper area (conductivity of aluminium to copper approximately 60 per cent) and details of the stranding (see *Figure 2*).

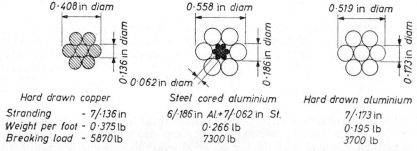

Figure 2. Comparison of three conductors of 0·10 sq in equiv. copper area

TABLE 4 shows the comparative mechanical characteristics of the main overhead line conductor materials.

TABLE 4

MECHANICAL CHARACTERISTICS OF THE MAIN OVERHEAD LINE CONDUCTOR MATERIALS

	Copper (hard drawn)	*Aluminium* (hard drawn)	*Steel* (galvanized)
Weight (lb/sq in/ft)	3·85	1·17	3·40
Tensile strength (lb/sq in)	60,000	23,500	194,000
Coefficient of linear expansion (per °F)	$9·44 \times 10^{-6}$	$12·78 \times 10^{-6}$	$6·4 \times 10^{-6}$
Modulus of elasticity (lb/sq in)	18×10^{6}	$9·9 \times 10^{6}$	28×10^{6}

4.2. *Insulators*

The electrical requirements for the insulation of overhead lines are outlined in Sect. 2.2. The principal insulator types in use will now be described.

The shape of an insulator is designed to avoid excessive current leakage and surface flashover under varying conditions of rain, fog and atmospheric pollution and its identity is related to flashover voltage characteristics under both wet and dry conditions, length of leakage path from conductor to earth, puncture voltage and mechanical strength. The two predominant insulating materials employed are toughened glass or porcelain with associated fittings usually of galvanized malleable cast-iron or steel.

Arcing horns are fitted in most cases to suspension and tension insulators to protect them from damage due to flashover (*Figure 3*d) by diverting the power frequency arc to the surrounding air. On lines employing the most modern protective devices (Sect. 2.2) they may be dispensed with, although it is usual to retain the horn at the conductor end as a safeguard against burning.

The main types of insulator are as follows:

(*i*)   *Shackle and bobbin type* (*Figure 3*a)—Low voltage lines.

(*ii*)   *Pin type* (*Figure 3*b)—High voltage lines, used up to 33 kV at intermediate positions. Standard mechanical strengths 400 lb and 800 lb working (factor of safety 2·5), applied as a cantilever load at the top of the spindle mounted insulator.

(*iii*)   *Suspension type* (*Figure 3*d)—High and extra high voltage lines, used at 33 kV and above at intermediate positions. Consisting of a suspended flexible string of interlocking disc shaped units, the number depending on electrical requirements.

(*iv*)   *Tension type* (*Figure 3*c)—All high and extra high voltage lines at terminal, angle and section positions. The same basic form as suspension insulators but used in a horizontal instead of vertical position. They have, therefore, to withstand the full conductor tension. The standard mechanical strength rating of both suspension and tension types ranges from 1,500 lb to 12,000 lb working (factor of safety 2·5).

(*v*)   *Stay insulators*—Unlike line insulators these are not normally under electrical stress but are inserted into the top end of staywires to insulate the earthed stay end from the top of wood pole supports and function both as a safety measure and to retain the insulation properties of the pole above ground. On low voltage lines they consist of a solid porcelain shackle but on unearthed high voltage lines their shape is entirely different, the insulating medium being wood or a synthetic material.

4.3. *Fittings*

Mechanical fittings and connections cannot be described or illustrated here in detail in view of their number and variety. Such information is available in manufacturers' catalogues. This section will confine itself to a brief outline of the parts which are an important and essential feature of the efficient operation of the line and to the basic principles which control their design. This group of fittings is associated with the conductor and insulators.

At intermediate positions the conductors must be held in suspension or supported on pin type insulators where the load on the fittings is normally that of the dead weight of the conductor in the span.

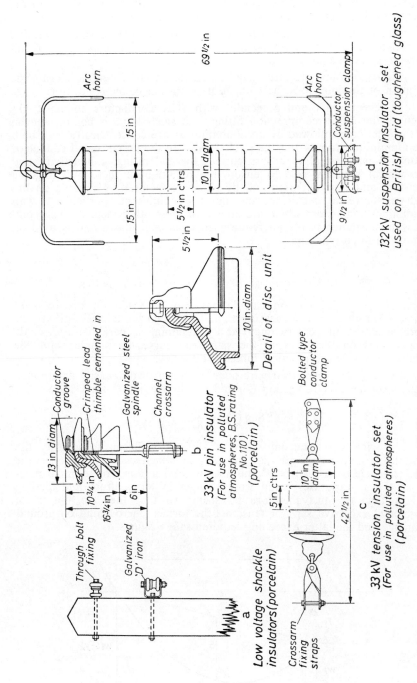

Figure 3. Typical examples of the main insulator types

In the first case the conductor is clamped into a metal saddle (see *Figure 3*d) and in the latter a wire binder is used. With both, allowance must be made, in degree of tightness, for a limited amount of slip in the event of a conductor breakage.

At angle and terminal positions a bolted (see *Figure 3*c) or compression type clamp is used which is normally required to take 95 per cent of full tension of the conductor without slip occurring.

Mid-span joints are often required on long sections and here again the strength of the joint must be compatible with that of the conductor.

In recent years and especially with SCA conductors emphasis has been on the use of compression fittings. A steel sleeve is compressed on to the steel core followed by an aluminium sleeve concentrically over both the aluminium strands and the steel sleeve. In the design of all conductor fittings it is essential to ensure correct thermal rating, conductivity and mechanical strength, also to ensure the retention of these by excluding moisture and contamination and by choosing material of suitable quality and resistance to corrosion; the latter is important, particularly with aluminium conductors which are anodic to most other metals. The compression technique fulfils all requirements outlined above and is used on almost all important lines.

5. CONDUCTOR SAGS AND TENSIONS

Conductor sag and tension calculations can be made on the basis of either a parabolic or catenary curve, and although the latter is strictly the more accurate, the errors involved by assuming a parabola are small. Calculations on the basis of the parabolic curve are simpler and the results are within the practical limits of accuracy.

The sag of a suspended wire under uniform load is easily determined if the span length (L), tension (T) and weight loading (w) are known:

$$\text{Sag } (S) = \frac{wL^2}{8T}$$

This simple relationship, however, is not sufficient to identify the possible variations in both sag and tension which occur when once the conductor has been suspended and anchored off at angle or terminal positions. These variations result from changes in temperature and loading and conductors must therefore be strung so that they do not cause subsequent excessive sags or tensions, the former encroaching on ground clearance and the latter exceeding required safety figures.

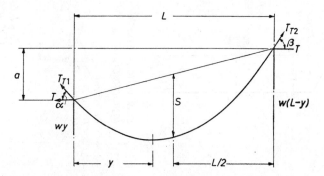

Figure 4. General case of the suspended conductor

5.1. *Fundamental formulae*

(a) *Symbols and definitions*

General

$L=$ Span (ft)
= horizontal distance between supports

$S=$ Sag (ft)
= distance measured in the direction of the resultant load between the conductor and the mid point of a straight line joining the two supports

$T=$ Tension (lb)
= Horizontal component of the tension under load w being uniform throughout any one span

$T_T=$ Tangential tension (lb)
= Actual tension at any given point in a conductor in the direction of the tangent to the curve

$w=$ Resultant load per foot of conductor (lb) (including weight of conductor)

$t=$ Temperature rise °F from initial to a final condition

$a=$ Difference in level of adjacent supports (ft)

$y=$ Horizontal distance of lowest point of curve from lower support (ft)

Conductor data

$A=$ Actual cross sectional area of conductor (sq in)

$d=$ Overall diameter of conductor (in)

$E=$ Modulus of elasticity of complete conductor (lb/sq in). Virtual modulus for composite conductors of materials a and b.

$$=\frac{E_a m + E_b}{m+1}\left(\text{where } m=\frac{\text{area of } a}{\text{area of } b}\right)$$

$c=$ Coefficient of linear expansion of complete conductor (per °F). Virtual coefficient for a composite conductor of materials a and b where E and m are as above

$$=\frac{c_a E_a m + c_b E_b}{m E_a + E_b}$$

$C_1=$ a constant $=\left(\dfrac{EA}{24}\right)^{\frac{1}{2}}$

$C_2=$ a constant $=cEA$

(b) *Formulae*

$$S=\frac{wL^2}{8T} \qquad \dots\dots\dots\dots(1)$$

$$\text{Length of conductor}=\left(L+\frac{8S^2}{3L}\right)\text{ or }\left(L+\frac{w^2 L^3}{24T^2}\right) \qquad \dots\dots\dots\dots(2)$$

$$\left(\frac{C_1 w_2 L}{T_2}\right)^2 - T_2 = \left(\frac{C_1 w_1 L}{T_1}\right)^2 - T_1 + C_2 t \qquad \dots\dots\dots\dots(3)$$

(The suffices 1 and 2 denote initial and final conditions respectively.)

$$y=\frac{L}{2}-\frac{aT}{wL} \qquad \dots\dots\dots\dots(4)$$

Vertical reaction at higher support $=w\ (L-y)$

Vertical reaction at lower support $=wy$

(c) *Example*—Determine the maximum sag at 122°F of a 0·10 sq in (copper equivalent) SCA conductor (6/0·186 in alum. + 7/0·062 in steel) on a span of 600 ft. Factor of safety $=2·0$ on breaking load at 22°F with $\frac{3}{8}$ in radial thickness of ice and wind load of 8 lb/sq ft.

$A = 0.1842$ sq in, $d = 0.558$ in, breaking load $= 7{,}300$ lb

$$E = \frac{9.9 \times 10^6 \times 7.7 + 28 \times 10^6}{7.7 + 1} = 11.98 \times 10^6 \text{ lb/sq in}$$

$$c = \frac{12.78 \times 10^{-6} \times 9.9 \times 10^6 \times 7.7 + 6.4 \times 10^{-6} \times 28 \times 10^6}{7.7 \times 9.9 \times 10^6 + 28 \times 10^6} = 11.07 \times 10^{-6} \text{per}^\circ F$$

$$C_1 = \frac{11.98 \times 10^6 \times 0.1842}{24} = 303 :$$

$$C_2 = 11.07 \times 10^{-6} \times 11.98 \times 10^6 \times \cdot 1842 = 24.4$$

From equation (3) find tension (T_2) *at* $122^\circ F$

$T_1 = $ initial tension at $22^\circ F = \dfrac{7300}{2} = 3650$ lb

$w_1 = $ resultant load in conductor at $22^\circ F$

horizontal component due to wind $= \dfrac{8 (0.75 + 0.558)}{12} = 0.874$ lb/ft

vertical load due to ice $(57 \text{ lb/cu ft}) = 1.243 \times 0.375 (0.375 + 0.558)$
$= 0.435$ lb/ft

vertical component ice $+$ self weight $= 0.435 + 0.266 = 0.701$ lb/ft
Hence $w_1 = (0.874^2 + 0.701^2)^{\frac{1}{2}} = 1.12$ lb/ft

$w_2 = $ Self weight of conductor $= 0.266$ lb/ft

$t = 122^\circ - 22^\circ = 100^\circ F$ (rise in temperature, therefore positive)

therefore $\left(\dfrac{48,300}{T_2}\right)^2 - T_2 = 1910$

T_2 is resolved by trial and error using a slide rule. In this case $T_2 = 910$ lb.

From equation (1) Sag S at $122^\circ F = \dfrac{0.266 \times 600^2}{8 \times 910} = 13.15$ ft

(d) *Corrections for special cases*—Although rarely encountered, corrections
can be made for serious departures from the basic assumption (*w* based
on horizontal span length and use of horizontal tension *T*) on the
following basis, *e.g.* very long or steeply sloping spans.

(i) *Corrected load per foot in the ratio of the mean of the conductor
length and line joining the supports to span length*

$$w \text{ (corrected)} = w \left\{ \sqrt{\left[1 + \left(\frac{a}{L}\right)^2\right]} + \frac{4}{3}\left(\frac{S}{L}\right)^2 \right\} \qquad \ldots\ldots\ldots(5)$$

(ii) *Tangential tension at support* (i.e. *actual max. conductor tension*)

$$T = T_{T2} \cos\left[\text{arc tan}\left(\frac{4S + a}{L}\right)\right] = T_{T1} \cos\left[\text{arc tan}\left(\frac{4S - a}{L}\right)\right] \qquad \ldots\ldots\ldots(6)$$

5.2. Application to complete lines

(a) *Equivalent span*—an overhead line is made up of spans of varying
length and calculations are based on the 'equivalent span' of sections of
line between rigid supports.

$$\text{Equivalent span} = \left(\frac{L_1^3 + L_2^3 + L_3^3}{L_1 + L_2 + L_3}\right)^{\frac{1}{2}} \qquad \ldots\ldots\ldots(7)$$

(Where L_1, L_2 etc. are the individual span lengths.)

This is based on the assumption that the conductor is free to move longitudinally (in line) at intermediate positions such that T is constant throughout the section. Suspension insulators are flexible enough to achieve this condition and with pin insulator lines the supports themselves may be assumed to deflect sufficiently. Angles and terminals with tension insulators are considered as the rigid supports, although as far as the former are concerned on pole lines this will depend on the staying arrangement adopted.

(b) *Conductor vibration*—Suspended conductors are often subject to mechanical vibration, involving high frequency bending stresses which are a maximum at conductor support points causing premature fatigue failures. It occurs usually under light steady winds and is a function of conductor tension and weight/diameter ratio. One invariable remedy apart from other precautions is to limit the 'everyday' conductor tension. This entails restricting the 'still air' tension of the conductor (*i.e.* tension under its own weight without any external loading) to a suitable proportion of its ultimate strength at an average temperature and can often be the controlling factor in sag and tension calculations. Light conductors such as SCA and h.d. aluminium are more prone to this trouble than h.d. copper which has a less diameter to weight ratio and as a rough guide the everyday tension of the former types may be limited to say 20 per cent and the latter 25 per cent of the ultimate strength.

Other counter-measures involve the attachment of dampers at support points to reduce the amplitude and dissipate the energy of vibration and reinforcement of the conductor by application of armour rods.

SCA conductors on British grid lines are strung to an ' everyday ' stress limitation and are also fitted with Stockbridge dampers.

(c) *Inelastic stretch*—Creep of the conductor material and the bedding down of strands under load result in increased sags which can cause infringement of ground clearance, unless due allowance is made. The effects are greater with aluminium and SCA conductors and because of the many variables involved, *i.e.* conductor material and stranding, tension, temperature, span length, degree and duration of loading, *etc,* the treatment of the problem, like that of vibration, is to a large extent arbitrary and based on experience.

Measures to counteract inelastic stretch may be taken during erection.

(i) *Pretension*—The conductor is tensioned high enough at the outset to remove the greater proportion of the inelastic stretch prior to final sagging, *e.g.* the conductor is pulled up to say, full design working tension for 30 minutes before sagging to the correct tension.

(ii) *Overtension*—The conductor is erected to a higher tension on the assumption that it will be reduced to the correct amount following a series of loading cycles over a period of time. For example British grid lines allow 9 per cent (erection sag reduced by 1 in for every foot of sag) with 0·175 sq in (copper equivalent) SCA conductors and standard span of 1,000 ft (305 m) and 15 per cent (greater area of aluminium) on 275 kV lines with 0·4 sq in (copper equivalent) SCA conductor, standard span 1,200 ft (366 m). The technique in America is to prepare separate charts of both erection and final sags, the former based on experimental values of the elastic moduli before and after loading the conductor up to 75 per cent of its ultimate strength.

Method (i) is commonly used for lines with relatively short spans and smaller conductor sizes. With large conductors and high tensions, however, pretensioning presents serious construction difficulties and method (ii) or a combination of (i) and (ii) is employed.

(*d*) *Low voltage lines*—Unlike high voltage lines those for low voltage are normally erected along roads with a large proportion of angle and service tapping poles and it is usual therefore for economic reasons to string the conductors at reduced tensions and short spans of 100–180 ft (30–50 m), a common standard being that of maximum sag of say 3 ft (0·9 m) at 122°F (50°C) on spans of 150 ft (46 m).

6. SUPPORTS

The function of overhead line supports and nature of the external loads which they incur, justify differences in treatment of stresses and concepts of safety from those adopted for structures such as bridges and buildings, where the principal loads are much less related to those arising from climatic conditions of wind and ice. Another important influence on design, especially in relation to lattice steel towers, is the regular practice of full scale testing of structures to their ultimate load capacity; a practice which was commenced in Great Britain in 1928.

Structure design, but not necessarily the form and material employed, depends initially on the electrical requirements as regards voltage, number of circuits, conductor size and type, insulation and clearances, and to some extent on the general configuration of conductors and earthwires. Apart from the application of these factors and that of mechanical loading, the following section is concerned more with features which are special to overhead line design practice than with those aspects which are common to structural engineering generally.

6.1. *Loading*

(*a*) *Components*

Horizontal transverse loads (*P*):

(*i*) Wind on bare or ice coated conductors. Calculated on basis of the support 'wind span'=half the sum of the adjacent span lengths (see *Figure 5*). (P_w)

(*ii*) Wind on supports. For square lattice structures wind on the leeward face is taken as half that on windward face, this shielding factor decreases with rectangular shapes until the full wind is taken on both faces. On cylindrical members, wind pressure is taken on 0·6 of projected area. (P_s)

(*iii*) Conductor tension at line deviations.

$$\text{Transverse load} = 2T \sin \frac{\theta}{2} \qquad \ldots\ldots\ldots\ldots(8)$$

(θ=angle of deviation and T=maximum conductor tension, see *Figure 5*). (P_a)

Horizontal longitudinal loads (*T*):

(*i*) Full conductor tension at line terminations. (*T*)

(*ii*) Out of balance conductor tensions due to broken conductors or earthwires. At supports with suspension insulators a reduced conductor tension, usually 70 per cent is allowed for the swing of insulators into the unbroken span. (0·7 *T* or *T*)

(*iii*) Out of balance conductor tension at angle or section positions. Only encountered in special cases, *e.g.* change from single to double earthwires. (T_x)

Vertical loads (V):

   (*i*) Weight of bare or ice coated conductors, calculated on basis of support 'weight span' as determined from equation (4) Sect. 5.1.   (V_w)

   (*ii*) Weight of insulators, *etc.*   (V_i)

   (*iii*) Support weight.   (V_s)

(*b*) *Wind and ice loads*—The relationship between wind velocity (V m.p.h.) and pressure (P lb/sq ft) used in British practice is as follows:

Flat surfaces $P = 0.0054\ V^2$ ....(9)

Round surfaces (*e.g.* conductors) $P = 0.0032\ V^2$ ....(10)

In most countries the maximum wind pressure is assumed to act on the full wind span regardless of length. Tests in recent years show that this assumption is conservative and that high velocity wind gusts act on a limited front only and, for spans above 300 ft at least, some reduction in pressure derived from true ultimate wind velocities is justified.

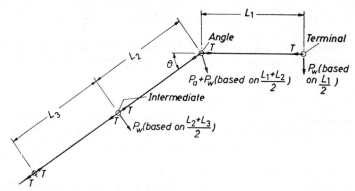

Figure 5. Horizontal loading relative to support positions

The build up and possible extent of ice loading on conductors is indeterminate and it is economically prohibitive to allow for excessive ice thicknesses that may occur only on rare occasions. The present practice of specifying a constant radial thickness of ice coupled with a 'factor of safety' (see Sect. 3) is, however, misleading in assessing the capabilities of conductors to support ultimate loads and impending changes in British regulations will incorporate the more logical treatment of prescribing the superimposed load at ultimate conditions related to the diameter of the conductor.

(*c*) *British grid lines*—This reference is included since the working loads specified are above the minimum permitted by regulations.

   (*i*) Conductors—8 lb/sq ft wind pressure acting on conductor coated with $\frac{1}{2}$ in radial thickness of ice.

   (*ii*) Supports—25 lb/sq ft on flat, and 15 lb/sq ft on round surfaces. Increased for heights above 150 ft, *e.g.* river crossing towers. Leeward face shielding factor dependent on support dimensions.

6.2. *Support types and materials*

(*a*) *Type*

Apart from structural form and materials the following are the recognized types of support used generally in construction (see *Figure 5*).

(*1*) *Intermediate*—At straight line positions and slight line deviations comprising the bulk of the supports used on a transmission line. Conductors supported on pin type or suspension insulators. Loading predominantly transverse unless a broken wire condition is involved (P_w, P_s, V, plus possibly P_a and $0.7T$).

(*2*) *Angle*—At line deviations (except those covered by *1*). The conductors are made-off to tension insulators each side of the support crossarm. Loading again predominantly transverse but with the greatest proportion from the conductor tension deviation load (P, V plus possibly T and T_c).

(*3*) *Section*—Basically a support with tension insulators, specially introduced to limit the length of section of unbroken line to facilitate erection and maintenance and also to afford a measure of line mechanical stability. In most cases this is met by the incidence of angles of deviation and in some cases by the necessity to make-off conductors at straight line positions involving conductor 'uplift' which cannot be obviated conveniently and economically by increasing the support height and retaining the use of pin type or suspension insulators. ('Uplift' with pin insulators is a condition of zero or negative weight loading tending to lift the conductor from the insulator, calculated from equation (4). Similar conditions apply with suspension insulators but additional factors are involved, see Sect. 6.3(*a*).)

(*4*) *Terminal*—Used at each end of a line with the conductors terminated with tension insulators. Loading predominantly due to the longitudinal conductor tension (P_w, P_s, T, V).

(*b*) *Structural form and materials*

This varies with the availability and cost of materials, natural hazards, construction difficulties and also the degree of importance of the line. The latter, for example, determines whether the supports shall be designed to withstand breakages of conductor and earthwire, in which case broad base towers are almost invariably used.

Generally the two most common and adaptable forms of support are wood poles, on all types of lines from low voltage upwards and bolted lattice steel towers principally for major high voltage lines.

Protection against corrosion is an important consideration to ensure long life. Efficient treatment of wood poles demands proper seasoning and pressure application of the preservative for complete penetration of the sapwood; creosote is the preservative normally employed. Practice for steel structures and fittings usually involves hot dip galvanizing; in Great Britain a minimum coating of 2 oz/sq ft is specified. Bolts are spun galvanized.

(1) *Wood poles*

(*i*) *Single poles*—As typified by B.S. 1320 lines in Great Britain and for design purposes including also unbraced 'H' poles (see *Figure 7*).

(*ii*) *Composite construction*—'A' braced 'H' poles and a type of construction widely used in North America for very high voltage lines, consisting of a widely spaced 'H' pole arrangement with timber cross arms and cross bracings forming a 'portalized' structure. This form is favoured because of available supplies of home-grown tall stout poles of southern yellow pine and Douglas fir and there is less concern for space limitations in construction.

(2) *Reinforced concrete and prestressed concrete poles*—Seldom used in Great Britain but extensively on the Continent, both single and composite types. As with (3) and to a lesser extent (4) their use is restricted where the supply cost and life of wood poles is satisfactory.

(3) *Tubular poles*—Painted or galvanized steel, used to a limited extent, mostly overseas, for low and high voltage distribution lines where wood is unsuitable. An EHV line in Canada provides an isolated example of the use of aluminium. Special circumstances surrounded this however and, as with (4) and (5), the structural use of aluminium alloy is uneconomical, despite savings in weight and resistance to corrosion.

(4) *Narrow base towers*—Mostly latticed structures of rolled steel and tubular sections, bolted or welded together and with single block foundations. There are many examples of use on important lines overseas, some of which involve the use of internal and external guy wires, a practice which may become increasingly favoured.

(5) *Broad base towers*—Steel lattice type construction usually with bolted connections, and with separate foundations for each leg. British grid towers are prominent examples (see *Figure 9*) which are constructed of bolted galvanized mild and high tensile rolled steel angle and flat sections. Tubular sections, either wholly or in conjunction with rolled steel, have not hitherto been used because of higher supply, fabrication costs and attendant difficulties in galvanizing sealed tubes. Open ended tubes present a maintenance problem. They are used to some extent on the Continent where painted structures are more common, as are concrete-filled galvanized tubular members.

6.3. *Design*

It is necessary to limit this paragraph to supports falling in the extreme categories (1) and (5) but which are representative of the majority erected in Great Britain at the present time. The principles enumerated will, however, provide a basic introduction to detailed design of all forms of support as previously mentioned.

(a) *Conductor configuration and support height*—With the electrical requirements resolved, the first step in support design is to decide upon the 'standard span' (*i.e.* the most economic span assuming level ground). Since the majority of supports are intermediate, exploratory design is centred mainly on these and the following interdependent factors which determine the general outline are taken into consideration.

(1) *Height to bottom conductor*—minimum specified ground clearance plus the maximum sag of the conductor. A curve of maximum conductor sag against range of span lengths will facilitate the study of alternative standard spans.

(2) *Conductor spacing*—There are two aspects.

(i) Minimum horizontal and vertical spacing to provide adequate mid-span clearance, dependent upon span length, sag and voltage, as well as factors such as ice shedding overcome by off-setting the conductors in vertical formation (*Figure 9*).

(ii) Minimum live metal to earth clearance taking into account the maximum swing of suspension insulators, related to horizontal (P_w and P_a) and vertical conductor loading (V_w and V_i).

A variety of conflicting formulae exist for the determination of (i) but, as applies also with (ii), the only reliable guide is progressive experience on existing lines. With pin insulators (i) is the principal criterion and, using B.S. 1320 as an example, the spacing allowed with 0·5 sq in h.d. copper conductors is 2 ft 6 in and 3 ft 6 in for a standard span of 350 ft, which is suitable for maximum spans of 400 ft and 500 ft respectively. A tolerance for single spans in excess of the 'standard' to take advantage of ground topography is necessary and should not be overlooked in deciding spacing, neither should the effect of conductor deviation at angle positions with both (i) and (ii). On broad base tower lines (ii) normally governs conductor spacing. Direct calculation from the factors mentioned usually gives insulator swings in excess of those known to occur in practice, largely because of wind pressure considerations (Sect. 6.1(*b*)). Current practice is to use design angles of swing (ω) between 30° and 35° to the vertical associated, as in Great Britain, with a minimum weight span equal to 35 per cent of the total weight of the conductors in the two adjacent spans (calculated at minimum temperatures in ' still air '—lesser weight spans correspond to an 'uplift' condition, Sect. 6.2(*a*)). *Figure 6* illustrates a simple wire clearance diagram and representative values of live metal to earth clearance (*x*) are given in Sect. 2.2.

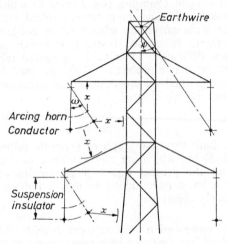

Figure 6. Wire clearance diagram

Similar considerations influence conductor jumper loops at angle positions where the swing allowed is smaller, approximately 20°.

(3) *Earthwire spacing*—The earthwire sag should be equal to or slightly less than that of the conductor and the relative vertical spacing is determined by the shielding angle (ψ) (Sect. 2.2. and *Figure 6*).

Four typical outlines of intermediate supports are shown in *Figures 7* and *9*.

6.4. Wood poles

Pinus silvestris (imported European redwood and home-grown Scots pine) and European larch are the timbers commonly used in Great Britain. Intermediate supports whether of single or unbraced ' H ' type (*Figure 7*) are designed as simple cantilevers on the ultimate extreme fibre stress of the pole. The following data is based on B.S. 1990; a handbook entitled *Wades' Tables* is another useful reference[18].

TABLE 5

	Ultimate extreme fibre stress (f_b)		Modulus of elasticity (E)	
	lb/sq in	kg/sq cm	lb/sq in	kg/sq cm
Pinus silvestris	7,800	548	1,520,000	106,870
European larch	10,000	700	1,640,000	115,300

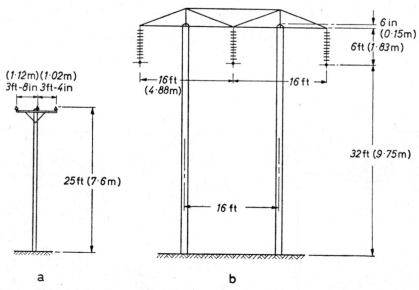

Figure 7. (a) *Intermediate wood pole support B.S. 1320 11 kV unearthed construction (0·05 sq in h.d. copper conductors—standard span 350 ft).* (b) *Intermediate wood pole support 132 kV unearthed construction (0·175 sq in (copper equivalent) SCA conductors—standard span 600 ft)*

From *Figure 8(a)* the section modulus (Z inch units) required at ground level for the intermediate pole=

$$\frac{\pi d^3}{32} = \left\{ \frac{(3P_w\,(H+h)+0\cdot5H\,P_s)\,12 \times \text{factor of safety}}{f_b} \right\}$$

[*H* and *h* ft, *d* (in), P_w and P_s (lb)]

Although the design of standard supports will be decided initially, actual pole sizes are determined in conjunction with profile (Sect. 8.1); British practice separates poles into three classes, Light, Medium and Stout, based on overall length (*L*) and minimum diameter (*d*), 5 ft from the butt. With a normal depth of setting (*D*) 5–7 ft, and an average pole taper of 1 in 10 the error involved in using the *Z* calculated at ground levels is negligible.

Stayed poles (*Figure 8b*) are designed on the thrust load developed in the pole with the point of stay attachment as near as possible to the centre of gravity of loading (common values of $\phi=30$ to $45°$).

Ultimate stay tension$= \dfrac{\{3\,(P_w+P_a)+P_s\} \times \text{factor of safety}}{\sin\phi}$ ....(11)

TABLE 6

Staywire sizes (45 ton quality galvanized steel strand)					
s.w.g.	Ult. breaking strength		s.w.g.	Ult. breaking strength	
	lb	kg		lb	kg
7/No. 12	5,992	2,718	7/No. 8	14,182	6,433
7/No. 10	9,079	4,118	19/No. 10	24,653	11,182

Ultimate thrust in pole$= \dfrac{\{3\,(P_w+P_a)+P_s\} \times \text{factor of safety}}{\tan\phi}$ ....(12)

Crippling load of the pole (lb)

$$= \frac{4140\, d_e^4}{l^2} \text{ for } pinus\ silvestris \text{ (increase in the ratio } \frac{10,000}{7,800}$$

$$\text{for European larch)} \qquad \ldots\ldots\ldots\ldots(13)$$

where d_e = effective diameter (inches)

$$= \text{diam at top} + \frac{L-D+3}{(L-5)\,3} \text{ [diam at 5 ft from butt} - \text{diam at top]}$$

and l = effective length (feet), taken as length between 1 ft from top
and 1 ft below ground level = $L - D$.

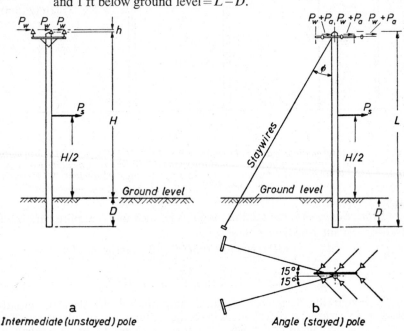

a   b
Intermediate (unstayed) pole   *Angle (stayed) pole*

Figure 8. Simple wood pole support loading diagrams

It will be seen that the above includes several approximations, *e.g.*
vertical loads and secondary bending stresses are ignored, and this is
reasonable for simple construction. These factors and aspects of deflection
and general stability should be considered when, for example, very tall
poles and masts are used both of wood and other materials. Crossarm
design for pole lines is straightforward involving either single or double
steel angles and channels acting as simply supported beams and cantilevers,
or simple triangulated frames.

6.5. *Broad base lattice steel towers*

(*a*) *Exploratory design*—With simple supports such as wood poles it is
comparatively simple to assess the alternative line costs with changes in
span length and conductor size, *etc.* When steel towers are involved an
approximate method is necessary to determine the tower weight.

$$\text{Tower weight above ground line (tons)} = kH\sqrt{M} \qquad \ldots\ldots\ldots\ldots(14)$$

(where H = the overall height of tower above ground level in feet, M = the
overturning moment at ground level in thousand lb ft and k is a ' constant ').
The constant k is critical and has to reflect a variety of factors, *e.g.*
factors of safety, material employed, *etc*, and it is desirable to study the

paper and discussion[19] to use the formula to best advantage. It also provides guidance on matters such as main leg slope, base width, plan bracing *etc.* Based on a range of designs in mild steel for both single and double circuit 33 to 132 kV lines, an average value of *k* for ordinary transmission line towers is given as 0·0016.

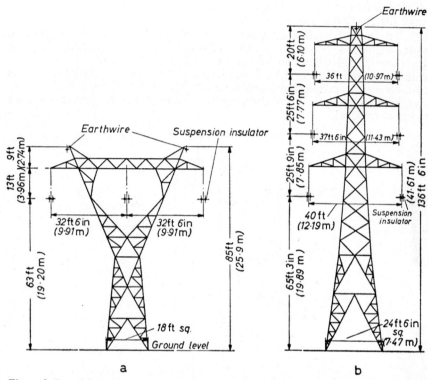

Figure 9. Broad base lattice steel towers. (a) CEGB—275 kV single circuit intermediate tower. (Conductors: twin 0·175 sq in (copper equiv.) SCA per phase. Earthwires: 0·07 sq in SCA. Standard span: 1,200 ft.) (b) CEGB—275/380 kV double circuit intermediate tower. (Conductors: twin 0·4 sq in (copper equiv.) SCA per phase. Earthwires: 0·175 sq in SCA. Standard span: 1,200 ft)

(*b*) *Final design*—Depending upon the circumstances, the exploratory work in calculating the standard span and other factors may extend to more detailed design. When the standard span has been decided the task of designing the most economic tower to meet the prescribed conditions can be initiated. Commencing with the intermediate or straight line tower, the most important, the basis of loading may for example be:

   wind span = standard + 10 per cent;
   weight span = twice standard;
   maximum single span = standard + 40 per cent.

The majority of support types include a small range of extensions to supplement or reduce the standard height tower which can be added or removed.

 From Sect. 6.3(*a*) the top hamper can be settled, torsion loading being an important influence on the tower width employed. A few exploratory studies can then be made to determine the most suitable base width and leg slope in relation to an economic leg member size. Base width variation influences the foundation size and the effect on overall costs should not be ignored.

Final design is undertaken graphically by means of 'stress diagrams', usually on the basis of working loads. The appropriate factor of safety (*e.g.* in Great Britain 2·5 under normal and 1·5 under broken wire conditions) is applied when the individual member loads are tabulated. Vertical loads ($V_w + V_i$, and appropriate percentage V_s) are omitted from the diagrams and are also introduced at the tabulation stage (shared equally over the four main legs).

The typical loading diagram illustrated in *Figure 10* for this type of tower includes a condition of any one conductor or the earthwire broken; (this condition is shown in brackets for a top conductor but it needs to be considered individually at each conductor and earthwire position). Points to note are the proportionate reduction of P_w and V_w for the broken wire condition and the practice of equating the wind on tower in equal proportions to crossarm level.

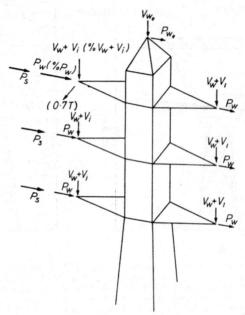

Figure 10. *Loading diagram for a double circuit intermediate tower*

In many cases an intermediate tower is expected to accommodate a small deviation load say up to 2° under which condition the wind span permissible at straight line positions would be appropriately reduced. In preparing loading diagrams for towers with deviation loads both maximum and minimum angles must be considered.

In *Figure 6*, between the crossarms is shown a form of bracing more common with narrow base towers but which may be used in the top hamper of lightly loaded, broad-base towers and involves 'split leg panels' (*i.e.* the bracings on adjacent faces do not connect at the same level on the two flanges of the main leg). Leg design must take into account the effects of torsion loading and the appropriate radius of gyration (*r*) on both the supported and unsupported lengths. The form of cross bracing above the bottom panel of the tower in *Figure 9b* is frequently used. Each pair of bracings is bolted at the centre and the load is considered to be shared equally between the two, such that one is in tension and the other in compression alternating down the tower. Strut design is based on minimum values of (*r*) and here again 'split leg panels' may be employed. The bottom two panels of the tower in *Figure 9*b, with 'K'-bracing are a typical feature of the tall towers in current use, particularly in the bottom panel and extensions. Secondary ' unstressed ' bracings are used both in elevation and in plan to support the main leg and are designed on a nominal maximum slenderness ratio basis.

Treatment of torsion loads due to broken wires depends on the tower being adequately braced in plan to prevent distortion, essentially at cross-arm level but possibly at other levels dependent on particular design features. *Figure 11* shows the reactions for a square cross section which is normal for towers of the type shown in *Figure 9*b and represents one extreme of the general case, the other being encountered in towers of the type shown in *Figure 9*a.

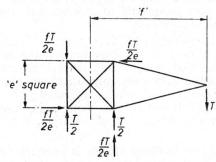

Figure 11. Torsion loading

(*c*) *Design stresses*—Ultimate design stresses (*i.e.* including factor of safety) in Great Britain are based on the elastic limit of tension members (also applied to bending) and the crippling load of struts.

(*i*) *Tension members*—Elastic limit stress, mild steel 36,000 lb/sq in (2,530 kg/sq cm). Elastic limit stress, high tensile steel 54,000 lb/sq in (3,797 kg/sq cm).

(*ii*) *Compression members*—There is no recognized standard strut formula employed in transmission tower design in Britain. A typical example for mild steel which is used with some variations of the constant in the denominator is given below. Alternatively a formula of the straight line type is employed.

$$\text{Ultimate stress} = \frac{36,000 \text{ lb/sq in}}{1 + (l^2/14,000 \, r^2)}$$

Standard practice requires a minimum member thickness of $\frac{3}{16}$ in with a limitation also of the maximum unsupported length of compression members, usually as follows:

Main members: $\quad \max \dfrac{l}{r} = 120$

Bracings and
other members: $\quad \max \dfrac{l}{r} = 200$

(*iii*) *Bolts*—Both mild and, to a less extent, high tensile steel bolts are used in Britain; diameters are usually $\frac{5}{8}$ and $\frac{3}{4}$ in with a maximum hole tolerance of $\frac{1}{16}$ in on the diameter.

Shearing stress (mild steel): 32,000 lb/sq in (2,250 kg/sq cm).

Bearing stress (mild steel): 64,000 lb/sq in (4,500 kg/sq cm).

7. FOUNDATIONS

The forces to be resisted by overhead line support foundations result largely from overturning moments with a consequent emphasis on horizontal and uprooting forces. The types employed can be broadly classified thus:

(i) *Side bearing*—Resistance depends on horizontal soil reactions, *i.e.* single foundations used for unstayed poles and narrow base towers.

(ii) *Uplift and compression*—Resistance depends on vertical soil reactions, *i.e.* at broad base towers, where each of the four legs has a separate foundation, and stayed poles.

Serious foundation failures on overhead lines are rare and practice has tended to remain unprogressive. Associated with this, design loadings are generally conservative. Present day costs are high, however, and much more attention is now being paid to experimental work in an effort to establish an improved technique.

An important influence with lines covering hundreds of miles and embracing a wide variety of soil conditions is the natural tendency to standardise and to base designs on 'normal ground'. Detailed site investigation and tests are normally only carried out when particularly poor soil conditions are encountered, which may entail piling or, very occasionally, raft foundations. It will be seen that a very great deal depends on individual judgement in the assessment of varying conditions intermediate between the two.

The usual practice in Great Britain is to apply nominally the same factor of safety to foundations as to supports. In determining the design values to be used, therefore, it is necessary to allow for the fact that the actual ultimate load of a foundation may entail several inches of movement, an important factor particularly with broad base towers.

7.1. *Side bearing foundations*

Figure 12 shows the pressure distribution assumed (neglecting the small values of direct horizontal shear) in two simple formulae used for wood pole and shallow concrete block foundations. In *Figure 12*a, parabolic distribution, the pressure developed is based on the horizontal movement relative to the pivotal point and assumes that soil resistance increases proportionately with depth.

$$P\left(H + \tfrac{2}{3}D\right) = \frac{kbD^3}{12} \text{ lb ft} \qquad \ldots\ldots\ldots\ldots(15)$$

(k = a constant, b = breadth of foundation,
dimensions in feet and loads in lb)

*Figure 12*b, involves similar assumptions but is related to constant soil resistance with depth.

$$P\left(H + \frac{(D-z)}{2} + z\right) = \frac{Kb\,(D-z)^2}{6} \qquad \ldots\ldots\ldots\ldots(16)$$

(where K = a constant, b = breadth of foundation, dimensions in feet and loads in lb. z = amount of top soil to be neglected, assume at least one foot).

The majority of side bearings encountered on overhead power lines in Great Britain concern wood pole suports which are buried direct in the ground with some inevitable disturbance of the soil surrounding the butt of the pole. Horizontal timber baulks are fitted to provide additional resistance where it is impracticable to increase depth for this purpose.

(Another widespread application is direct cast concrete block mast foundations for overhead railway electrification, with mechanically augered holes.) Formula (15) is the most commonly used with values of $K=1,000$ to 2,000 lb/sq ft per foot of depth working pressure, based on experience in all types of soil including clay (despite the theoretical assumptions of the formula). Even when taking into account the particular circumstances mentioned below and the shallow depths involved (maximum usually in the region of 8 ft) values greater than the minimum are difficult to justify for average conditions. In comparison with formula (16), using $K=4,000$ lb/sq ft working pressure for average conditions of 'undisturbed' clay, it will be seen that similar results are obtained for depths up to approximately 7 ft but beyond this there is an increasing divergence with depth.

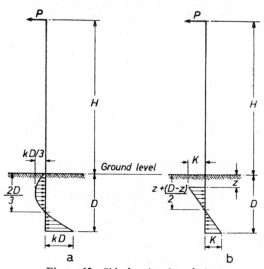

Figure 12. Side bearing foundations

Maximum loads are rarely, if at all, encountered in practice and are then of short duration. The constants employed are very much higher than would be derived from normal theoretical considerations and whilst the pressure distributions assumed are reasonable for the conditions on which they are based, *i.e.* before any rupture of the soil occurs, it is doubtful if they hold good at failure. A better appreciation of the many factors involved can be obtained from the recent tests carried out in Britain, France and Sweden[50], the latter being concerned with large block foundations for narrow base towers with high vertical reactions in which the base provides a large proportion of the resistance obtained.

7.2. *Uplift and compression foundations*

Figure 13 shows that with an overturning movement in a given direction, one pair of foundation blocks will tend to be uprooted (uplift) and the other pair forced downwards (compression).

The foundation load consists of the tower leg load (tension or compression) plus or minus the vertical components in the bracings on the two adjacent faces. Normal practice is to continue the leg of the tower down into the foundation block, thus avoiding the application of a large shear component at ground level. The leg is jointed just above ground level to facilitate erection and the section extending into the foundations is termed the stub. The horizontal shear component in the bottom bracings is resisted, in the case of concrete foundations, by making the chimney of suitable width and with steel grillage foundations it is customary to connect the bottom bracing below ground level where the soil is more able to provide the necessary resistance.

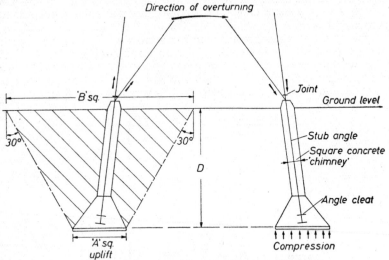

Figure 13. Uplift and compression foundations

With intermediate and small angle supports the loading is largely due to wind and is reversible so that all four footings are identical. Ultimate uplift resistance, the most critical condition, is calculated on the basis of an assumed frustum of earth above the foundation block (*Figure 13*). In Britain the angle of the sides to the vertical assumed for normal conditions is 30°; the weight of earth is taken as 100 lb/cu ft and of concrete 140 lb/cu ft.

$$\text{Volume of frustum for square base} = \frac{D}{3}[A^2 + B^2 + (A \times B)] \quad \ldots\ldots\ldots\ldots(17)$$

This theory is related to the resistance expected from dry compact sand with an angle of repose of 30°, but is applied to all types of soil. Cohesion is ignored because of the variable factors involved although it may contribute substantially to overall resistance. This aspect is receiving particular attention in the previously mentioned experimental work now being carried out. The corresponding ultimate bearing pressure for compression loads is approximately 7,000 lb/sq ft.

The type of foundation shown in *Figure 13*, consisting of a shallow concrete pad surmounted by a truncated pyramid and chimney enclosing the stub angle, is commonly employed in Great Britain and has the advantage that it avoids the use of reinforcing steel. Alternative forms involve a protruding bottom slab which facilitates soil undercutting. Also, although abandoned in Britain, the steel grillage type without concrete, the base consisting of suitably spaced channels or beams is used overseas where concreting is expensive.

The ultimate bond stress between galvanized steel and concrete is 150 lb/sq in; additional anchorage, where required, is provided by angle cleats bolted to the stub.

In the case of stayed poles sufficient area under the pole should be allowed to take compression loads, and with wood poles this may entail additional timber baulks. Anchorage for the stay wire should be calculated from similar uplift considerations already outlined. It is important, however, to install the stay blocks against virgin soil as far as possible and for this reason a long rectangular as opposed to a square shape is preferable.

8. CONSTRUCTION

Prior to the construction of an overhead line extensive preliminary work has to be undertaken. Statutory permission has to be obtained in Britain from the Ministry of Power, from the Air Ministry, Post Office, Railways and the County and Local Authorities concerned and finally wayleaves must be negotiated with property owners whose interests are affected.

Line construction is predominantly a civil engineering matter, with the exception of earthing and bonding arrangements and final electrical tests following completion. The sequence of operations may be segregated thus:

(i) Survey, (ii) Foundation installation, (iii) Support erection, (iv) Conductor erection.

Co-ordination of labour, transport, sorting and delivery of materials at suitable places along the line and general forward planning, *etc*, is an important feature of groups (ii), (iii) and (iv) especially with long lines which may involve anything up to 500 support positions.

8.1. *Survey*

The general route may be selected from survey maps followed by a preliminary walk-over survey which may be integrated with preliminary wayleave negotiations. Aerial survey has been found of use overseas for this preliminary work, particularly in difficult country and has been used on rare occasions for the ultimate survey.

A final detailed survey must be made with adjustments on any outstanding angle positions and general alignment between these positions with the setting of line pegs at regular points. Ground level readings are taken at regular and frequent intervals for the preparation of a profile along the whole centre line of the route. This work involves the use of a theodolite, level, levelling staff, chain and ranging rods. The profile is subsequently plotted on squared paper to a suitable scale (1 in = 20 ft vertically and 1 in = 200 ft horizontally are common) incorporating information such as side slope either side of the centre line, details of road and power line crossings and notes on superficial ground conditions, *etc*.

The purpose of the profile is to enable each intermediate position and support height generally to be determined, with due regard to provision of minimum statutory ground clearances and special requirements arising from crossings of roads, railways, *etc*. The limiting factors of support design, maximum wind span, weight spans, *etc*, must also be taken into account. The support positions and curve of the bottom conductor at maximum sag (*i.e.* at maximum temperature) are plotted and for this purpose it is necessary to prepare a 'sag template'. A similar template, for the sag at minimum temperature in still air, is also used to check for 'uplift' conditions. These are devices for drawing the conductor curve, based upon the profile scales, and can be made from cardboard or a transparent material when both the minimum and maximum curves can be incorporated on the same template. A set of say six templates may be required to cover the range of equivalent spans encountered in suitable steps either side of the standard span. On completion, a schedule is prepared with details of support height and types, span lengths, insulators and fittings, *etc*, for the dual purpose of ordering materials and construction.

The final survey operations are to peg out the supports positions on site and in the case of broad base towers the excavation boundaries for the foundations.

8.2. *Foundation installation*

On pole lines, wood, reinforced concrete, steel, *etc,* foundation work is normally combined with support erection but with broad base towers, foundation installation constitutes a separate operation. A large proportion of foundations are hand excavated although power driven augers, common capacity up to 3 ft diameter × 12 ft deep holes, are now used extensively with single member foundations such as are required with pole lines.

With broad base towers excavations must first be accurately set out and the bottoms of the four holes are then dug to a common level. When there are steep side slopes special tower extensions may be used to reduce foundation excavation. The stub angles are usually set by means of a ' stub setting template ' composed of a light rigid framework which holds them at the correct position and slope. Steel or timber formers are used in placing the concrete to the required shape, although expendable formers of special paper have also been successfully used for this purpose. A normal minimum period of 48 hours is allowed before the formers are stripped, an operation which is virtually eliminated with the expendable type, and the earth reinstated, usually with hand ramming only. Concrete mixing in most cases is carried out at each individual site, employing a nominal 1, 2, 4 mix, and follows the normal pattern of concreting technique and practice, as is the case with other aspects such as timbering, pumping, de-watering *etc.*

8.3. *Erection*

The majority of wood poles are erected by man-handling into position using pole pikes or ladders but with long or heavy poles, including steel and reinforced concrete, a derrick is employed. This may consist of a single pole or a pair of poles used as shear legs or alternatively ' falling ' type derricks can be used. A skid board is fitted vertically at the back of the excavation to facilitate the placing of the butt of the pole. Power driven augers if used, are usually equipped with lifting gear. Crossarms are often fitted to the pole before erection, side guys are employed for steadying the lift and as temporary support during concreting and earth reinstatement.

To reduce land damage steel towers are usually built up piecemeal using a wood or tubular steel derrick pole and hand or power winch for lifting. This may involve either erecting the legs in stages and filling in the bracings or building the tower up in panels. In complete contrast, an alternative method is to assemble the tower horizontally on the ground and to erect it as a complete unit. In the United States mobile cranes are used for this purpose.

Individual tower members are stamped with erection marks to facilitate sorting and assembly.

8.4. *Conductor erection*

Prior to running out the conductors over the section of the line concerned (*i.e.* between angle to angle or angle to terminal) some preparatory work is needed such as tree felling, erection of scaffolding to carry the conductors over road and other crossings, *etc.* In addition consideration must be given to fitting temporary back stays and other methods of relieving the terminal type loading, to which the angle supports at the ends of the section are subjected during conductor stringing, both from the viewpoint of strength and deflections likely to cause inaccuracies in sagging.

The drums of conductor, which may weigh up to five tons are then placed in position at the end of a section and mounted to revolve freely and are controlled by a brake to prevent over-running. A tractor may be used to pull the conductors over the ground in pairs or more, alternatively they may be pulled in with a bondwire and winching device. As the conductors pass each support, pulling is stopped to allow them to be fitted through running blocks which are then lifted and attached to the crossarms. In the case of suspension insulators they are either suspended from the string itself or from a separate 'dropper' wire of equivalent length. When run out the conductors are made-off in the tension insulator set clamps at one end and then pulled up clear of the ground from the opposite end of the section using a power winch or other means, preparatory to final sagging. This completes the first stage which will also include the making of any necessary mid-span joints. The greatest emphasis during the whole operation is on avoiding damage to the conductors. This factor has now assumed such importance in relation to the reduction of corona and radio interference that in the erection of extra high voltage lines in many countries methods have been devised to run out conductors clear of the ground. Such methods involve, to a varying degree, running-out the conductors under tension which is absent when they are pulled out over the ground. Extra mechanical plant is necessary which must be carefully designed to avoid internal damage to the conductor whilst under tension.

The usual method of erecting conductors to their correct tension is based upon direct measurement of sag by sighting between the two supports of the span chosen for the purpose, at a distance down from the conductor suspension points equal to the appropriate sag. On short span lines a 'sighting board' is placed on each of the two supports and observation made by naked eye, for longer spans one of the 'sighting boards' is replaced by a specially mounted level reading on the other. The span selected should be as near level as possible, the sag for which at the relevant temperature is obtained from an erection sag chart. A series of these charts is prepared for the line covering the various equivalent spans in suitable steps and each of which shows a series of curves of sag against spans for the range of erection temperatures together with the corresponding tensions. A suitable system of visual signals or other means of communication is employed between the winch operator and the 'sagger' so that the conductor can be raised or lowered to the correct height. On completion the final clamp position is marked at the pulling end and the conductor lowered to the ground where it is made-off permanently to the tension insulator set clamp. It is then pulled up again and the tension set is attached to the crossarm. Subject to a general check along the line the operation is completed by clamping on the conductor at each suspension point and fitting vibration dampers, spacers, *etc*, as required. When all the conductors have been strung, the jumper connections at angle positions can be made, earthing and bonding arrangements completed, anti-climbing devices, *etc*, fitted and general clearing up at all site positions. The line is then ready for inspection and, subject to routine electrical tests, for handing over.

The authors are indebted to British Insulated Callender's Construction Company Limited for permission to contribute this chapter.

REFERENCES

[1] Westinghouse Electric Corporation. *Electrical Transmission and Distribution Reference Book* 4th ed. (1950)
[2] RISSIK, H. *Power System Interconnection*
[3] STARR, A. T. *Electrical Power*
[4] LEWIS, W. W. *Protection of Transmission Systems Against Lightning*

[5] THOMAS, A. M. and OAKESHOTT, D. F. Choice of insulation and surge protection of overhead transmission lines of 33 kV and above, *J. Instn elect. Engrs* 104, Pt A, No. 15 (1957)

[6] A.I.E.E. Report. A method of estimating lightning performance of transmission lines, *Elect. Engng, N.Y.* 69 (1950)

[7] *Overhead Line Regulations E.I.C.53* (1947 revise) H.M.S.O., London

[8] FORREST, J. S. Service experience of the effect of corrosion on steel cored aluminium conductors *J. Instn elect. Engrs* 101, Pt 2, No. 1 (1954)

[9] BOYSE, C. O. and SIMPSON, N. G. The problem of sagging on overhead transmission lines, *J. Instn elect. Engrs,* 91 Pt 2 (1944)

[10] McCOMBE, J. *Overhead Line Practice*

[11] LUMMIS, J. and FISCHER, H. D. Practical application of sag and tension calculations to transmission line design *Trans. A.I.E.E.* Paper No. 54–501

[12] DOUBLE, E. W. W. and TUCK, W. D. Vibration of overhead line conductor, *J. Instn elect. Engrs,* 186 (1940)

[13] STURTON, G. P. Sagging twin 0·4 sq in. copper equivalent SCA conductor, *Proc. Instn civ. Engrs* 4, Pt III (1955); and written discussion, 5, Pt III (1955) 263

[14] GRIMMITT, H. W. Overhead line regulations, *J. Instn elect. Engrs* 96, Pt I, No. 101 (1949)

[15] DODGE, C. C. A 230 kV spar arm H-frame transmission line design and tests, *Trans. A.I.E.E.* Report No. 57–154

[16] SOTTER, Dr. K., LAWTON, F. L. and SOOSAAR, A. Aluminium towers on the transmission line, *Engineering* (Nov. 1954)

[17] SAYERS, D. P., FORREST, J. S. and LANE, F. J. 275 kV developments on the British grid system, *Proc. Instn elect. Engrs,* Pt 2 (1952)

[18] Gabriel, Wade and English Ltd. *Wades Tables*

[19] RYLE, P. J. Steel tower economics, *J. Instn elect. Engrs* 93, Pt 2

[20] KURTZ, E. B. *The Lineman's Handbook*

British Electrical and Allied Industries Research Association Reports
[21] F/T 83, 1934. *Variation in the Distribution of Wind Pressure on Overhead Lines*
[22] F/T 84, 1935. *Wind Pressure on Latticed Towers—Tests on Models*
[23] O/T 4, 1952. *Handbook on Electrical Characteristics of Overhead Lines*
[24] O/T 7, 1952. *The Bond Strength of Galvanized Steel Angle in Concrete*

British Standards
[25] B.S. No. 4. *Dimensions and properties of channels and beams for structural purposes*
[26] B.S. No. 4A. *Dimensions and properties of equal angles, unequal angles, and T-bars for structural purposes*
[27] B.S. No. 15. *Structural steel*
[28] B.S. No. 77. *Voltage for a.c. transmission and distribution systems of authorized undertakers*
[29] B.S. No. 125. *Hard-drawn copper conductors for overhead power transmission purposes*
[30] B.S. 137. *Porcelain and toughened glass insulators for overhead power lines (3·3 kV and upwards)*
[31] B.S. No. 182–4. *Galvanized iron and steel wire for telegraph and telephone purposes*
[32] B.S. No. 215 (Pt 1). *Aluminium conductors for overhead power transmission purposes*
[33] B.S. No. 215 (Pt 2). *Steel-cored aluminium conductors for overhead power transmission purposes*
[34] B.S. No. 548. *High-tensile structural steel for bridges etc and general building construction*
[35] B.S. No. 607. *Reinforced concrete poles for electrical transmission and traction systems*
[36] B.S. No. 729. *Method for testing the zinc coating on galvanized articles other than wire (copper sulphate test and visual examination)*
[37] B.S. No. 913. *Pressure creosoting of timber*
[38] B.S. No. 916. *Black bolts screws and nuts*
[39] B.S. No. 1320. *High voltage overhead lines on wood poles for line voltages up to and including 11 kV*
[40] B.S. No. 1990. *Wood poles for overhead lines*

International Conference on Large Electric Systems (C.I.G.R.E.)

[41] Paper No. 226 (1948). Percivall, A. E. *Mechanical Design of 264 kV Transmission Lines in Great Britain*

[42] Paper No. 202 (1950). *11 kV and 220 kV Power Lines in the Network of Imatra, Voima Oy in Finland*

[43] Paper No. 223 (1950). *New Transmission Line with Concrete-filled Steel Type Towers*

[44] Paper No. 227 (1952). *Pre-stressed Reinforced Concrete Poles for Overhead Lines*

[45] Paper No. 202 (1954). *Wind Pressure on Overhead Transmission Line Conductors*

[46] Paper No. 203 (1954). *Technical and Economic Comparison Between H-frame and Corset Type Tower Design Based on Swedish Transmission Line Regulations and Prices*

[47] Paper No. 212 (1956). *Tests on Overhead Line Towers at Erlinsbach*

[48] Paper No. 224 (1956). *Contribution to the Study of the Laying and of the Tensioning of Conductors on Very High Voltage Electric Lines*

[49] Paper No. 228 (1956). *Report on the work of International Study Committee No. 6: Mechanical Calculation of Overhead Lines*

[50] Paper No. 230 (1956). *Report on the work of International Study Committee No. 7: Towers and Tower Foundations*

TUNNELLING PRACTICE

H. D. MORGAN, M.Sc., M.I.C.E.

IN the last few years there have been remarkable developments in the technique of tunnelling, brought about mainly as a result of research into the solution of civil engineering problems and by exploiting new methods of construction, advances in mechanization, and improved materials. The advances made in soil mechanics have also assisted considerably in predicting and overcoming difficulties in driving tunnels.

PLANNING

Geological survey

In carrying out any tunnelling work the first and most essential operation is to determine the geological and physical characteristics of the site, for only thus can the best method of tunnelling be determined in the light of all existing circumstances. In Great Britain there is the well organized and excellently conducted Geological Survey, which has vast sources of information available and many of its published maps and memoirs can be consulted at the Survey offices and at libraries. It is now obligatory for the results of borings down to 100 ft (30 m) and over to be reported to the Survey. Thus the would-be tunneller should have a stock of information readily at hand which will at least give him some indication of the problem to be tackled.

Use of models

Tunnelling in built up areas presents many special problems of its own, for in addition to detailed knowledge of geological structure there is the need to plan the sequence of operations with great care and forethought, as emphasized by HARLEY-MASON[1] when he carried out remarkable work during reconstruction of Aldgate East station. For such work, complicated by sewers, pipes and mains, and by the existing layouts of rail tracks and roads, use of models prepared from surveys and other information proves to be of great value in planning the work, especially as regards street occupations and order of priorities.

Site investigation

The need for detailed site investigation cannot be emphasized too strongly. This matter was stressed in a paper by HARDING[2], in which he drew attention to the fact that ground can vary very rapidly in three dimensions and in its nature, slope and properties; moreover, slight variations in the level of ground water can completely alter the behaviour of some soils during working, a matter of great importance to the tunneller. As Harding states much trouble can arise by mistaking boulders for bedrock, in the case of a ' buried channel ' (see also p 85).

Other examples are described in this paper[2] including that of Braehead power station on the site of which there was found a complex combination of dense gravels with soft and very variable silt between this and bedrock. Tunnelling in such ground will also have its special problems.

METHODS AND EXAMPLES OF TUNNELLING

Having determined site conditions, and having measured the physical properties of the ground through which he has to tunnel, the engineer must now determine the best method to be adopted. Much will depend upon local circumstances; in all civil engineering operations, especially in tunnelling, it is impossible to lay down exact rules as to what shall be done because every job is different. Moreover, it is generally true to say that below ground there are often startling variations in the strengths and physical properties of soils within a limited area.

Today the tunnelling engineer is fortunate in having at his command a wide variety of geotechnical processes from which he can choose when called upon to tunnel through difficult or water-bearing ground.

Ground consolidation by injection process

These processes are conveniently grouped into single fluid and two fluid. When using a single fluid method as much fluid as the permeability of the soil will allow is pumped into the ground and either sets or forms a gel after a short interval of time. The two fluids in the other system, however, are injected one after the other into a strictly limited volume of ground. These solutions react almost instantaneously to precipitate a cementing substance, consequently the injection points are usually only about 2 ft apart and no more than 18 to 24 in in depth of consolidated material is achieved at a time.

Solutions

A large number of single fluid processes have been patented for the injection of sand with mixtures in which the essential ingredient is sodium silicate. Other salts which react with it are added at the time of injection and precipitate silica gel after a short interval. Permeability of soils with a 10 per cent size down to 0·1 mm can be reduced considerably, but cohesion is not greatly increased.

The Joosten two fluid chemical consolidation process is applicable to gravel and sand, whether water-bearing or dry, and up to a certain point whether clean or containing a small proportion of other matter. Sands with an effective grain size of less than 0·1 mm are too fine for injections, clays, silts and peat being also unsuitable for this process. Two chemical solutions are injected into the ground, which react rapidly with each other to bind the sand grains together and thus to form an artificial ' sandstone '. A silica gel is precipitated from a solution of sodium silicate by the action of calcium chloride, the free silicic acid thus formed sticking to the sand particles and binding the whole mass together in a watertight block. A third solution, sodium carbonate, is sometimes used in order to reduce viscosity and encourage penetration of fine soils.

Figure 1 shows an interesting application of this process at the Bank-Monument station, London. Here the London clay was 3 ft 6 in (*c* 1 m) below the crown of the tunnel, with very loose sandy gravel above; the consolidated ground was quite firm, the 26 ft (8 m) diam arch standing unsupported while each ring of cast iron was built. An arch of solidified ballast was first formed by driving pipes radially from inside an old sewer for a sufficient length to cover fourteen rings of 26 ft diam tunnel. When these had been excavated the arch of solidification was extended by driving similar pipes and injecting on section *CD*.

Cement grout

The use of cement grout for sealing water-bearing fissures in rock appears to have been adopted first in the sinking of a shaft at Lens in 1882.

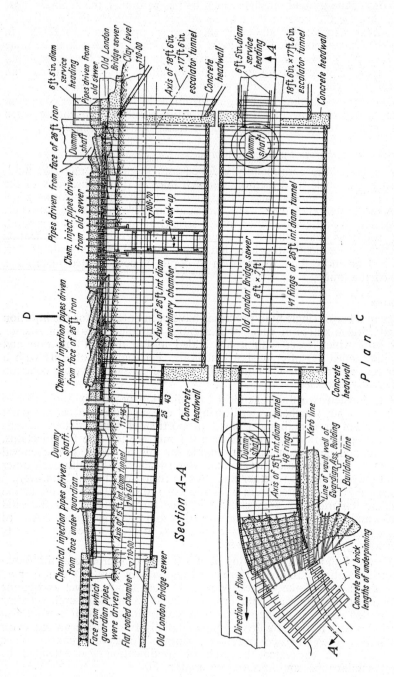

Figure 1. Chemical consolidation process as applied to 26 ft tunnel at Monument Station

Cement grout is effective in closing fissures over 0·1 mm in width, but cannot be used in cavernous ground. TERZAGHI[18] has pointed out that cement injections have a limited application to soils with a 10 per cent particle size not less than 0·5 mm when loosely packed or 1·4 mm for dense sands. Experience shows that cement grout in fine and medium sands merely displaces the sand laterally, without penetrating the voids, and forms cement nodules. A classic example of what can be achieved by cement grouting was the work on the Severn tunnel described by CARPMAEL[3].

In an interesting paper recently PELLETIER[19] describes how a combination of single fluid processes was used to consolidate a wet crushed quartzite seam which was met in the Malgovert tunnel in France. A series of four injections was made: first a sodium silicate solution was used to prepare the ground to facilitate pressure cement grouting which followed and produced circulation passages and compressed the quartzite. The third injection, a sodium silicate and phosphoric acid solution, formed a gel coating the sand grains, dried the ground, and produced cohesion. A final pressure cement grouting was used to give perfect keying to the ground by compression.

Thixotropic suspensions

Certain naturally occurring clays form thixotropic suspensions in water and certain other clays can be made to acquire this characteristic by chemical base exchange. Such suspensions are pumped into coarse sands as liquids which then transform into a gel when left undisturbed for a while and greatly decrease the permeability of the sand.

The Soletanche system which has been used with great success in France uses this principle to produce clay–chemical and clay–cement grouts to suit particular characteristics of the ground to be treated, covering a wide range of permeability. Bentonite, a processed clay, is used in varying proportions with cement and reagents and the viscosity of this type of grout can be reduced by agitation to enable soils with 10 per cent particle size down to 0·1 mm to be penetrated. A paper by KELL[20] describes the use of this system recently on the Dartford tunnel under the River Thames. It was used in this case to minimize the loss of compressed air through sand and gravel distributed irregularly in layers.

Bitumen emulsion injections

Another method of dealing with difficult ground is by injecting bitumen emulsions, such as the Shell-Perm process, a single fluid process employing a coagulator. This reduces the permeability but does not increase the strength of ground. When considering the adoption of any injection process careful consideration must be given to the suitability of the ground and the ease with which the seat of operations can be reached. It is found in practice that most granular materials contain more than 30 per cent of voids, and that to solidify them it is therefore necessary to handle and to inject 30 per cent of the volume to be treated.

Freezing

The freezing process has been very successfully applied on tunnelling operations, MUSSCHE and WADDINGTON[5] having described its use on the construction of the Moscow metropolitan railway. During the period 1932 to 1935, 94,200 cu yd (72,000 cu m) of ground was frozen at five different sites in connection with deep galleries and entrance tubes to various stations. Freezing of inclines to the stations proved to be a very difficult operation; it was therefore decided to freeze a cylinder of ice around the inclines to be installed, which involved the drilling of boreholes at an angle of 30 degrees to the horizon in running sands.   For the excavation of the underground galleries, fifty to sixty boreholes were drilled to an average depth of 80 ft (24 m); many of them were replaced by inclined holes in order not to obstruct the traffic.

Compressed air

The use of compressed air to exclude water from excavation is a well known process confined to tunnels and vertical shafts.   As 50 lb/sq in is generally considered to be the maximum to which workmen should be exposed, or in which they can conveniently work, this method is restricted to hydrostatic heads not greater than 110 ft (33·5 m).   Silts and clays of a consistency approaching the liquid limit can be prevented from flowing and controlled by compressed air.   Fine running sands which cannot be dewatered by draining to sumps are converted to firm compact material by applying compressed air which eliminates the internal pore pressure of the soil and drains the water back from the face.

In coarse sands and gravel loss of air may make this process unworkable unless some method is used to seal the soil, as mentioned in the case of the Dartford tunnel, or by laying a clay blanket over the tunnel route.

SHIELD TUNNELLING

Tunnelling by means of the shield has developed considerably since the pioneer work of Brunel who in 1818 took out the first patent which refers to the shield as a 'casing or cell intended to be forced forward before the timbering which is generally employed to secure the work'.   He employed this device for driving the Thames tunnel between 1825 and 1828, later application of his idea being made possible by Lord Cochrane, who in 1830 took out the first patent for using compressed air in caisson work.

The Thames tunnel was carried out in free air only by dint of the utmost perseverance and almost superhuman courage.   Its cost on this work was so high that for many years shield tunnelling suffered a severe setback, until in 1869 Greathead employed it with outstanding success for driving the Tower subway.   Originator of the famous shield which bears his name, Greathead was the patentee of the cement grouting pan, and his employment of compressed air with cast iron tunnel lining facilitated the economic development of sub-aqueous tunnelling.   The first large scale employment of the Greathead shield was in 1884 on the City and South London railway; it was also used successfully for a tunnel under the Hudson river, under the Thames at Blackwall, and for the Central London railway.

The method of operating the Greathead shield in London clay, or in similar homogeneous material, is shown schematically in *Figure 2*.   The device comprises a skin A with a cutting edge D, driven forward by the rams operated by hydraulic pressure and bearing against the cast iron lining segments C; in this instance a small pilot heading E is being driven ahead of the shield, and the needles F are driven through the ground to break it up as the shield advances.   The rams are shown ready to move the shield forward.   Water may be used as the hydraulic medium in these rams, but oil operated rams have advantages and are gaining favour.   The annular space left between the cast iron segments and the ground is filled with cement grout. The shield is an extremely simple device to operate, experience proving that unskilled men of reasonable

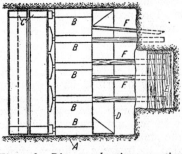

Figure 2.   Diagram showing operation of Greathead shield

intelligence can master the technique in seven days. When driving the South London tunnels, for example, an average advance of 13 ft (4 m) for 24 hr was constantly maintained.

The shield is a very adaptable apparatus, proof of which is provided by the enlargement work carried out on the City and South London railway tunnels[6].

Eight exceptionally strong tunnelling shields were employed on the driving of the Fulton Street—East River tunnels, New York[7], work rendered extremely difficult owing to the proximity of tall buildings and the need for carrying out operations under an air pressure which varied from atmospheric to 48 lb/sq in (3·4 kg/sq cm). Each shield was of the open type, with a platform extending across the horizontal diameter, the vertical members dividing the shield into three compartments, the lower middle pocket being large enough to allow a skip to pass through to the working face. The external diameter of the tunnel lining was 18 ft 3 in (5·56 m) and that of the shield was 18 ft 10 in (5·74 m), the thickness of the skin being 2½ in (63·5 mm); there was thus a radial clearance of 1 in between the outside of the iron and the inside of the tail of the shield. This was found to be adequate; in Manhattan two shields travelled around curves of 335 ft (102 m) radius without experiencing any binding against the lining. Hoods were provided on both land and river shields, extending 2 ft 10 in (0·86 m) beyond the cutting edge; hoods on the land shields extended down to 1 ft (0·3 m) below springing line and those on the river shields to 1 ft above springing line. The eighteen 10 in (25·4 cm) diam hydraulic jacks on each shield exerted a thrust of 4,000 ton (4,064 tonne) and were supplied with hydraulic pressure at 6,000 lb/sq in (422 kg/sq cm). A segment erector was mounted at the edge of the horizontal platform, rotation being effected through a pinion, and extension or withdrawal by means of an hydraulic cylinder within the erector.

A very interesting type of shield was used on the construction of the Lincoln tunnel, New York[8]. This was provided with a closed face in which two rectangular openings were cut; the silt through which the shield was driven was squeezed through these openings, the operation being termed 'silt displacement'. A long ribbon of silt came through each opening, like tooth paste coming through a tube, and it was cut up into reasonably sized pieces by men using wires, in much the same manner as a grocer cuts cheese. An interesting feature was the mechanical bolt tightener, devised and patented by Parker.

Mechanical excavation

High speed tunnelling on the London tube through clay was made possible in certain cases by employing the Price rotary excavator, shown in *Figure 3*. This was employed in conjunction with a portable belt conveyor driven by a 10 h.p. electric motor. The excavator head proper employed six radial arms on which were mounted suitably disposed cutters and scoops, the excavated material being discharged into a chute. An electric motor of 52 h.p. was employed to drive the machine, and on the Strand line of the London tube an excavator of this type attained a weekly progress of 109 rings or 180 ft (55 m) of cast iron lining.

In America recently a 26 ft (7·93 m) diameter shield of this type called a 'giant mole' was used to drive six tunnels through weak shales in the Oahe hydro-electric scheme[21] on the Missouri river. These tunnels were driven in a quarter of the time required by conventional tunnelling methods. Steel supports were erected from a jig behind the shield and concrete lining followed up. The shield was maintained on line partly

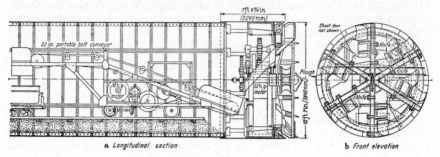

a *Longitudinal section*   b *Front elevation*

Figure 3. Price rotary excavator

by a central pilot bit and partly by arranging that some of the cutters on an annular ring rotated in the opposite direction to those on the central cutting face.

Hallinger shield

An interesting development of shield tunnelling is shown in *Figure 4* which is a longitudinal section taken through the hemispherical cutter assembly. The patented invention of Hallinger[9], this shield is fitted with a specially designed hemispherical excavator, with cutters on its surface which are spaced 1 m (3·3 ft) apart, or even closer together. Behind each blade there is a slot through which the ground cut passes into the inside of the hemisphere. The blades are set so that each projects 20 mm (0·78 in) further forward than the one below it; thus, if the cutting edge of the first row is 20 mm from the face of the hemisphere, the second row will be 40 mm and the third 60 mm. The hemisphere is rotated about a horizontal axis by means of two hydraulic cylinders mounted in a vertical plane, the rams of which carry sprocket wheels and chains, one end of each chain being attached to the hemisphere, which is rotatable through 130 degrees.

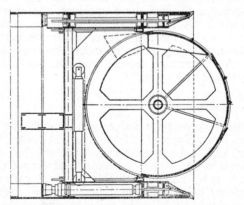

Figure 4. Hallinger shield

When the shield starts work the ram which rotates the hemisphere in an upward direction is at the outer end of the stroke. The other ram is then operated so that the hemisphere rotates downwards, excavating a layer of earth 10 or 20 mm thick; the first ram then moves the hemisphere into the original position, spoil passing through and below the hemisphere into the completed tunnel. No independent shoring of the tunnel is required, even when driving through water bearing sands. In order to counteract the tendency of the shield to travel downwards the cutting edge of the shield is so formed as to cause a slight upward pressure, this correction operating automatically when a straight tunnel is being driven.

The Hallinger shield was used with great success on the construction of two tunnels under the Danube for the Metropolitan Water Board of Budapest, where two tunnels were driven through clay, sand and gravel, having lengths of 657 yd (600 m) and 619 yd (565 m) with an internal diameter of 9 ft 2 in (2·8 m). At Dortmund, Germany, the shield was used to drive a tunnel having a diameter of 13 ft 9 in (4·2 m) about 2,000 yd (1,800 m) long through sand, water-bearing clay, soft sand and hard marl. The Hallinger shield was used in conjunction with a pre-cast concrete lining. Average daily progress on the Budapest tunnels was 12 ft 6 in (3·8 m) and 20 ft 6 in (6·2 m) respectively; the best day's work on the first tunnel was the erection of twenty-one lining rings, and on the second tunnel thirty lining rings. A complete ring could be erected in from 12 to 15 min, the best time being 8 min.

SIMPLON TUNNEL

The difficulties encountered in driving the Simplon tunnel through the Alps are described in a classic paper by Fox[10]. While driving the pilot tunnel through a decomposed calcareous mica schist formation, heavy timbering and heavy rolled steel joist supports with heavy timber baulks bolted between them were successively crushed. Eventually by interfilling rammed concrete between close spaced steel joists this section of the tunnel was driven. Opening out this pilot tunnel to the full section was most difficult and expensive and it is an excellent example of a devastating situation overcome by determination and unremitting toil. For further details of this tunnel see the following chapter on Tunnels and Tunnelling in Switzerland.

OPENING OUT TUNNEL SECTION

Although work on the Simplon tunnel was unique in size and difficulty, the method of opening out the tunnel to its full section embodies the essential principles of the 'bar and sill' method. Successive stages of this method are illustrated in *Figure 5,* which shows in diagrammatic form the opening out of a double track railway tunnel, the drawings being diagrammatic and not referring to any specific work. The first task is to drive pilot headings, the arrangement and size of which depend to a large extent on the nature of the ground. In very loose or broken material the top heading should be driven only slightly in advance of the finished length, but wherever possible it is wise to drive the top heading for the full length of the tunnel, which will facilitate speed and ventilation during construction.

At intervals throughout the length 'break ups' will be put in hand. Assuming that arch and side walls are taken out in 12 ft (3·7 m) lengths, the first operation consists of erecting and propping the three 'crown bars' on a short sill in the pilot heading as shown in *Figure 5*a. Each crown bar may be a 10 in by 5 in rolled steel joist about 20 ft long; excavation of the arch will then proceed in a fanwise manner for the erection of more bars and the placing of the 'nipper sill'. The bars are propped from the latter and in the final stage of arch excavation the main props and main sill are placed in position. For a 12 ft length of arch the bars (other than the three crown bars) will probably be 17 ft long and may be of 8 in by 6 in section or of 10 in by 5 in section, according to the nature of the ground.

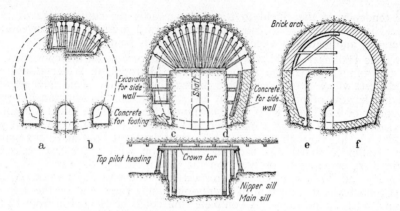

Figure 5. Opening out tunnel by bar and sill method

Where ground pressure is very heavy it may be necessary to build in bars behind the arch, when it is essential to set them at such a height that they will be well clear of the extrados of the arch, thus ensuring that the full section of the arch is not in any way affected by the bars. It is also essential to leave space between the bars and the extrados which can be packed with clean rubble filling; this not only facilitates drainage but also distributes ground pressure over the whole arch and thus prevents local stress building up. The arch section having been fully excavated, the rock is broken down at the sides and the footing and side wall concrete placed as shown in *Figure* 5c and d. Final operations are indicated at *Figure* 5e and f, the former showing the type of structural steel centering to be used in conjunction with timber laggings. If possible all poling boards should be removed in order to ensure that all cavities above them are well packed with rubble filling or concrete.

Steel supports are gaining favour when opening out a tunnel as they have many advantages[32]. They can be erected faster, leave clearer working spaces, and often require less unpaid excavation. The use of steel supports in the particularly difficult rock encountered in the Woodhead new tunnel is described in a paper by SCOTT and CAMPBELL[27]. Several classical tunnelling methods were tried in this double-line railway tunnel, but full face enlargement was adopted with complete steel ribs erected immediately after excavation.

Another means of support which has developed considerably in recent years is the technique of roof bolting. This method utilizes the natural arch effect in the rock above a tunnel to provide self support to the rock in the crown of the tunnel. Long bolts are inserted into holes drilled in the rock and secured by wedging, by expanding sleeves, or by cementing. Cemented bolts have the advantage of providing continuous contact with the rock. Timber or rolled steel sections may then be attached to the bolts as necessary in order to support the roof. This method has been used extensively in underground excavations in Sweden and the use of wedged bolts at Bowland water supply tunnel is referred to in a paper by GRUNDY[28]. Cemented bolts are considered to be an improvement on wedged bolts. One method introduced in 1954 consists of inserting into a bored hole a perforated metal tube which has been previously filled with cement mortar and then driving into the tube a plain or ridged bolt. This forces some of the mortar through the tube and into contact with the rock thoughout the length of the bolt, providing a homogeneous assembly and excellent strength.

Where the ground is very wet ample drainage should be provided. A valuable lesson on the need for this was provided by experience gained during the opening out of Cofton tunnel on the (at that time) London, Midland and Scottish railway[11]. Iron sheeting had been laid on the extrados of the four ring arch of this tunnel for its entire length, extending well down the haunch on either side. This sheeting was found to have been badly corroded proving that it had been laid to protect green brickwork from water in the crown, but it had the effect of concentrating water at the side walls, in which the mortar was found to have deteriorated.

EXAMPLES OF DIFFICULT DRIVING

It can be generally laid down that where there are any signs of joint planes or crustal disturbances in the rock, some form of lining should be adopted. An outstanding example of what can happen in shale, one of the most treacherous rocks, was provided by the case of the Galo Tara tunnel on the Khyber railway[12]. Here the pilot tunnel was driven through very hard slaty shale. All went well, except in one place where the roof caved in during the enlargement of the heading. Here a pocket of soft shale overlay the hard shale, resulting in the formation of a large domed cavern. Attempts to timber this failed, and the enlargement was on such a scale that daylight was clearly visible 70 ft (21·3 m) above. Movement continued until the shaft so formed was stabilized.

An even more striking illustration of what may happen in shale was provided by the Michni tunnel on the same railroad; this penetrates a steep ridge of shale which, at the time of construction, gave no indication of containing water. As soon as heading driving started, however, a serious state of affairs was revealed. This portion of the tunnel consisted of wet, muddy shale, which was very surprising. It was believed that the tunnel passed through an underground reservoir, a theory later substantiated by the fact that vigorous drainage took place down the 1 in 25 gradient over a period of four years, the time of construction. Fortunately this bad portion of the tunnel was only 800 ft long; it was lined completely with an invert, consisting of six or seven rings of brickwork set in cement mortar.

Shale caused very difficult driving for about three quarters of the 3 mile long Woodhead tunnel[27] for double-line railway. The dip of the shale was about 8 deg. to the tunnel axis and, although carefully packed heavy steel ribs were placed 6 ft (1·9 m) apart when the full face was opened out, several heavy falls of rock occurred. It was found that satisfactory support could be provided by following up the excavation closely with a concrete primary lining. On occasions it was necessary to take this lining as close as the steel support immediately behind the face, but it was still possible to fire a round close to this green concrete.

An interesting example of what may happen owing to the combined effects of bad ground and abundant ground water is provided by *Figure 6*, which shows a short section of the Colorado river aqueduct[13]. This is the shear zone near the Potrero shaft, which delayed construction for some ten months; a flow of water estimated at 7,500 gal/min (34,000 l/min) broke into the heading and carried with it 1,000 cu yd (760 cu m) of debris. Since the capacity of the pumps was only 2,500 gal/min (11,000 l/min), they were soon flooded and the water filled the shaft to a depth of 647 ft (197 m). After de-watering this a second flood occurred, which was also surmounted and timber bulkheads were built so that a top centre drift could be started. A drift was then excavated on the north side of the tunnel in an attempt to lead the then flow of 6 cu ft/sec (0·17 cu m/sec) away from the working face, but this was unsuccessful. Exploratory core drilling was then put in hand which proved that there were favourable conditions for a detour of the tunnel. Fissures in the rock were grouted successfully and the top heading was driven as shown in *Figure 6*. The tunnel section in the shear zone was excavated to allow for a thickness of from 15 to 30 in of concrete; to support running ground in the shear zone a length of 24 ft was treated with gunite to a thickness of 2 ft. A further 6 in of concrete was added during concreting of the lining and several tons of cement grout were injected behind the lining as a further precaution.

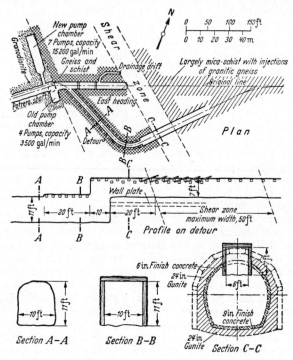

Figure 6. Shear zone at Colorado river aqueduct

MATERIAL HANDLING PLANT

In tunnelling through hard homogeneous rock the main problems confronting the engineer are the efficient use of explosives, rapid disposal of excavated spoil and organization of the work so that speed is the criterion. The high speed rocker shovel incorporates the fruits of more than thirty years of experience in its design. One model of this machine, for example, has a bucket of $\frac{1}{2}$ cu yd (0·38 cu m) capacity which loads into a hopper fitted with a variable speed conveyor mounted on rubber covered rollers; the machine may be operated either electrically with hydraulic servo control, or by compressed air. Another example of this loader was used with great success in driving the 6 mile (9·7 km) drainage tunnel for a gold mine in Colorado. The tunnel was driven through volcanic breccia, section 10 ft wide and 11 ft high, and a steady rate of 1,500 linear ft a month was maintained. Record drive for one day was 74 linear ft, and in a 31 day month it was 1,879 ft. The loader employed on this work handled an average quantity of 34 cu yd (26 cu m) of shattered rock after each round fired.

The gate end loader, familiar to mining engineers, has been very successfully employed in driving a pit tunnel at Newton colliery[14]. This tunnel is 1,200 yd long and has a finished cross section 14 ft by 12 ft; in several cases a complete six yard advance was made in 48 hr, equivalent to 18 yd of drivage for a week of six days. Some 140 tubs were filled after each round, equal to a 2 yd advance; debris was loaded into the tubs by a gate end loader, two men filling on either side of the gathering end of the loader, while a fifth man scraped down the debris and broke up large pieces of rock. Strata consisted of inferior shales and mudstones with much faulting.

Conveyor belts are being adopted extensively for the removal of spoil as at Potters Bar[26] where the belt moved forward with the shield. Vertical chutes feeding all the shield galleries carried the spoil to the conveyor belt which fed it to the hopper loading point for removal by light railway.

A specially designed vehicle used to remove the broken rock at Allt-na-Lairige[24], in Argyll, enabled a rate of driving of 444 ft (135 m) in seven days to be achieved in this 8 ft by 6 ft 6 in (2·4 m by 2 m) tunnel. The vehicle was 70 ft (21·3 m) long and had sufficient capacity to take all the muck from a pull of 7 to 8 ft. The rock was loaded by means of a rocker shovel at one end of the car and carried steadily back along the car on a steel slat conveyor belt floor thus avoiding delays due to changing cars at the face. The vehicle was drawn by a diesel locomotive, and enabled the mucking time to be reduced to half that required when using small cars and by-passes.

EXPLOSIVES

In recent years the rapid development of commercial explosives has had a profound influence on the speed at which tunnels can be driven. The subject has been reviewed by LORIMER[15] and is dealt with in detail in the chapter on Explosives.

The pattern of the drill holes to be used in tunnelling will depend upon the type of rock and on the site conditions and the best pattern for arranging the shot holes in any particular rock can be worked out only by trial. For examples, see the chapter on Explosives.

In high speed tunnelling the drill 'jumbo', or drill carriage, which may be mounted on wheels, is found to be extremely useful. With a large 'jumbo' it is possible to drill eighty or more shot holes in one round, the loading, connecting and stemming being a considerable operation.

This type of machine is now being replaced by rock drills fitted with a self adjusting pneumatic feed leg or 'air-leg'. These are not so heavy as a drifter and are easier to handle. They consume only about half the quantity of compressed air in performing the same amount of work as a drill carriage drifter, but the rate of drilling is slightly slower. Rock drills with air-legs were used in the Woodhead tunnel[27] and in the rock tunnels in Scotland (Allt-na-Lairige[24]) and Sweden (Harresele) where record drives have recently been made.

Stemming is very important to ensure maximum explosive efficiency. When driving headings with delay firing, stemming is also necessary to ensure that charges which are connected by wire are not drawn out of the hole by the debris of previous shots jerking on the connecting wires.

Lorimer states that when the cut shots have been fired the result should be a hole about 12 to 15 in diameter into which all rock has been shattered and partially ejected, thus providing a free face to which the rest of the round can break. If a round has been correctly planned there should be no sockets left in the holes; moreover, the debris pile from a well designed round is not scattered back from the face and is thus in a very good position for loading into skips by mechanical means.

TUNNEL LINING

A very important matter in all tunnelling operations is to decide on the best form of lining to adopt. Rate of progress in shield driven tunnels is largely dependent upon the rate at which the tunnel lining can be erected.

Flanged cast iron segments built up in the tail of the shield into rings and bolted together have for many years been the most common lining for such tunnels. Structural steel lining segments have also been employed with considerable success for lining sub-aqueous tunnels, but in Great Britain they have usually been restricted to secondary linings.

An interesting development of tunnel lining methods in Great Britain has been the increasing use of bolted concrete segments. Reinforced concrete segments were first used in practice in about 1938 though much research was carried out before this. An interesting example of work carried out with pre-cast concrete segments has been provided in a paper by PATTENDEN[16]. The tunnels were 8 ft, 12 ft 3 in, and 16 ft 6 in internal diameter all lined with circular pre-cast concrete segments as described by GROVES[17].

Reinforced concrete segments are particularly suited for tunnels with limited cover where tensions may be set up in the lining. In general, cast iron may be subjected to a greater external pressure than reinforced concrete segments and can be more readily caulked against seepage.

These several types of lining being assembled inside the shield, an annular space is left around the lining which normally must be grouted by means of a bougie or pressure-grouting pan of the Greathead type. HARDING[4] has emphasized the point that considerable quantities of water are needed to carry the cement and that unless excess water is removed the full effect of grouting cannot be achieved. Also, a secondary lining is frequently required in order to provide a flush surface for the sake of appearance or to improve hydraulic characteristics. More recently attention has been turned to developing the technique of lining tunnels in soft ground with pre-cast concrete segmental blocks which overcome both these disadvantages.

The Don-Seg wedge block lining developed and successfully used in the construction of a raw water tunnel for the Metropolitan Water Board[22, 23] is applicable to small diameter tunnels driven in clay. The blocks are wedge shaped and placed in a ring with the wide and narrow ends leading on alternate blocks. By operating the shield rams in a certain order the ring is driven home against the previous ring and expanded by wedging action to bear tightly against the surrounding soil. The rate of advance in the circular tunnel of 8 ft 10½ in (2·7 m) internal diameter complete with lining was 180 ft (55 m) per week using hand tools for mining, but this was stepped up to 240 ft (73 m) per week when a shield equipped with rotary cutters was introduced.

A further advance in the development of pre-cast concrete linings was successfully used in the Greenwood—Potters Bar tunnels constructed for British Railways (Eastern Region)[26]. These tunnels have a 26 ft 6 in (8·1 m) internal diameter for double track railway and the lining is built in 18 in wide rings consisting of a pre-cast reinforced concrete invert unit and nineteen interlocking pre-cast concrete voussoirs without reinforcement. Certain of the voussoirs are specially shaped to admit hydraulic jacks used to stress each ring against the surrounding ground. A steady rate of advance of 70 ft (21m) per week of completed tunnel was obtained by this method of construction.

A difficult problem when constructing a concrete lining *in situ* is the control of water entering the tunnel while concrete is being placed. This problem has been considerably eased by the introduced of quick setting cements. It is now possible to control the entry of water from fissured rock by sealing with quick setting mortar and incorporating drainage channels. Flow from porous rocks can also be treated with a quick setting rendering and the flow concentrated at convenient points.

A further advance in providing *in situ* concrete tunnel linings is the development in Switzerland of the concrete gun. It is now possible to apply concrete containing up to 1 in aggregate and build up a lining 4 in thick in three coats, or a greater thickness if required. This provides a dense concrete, strength approximately 4,000 lb/sq in (281 kg/sq cm) at 7 days which, being forced into any crevices in the rock, is well keyed, and 20 to 30 cu yd of concrete per hour can be placed with a minimum of interference to other operations in the tunnel.

DESIGN OF TUNNEL LININGS

The primary lining of a tunnel may be classified under one or other of two distinct types:

(1) An *in situ* lining of concrete, brickwork or masonry;

(2) Built in purpose-made units or segments, usually constructed in complete rings of lining.

In general, an *in situ* lining is the most suitable for rock tunnels on account of the uneven shape of the excavation and the fact that the permanent lining does not normally require closely to follow the advance of the working face. In shattered rock where a lining is required close to the face, it is normally found expedient to provide temporary supports for this purpose; alternatively a cast iron lining may be used in such circumstances.

Rock tunnels frequently remain unlined; this is particularly the case with large intake and discharge tunnels in consistently sound rock for hydro-electric power stations[29], where the resulting roughness is not a considerable factor. Certain types of schists are notorious for softening and swelling when exposed to the atmosphere and a rock that appears initially to be sound rapidly weathers and deteriorates. In such circumstances a most rigorous examination must precede any decision to leave a tunnel unlined.

When tunnelling in soft ground, *i.e.* any ground other than rock, it is normally necessary for the lining at all times to follow closely the working face or, where a shield is used, the trailing edge of the shield.

It is not possible completely to separate the design from the construction of a tunnel. As an example, it is sometimes the case that the thickness of a concrete lining is determined by the size of steel supports to be built into the work. The basis of the design of a tunnel lining in rock is to ensure that the resulting system of active and passive forces will nowhere induce stresses in the lining or in the rock in excess of permissible values. Such a criterion often allows a wide choice of profiles of a rock tunnel and the shape will often be selected from considerations of the users' viewpoint and the construction methods.

A certain amount of data concerning the physical characteristics of particular rocks have been determined *in situ*[30] for individual projects and a theoretical analysis of stresses around tunnels, based on the elastic properties of rocks, has been developed by TERZAGHI and RICHART[31]. A common error in the application of such analysis is in the differentiation between the very different cases of an intact and a fissured rock. Special problems arise in the design of linings for pressure tunnels and a considerable bibliography of this subject has been compiled by JAEGER[30]. See also chapter on Hydraulic Power Plants.

Methods of analysis are often given in textbooks in which the vertical loads on the crown of the tunnel are estimated as a function of the depth from the surface of the ground and the unit weight of the overlying material. In rock, the load on the crown is alternatively based on the dimensions of the tunnel and the unit weight of the overlying material[32]. The lateral forces on the side walls are then estimated by using one or other of the classic methods, such as Rankine's theory, while the pressures on the invert are usually assumed to be uniformly distributed with a resultant equal to the vertical component of the estimated forces on the crown and side walls.

In practice a competent engineer may not place too much confidence in these methods of analysis since so many factors unknown or incapable of exact assessment enter into the assumptions made and he is obliged to rely to a substantial extent on his experience of similar works. As an example of the complications which may arise, some thought should be given to the situation in which the vertical loads may deflect the crown or arch rib, resulting in elastic deflection of the side walls. This latter movement calls into play passive forces which may exceed, sometimes to a considerable extent, the active pressures estimated by classical theory. There is an unfortunate tendency in textbooks to evade these issues. It should be clear that deflection of the tunnel lining can cause significant modifications to the magnitude and distribution of the pressures which are in operation. These modifications are frequently favourable to the structure since they tend to reduce the critical bending moments in the arch rib and may sometimes eliminate tensile stresses.

Problems of special interest arise when dealing with tunnels which are to be situated in cohesive ground such as the London blue clay in which the majority of the London underground railway tunnels have been driven. Linings circular in cross section are invariably adopted for these comparatively deep tunnels; this implies the simplifying assumption that the pressure is of the 'hydrostatic' type *i.e.* uniform in magnitude at all points on the lining and acting always normal to the surface. It is frequently assumed that this condition exists when the depth below surface is fairly large compared with the tunnel diameter, but the assumption is not necessarily valid even in clay. The relationship between the initial vertical and horizontal pressures (p and p_h) in a clay are determined by its geological history but for normally consolidated clays it is frequently found that p_h/p lies between 0.5 and 0.75. Such a relationship appears to be consistent with observations in tunnels in clay which usually indicate that, after construction, a tunnel tends to deform slightly into an ellipse with its major axis horizontal; this is the normal behaviour in London clay. So long as such distortion does not cause stresses in the clay beyond the elastic limit, a state of equilibrium will soon be attained on account of the passive pressures developed in the clay. Where two or more tunnels are to be built close together, the effects of partial release of the ground supporting the first tunnel during the construction of a subsequent tunnel must be carefully examined; the safe minimum spacing between tunnels depends on many factors.

It is frequently found that engineers will assess the relative strengths of different types of tunnel lining by comparing the different moduli of cross section of ring per unit length of tunnel; in the author's view this practice is not always rational and in some circumstances, where the possibility of failure on account of instability may occur, the proper criterion should be the value of the moment of inertia of the different sections. The tunnel is then considered as a thin tube, or a series of slender rings, subjected to external pressure and the analysis follows that of Timoshenko or Southwell.

It is a matter for the engineer's judgement to determine how stiff a lining to provide for a tunnel. In general, the stiffer the lining the higher the bending stresses that it will be subjected to. A typical thickness of a concrete lining in rock for preliminary design is that of one inch of thickness for every foot of diameter; similar figures are used for brickwork or masonry.

In soft ground, if the engineer is fairly confident that he can assess the vertical and lateral pressures with a reasonable degree of accuracy, the bending moments M in the lining may be evaluated by means of the following general equations, summation being performed from the crown round the ring and back to the crown again where x and y are co-ordinates on two transverse axes in the plane of the tunnel section.

$$\Sigma M . x = 0 \qquad \dots\dots\dots\dots(1)$$

$$\Sigma M . y = 0 \qquad \dots\dots\dots\dots(2)$$

$$\Sigma M = 0 \qquad \dots\dots\dots\dots(3)$$

In this brief review of a vast and fascinating subject, the writer has only been able to touch upon a few of the outstanding tunnelling works carried out in recent years, and to refer to some of the many advances in tunnelling techniques which have contributed so much to the speed and safety with which such work can now be carried out.

REFERENCES

[1] HARLEY-MASON, J. H. Reconstruction of Aldgate East Station *Instn civ. Engrs Paper No. 5211*, 1939

[2] HARDING, H. J. B. Site Investigation including Boring and other Methods of Sub-Surface Exploration *Instn civ. Engrs Works Constr. Paper No. 12*, 1949

[3] CARPMAEL, R. Cementation in the Severn Tunnel *Proc. Instn civ. Engrs* 234 (1931-32) 277

[4] HARDING, H. J. B. The Choice of Expedients in Civil Engineering Construction *Instn civ. Engrs Works Constr. Paper No. 6*, 1946

[5] MUSSCHE, H. E. and WADDINGTON, J. C. Applications of the Freezing Process to Civil Engineering Works *ibid No. 5*, 1946

[6] JONES, I. J. and CURRY, G. Enlargement of the City and South London Railway Tunnels *Proc. Instn civ. Engrs* 224 (1926-27) 176

[7] KILLMER, M. I. *Fulton Street–East River Tunnels, New York* American Society of Civil Engineers Constr. Div., 1930

[8] KING, H. L. Subaqueous Tunnel Construction *Civil Engng* 9 (1939)

[9] HAJNAL-KONYI, K. The Hallinger Shield and Erdelyi and Vajda Tunnel Lining *Engineering* 149 (1940)

[10] FOX, F. The Simplon Tunnel *Proc. Instn civ. Engrs* 168 (1907) Paper No. 3651

[11] McCALLUM, R. T. The Opening Out of the Cofton Tunnel, London, Midland & Scottish Railway *ibid* 231 (1930-31) 161

[12] BAYLEY, V. The Khyber Railway *ibid* 222 (1925-26) 1

[13] WEYMOUTH, F. E. Tunnel Construction—Colorado River Aqueduct *Civil Engng* 4 (1934)

[14] FAULKNER, M. I. Paper presented to Lancashire Branch of National Association of Colliery Managers, 1940

[15] LORIMER, J. Some Uses of Explosives in Civil Engineering *Instn civ. Engrs Works Constr. Paper No. 3*, 1945

[16] PATTENDEN, B. Tunnelling with Pre-cast Concrete *Instn civ. Engrs Works Constr. Pap. No. 5453*, 1945

[17] GROVES, G. L. Tunnel Linings with Special Reference to a New Form of Reinforced Concrete Lining *J. Instn civ. Engrs* 20 (1934) 29

[18] TERZAGHI, K. Methods of Improving the Physical Properties of Soils for Engineering Purposes *Proc. Harvard Conf. on Soil Mechanics*, Vol. III, p 180, 1936

[19] PELLETIER, J. The Construction of the Tignes Dam and Malgovert Tunnel *Proc. Instn civ. Engrs* 2, Pt III (1953)

[20] KELL, J. Pre-Treatment of Gravel for Compressed Air Tunnelling under the River Thames *The Chartered Civil Engineer* March, 1957

[21] Driving Power Tunnels, *Water Power* (Aug. 1957) 316

[22] SCOTT, P. A. A 75-inch Diameter Water Tunnel: A New Method of Tunnelling in London Clay *Proc. Instn civ. Engrs* 1, Pt I (1952)

[23] TATTERSALL, WAKELING and WARD. Investigations into the Design of Pressure Tunnels in London Clay *Proc. Instn civ. Engrs* 4, Pt I (1955)

[24] ALEXANDER, H. J. An Experiment in High Speed Tunnelling *Water Power* (July 1955) 261

[25] ARCHER, G. J. Tunnelling Plant and Equipment *Proc. Instn civ. Engrs* Sept. 1, Pt I (1952)

[26] Tunnelling Operations at Potters Bar *Civil Engineering* (June 1957) 675

[27] SCOTT, P. A. and CAMPBELL, J. I. Woodhead New Tunnel *Proc. Instn civ. Engrs* 3, Pt I (1954)

[28] GRUNDY, C. F. Notable Water Tunnel *Water Power* (Jan. 1951)

[29] HAGRUP, J. F. Swedish Underground Hydro-Electric Power Stations *Proc. Instn civ. Engrs* 3, Pt III (1954) 321

[30] JAEGER, C. Present Trends in the Design of Pressure Tunnels and Shafts for Underground Hydro-electric Power Stations *Proc. Instn civ. Engrs* 4 (1955) 116

[31] TERZAGHI, K. and RICHART, F. E. Stresses in Rocks about Cavities *Géotechnique* 3 (1952) 57

[32] PROCTOR, R. V. and WHITE, T. L. *Rock Tunnelling with Steel Supports* The Commercial Shearing and Stamping Co., Ohio, 1946

TUNNELS AND TUNNELLING
IN SWITZERLAND

C. ANDREAE

A GREAT deal of tunnelling has been and still is necessary in Switzerland owing to the very mountainous nature of the country. There are altogether 660 Swiss railway tunnels, with a total length of 182 miles (300 km); seven of them being over 5 miles (8 km) long. Road tunnels are now needed and galleries of even greater length but of smaller cross section are made to convey water to hydraulic power plants.

DESIGN OF LONG TUNNELS THROUGH HIGH MOUNTAIN RANGES

The first essential in the design of long, deep tunnels is a thorough geological survey of the ground, covering the kinds of geological strata to be met, their direction and fall. It is also important to study the hydrological features of the mountain, and to determine the probability of meeting wells and springs.

At great depths ground temperatures are high, and it is important to know what these are likely to be. The moisture content of the air in tunnels is always high, and in saturated air the efficiency of labour falls when the temperature exceeds 77°F (25°C), dropping almost to zero at 95°F (35°C). If temperatures of this kind are to be expected special means must be provided for ventilation or even for cooling the air. Investigation of the probable temperatures will therefore be an important part of the preliminary survey for the design of any tunnel the cover of which reaches 5,000 ft (1,500 m) or more.

Ground temperature

The normal geothermal gradient under plains amounts to 0·017-0·018°F/ft (0·031-0·033°C/m), the reciprocal geothermal gradient being 56-59 ft/°F (32-33 m for 1°C). Where the earth's surface is mountainous the gradient becomes greater (the reciprocal gradient smaller) under valleys and smaller (the reciprocal gradient larger) under the ranges, *Figure 1*. At great depth the planes of equal temperature (geoisotherms) become parallel again, the gradient and the reciprocal gradient becoming normal.

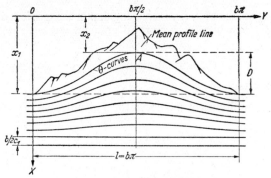

Figure 1. Geothermal gradients

383

The gradient found by experience in one tunnel cannot be assumed in another without further investigation. By applying the gradient of the St. Gothard tunnel the temperature of the Simplon tunnel was expected to be about 108°F (42°C). It was in fact found to be about 132°F (55°C). This discrepancy led to numerous investigations of the problem.

Theoretical determination of isotherms[1, 2, 3, 4]

According to Fourier the equation for equilibrium condition of heat flow along to a vertical section through the mountain containing the centre line of the tunnel is

$$\frac{\partial^2\theta}{\partial x^2} + \frac{\partial^2\theta}{\partial y^2} = 0 \qquad \dots\dots\dots\dots(1)$$

where θ is the temperature.

According to Thoma a solution of this equation for an undulating surface is given by

$$\theta = C_1 \log_e \{ A + \sqrt{(A^2 - 1)} \} + C_2 \qquad \dots\dots\dots\dots(2)$$

where

$$A = e^{2x/b} + \sqrt{\left\{ 1 - \left(2\cos\frac{2y}{b} - e^{2x/b} \right) e^{2x/b} \right\}} \qquad \dots\dots\dots\dots(3)$$

and C_1 and C_2 are constants. The period of this function is $b\pi$, and the θ lines or isotherms are undulating.

Below the ranges, $y = \dfrac{b\pi}{2}$, so that

$$\theta = 2C_1 \log_e \{ e^{x/b} + \sqrt{(e^{2x/b} + 1)} \} + C_2 \qquad \dots\dots\dots\dots(4)$$

and the temperature gradient is given by

$$\frac{d\theta}{dx} = \frac{2C_1}{b} \cdot \frac{e^{x/b} \{ e^{x/b} + \sqrt{(e^{2x/b} + 1)} \}}{e^{x/b} \{ e^{x/b} + \sqrt{(e^{2x/b} + 1)} \} + 1} \qquad \dots\dots\dots\dots(5)$$

With increasing values of x, *i.e.* increasing depth, the gradient increases also and approaches $2C_1/b$, while the reciprocal gradient diminishes and approaches $b/2C_1$.

Below the valleys, $y = 0$ or $b\pi$, hence

$$\theta = 2C_1 \log_e \{ e^{x/b} + \sqrt{(e^{2x/b} - 1)} \} + C_2 \qquad \dots\dots\dots\dots(6)$$

and the temperature gradient is

$$\frac{d\theta}{dx} = \frac{2C_1}{b} \cdot \frac{e^{x/b} \{ e^{x/b} + \sqrt{(e^{2x/b} - 1)} \}}{e^{x/b} \{ e^{x/b} + \sqrt{(e^{2x/b} - 1)} \} - 1} \qquad \dots\dots\dots\dots(7)$$

With increasing values of x, *i.e.* increasing depth, the gradient diminishes and approaches $2C_1/b$, while the reciprocal gradient increases and approaches $b/2C_1$.

$2C_1/b$ is equal to the normal gradient, $\left(\dfrac{d\theta}{dx}\right)_{x=\infty}$, which determines the value of the constant C_1.

If D is the amplitude of the curve for a given value of θ, C_2 is given by

$$\theta = C_1 \log_e \left(\frac{e^{D/b} + 1}{e^{D/b} - 1} \right) + C_2$$

or

$$C_2 = \theta - C_1 \log_e \left(\frac{e^{D/b} + 1}{e^{D/b} - 1} \right) \qquad \dots\dots\dots\dots(8)$$

If one isotherm θ can be derived from the temperature at the surface the origin 0 of the coordinates can be found as follows:

$$x_1 = b \log_e \tfrac{1}{2} \{ e^{+(\theta-C_2)/2C_1} + e^{-(\theta-C_2)/2C_1} \} \qquad \ldots\ldots\ldots\ldots(9)$$

$$x_2 = b \log_e \tfrac{1}{2} \{ e^{+(\theta-C_2)/2C_1} - e^{-(\theta-C_2)/2C_1} \} \qquad \ldots\ldots\ldots\ldots(10)$$

Application—Small peaks, elevations and depressions of the surface have practically no effect on the temperatures at the depth of the tunnel. The shape of the geotherms is determined by the mean shape of the mountain range; the mean profile along the line of the tunnel must therefore be drawn. This is obtained by drawing the cross sections through a series of points on the centre line of the tunnel, the width of each cross section bearing a certain relationship to the vertical distance from the tunnel level to the surface (two or three times the vertical distance), the mean heights of the cross sections being plotted as offsets for the profile line. It is then necessary to know the soil temperatures at several altitudes of the mountain, measured in boreholes about 30 to 35 ft deep, and from these temperatures that of the top of the mean profile line is computed. By applying a probable gradient the top of an isotherm, for instance that corresponding to the temperature at the foot of the mountain (A in *Figure 1*), can be found, and for that isotherm x_1 and x_2 are then calculated by means of equations 9 and 10. The difference $(x_1 - x_2)$ should be equal to D. The curve thus obtained for θ should then satisfy equations 2 and 3.

The thermal conductivity of the rocks depends upon the fall of their strata and is greater in a direction parallel to the direction and fall of the strata than in one perpendicular to them. If the strata are vertical or nearly so the geothermal gradient is small, and the reciprocal gradient large; if on the other hand they are horizontal or only slightly falling the gradient will be greater and the reciprocal gradient smaller. Values for $2C_1/b$ as recommended by Koenigsberger, Thoma and Goetz are given in TABLE 1.

Standard sections and lining

Figures 2a and b shows two sections of Swiss tunnels. The shape of a railway tunnel section depends upon the structure gauge for railways, which on the Continent is somewhat different from that in Great Britain, but its lining must be shaped and dimensioned to suit the geological conditions of the ground. Short tunnels in solid rock may be left unlined: long tunnels are always lined along the whole of their length, even in good rock. Unlined tunnels need much supervision, which for long tunnels is too expensive and not sufficiently safe. For small depths in soft but homogeneous ground the stresses in the lining and its dimensions can be computed by using the rules for earth pressures, *Figure 2b*. At depths of about 80 ft (25 m) or more the static computation becomes rather questionable because it is difficult to tell how much of the ground will take part in the action. If, as is generally true in mountain tunnels, the ground is not

TABLE 1

$2 C_1/b$ ACCORDING TO KOENIGSBERGER, THOMA AND GOETZ

Fall of strata	Vertical or nearly		About 45°		Horizontal or nearly	
	°C/m	°F/ft	°C/m	°F/ft	°C/m	°F/ft
Gneiss	0·027-0·028	0·014-0·015	0·033	0·018	0·034-0·036	0·018-0·019
Granite	0·027-0·028	0·014-0·015	0·033	0·018	0·034-0·036	0·018-0·019
Mica schists	0·027-0·028	0·014-0·015	0·034-0·036	0·018-0·019	0·037-0·041	0·020-0·022
Phyllites	0·027-0·028	0·014-0·015	0·031	0·017	0·032-0·033	0·017-0·018
If wet: less	←		5-8 per cent			→

CERB 13

TABLE 2

DETAILS OF THE SEVEN LONGEST SWISS TUNNELS

Tunnel	Length		No. of tracks (standard gauge)	Years of construction	Culminating point		Range	Height of cover (max)		Geothermal gradient Mean		Reciprocal geothermal gradient Mean		Max. temperature	
	m	ft			m	ft		m	ft	°C/m	°F/ft	m	ft	°C	°F
Simplon I	19,803	64,974	1	1898-1906	704·5	2,311	Alps	2,200	7,218	0·027	0·014	37	121·4	55·4	131·7
Simplon II	19,824	65,042	1	1912-1921[1]	704·5	2,311	,,	,,	,,	,,	,,	,,	,,	,,	,,
St. Gothard	15,003	49,225	2	1872-1882	1,154·6	3,788	,,	1,700	5,578	0·021	0·011	47	154·2	30·7	87·3
Loetschberg	14,605	47,919	2	1906-1912	1,242·8	4,078	,,	1,570	5,151	0·022	0·012	46	151·0	34·0	93·2
Ricken	8,604	28,230	1	1903-1910	622·0	2,041	Prealps	570	1,870	—	—	—	—	24·0	75·2
Grenchenberg	8,578	28,144	1	1911-1915	545·05	1,788	Jura	885	2,903	—	—	—	—	21·0[2]	69·8[2]
Hauenstein	8,134	26,688	2	1912-1915	451·72	1,482	,,	480	1,575	—	—	—	—	25·6[3]	78·1[3]

1 Interruptions due to the World War I   2 Much water   3 Dry and partly horizontal strata

TABLE 3

THICKNESSES OF TOP OF ARCH

Simplon I and II	0·35-0·70 m (1 ft 2 in-2 ft 4 in), except on a length of 50 m (164 ft), 1·87 m (6 ft 2 in) in quite soft ground
St. Gothard	0·40-1·00 m (1 ft 4 in-3 ft 3 in)
Loetschberg	0·40-0·80 m (1 ft 4 in-2 ft 7 in)
Ricken	0·45-0·75 m (1 ft 6 in-2 ft 6 in)
Grenchenberg	0·35-0·60 m (1 ft 2 in-2 ft 0 in)
Hauenstein	0·40-0·80 m (1 ft 4 in-2 ft 7 in)

homogeneous, the dimensions of the lining can be decided by practical experience alone, for the forces acting vary continuously with geological conditions, with ground humidity, even with the seasons, and also depend on the methods used for excavation and lining and on the skill of the builder.

The thicknesses given in TABLE 3 were adopted for the top of the arch in the seven long tunnels mentioned in TABLE 2.

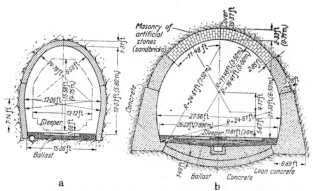

Figure 2. a *Single track tunnel in good rock (Rickentunel)* b *double track tunnel in earth under a cover of 12 m (39·37 ft) (Ulmberg-Zürich). Scale 1:180*

At the great depths reached by the long tunnels through the Alps movement has occurred due to the weight of the cover when the latter reached a height of about 5,000 ft or more. Such movement has been observed in all kinds of rocks, including granite, gneiss, limestone and others which are normally quite solid and resistant; it is due to the elastic or plastic expansion of the compressed rock. The pressures due to these movements are mainly side pressures: they are not very high but quite continuous. A relatively small amount of counteraction by a somewhat stronger lining will bring them to a standstill[5]. It can be reckoned that in such places the lining has to be reinforced by about 50 per cent.

Most of the railway tunnels in Switzerland have been lined with masonry in Portland cement mortar. In many of them good quality artificial stones have been used for the arch as bricks were not suitable. Some new tunnels are lined in concrete, but even then the top part of the arch is sometimes constructed in masonry. The use of concrete for lining railway tunnels is new, and few data are available about its condition after many years, although it must be stated that the condition of some old tunnels is not very encouraging. It is very important that all lining should be made good to the ground behind the arch as well as behind the sidewalls. All overbreak must be filled with concrete or with rubble masonry in mortar. Water found in the tunnel must on no account be used for making mortar or concrete. Stones and aggregate from the excavated material may be used but they should be examined and cleaned outside the tunnel first.

If water is met with, the arch must first be covered with a coating of bitumen between two layers of cement mortar: the space between the arch so covered and the ground may then be filled with stones without mortar. It is advisable to protect the insulating coat with a layer of artificial or very flat stones; this should only be done locally where the water actually emerges. If water appears over a greater length of the tunnel, the space between the coat and the ground may be filled with stones without mortar in lengths of 3 ft to 6 ft which alternate with sections of about the same length where the space is filled with concrete or with rubble masonry in mortar as shown in *Figure* 3a. The water must be collected at the springing

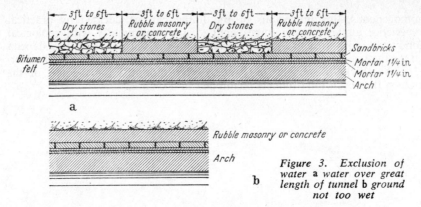

Figure 3. Exclusion of water **a** water over great length of tunnel **b** ground not too wet

of the arch and led down behind the side walls through a vertical pipe or drain shaft to the channel. Where the ground is not too wet the arch may be covered as shown in *Figure 3b*. It is always advisable to tighten the masonry by means of cement injections.

Ventilation of tunnels during operation[6-8]

All long tunnels to be used by steam trains should be ventilated. In Switzerland the old Saccardo system was adopted in the St. Gothard tunnel, before the electrification of the Gothard line. This system is not very efficient and other long tunnels (Simplon, Loetschberg and Grenchenberg) were provided with a different system, a curtain closing one portal. Air is introduced

Figure 4. Temperature variation inside and outside tunnel

behind the curtain at a pressure sufficient to overcome the frictional resistances of the lining and any opposing natural draughts which may occur. In tunnels there is always a natural draught due to:

1 the difference between the temperature inside the tunnel and that outside. The pressure arising from this difference will be (*Figure 4*)

$$h_t = \rho H \frac{\alpha(t_1 - t_2)}{1 + \alpha t_1} \qquad \dots\dots\dots\dots(11)$$

where ρ is the density of air, H the difference between the levels of the two portals, t_1 the temperature inside the tunnel, t_2 the temperature outside the tunnel, and $\alpha = 1/459$ for F scale (or $1/273$ for C scale).

2 the pressure arising from the difference of barometric pressure, reduced to the same level, given by

$$h_b = \beta b \qquad \dots\dots\dots\dots(12)$$

where b is the difference in barometric pressure and β is the density of mercury.

3 pressure of wind blowing against a portal, given by

$$h_w = \frac{w^2}{2g} \sin^2 \gamma \qquad \dots\dots\dots\dots(13)$$

where γ is the angle between wind direction and portal face, and w is the wind velocity.

The natural pressure h_n of the air in the tunnel will be the sum of h_t, h_b and h_w:

$$h_n = \pm h_t \pm h_b \pm h_w \qquad \dots\dots\dots(14)$$

The small amount of compression permits the assumption for practical purposes of a constant volume of air and the application of the ordinary formulae of hydraulics.

The ventilation pressure must therefore be

$$h = h_n + z + \frac{\rho v^2}{2g} = h_n + \frac{\rho v^2}{2g}\left(1 + \frac{fL}{m}\right) \qquad \dots\dots\dots(15)$$

where z is the resistance due to the lining of the tunnel, given by

$$z = \frac{f\rho v^2 L}{2gm} \qquad \dots\dots\dots(16)$$

f is $0\cdot007$ for a lined section of the tunnel, p the density of air, v the air velocity $= V/A$, L the length of tunnel, m the hydraulic radius of the tunnel section $= A/P$, A the area, P the perimeter of the tunnel section, and V is the volume of air per second.

The required power p of the ventilating apparatus will then be:

$$p = \frac{Vh}{102\eta} \text{ kilowatts} \qquad \dots\dots\dots(17)$$

or, if V is given in cusec and h in lb/sq ft,

$$p = \frac{Vh}{550\eta} \text{ horse power} \qquad \dots\dots\dots(18)$$

where η is the efficiency (about $0\cdot6$).

TUNNELLING METHODS

Pilot heading

In all the Swiss tunnels driven before World War II a pilot heading was used, a method which offered the following advantages:

a the section of the pilot heading being small, the debris removing period after each blast is short and drilling can start again after a short interruption. Progress is therefore fast. The excavation of the full section and the lining can be made to keep up with any speed attained by the pilot heading, for this is only a question of labour, transport and organization.

b the heading probes the ground. If it meets a difficulty which holds up its advance for a time, the rest of the work is not affected and can continue to progress normally. By the time the following work has reached the end of the heading the difficulty will usually have been overcome and the heading can advance again, whereas with a 'full face' advance any obstacle, such as bad ground or water, will stop the whole of the work.

c the method is economical in explosives.

d the method makes it possible to suit the methods of working down and lining to the geological conditions, and to choose an economical system to provide adequate safety and stability.

For long tunnels the pilot heading must always be driven as a bottom heading, in order to provide a continuous route for the transport system and for water running off at formation level. The St. Gothard tunnel was driven

TABLE 4

RATE OF PROGRESS (FROM ONE SIDE ONLY) AND CONSUMPTION OF EXPLOSIVE DURING
CONSTRUCTION OF THE MORE IMPORTANT SWISS TUNNELS

Tunnel	Ground	Section of pilot heading		Advance per day				Consumption of explosive				Types of machine drills used
				mean		max		heading		excavation		
		sq m	sq ft	m	ft	m	ft	kg/cu m	lb/cu ft	kg/cu m	lb/cu ft	
St. Gothard	Mica schists Granite	6·4	68·9	3·01	9·87	7·30	23·95	3·9	0·24	<1	<0·06	Ferrous and others (compressed air)
Simplon	Phyllites Mica schists Gneiss Granite	4·6-6·8	49·5-73·2	5·2	17·06	—	—	4·47	0·27	1·22	0·07	Brandt (water of 80-100 atm.)
Loetschberg	Limestone Gneiss Granite Mica schists	6·2	66·7	6·1	20·01	13·0	42·7	3·9	0·24	0·8	0·05	Meyer (North) Ingersoll-Rand (South) (compressed air)
Hauenstein	Limestone	6·0	64·6	10·4	34·1	14·7	48·2	2·2	0·13	0·5	0·03	Pneumatic hammers (Westfalia, Meyer, Flottmann)

with a top heading, with poor results both technically and economically. A top heading may be used quite successfully for short tunnels provided that the excavation is done according to the Belgian system.

Methods for enlarging heading and finishing tunnel
The two methods mainly used in Switzerland are known as the Austrian method (sometimes called the English-Austrian, being developed from the old English method, which advanced with full section), and the Belgian method.

Austrian method—The principle of the Austrian method, *Figure 5* a and b is first to excavate the whole section, then to commence lining with the side walls, and finish with the arch.

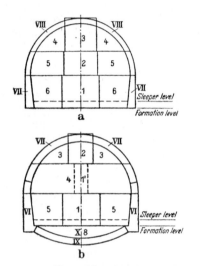 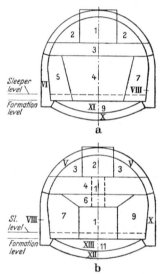

Figure 5. Austrian method   Figure 6. Belgian method a from top
a in rock b in soft ground   heading b from bottom heading

In solid rock, or rock which is not too brittle, the most economical method is to dig a cutting from the bottom heading up to the top of the full section (2 and 3 in *Figure* 5a). This is generally done in two steps. The rest of the excavation then follows as shown in *Figure* 5a.

One advantage of the Austrian method is that it permits the use of rational timbering, if necessary, capable of withstanding pressures from varying directions, including side pressures. Being economical it is the method generally used for long tunnels, especially at great depths where the walls of the excavation may yield to the weight of the cover (see above).

Belgian method—The Belgian method, *Figure* 6a and b, can be started either with a top heading, *Figure* 6a which is the more general, or by a bottom heading, *Figure* 6b. The underpinning of the arch is rather a delicate job but the advantage of the method is that the roof can very quickly be supported by the arch. The springing of the arch must be placed on a sill of reinforced concrete in order to prevent its sinking during the excavation for the side walls and their construction. The arch itself offers little resistance to side pressures until the side walls are built; for this reason the method should not be adopted where side pressures are expected, as, for example, in depths greater than about 5,000 ft. The method was, in fact, used for the St. Gothard tunnel and proved unsatisfactory. On the other hand it gives very good results in soft ground, where the height of cover is small and where the surface must not be disturbed *e.g.* where there are buildings. Another advantage is that less timbering is required.

Nowadays these methods are only used in soft ground. They require too much manual labour. The most expensive and toilsome part of the work is the loading of the excavated material and this work is now done mechanically by means of shovels driven by compressed air or electricity. These heavy and expensive machines work economically only if the whole excavation is concentrated in one place. This means that the excavation must not be done, as before, in several steps but the tunnel must be driven full section at once (full-face driving). That method is now used for all tunnels driven through solid or not too soft ground. Where a tunnel meets very bad ground, one of the old classic methods mentioned above must be adopted. In brittle rock steel supports may be used instead of wooden ones. At large depths where the elastic compressed rock expands into the excavated space it can also be fixed by means of pinning or bolting (see also chapter on Tunnelling Practice). At very great depths the rock might become plastic. It depends upon the degree of plasticity whether steel supports must be used or if bolting will do[9].

Ground movements

As a general rule it is more economical, and shows a greater degree of skill, to avoid or prevent ground movements than to overcome them.

Ground movements are a function of the size of the excavation, but an even more rapidly increasing function of the time during which the excavated space is left without lining. If the tunnel is in ground likely to move the method chosen must be one which will permit the expected movements to be opposed by lining as soon as possible once excavation has begun.

Transport system

It must be possible to transport all excavated material out of the tunnel and to bring in all materials required for the work, including timbering and lining, in quantities appropriate to the rate of progress. For long tunnels this requires thorough study and very careful organization; the economic success of the work as a whole depends largely on that organization. The track must be well laid out and well maintained. In a railway tunnel with full-face driving the gauge of the track for material transport may be 1 m (3·28 ft). If the tunnel is driven through bad ground by means of one of the classic methods mentioned above, the gauge should be smaller, about 0·75 m (2·5 ft). For a long tunnel a large gauge is advantageous because it allows a higher speed. In the tunnels through the Alps compressed air locomotives were used, but, compressed air being expensive, electric locomotives are used today.

The whole transport system must be controlled by a carefully drawn up timetable which must be observed as strictly as those for ordinary railway service.

Ventilation during construction of tunnel

The volume of air normally required for ventilation only, without refrigeration, can be assumed to be about 18 cu ft/min ($\frac{1}{2}$ cu m/min) multiplied by the number of men working together inside the tunnel. To that must be added about 5,000 cu ft per lb (300 cu m/kg) of explosive used.

Example—For a crew of 200 men using 500 lb of explosive per shift of eight hours the volume of air required is given by:

$$200 \times 18 = 3,600 \text{ cu ft/min}$$

$$\frac{500 \times 5,000}{8 \times 60} = 5,200 \text{ cu ft/min}$$

Total $= 8,800$ cu ft/min (or 147 cusec)

Such a small volume of air can easily be conveyed to the works by means of a pipe, diam $d=1$ ft 6 in. Assuming compression with constant volume, the pressure to be given to the air at the tunnel entrance will be (see equations 15 and 16):

$$h = \frac{\rho v^2}{2g}\left(1 + \frac{fL}{m}\right) \qquad \dots\dots\dots(19)$$

For a circular pipe $m = \dfrac{\pi d^2}{4\pi d} = \dfrac{d}{4}$ $\qquad \dots\dots\dots(20)$

Taking[10] $4f = \lambda = 0{\cdot}02 - 0{\cdot}03$,

$$h = \frac{\rho v^2}{2g}\left(1 + \frac{\lambda L}{d}\right) \qquad \dots\dots\dots(21)$$

and the required power will be as given in equations 17 and 18, *i.e.*

$$p = \frac{Vh}{102\eta}\,\text{kw} \qquad \text{or} \quad p = \frac{Vh}{550\eta}\,\text{h.p.} \qquad \dots\dots\dots(22)$$

where η is the efficiency, about $0{\cdot}6$.

The pipe diameter chosen is important. The resistance of the pipe is

$$z = \frac{\lambda \rho v^2 L}{2gd}\,(\text{kg/sq m or lb/sq ft}), \qquad \dots\dots\dots(23)$$

velocity $v = V/A$, where $V =$ volume per second and $A =$ area of pipe section $= \pi d^2/4$.

Hence $$v^2 = \frac{16V^2}{d^4\pi^2}$$

So $$z = \frac{8\lambda \rho V^2 L}{g\pi^2 d^5}\,(\text{kg/sq m or lb/sq ft}) \qquad \dots\dots\dots(24)$$

The resistance of a ventilation pipe to the movement of air within it is proportional to the length, to the square of the volume of air passing in unit time, and inversely proportional to the fifth power of the diameter[10].

If the tunnel reaches a depth where the temperature is high a much greater volume of air must be provided. During the construction of the Simplon tunnel, 25–35 cu m/sec (900–1,250 cusec) was sent into the tunnel. (The volume was limited by the cross sectional area of the heading the air must pass through. The velocity should not exceed about 13 ft/sec where men are working.) Such a volume cannot be supplied economically through a pipe as the resistance would be far too high. Through the finished part of the tunnel a pipe of large diameter, say 2 ft 6in to 3 ft 6 in, may be laid, but through the length under construction a diameter of 1 ft 9 in will be about the maximum permissible.

A volume of 35 cu m/sec would have required 11,800 kW or 16,000 h.p. For this reason the Simplon tunnel was not built as a double track tunnel, but as two parallel single track tunnels 17 m (56 ft) apart from centre to centre (*Figure 7*). Only one was completed in the first operation, while the heading only of the second was driven, and used for ventilation. Every 200 m (656 ft) the two headings were connected by a transverse heading, *Figure 8*. Air was blown through heading *II* and passed through the last transverse heading (which was the only one left open, the others being closed as soon as a new one was through), so entering tunnel *I* and leaving by portal *I*, passing the excavation and lining work. For the advancing fronts of the two headings a small amount of air, corresponding to the number of men working there, was taken off the main current at *A* (*Figure 8*) by means of small ventilators, and led[10] through pipes of diameter 0·40 m (1 ft 4 in).

The pressure and power required by such a system can be calculated with the help of equation 19

$$h = \frac{\rho v^2}{2g}\left(1 + \frac{fL}{m}\right)(\text{kg/sq m or lb/sq ft}) \quad \ldots\ldots\ldots\ldots(30)$$

where $m = A/P$ (cross sectional area/perimeter of the heading or tunnel) = hydraulic radius, and f for unlined heading, according to Murgue[10] = 0·0175; for finished and lined tunnel, according to Mermier = 0·007.

Equation 19 can also be used for the pipe line supplying compressed air to the penumatic tools.

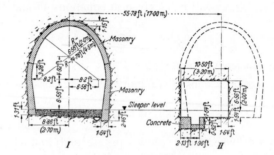

Figure 7.   Section of Simplon tunnel
as first built.   Scale 1:180

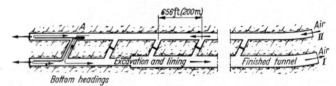

Figure 8.   Plan of Simplon tunnel

If temperatures are high, as they were in the Simplon tunnel, the air must be cooled with cold water before it reaches the working sites[11].

In a railway tunnel or in a gallery of a similar section driven with full-face, a pipe with a diameter of about 1 m (3·28 ft) can be used for the ventilation up to the advancing front.   That eases the solution of the problem.

REFERENCES

[1] THOMA, E. *Ueber das Wärmeleitungsproblem bei wellig begrenzter Oberfläche und dessen Anwendung auf Tunnelbauten* (The Problem of Heat Conduction below an Undulating Surface and its Application to Tunnelling) Karlsruhe, 1906

[2] KOENIGSBERGER, J., THOMA, E. and GOELZ, H. Versuche über primäre und sekundäre Beeinflussung der normalen geothermischen Tiefenstufe (Experiments on Primary and Secondary Influences on the Normal Reciprocal Geothermal Gradient) *Ecl. geol. Hel.* 10 (1908)

[3] ANDREAE, C. Die Temperaturprognose im Tunnelbau (The Prediction of the Temperatures in Tunnels) *Schweiz. Bauztg* (1953)

[4] ANDREAE, C. *La prévision des températures souterraines* (The prediction of the temperatures underground) Annales des Ponts et Chaussées, Paris, 1958

[5] Maillart, R. Ueber Gebirgsdruck (On Earth Pressure at Great Depth) *Schweiz. Bauztg* (1923)

[6] Rothpletz, F. Die Ventilationsanlage des Simplon-tunnels (The Ventilating Plant for the Simplon-Tunnel) *Schweiz. Bauztg* (1919)

[7] Andreae, C. *Der Bau langer, tiefliegender Gebirgs-tunnel* (The Construction of Long, Deep Tunnels) Berlin, 1926

[8] 'Andreae, C. *Les grands souterrains transalpins* (The Great Tunnels through the Alps) Zürich, 1948

[9] von Rabcewicz, L. Die Ankerung im Tunnelbau ersetzt bisher gebräuchliche Einbaumethoden (Bolting replaces Timbering Methods used hitherto) *Schweiz. Bauztg* (1957)

[10] Wiesmann, E. *Küustliche Lüftung im Stollen-und Tunnelbau sowie von Tunnels im Betrieb* (Artificial Ventilation of Headings and Tunnels during Construction and of Tunnels during Operation) Zürich, 1918

[11] Mermier, E. La Ventilation et la Réfrigération du Tunnel du Simplon (Ventilation and Refrigeration of the Simplon Tunnel) *Bull. tech. Suisse rom.* (1907)

LAND DRAINAGE

G. R. McKay, B.Eng., Ph.D., A.M.I.C.E.

Revised by H. Cheetham, M.B.E., B.A., A.M.I.C.E.

LAND DRAINAGE ORGANIZATION IN GREAT BRITAIN

Land Drainage Act 1930.

River Boards Act 1948.

Rivers (Prevention of Pollution) Act 1951.

Although there are a number of Acts affecting land drainage, some obsolete, dating back to the reign of Henry VIII, the Land Drainage Act 1930 is the basis of all modern land drainage legislation. This Act set up Catchment Boards which covered the larger part of England and Wales. In Scotland where the need for extensive land drainage works is not so widespread, land drainage matters are dealt with by the Department of Agriculture for Scotland.

Each catchment board covered a geographical catchment area. Large rivers such as the Severn, Trent, Yorkshire Ouse *etc,* had a separate board, but smaller river catchments were grouped into convenient administrative areas such as Essex Rivers, Sussex Rivers *etc.*

The catchment area of a river is that area, the rainfall on which ultimately drains into the river. In most cases natural water-sheds exist, but in others artificial drainage and the construction of floodbanks have cut off the natural drainage of an area to one river and diverted it to another. For example the River Don was originally a tributary of the River Trent, but was diverted some 300 years ago to the Yorkshire Ouse by the Dutch engineer Vermuyden.

The Catchment Board members were appointed by County Councils and County Boroughs and by the Ministry of Agriculture and Fisheries after consultation with Internal Drainage Boards within the catchment area. For the first time the principle of responsibility of passage of water to the sea was adopted in the financial provisions of the Act, and the Catchment Board had power to levy a rate which was collected as a precept on the rating authorities within the area. Additional revenue was obtained by the Catchment Board by precepts on Internal Drainage Boards and in special circumstances by contributions from local authorities for special schemes of direct benefit to such authorities. Government grants were also received for new works and improvement schemes.

The direct authority of the Catchment Board was limited to its statutory 'main river'. There was no definition of 'main river' which was an arbitrary portion of the principal river and tributaries marked in red on a map prepared by the Ministry of Agriculture.

The Board had power to carry out works on the main river and banks for the purposes of land drainage in its widest term including flood prevention and conservation of water, but not navigation. In the Act provision was made for the formation and supervision of Internal Drainage Boards. Internal Drainage Districts are districts within the catchment boundary, usually low lying areas where land drainage is of paramount importance. The boundary of an internal drainage district is not specified under the Act, but normally an area up to a level of 8 ft above highest known flood level in the case of agricultural land and up to highest known flood level in urban areas is included in an Internal Drainage Board. Such an area was recognized as receiving special benefit from land drainage works carried out either by the Catchment Board or the Internal Drainage Board and as such was charged a drainage rate on the schedule 'A' value of the land and property, capital costs being an owners' rate and maintenance costs an occupiers' rate. In some cases Internal Drainage Boards are quite small, some only a few hundred acres and others as large as a hundred thousand acres.

The 1930 Act gave the Catchment Board powers to prevent any person obstructing any stream by building a dam *etc,* and also gave certain powers of land drainage to County Councils in connection with minor watercourses outside Internal Drainage Boards.

The River Board Act 1948 covered the whole of England and Wales except for the metropolitan area of London and the Thames Conservancy Catchment Board and the Lee Conservancy Catchment Board, which had more comprehensive powers. In all 32 River Boards were formed and some of the smaller areas set up under the 1930 Act were amalgamated into larger units. It brought under one control land drainage, fisheries and pollution prevention and in addition made the Boards responsible for collating all information regarding river flows.

The land drainage duties of the new Boards were similar to those of the old Catchment Boards; existing Fishery Boards were taken over and the responsibility of dealing with pollution was transferred from the local authorities. The River Boards consist of not more than 40 members of which not less than 3/5ths are nominated by the County Councils and County Boroughs and the remainder are appointed by the Minister of Agriculture and Fisheries; one of which represents the Minister and the others represent Internal Drainage Boards interests. In the case of the Yorkshire Ouse and River Trent Boards only, an additional member is appointed by the National Coal Board as there are considerable land drainage problems which arise from subsidence caused by the mining of coal in low lying areas.

The catchment areas of the River Boards were delineated in the same manner as for the old Catchment Boards. The revenue of the River Boards is raised in the same manner as the old Catchment Boards, *i.e.* precept on Internal Drainage Boards, precept on local authorities, Government grants and special contributions.

The Rivers (Prevention of Pollution) Act 1951 was passed to make new provision for maintaining or restoring the wholesomeness of the rivers and other inland or coastal waters of England and Wales in place of the Rivers Pollution Prevention Act 1876 and certain other enactments.

Briefly summarized, a person commits an offence if he causes or knowingly permits to enter a stream any poisonous, noxious or polluting matter or matter which tends to impede the proper flow of the water of the stream in a manner likely to lead to a substantial aggravation of pollution.

The 1951 Act enables River Boards to make by-laws for prescribing standards for the purpose of determining when matter is to be treated as poisonous, noxious or polluting, and states a guiding principle that in exercising these powers a River Board shall have regard to the character and flow of the stream and to the extent to which the stream is or may in the future be used for industrial purposes, fisheries, water supply, agriculture, transport or navigation.

The Act also includes provisions making it necessary to obtain the consent of River Boards to the bringing into use of new or altered outlets and to the making of new discharges of trade or sewage effluent to streams, and enables conditions with respect to nature, composition *etc* to be imposed.

Section 6 provides for the extension of all or any of the provisions of sections 2 to 5 of the Act to tidal waters or parts of the sea by means of an order.

DESIGN OF DRAINAGE SCHEMES

The information required for the design of drainage schemes will be considered under the following headings: rainfall; resultant discharge and flow in the rivers or run-off; details of the catchment area and surveys.

RAINFALL

Rainfall records are collected by the British Rainfall Organization, the Meteorological Office, and the Air Ministry. The Organization relies largely on voluntary observers who forward copies of their daily readings to the office at the end of each month or year. Over 5,000 stations are in operation. The Organization has two publications: *British Rainfall*, which contains tables of rainfall at nearly all the stations for the previous year, with maps, tables and descriptive matter dealing with the distribution of rainfall in each month and in the whole year, and *The Meteorological Magazine* (monthly), which contains tables of rainfall in the previous month.

Although extremely useful in a general sense, rainfall records are not sufficient, as set out, as a basis for land drainage design. Most River Boards obtain a copy (monthly) of the daily records of the observers in their area. As the system is a voluntary one, the number and in particular the distribution of stations throughout the area is usually inadequate. Additional stations are set up and maintained by River Boards. In test areas on one or more tributaries, temporary stations can be set up and maintained long enough to allow a reasonable estimate of the rainfall in the test area to be interpolated from the main permanent station records.

In land drainage, interest lies only in extremes of rainfall *i.e.* long periods of continuous heavy rain and three or more weeks of drought. 'Long periods' vary with the size of the catchment of the river concerned, from three days in smaller areas to twenty or more in larger. Short storms of a few minutes' duration but of great intensity are of no account. Daily readings are normally sufficient for large catchment areas, but can be very misleading for small areas of the order of 100 sq miles. For instance two daily readings of 1 in might indicate an intensity of 1 in in 24 hours whereas in fact all the rain fell in the last 12 hours of the first rain day and the first 12 hours of the second rain day, an intensity of 2 in in 24 hours, 100 per cent greater than indicated. Autographic rain gauges are very useful especially in small areas, but are expensive. In most cases daily readings, combined with local information regarding the approximate times of the storm, will be sufficient. Of particular, if special, interest is snow,

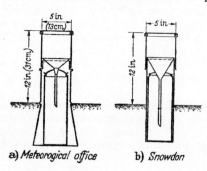

Figure 1. Types of approved rain gauges for daily readings

a) *Meteorological office*   b) *Snowdon*

so that the type of gauge which allows the most accurate estimate of the equivalent rainfall should be used. The Meteorological Office gauge and the Snowdon gauge are both recommended (*Figure 1*).

RUN-OFF

The land drainage engineer is primarily concerned with the result of rainfall—the run-off or resultant discharge of the rivers. It is important therefore to know not only the rainfall but what the effect of this rainfall will be. The relationship between rainfall and run-off is not a simple one and as yet there is no satisfactory theory or empirical formula generally correlating the two. A detailed study of rainfall records and the corresponding run-off or discharge will, however, allow a reasonable estimate of the maximum discharge likely to occur in an area to be made.

The following factors influence run-off:

a size, topography and geology of the catchment area

b shape of catchment area and length of river

c season of year

d weather

e duration, intensity and direction of the particular rainstorm.

a and *b* are constant and virtually unalterable features; if, as is often assumed, they were the only factors affecting run-off there would be a definite relation between rainfall and run-off which could be determined by measurement for all time. *c, d* and *e* (and other factors to a lesser extent) have a far greater influence on run-off than is usually allowed. It is these factors, so extremely variable and indeterminate, which produce the apparent paradoxes which observations show to occur.

Observations show that a period of rain falling in a summer month will only produce less than two thirds of the discharge of a similar period of rain falling in a winter month. (Summer and winter are taken as the growing and non-growing seasons of the year, approximately 1 April to 30 September and 1 October to 31 March respectively. The change is definite and with no intervening period.) This difference is due to direct evaporation and to absorption by growing vegetation. When it is realized that a single tree will absorb up to 80 gallons (250 litres) per day and an acre of corn about 1,000 tons (1 hectare of corn about 2,500 tonnes) in a season, the difference in growing and non-growing seasonal discharges can be readily understood.

In studying run-off, a particular rainstorm must not be separated from the rainfall and other weather conditions which preceded it. Thus an inch of rain in twenty four hours falling on a snow laden, frozen country-side will produce a different effect from the same amount falling after ten days averaging half an inch per day, which again will be different from the same amount falling after ten dry days. Snow must always remain a special case. The discharge from snow depends on the rate of thaw (which is in itself independent of rainfall) rather than on the amount of snow.

The direction of the rainstorm and its distribution over the area finally determines the flow in the river and it is the effect of this factor which is the most difficult to estimate or to account for in design. Each river consists of the main stream fed by numerous tributaries and it is the incidence of the flood waves in the tributaries at the main stream which determines the peak discharge there.

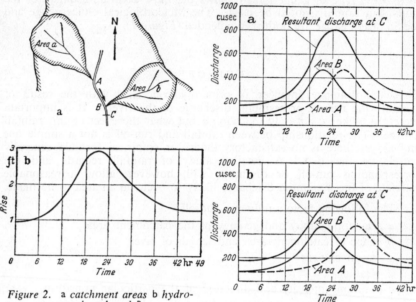

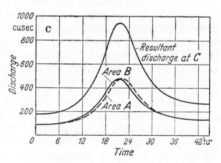

Figure 2. a catchment areas b hydrograph at A and B

Figure 3. Discharge/time curves for
different rainfall conditions

Example—Consider two equal and similar catchment areas *a* and *b* discharging into a river at A and B respectively, *Figure* 2a, so that A is about ten miles above B. The hydrograph for a particular storm is given in *Figure* 2b. It is a portion of the automatic recorder chart for that time. From this hydrograph and the stage discharge curve (see p 401) the discharge can be plotted against the time.

Consider both areas subjected to a uniform rainstorm at the same time and consider the flow from the two areas at *C*. At 0 hours both areas are contributing a normal flow of 90 cusec (cu ft/sec: 1 cusec = 0·028 cu m/sec) each. Then the contribution from *b* starts to increase. The flood wave from *a* will move down the river at about two miles/hr so that the contribution from *a* will not increase until five hr after that from *b* (*Figure* 3a). Adding the contribution from *b* to the contribution from *a* at any time we get the resultant discharge in the river at *C* at that time. The maximum discharge of each catchment is 470 cusec. The maximum discharge in the river at *C* is 800 cusec.

Consider a rainfall of the same intensity but moving north west so that it takes about four hours to move across from *b* to *a*. Then the contribution from *a* arrives at *C* about nine hr after that from *b* (*Figure* 3b). The maximum contribution from each area is unaltered but the maximum discharge in the river at *C* is only 690 cusec.

If the same rainstorm is moving south east, the contributions from each tributary arrive at *C* within an hour of each other (*Figure* 3c). The maximum discharge at *C* is then 930 cusec.

In all these three conditions the rain gauges in areas *a* and *b* will register the same amount. The resultant discharge at *C* is 800, 690 and 930 cusec respectively, the total discharges over a period being equal. It is clear that there can be no simple relation between rainfall and maximum discharge.

A method of ascertaining maximum flood flows is the use of ' unit hydrographs '[1], if the necessary hydrology information is available[2].

As a rough guide, the run-off is often assumed to be 14 cusecs per thousand acres for flat agricultural land, increasing to 30 cusecs per thousand acres for undulating or hilly land. Where part of the area is urban the run-off is increased to 40–80 cusecs per thousand acres for the whole area, depending on the amount of development. In agricultural areas it is uneconomical to design for very rare catastrophical storms. In a storm in the Midlands in August 1957 the rainfall was nearly 6 in in 6 hours, and resulted in an estimated discharge of 1,000 cusecs per thousand acres on a catchment area of 7,000 acres.

MEASUREMENT OF DISCHARGE

Irrespective of the flow in the river, it is the level of the river which is all important and it is the object of flood relief works to attain control of the river level. A water level can be easily recorded and as a flood is a serious occurrence for those within the flooded area there is usually a wealth of information about each and every major flood for many centuries. The highest level likely to be reached at any place along the river can be determined, and also the maximum height of any single flood. In studying this information due allowance should be made for any changes which may have taken place in the river.

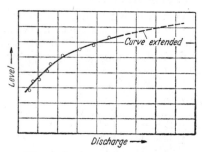

Figure 4. Stage discharge curve

To design flood relief works it is necessary to be able to determine the maximum height of the river after the works have been carried out. To do this it is necessary to know the maximum discharge and hydraulic conditions of the river at this discharge. The anticipated maximum height can then be calculated or determined from the results of tests on scale models. The latter is probably the better method but facilities for building and operating models may not always be available. In either instance a detailed and intimate knowledge of the regime of the river is necessary before accurate and economic design can be accomplished.

It is relatively easy to determine the maximum level attained along a river by a flood but this does not represent a condition of flow. The maximum levels are not reached at the same time. The line joining the maximum heights, often termed the flood gradient, merely represents the envelopment of the flood (wave) as it passes down the river. The level in the upper reaches is usually falling while that in the lower reaches is rising. Any calculation of discharge using cross sectional area of flow and flood gradient may give a wrong discharge. The effect of any modification varies with the discharge so that an accurate estimate of the discharge is essential to good design.

There are no data which can be given for general use to compute or estimate the maximum discharge of a river. Such reliable measurements as have been made show no general relationship between discharge and the factors which might be expected to affect it. The maximum discharges of rivers of comparable catchment areas vary so widely that figures taken from such sources to estimate discharge would only be misleading. The only satisfactory method is, with the aid of actual measurements, to create a stage discharge curve (*Figure 4*). This curve is the graphical representa-tion of the relation between the discharge and the level of the river at the

point of measurement. While some time must elapse in the collection of
the necessary data it is not necessary to wait for the maximum flood before
use can be made of the curve.

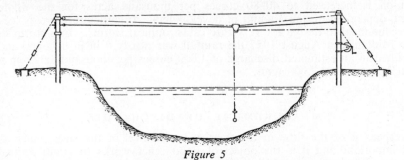

Figure 5

Cable station for river discharge measurement

The first criterion for accuracy in river discharge measurements is
that the whole flow should pass through the station at all discharges and
with as little local disturbance as possible. A single span bridge with
abutments back from the bank of the river is an ideal site; failing this
it is necessary to erect a cableway across the river at a point where the
banks are high and unlikely to be inundated (*Figure 5*).

Whatever the type of equipment chosen it is essential that a complete
gauging can be carried out quickly. At large discharges a small increase
in level will give a large increase in discharge, so if there is difficulty in
moving the meter from point to point an indeterminate average of the
discharges between levels will be recorded.

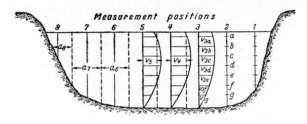

Figure 6

Discharge by gauging

An initial survey of the cross section of the river at the station is
made and plotted. The section is divided into equidistant vertical lines and
velocity measurements are made at varying depths on these verticals. The
average velocity v_1, v_2 for each vertical can be found. From the section
and the water level at the time of measurement the effective areas a_1, a_2
can be determined, then the total discharge (see *Figure 6*) is given by

$$Q = a_1 v_1 + a_2 v_2 + \qquad \qquad \text{............(1)}$$

The velocity is measured by means of a current meter. A current
meter operates by counting the revolutions in a fixed time of an impeller
turned by the flowing water. The makers supply a chart showing the
relation between the revolutions per minute and the water velocity. A
current meter requires great care in handling to yield good results. The
need for regular calibration (determination of the relation between r.p.m.
and velocity) cannot be stressed too strongly. Calibration will be carried
out by the makers or by the National Physical Laboratory, Teddington.

Discharge measurements should, at first, be carried out at regular intervals and also throughout high or flood flows. The measurements when plotted will not lie exactly on a smooth curve. Measurement to within 5 per cent is excellent. The discharge at a level on a rising flood will exceed that at the same level on a falling flood and will vary also with the ultimate height of the flood. A note should be made at the time of measurement whether the river is rising or falling, the duration of the gauging and, later, the ultimate height of the flood.

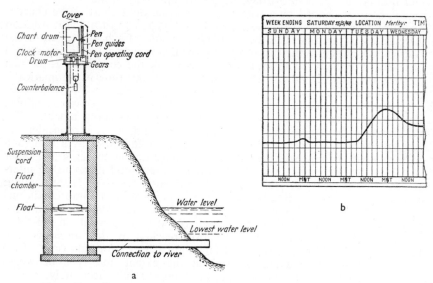

Figure 7. a *float type level recorder* b *typical chart 10 ft range, drum type*

Level measurements are taken continuously by means of an automatic recorder checked by a gauge board. Each measured discharge is plotted against its corresponding level. When a number of points at reasonable intervals have been obtained a smooth curve is drawn through them. This is the stage discharge curve, which for any level gives the corresponding discharge. The curve is extended beyond the measured limits to allow estimation of the discharge at levels higher than those yet recorded. As occasion permits this extension is amended to conform to actual measured results.

In a large catchment area with a system of tributaries it is necessary to set up, at least temporarily, more than one gauging station in order to obtain a relation between area of catchment and discharge. The discharge is not directly proportional to the area of catchment. Two tributaries each with a recorded maximum flow of 5,000 cusec will not produce, normally, a flow of 10,000 cusec below their confluence. The relation between area of catchment and the resultant run-off is a function of the duration and intensity of the rain but a study of records will allow a reasonable estimate to be made. Thus, measured results for one area of a given size can be interpolated with reasonable accuracy to that of a different size. The gauging stations should therefore be chosen to be representative of widely varying areas.

Automatic recorders

In addition to gauging stations at a few points in the catchment area it is necessary to know the level at salient points along each tributary and the main river at the same time. Gauge boards are not sufficient for this purpose, for if they are read, as is usual, once daily at a fixed time, much useful information will be lost. Automatic recorders are set up as at gauging stations. Wherever possible, float operated automatic recorders should be used, although the initial installation is comparatively costly. In silt laden rivers and sites where wave action is prevalent, special precautions have to be taken in the design of the inlet pipe.

An alternative type of automatic recorder, the pressure operated type, is cheaper to install, but the float operated type is considered more accurate and positive for river recording, especially on isolated sites.

A float suspended by a wire activates a pen on a chart. The chart is on a drum or disk rotated by clockwork and geared to turn one revolution in seven days, the time scale being divided to suit. Each movement of the float is transmitted to the pen through a parallel movement reducing system of levers or pulleys. The drum or disc is set to the correct time, the pen to the correct level and for a week the level at any time is automatically recorded, *Figure 7*.

Time, money and trouble spent on gauging and level recorder stations, and the necessary office work, will be quickly and amply repaid. The certainty which can be introduced into design will result in considerable saving, either by the removal of the possibility of failure or by a reduction in the extent of the works proposed. The stage discharge curve and other measured features will allow the known previous flood levels to be interpretated as discharges, which can be compared with the corresponding rainfall. Then from rainfall records the worst possible rainfall conditions can be estimated. Comparison with discharge records will allow the translation of these conditions to a discharge at various points in the river. From the stage discharge curve the level reached by this discharge can be determined. Also an equivalent factor for Chézy's formula ($v = C\sqrt{mi}$) can be calculated. Having determined the extent and type of works required the effect of these works can be estimated quite accurately.

DETAILS OF CATCHMENT AREA: SURVEYS

The boundary of a catchment area can best be obtained from the coloured $2\frac{1}{2}$ in or 1 in to 1 mile ordnance sheets. These show the contours clearly marked. The boundary follows the water-shed or parting of the hills and by starting at the point on the river to which the catchment area is required and following the ridges of the contours between the highest points of adjacent hills the boundary can be delineated, *Figure 8*. If greater detail of the boundary is required *e.g.* for legal documents, the boundary as marked on the 1 in sheet is transferred to the 6 in sheet, the line walked and amendments made by observation on the ground. For technical calculations the area as delineated on the 1 in sheet suffices. The area is measured by planimeter or by one of the standard methods for calculating the areas of irregular shapes.

As a general reference it is useful to 'milepost' a river. The mileage along the right bank differs from point to point from that along the left bank. (Right and left are designated looking downstream.) An arbitrary point representing the start of a river, mouth or confluence, is chosen and the mileage scaled on the map along the centre line of the river. A line is drawn through each mile point at right angles to the river and permanent marker posts placed on this line on each bank of the river.

For river improvements works, cross sections of the river are required. They should normally be taken at regular intervals, 'typical' sections being avoided, except in special cases, where common sense indicates that 'typical' sections for stated lengths of river would give more accurate results. The interval depends on the use and extent of the survey. All that is required

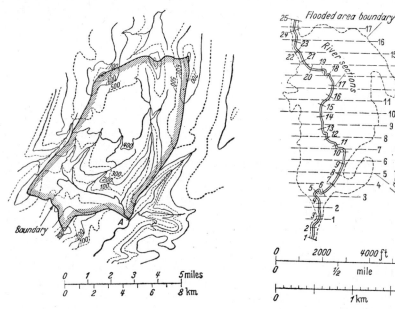

Figure 8. Contour map of a catchment area

Figure 9. Setting out river and land sections

is to obtain a fair average. On a large river probably 8 sections per mile might be sufficient, and on a small river sections every 50 ft might be necessary. Cross sections are taken at right angles to the river at the point of sectioning and distances between sections are measured along the centre line of the river. As the intervals between sections should normally be constant, so also should the intervals between soundings: 5 ft for smaller rivers, 10 ft for larger. Soundings are taken from water level to the nearest 3 in. Water levels are measured to the nearest inch. Water level at the last section taken on one day should be taken first the next morning to obtain the surface fall throughout the length. Cables or pipelines crossing above or below the river should be noted. The sections are required mainly for calculation purposes and should be plotted to 1/10, 10 ft to 1 in or 20 ft to 1 in scale. They must be plotted to the same horizontal and vertical scales otherwise it would not be possible to determine the wetted perimeter. There are two conventions for plotting river sections:

1 looking downstream. The farthest upstream section is No. 1; it is plotted looking downstream and is placed at the bottom of the sheet so that the right bank is on the right hand side of the paper. The other sections are plotted successively above each other

2 looking upstream. The farthest downstream section is No. 1; it is plotted looking upstream and is placed at the bottom of the sheet with the right bank to the left of the paper. The sections are plotted successively above one another.

Both methods offer a visual picture of the river, and the former method is usually preferred. In the second method it is at first a little confusing to have the right bank on the left of the paper and vice versa.

For flood alleviation schemes details of the land adjoining the river are also required. These are again obtained by cross sections. The intervals between sections are determined in the same way as for the river sections. They should be taken at right angles to the general direction of flow through the area and should be set out on the map first before being taken on the ground, *Figure 9*. They should extend from each bank of the river to land which is 10 ft or more above flood level. Care should be taken to see that there is not a low lying area behind the higher ground. If there is it should be included in the section. In addition to field levels at regular intervals across the section, levels should be taken where the line cuts ditches, drains, roads and railways. Inverts of bridges and culverts in the area are also required. Land sections also should be plotted to scales which allow easy calculation, but different vertical and horizontal scales are used to show up the relatively small changes in level. A useful combination of scales is 10 ft to 1 in vertically and 100 ft to 1 in horizontally. The land sections should be plotted to the same convention as for river sections.

For internal drainage schemes a detailed contour survey of the area is required, with 1 ft contours of the flat low lying portions and 5 ft contours of the relatively higher ground. The survey should include all land within 10 ft of the highest water level or the lowest land level, whichever is higher. In addition to the contours spot levels will be required along all roads, embankments and main drains in the area, and the inverts and soffits of bridges, culverts *etc*. In urban areas adjoining the river additional information will be required of all openings and discharges into the river, such as loading bays, sewers, storm overflows, the purpose of such openings and an indication of the effect of increasing the highest level or reducing the lowest river level. Most of this additional information will be available from the engineer to the local authority.

ALLEVIATION OF FLOODING

Flooding is best defined as the inundation of natural washlands within a river valley, and the problem is to convey water through any particular area without flooding taking place. The flooded area may be mainly urban or rural. The principle of improvements will depend upon the nature of the area. In many urban areas land liable to flood, being cheap, has been too often used for building sites and it is now desirable to prevent any further flooding absolutely. Such a goal is hardly technically possible. No matter what circumstances are taken as the worst possible, sooner or later there will occur that series of circumstances which will exceed expectation and the area will be flooded. The interval between such floods, however, is long enough to speak of total prevention. Such a scheme is usually costly but as the damage done in an urban area by a flood is enormous and affects many people, the money is often available. The problem in a rural area is somewhat different. A flood in the growing season is a disaster, whether the land affected is arable or pasture, but flooding in the non-growing season can be of benefit. Farm buildings are usually situated outside or above the flooded area. The remedy in both urban and rural areas is one of degree, but in urban areas the remedy is often restricted by virtue of the adjacent property.

The chief methods of dealing with floods are, in general:

    a enlargement of existing channel
    b construction of by-pass channels
    c construction of flood banks
    d use of control areas
    e removal of cause of flooding

or a combination of one or more of these. The choice will depend on local circumstances but the advantages and disadvantages of each method will have a part in this choice.

ENLARGEMENT OF EXISTING CHANNEL

Distinction must be made between extensive cleaning and enlargement of the channel. The bank full capacity of a natural river is normally about one third of the maximum flood discharge. All rivers have or have had a summer channel, now termed the river, and a winter channel. The winter channel can be traced in rural areas and may vary in width from the river to two or three miles. In natural form flood discharges are accommodated in this double channel. Fundamentally it is only because of man's insistence on the use of the land within the winter channel, either for agricultural or urban development, that he has to endure ' flooding '. Flood discharges occur at the most on a few days each year as the river channel is sufficient to accommodate average flows. To enlarge the channel to carry flood flows is in direct contradiction to natural requirements and it is to be expected that the natural forces will endeavour to restore the original conditions. This attempted restoration may be slow and easily dealt with by normal maintenance. It may however be extremely rapid and costly to handle. Banks may be seriously eroded, shoals form in the bed and creeping shoals of ballast may move down the river into the enlarged portion.

With modern machinery the excavation may be both cheap and easy. For total prevention the quantity of excavation will be large and the disposal of the soil may be troublesome and expensive. Agricultural amenities, fences, drinking places *etc* must all be given attention. In the new cut the normal depth will be considerably less than that in the old river, and so shallow that cattle may be able to wander across the river. This would entail the expense of fencing along both sides of the river. In urban areas the application of this method is limited.

CONSTRUCTION OF BY-PASS CHANNELS

If it is not possible to restrict flood discharges to defined limits through an area liable to flood it may be possible to prevent flooding in that area by diverting part of the flow above the area to rejoin the main flow below the area. For economy it is obvious that the existing river should be used to carry the maximum possible flow without flooding, and the by-pass channel should be designed to carry only the balance. If the entrance to the by-pass is unrestricted it will carry a proportion of all flows, with all the resultant disadvantages of enlargement of the river channel. The by-pass or the river channel will silt up within a few years. The discharge into the by-pass is controlled by means of a weir or sluices.

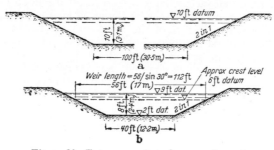

Figure 10. Entrance weir to by-pass channel

Theoretically the existing river should carry all the discharge up to that which causes flooding, then the by-pass should carry any further increase. This is rarely practically possible. The detail design of a by-pass entrance is not easy to calculate with any accuracy, but the problem can be solved without difficulty by a model. A first approximation can be derived.

> *Example*—A river, slope 1:2,000 and of section shown in *Figure 10*a, has a maximum discharge of 7,000 cusec when the depth of flow is 10 ft. At some point lower down flooding occurs when the river is 8 ft deep. By calculation, when the depth is 8 ft the discharge will be 5,000 cusec. Therefore the by-pass will have to carry 2,000 cusec of the maximum discharge. The slope of the by-pass will approximate to that of the river *i.e.* 1:2,000. The channel required has 40 ft bottom width, 2:1 side slopes and 8 ft depth, *Figure 10*b. If the by-pass channel takes off from the river at 30° then the length of weir possible will be about 110 ft. The head to discharge 2,000 cusec over this weir is about 3 ft. There will be a fall in the water surface along the length of the weir. Assume the fall is straight, uniform from 10 ft to 8 ft, and the average level of water is 9 ft. Therefore the crest of the weir will be at 6 ft. The weir will operate whenever the river level reaches 6 ft, *i.e.* when the discharge is 2,800 cusec. If it is determined that this is too often then the shape of the outlet could be altered to give a longer weir or sluices could be added to the crest, opening at some predetermined level, say 7·5 ft.

Care must be taken that the by-pass is of uniform carrying capacity along its length otherwise flooding may occur in some areas along its banks not previously affected. At normal flows the by-pass will be dry; this will lead to the growth of weeds. If, however, arrangements are made to drain adequately the bottom of the by-pass, cattle will be able to graze it and keep down growth. The nuisance of stagnant pools will also be avoided. Although a dry by-pass is preferable, it is not usually practicable in Great Britain. A narrower and deeper by-pass with a very small normal flow is more economical, and is efficient if the entrance is properly controlled. A by-pass scheme is costly, too often necessitating the construction of bridges and such ancillary works. It does however provide a solution for urban areas and does not interfere with the normal regime of the river and the amenities it may offer.

CONSTRUCTION OF FLOOD BANKS

This method is a compromise with nature. The normal flow is confined to the river, and flood flows are allowed to spread to a limit determined by the flood banks. If the flood banks can be set back at a reasonable distance from the river and the area between the flood banks can be kept free of obstructions the method is good and full use can be made of the whole cross sectional area between the flood banks to carry the flood discharge. If the flood banks are constructed close to the river bank any erosion of the river bank will weaken the flood bank and make it liable to fail, with resultant flooding. The more the flood flow is confined the higher it will be and the risk and the consequences of a breach are increased. Along most rivers, in areas liable to flood, the land near the river is higher than that farther back. As a result the flood banks required away from the river may actually be higher than those required on the river edge. The reduced level of the flood and the banks will, however, be lower. They will be far more stable and less liable to be affected by changes in the river and to breach under load.

The capacity of a double channel can be estimated with reasonable accuracy by considering it made up of two channels, a deep one and a shallow one. Thus in *Figure 11* we have channel of area $KCDEFL$ and wetted perimeter $CD+DE+EF$, and channel of area $ABCK+LFGH$ and wetted perimeter $AB+BC+FG+GH$. Hydraulic formula can be applied to each separately.

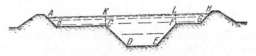

Figure 11. Section of embanked river

The land between the embankments will, of design, be subject to periodic flooding and cannot generally be used profitably as arable land. (During the World War II some land of this type was ploughed up for the first time in history.) It will make good pasture for cattle or sheep. To be used as pasture it must be fenced to prevent cattle straying on to arable lands behind the flood banks. The fencing should be on the land side of the flood banks so that the cattle or sheep can graze the banks, sheep being better than cattle in this respect. This both consolidates them and encourages a good grass surface. Cross barriers will be required between farms; these should be post and wire fences, not hedges, to restrict the flow as little as possible. Where cattle cross the banks, stoned ramps should be constructed; this prevents the bank being trodden down as the cattle scramble up, with consequent danger of overtopping at such points and probable failure.

It is usually too costly to import materials for the construction of flood banks and they are, therefore, constructed of the most suitable material available locally. They should have sufficient mass to be structurally stable, and wide enough to prevent any seepage. TABLE 1 gives the minimum dimensions which should be used, *See Figure 12.*

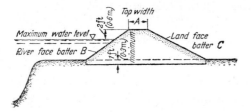

Figure 12. Cross section of flood bank

TABLE 1

FLOOD BANK DATA

	Min top width A, ft	River face batter B	Land face batter C
Clays	6	$1\frac{1}{2}:1$	2:1
Loams	6	2:1	$2\frac{1}{2}$-3:1
Sandy clay or loam	6	2:1	3-4:1

In every case the hydraulic slope through the floodbank from maximum water level to the landward toe should not be steeper than 1 in 4. Where poor ground conditions exist, a full soil mechanics investigation should be carried out.

The bank should be constructed 2 ft higher than the maximum water level to prevent waves spilling over the bank and to allow for treading and local settlements. This freeboard should be maintained as a safeguard for exceptional floods. Banks should be covered with a good top soil and grassed or turfed. Cultivation and seeding is much cheaper than turfing, and the latter is only usually carried out where immediate erosion is anticipated. In turfing banks it is useful to cut the turfs in bricks, making the angle of cut that of the angle of the face of the bank, *Figure 13.*

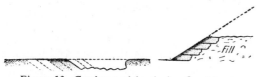

Figure 13. Cutting turf for facing flood banks

The turf bricks can then be laid in horizontal courses without difficulty. Only the river face need be turfed. The material should be well consolidated in thin layers of about 1 ft, depending on the type of consolidating plant used. Allowance of approximately 1 in per ft should be made to all vertical measurements for settlement after construction is finished. The

TABLE 2

FLOOD BANK FAILURE

Causes of failure	Remedy
Erosion of berm and slip of flood bank into river	Set bank back as far as possible from top of river bank and protect river bank as soon as erosion begins
Erosion of the river face of the bank	Maintain a surface of grass
Seepage of water through bank due to:	
a vermin burrows	Destroy vermin and rebuild
b drying out cracks	Maintain a surface of grass on a good top soil
c rise in seepage gradient owing to sustained pressure	Widen bank on land side or introduce a clay core
Erosion of land face by spillage	Raise the bank to increase freeboard
Slip of land face	Set back internal drainage ditch and reinstate with flatter slope

site of the bank should be stripped of turf and top soil, which can be used later to surface the bank, and excavated to at least 1 ft or to material at least as good as that of which the bank is to be constructed. In ballast or sand a clay core should be inserted and brought up with the bank as work proceeds, *Figure 14*. Alternatively, if the bank covering is of clayey soil, then this can be continued to about 3 ft below ground level on both toes instead of the central core.

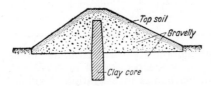

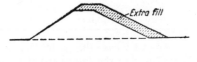

Figure 14. Flood bank with clay core

Figure 15. Extra volume to increase height of flood bank

It should be noted that when the height of a bank is to be increased it is not sufficient just to add to the top. The width of the bank must also be increased, *Figure 15*: this means the addition of a considerable volume of material. To increase a 6 ft bank to 7 ft an addition of 37 cu ft per ft is required compared with the original volume of 104 cu ft per ft. The top soil should be removed from the top and land face. The bank is broken down to give the new width, the extra material added to form a new top, and the soil is then replaced.

Constant and effective maintenance is necessary on all embankments. One breach will destroy the value of the scheme. Rank, undisturbed vegetation will destroy the texture of the banks and will also offer concealment for vermin, which will undermine the bank and cause failure under load. Where large areas are affected it is usual to build barrier banks at right angles to the river extending from the flood banks to the higher ground. In this way the area flooded by a breach is limited to the area between barriers.

With an embankment scheme there must be coupled a scheme for the internal drainage of the area protected. The flood water must be prevented from entering the area at any point, so that any free opening to allow discharge of water from the area must be dealt with.

USE OF CONTROL AREAS

Distinction is made between controlled flood areas and the area between flood banks. In the latter the water flows across the whole area between the flood banks while in the former the area is used essentially for storage. During the peak of a flood, water is stored in the area, where little or no damage will result, in order to prevent flooding below in a more vulnerable area. The application is limited. The control is only effective so long as a fair proportion of the discharge is passing into the area—while the water level in the control area is below that of the river. Thus 83 acres are required of 1 ft depth per 1,000 cusec per hr. Only that depth below flood level is effective. In larger rivers the surplus flow may well be 5,000 to 10,000 cusec for 12 to 24 hr. The area must be such that there is no flow out of the area at the same time as there is flow into the area. A controlled flood area has an application in tidal reaches, where flooding is the result of a high fresh meeting rising spring tides. The period of flooding each day is limited to high tide periods as the height of the tide falls off quite quickly. A proportion of the water stored in the area can be discharged back into the river during low tide periods, thus the area required is reduced to reasonable limits. In these circumstances it can be effective and cheap. A flood bank along the controlled area is strengthened to allow overflow at a certain river level, with possible adjustment to the internal drainage system, including the enlargement of the main outfall of the area, and even a large capacity low lift pump to clear the area of water at the end of the flood period. The greatest difficulty is to obtain the agreement of all the landowners concerned and a basis for compensation.

Normally, upland water supply reservoirs cannot be used for flood control. A reservoir for flood control would need to be kept empty in normal periods. However, composite reservoir schemes have been carried out in the United States (Tennessee Valley) and at Lake Bala in Wales, where an amount of freeboard is maintained for flood control.

REMOVAL OF CAUSE OF FLOODING

In a few instances local flooding may be caused by obstructions and restrictions in the river channel and their removal will eliminate or at least alleviate the condition. The hold up or backwater effect of a weir is limited. In *Figure 16* AB represents the water surface in a channel in which a weir is then built which raises the water level at the weir to C If CD is horizontal and E the limit of the effect of the weir then CE is approximately $2\frac{1}{2}$ to 3 times CD. The effect of this hold up diminishes as the flow increases, see *Figure 17*, so few weirs are important in flood relief works. If land between C and E only is flooded then removal of the weir may eliminate flooding but the removal will have no effect on the conditions above E. Narrow bridges or culverts are not important until they restrict over 50 per cent of the free flow area. As in the case of weirs, the hold up is limited and appears to be more than it actually is,

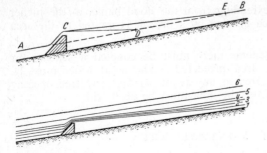

Figure 16. Hold up at a weir:
backwater effect

Figure 17. Diminishing backwater effect of a weir with
increasing discharge

Figure 18: again CE equals 2½ to 3 times CD. When investigating the effect of obstructions, it is important to check the longitudinal sections for a considerable distance both upstream and downstream to ascertain whether the general bed level has been enhanced locally.

The primary effect of a flood relief scheme is limited to the reach in which it is carried out. Draw down effects are less even than backwater effects. In *Figure 19* AB represents the free flow water level in a river channel. Channel improvements are carried out and extend to C. The water surface in the improved channel falls to DE with the same discharge, h ft below AB. F is the limit of the draw down effect in the unaltered portion of the channel: CF rarely exceeds 100 h. Below the works, conditions are not materially altered. The improved channel does not draw down any more water. The flow at C is determined by the old

Figure 18. Hold up at
bridges

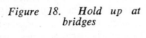

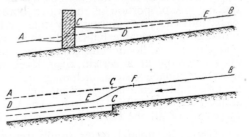

Figure 19. 'Draw down'
effect

channel, therefore no more water can be leaving the lower end of the improved channel. Improved channels simply carry the same quantity of water at a lower level.

The discharge in a river is largely dependent on the rate of discharge of its tributaries, in turn dependent on their feeder streams and so on to the field ditches and drains. A flood relief scheme will not, in itself, materially alter the discharge. Such a scheme will tend, however, to make landowners and farmers conscious of the benefits of drainage and to encourage them to improve field drainage. The extent of these activities and their relation in time to maintenance or improvement work in the main river will determine the probability of flooding along the river. Allowance must be made for all these factors in the preparation of schemes. The general improvement of drainage will result in the runoff reaching the main river in a shorter time. The possibility that the maximum discharge of the tributaries into the main river will occur at the same time may be increased, see *Figure 2*. On the other hand the improvement of the river will encourage discharge and hence a greater quantity of water will be discharged on the rising flood, see *Figure 20*. The net effect will be to reduce the heights of smaller floods. Normally, major floods will not be altered, but large schemes should receive special investigation. For instance, even where comparatively large areas are protected from flooding, *e.g.* the Nottingham Flood Protection Scheme[3], the discharge will not be affected if the flooded area acting as an uncontrolled reservoir is practically full at the peak of the flood.

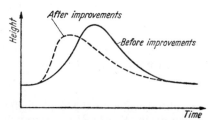

Figure 20. Effect of channel improvements on a flood hydrograph below the improvement

REGULATION OF CHANNELS

Rivers tend constantly to change in shape and course. The causes of these changes may be the immediate effect of some natural or artificial change or may be remote both in time and distance. A river also appears to conform to some sort of cycle of change. The changes may not only interfere with the function of the river as a conveyor of surplus water to the sea but may also seriously affect other interests such as water rights, roads, waterways or railways. It is possible by carrying out a comprehensive scheme to regulate the river so that a reasonably uniform channel is created which can be maintained with normal maintenance.

The problems of meandering and methods of regulation are described in the chapter on Hydraulics of Canals and Rivers of Mobile Boundary.

INTERNAL DRAINAGE AND IRRIGATION

Waterlogged land is of little use but it can be improved by proper drainage. Regular maintenance of the drainage system is, however, essential and neglect of hedging and ditching and of other drains will soon result in the land again becoming derelict. In undulating country the surface slopes are sufficient to carry off the surplus water into the ditches and streams without artificial aid. Occasionally waterlogged land occurs on hillsides usually just below a change of slope. This is due to the water table being unable to conform to the slope of the ground and appearing above or close to the surface. Longitudinal drains across the slope of the ground will correct this defect. In other instances small areas will be boggy owing to the basin like formation of the underlying clay or rock. It may be possible to break up this formation with a rotary tiller or to drain the area by drilling a hole through to a pervious stratum below, but such areas are rarely large enough to warrant the expenditure necessary for their drainage.

Low lying flat areas have, as a rule, been laid down comparatively recently by the river itself and are, therefore, invariably near or below the flood level of the river. In order to make use of the area the river must first be prevented from flooding it, usually by the construction of flood banks. Arrangements have then to be made to collect and dispose of the water otherwise entering the area. The area may be so low that gravity discharge is not possible at any time. Such conditions occur in Holland. It may be high enough to allow discharge into the river at all states of the river, but is so flat that it is not possible, without artificial aid, to convey the water to the river fast enough to avoid flooding in the area; there is also every intermediate stage. The problem, then, is to collect and convey the water entering the area to a discharge point and thence pass it into the river either by gravity or by pumping.

TYPES OF DRAIN

Field drains

Field drains carry the subsoil water to the field ditches. The commonest form is the tile or French drain, *Figure 21* a. A trench about 1 ft wide is dug and in the bottom is placed a porous stoneware pipe which is surrounded by stones. The stones should be well graded and the open joint between pipes covered with hessian so that soil is prevented from entering the drain and eventually blocking it.

Stone drains, *Figure 21* b, are similar to the tile drains but without the porous pipe. They are not nearly so efficient as tile drains and the slight saving in cost is rarely justified.

Turf drains, *Figure 21* c, are useful when stones have to be imported. A trench is dug, the turf being carefully removed. The bottom of the trench is dug with a lip on both sides and the turf placed spanning across the lips and then backfilled. The life is limited to about 10 years.

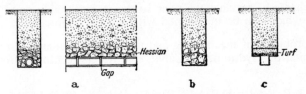

a   b   c

Figure 21. Types of field drains a *tile or French drain* b *stone drain*
c *turf drain*

Mole drains are formed by pulling a torpedo shaped form through the earth, displacing the earth and leaving a hole. The method is only suitable in clay soils.

The drains are laid following the contours of the field, *Figure 22*a; gridiron, *Figure 22*b; herringbone, *Figure 22*c; or parallel, *Figure 22*d. Herringbone and gridiron are common in clay soils. The gridiron formation has the advantage that four adjacent drains have to be blocked before it becomes ineffective. Blocked drains are indicated by a wet patch in the field. A simple map related to nearby fixed points should be made when laying drains in order to facilitate their location in the future. To be most effective field drains should be laid where the percolating rain water meets the rising ground water; in clay soils this zone is indicated by traces of manganese dioxide. Usually the drains are placed 2 to 3 ft deep where they will be undisturbed by ploughing and other farming operations.

TABLE 3

Spacing of drains

Type of subsoil	Distance apart ft
Clay	25-30
Sandy clay	40-45
Clay loam	50-55
Loam	70-75
Sand	100

The size of the drain is not important, 3 in or 4 in being usual.

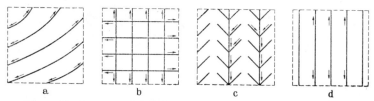

Figure 22. Layout of field drains a *natural* b *gridiron* c *herringbone*
d *parallel*

FIELD DITCHES

The object of the field ditches is to collect the surface water from the
fields and the percolation water from the field drains. The maximum
surface run-off is taken as

$$Q = 0.25\ cA \qquad \qquad \ldots\ldots\ldots\ldots(2)$$

where Q is the run-off in cusec, A is the area in acres, c is a run-off factor.
Values of c are as follows:

$$\begin{aligned}
\text{clay soils tilled} && c &= 0.50 - 0.80 \\
\text{clay soils pasture} && c &= 0.40 - 0.70 \\
\text{loam soils tilled} && c &= 0.10 - 0.30 \\
\text{loam soils pasture} && c &= 0.20 - 0.50
\end{aligned}$$

The field drains will not discharge their maximum until 5 or 6 hr after
the storm so that the ditches have not to accommodate both flows at
the same time.

The size of field ditches is determined not by their discharge capacity
but by the minimum size it is reasonable to dig. The bottom of the
ditch must be below the field drains. The depth then is 3 ft 6 in to
4 ft 6 in. With a 2 ft bottom width the area will be at least 12 sq ft so
that, running full, the average velocity in the drain from a 10 acre field
will only be 0.10 ft/sec.

Subsidiary or feeder drains

These are considered as uniform channels capable of conveying the
discharge from the field ditches and to discharge it into the main drains.

Main drains

The flow in the field ditches and the subsidiary drains is comparatively
small and the falls are negligible. For the calculations for the main drain
the level in the area served by a subsidiary can be taken as the level at its
point of discharge into the main drain.

The main drain conveys the water from the subsidiaries to the outfall
and thence into the river. The flow conditions depend on: *1* size of drain,
2 shape of drain, *3* water level at outfall, *4* water level at confluence of
the feeder most remote from the outfall or at the feeder from the relatively
lowest area, and *5* the inflow.

The principle of design is to keep the water level everywhere in the
main drain to not higher than 18 in below ground level at any time.

DESIGN OF INTERNAL DRAINAGE SYSTEM

TABLE 4 shows the relation between rainfall, duration of rainfall and run-off
which can be taken for calculation of requirements in an internal drainage
area. The figures are compiled from the rainfall records for England.
A run-off factor of 0.50 has been assumed.

TABLE 4
RAINFALL AND RUN-OFF DATA

Duration of rainfall hr	Once a year			Once in ten years			Once in fifty years		
	Total rainfall in	Intensity in/hr	Q run-off per 1,000 acres cusec	Total rainfall in	Intensity in/hr	Q run-off per 1,000 acres cusec	Total rainfall in	Intensity in/hr	Q run-off per 1,000 acres cusec
1	0·50	0·50	84	1·00	1·00	167	1·50	1·50	251
2	0·60	0·30	37	1 20	0·60	75	1·82	0·91	114
3	0·70	0·23	23	1·30	0·43	43	2·05	0·68	68
4	0·73	0·18	15	1·38	0·35	28	2·15	0·54	45
12	0·90	0·075	18	1·68	0·14	30	2·55	0·21	50
24	1·00	0·04	20	2·00	0·08	40	3·00	0·12	60

For short storms the run-off Q, cusec, has been calculated from

$$Q = \frac{cAI}{2+T} \qquad \qquad \text{..........(3)}$$

when c is the run-off factor, A is the area, acres, I is the intensity of rainfall, in per hr, T is the duration of the storm, hours. For longer periods of rain, conditions change and become more uniform. The run-off increases slightly for periods of rain exceeding 4 hr and remains almost constant for rain extending over 24 hr or more.

For design, storms of 1 hr duration are used and, if necessary, adjustment is made for storms of longer duration. The maximum flow is given by the one hour storm and the main drain must be capable of carrying this flow to the outfall. The size of the outfall is also determined by this flow, see p 423. The level outside the outfall is that of the river. It should be arranged so that with gravity flow the level inside the outfall with maximum discharge is that of the normal river level plus the fall through the outfall. It cannot be below, and if it is above, full use is not being made of the available fall.

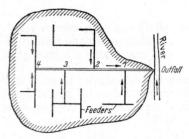

Figure 23. An internal drainage area

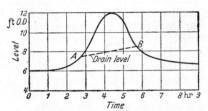

Figure 24. Hydrograph for worst conditions in river of Figure 23

A hydrograph of the river at the outfall is also required for design of the internal drainage system. It should show the worst river conditions likely to occur once a year, once in ten years or once in fifty years. For gravity flow conditions the ten year probability is the most suitable. The probability of the worst rainfall in ten years coinciding with the worst river conditions in the same period offers ample protection.

Example—Consider a flat area at 10 ft O.D. (Ordnance Datum), 1,000 acres in extent, with a main drain 2,000 ft long fed by subsidiary drains at regular 500 ft intervals, *Figure 23*. The hydrograph for the worst conditions in the river is given in *Figure 24*, based on a ten year probability.

Design procedure

Assume gravity flow, and a channel of uniform grade.

Normal water level at outfall=6 ft O.D.

Water level at *4*, the furthermost feeder as a first approximation=8 ft O.D.

Permissible slope=1:1,000

Side slopes=2:1 (determined by the type of ground)

Discharge *0* to *1* (*Figure 25*)=167 cusec

Discharge *1* to *2*=134 cusec, and so on.

It will be found that the channel illustrated in *Figure 25* will carry the discharges to these conditions. It will also carry the discharge whatever the level of the river above 6 ft O.D. provided the drain can discharge fully into the river.

When a storm in the area coincides with a flood in the river the whole of the run-off from the storm will have to be stored in the area.

The storage required will be 167 × 3,600 *i.e.* 601,200 cu ft. Storage is available in the main drain, in the subsidiaries and in the field ditches.

Storage in main drain

Allow the water level to rise to 8·0 ft O.D. at the outfall and calculate the surface slope with the maximum discharge. First approximation: assume the section of flow *0* to *1* is that as at the outfall and calculate the necessary surface slope with this section of flow. This will determine the water level at *1* which determines the section of flow *1* to *4* and so on up the drain. It will be found that the water level at *4* is 8·5 ft O.D. The storage available in the main drain is the volume between the free flow surface and this surface, which represents the maximum water level conditions. The storage is 65,000 cu ft.

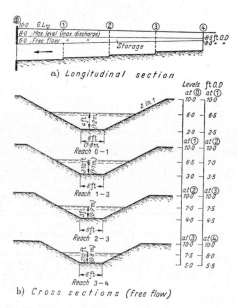

a) *Longitudinal section*

b) *Cross sections (free flow)*

Figure 25.

Storage capacity of feeders and ditches

The bulk of this storage is only available when the water level in the drain approaches the maximum. The amount of storage can be estimated from survey but failing information it can be taken as in the order of:

Per 100 acres of land more than 2 ft 6 in above drain level, zero

Per 100 acres of land between 2 ft 0 in and 2 ft 6 in above drain level, 10,000-20,000 cu ft.

Per 100 acres of land between 1 ft 0 in and 2 ft 0 in above drain level, 20,000-40,000 cu ft.

The whole of this area is between 1 ft and 2 ft of the water surface at maximum conditions, therefore maximum storage available in feeders and ditches is 400,000 cu ft. Total storage is 465,000 cu ft.

The storage lacking is 136,000 cu ft. This storage must be provided by enlarging the main drain. Near the outfall no purpose would be served by deepening the drain. The free flow surface is controlled by the river level. At the upper end, however, the free flow level is near maximum and little storage is available. Assume another section, larger than before with a uniform bed grade and no steps. Determine the free flow profile and the maximum level profile and re-determine the storage available. It should be noted that as the drain section is now so much larger the surface slopes will be smaller,

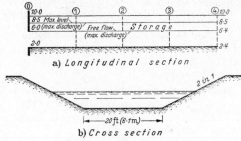

a) Longitudinal section

b) Cross section

Figure 26. Designed channel

therefore the water level at the outfall can rise higher than before and still satisfy the condition that the water level is everywhere 18 in below the land.

It will be found that a channel of section shown in *Figure 26* with a slope of 1:6,500 will satisfy all the requirements.

The area will not be flooded, therefore, by storms of short duration. Consider continuous rain over the area for longer periods. The run-off is 40 cusec which the drain can obviously carry to the outfall. Determine the water profile in the drain when the river is at its normal level, 6 ft O.D. If the maximum rate of rise of the drain exceeds the rate of rise of the river, the level inside the outfall will be that of the river. When the rate of rise of the river exceeds that of the drain the gates will close and there will be no further discharge until the river level falls below that of the drain. Plot the rise in the drain, with an inflow of 40 cusec, against time. The level at which the slope of the tangent to this curve is equal to the slope of the tangent to the hydrograph is the level at which the gates will close. Or by calculation, see TABLE 5, the gates close at 7·5 ft O.D.

TABLE 5

Level ft O.D.	Storage between levels cu ft	Time to fill storage at 40 cusec sec	Rate of rise in/hr	Rate of rise of river in/hr from hydrograph	Remarks
6·0					
	37,000	925	23·4		
6·5				9·0	
	39,000	975	21·6		
7·0					
	20,250	506	21·3	15·0	
7·25					
	20,750	519	20·9	18·9	
7·5					
	71,250	1,781	16·5	20·3	*Gates close*
7·75					
	121,750	3,044	13·6	25·1	
8·0					
	122,250	3,056	13·4		
8·25					
	122,750	3,069	13·2		
8·5					

The point of closure is A in *Figure 24*. Continue to plot the rise time curve for the drain from point A on the hydrograph. Discharge will commence at B where this curve cuts the hydrograph again. If B is below the maximum permissible level there is sufficient storage in the drain; if above, extra storage must be provided. Time for the drain to rise from 7·5 ft O.D. to 8·5 ft O.D. is 3 hr; 3 hr after the gates close the river has fallen to below 8·5 ft O.D., therefore discharge will have previously recommenced.

The size of the outfall is more or less arbitrary. The free flow area in the drain at outfall is 56 sq ft. Outfall 75 per cent of this area, 42 sq ft. Therefore two gates each 5 ft × 4 ft would suffice. The average velocity at maximum discharge through the outfall would be 4 ft/sec. It should be noted that the flow through an outfall, if it is submerged, depends only on the relative levels of the drain and the river and not on the actual level. If the drain level exceeds the river level by 1 in the discharge will be constant no matter what the actual level of the river.

PUMPING

Provision for pumping the water from the area into the river is made when,

1 it is not possible for the water to flow by gravity

2 the size of the drain is such that its cost and maintenance exceed the cost of installing, maintaining and running the pumping installation required for equal benefit.

The cost of the gravity scheme will be made up of:

a excavation of drains

b construction of ancillary works; bridges, outfall *etc*

c maintenance.

The cost of the pumping scheme is made up of:

a excavation of drains

b ancillary works to the drains

c pumping station structure, which may or may not incorporate the outfall

d pumps and engines

e maintenance, running costs and attendance.

As for the gravity flow, the pumping scheme is arrived at by a system of trial and error. The cost of the pumping installation depends on:

1 maximum demand; the station must be capable of pumping the maximum demand and this determines the size of the pumps and engines

2 number of hours of pumping per year

3 efficiency of pumping. It is cheaper to develop the same power for ten continuous hours than the same power each hour for every other hour.

It is essential, therefore, to discharge as much as possible by gravity; to reduce the maximum demand by making use of all the available storage; to balance the drain system to the pumping capacity. The drains must bring the water to the pumps; the pumps cannot draw it down the drain. The drains must, however, be as small as is compatible with this condition.

Example—In the previous example consider the area sloping uniformly from 11 ft O.D. to 10 ft O.D. at the upper end of the main drain. The maximum run-off is 167 cusec and the drain required to carry this discharge to the outfall under gravity flow conditions is that given in *Figure 25*. If a storm occurs when the river is high, the pumps must operate. If the pumps are used to pump 167 cusec the level at the outfall will remain at 6 ft O.D. If the highest river level is 12 ft O.D. the water horse power required would be $(62 \cdot 4 \times 6 \times 167)/550 = 115$.

Such a capacity is unnecessary. A proportion only could be pumped into the river and the remainder would then raise the level in the drain. It has been shown that if the level at the outfall rises to 8 ft O.D. there is no flooding in the area. The total runoff during the storm has been calculated as 601,200 cu ft. The storage in the drain is 65,000 cu ft and in the ditches *etc* 100,000 cu ft.

Total quantity stored	165,000 cu ft
Amount to be pumped	436,000 cu ft
Average rate of pumping	121 cusec

As the water in the drain rises the head to be pumped decreases. The power required therefore is less than that to pump 167 cusec 4 ft *i.e.* 76 h.p. To determine the horse power required, estimate the storage in the drain between each 6 in rise in level.   Assume a power less than 76 and for each 6 in rise interval determine the discharge of the pump. The rate of storage for this interval is then 167 less the pump discharge. Calculate the time to fill the storage. Add the storage times for each interval: this will give the time to reach the maximum permissible level. If this time exceeds the duration of the storm the pump is too big: if less than the duration of the storm it is too small. In the example it will be found that 62 h.p. will suffice.

The pump suppliers will require to know the discharge at the lowest drain level and the discharge at the highest drain level. Allowing for losses at inlet, in the pipes and at outlet they will determine the diameter and speed of the pump and the horse power of the engines.

In the trial and error design of an internal drainage system there is little point in pressing mathematical calculations to absolute accuracy. Even in the final layout an accuracy of 5 per cent to 10 per cent is sufficient. If the calculations show that a storage of 600,000 cu ft is required and that 580,000 cu ft are available it can be accepted as an adequate solution. The calculations can be reduced considerably by the use of a nomograph[4], a semi-graphical method to determine the profile of the water in a drain.

PUMPING STATIONS

Before 1930 the well established centrifugal type of pump was used almost exclusively for land drainage. The development of the screw pump, a modified axial flow type, has led to its adoption in many modern stations and it will probably supersede the centrifugal for land drainage.

The characteristic curves of centrifugal pumps are given in *Figure 27*a. They show the relation between discharge and head; power absorbed and efficiency at constant speed. The characteristics of the screw pump are given in *Figure 27*b. In a centrifugal pump a small decrease in head causes a large increase in discharge and a corresponding increase in power absorbed. A screw pump is not sensitive to small changes in head; it will be noticed that as the head decreases the discharge increases but the power absorbed decreases.

Land drainage pumps have to discharge large quantities at low heads, normally less than 20 ft, and the head varies owing to changes in inflow and river levels. The characteristics of the screw pump make it suitable for these conditions. Unlike the pure axial flow pump it can be started up against a closed valve but still retains the inherent advantage that there is no possibility of overload on the prime mover should the head be reduced below the design point. The screw pump with its end on drive allows simpler and smaller accommodation and requires less complicated foundations than the centrifugal. Some diagrammatic layouts are shown in *Figure 28*.

The costs of pumping stations depend largely on local conditions and are not comparable station to station. The duties to be performed by the pumps determine the size and speed. This in turn determines the size and power of the engines. The

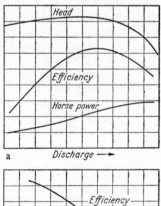

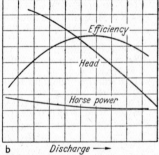

Figure 27. Characteristic curves a centrifugal pumps b screw pumps

cost of the building to house the machinery will vary accordingly and also depends on site conditions *e.g.* whether piling is necessary, the type of layout *etc.* Pump manufacturers will give advice and preliminary estimates of price, size and number of pumps, power and weight of engines, auxiliary plant likely to be required, evacuators, heat exchangers *etc* and information as to the running costs. To do this they require to know:

- *a* difference in delivery and suction levels and the range of variation of these levels at which pumping is likely to take place
- *b* discharge required
- *c* probable layout, in order to estimate frictional losses in the pipe line and to be able to advise on the type of pumps.

When tenders are being let for pumping machinery it is usual to ask for a guarantee of performance, efficiency and fuel consumption of the plant, with a stated penalty for failure to comply with the guaranteed

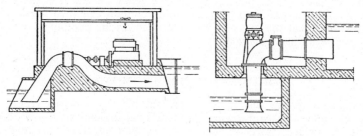

Figure 28. Typical layouts with axial flow pumps

figures. For the large pumps in land drainage this clause is somewhat useless as there is no method of measuring the large volume of water to the required degree of tolerance. The pump must be capable of handling the maximum demand, but the occasion of this demand will be rare and the greatest amount of pumping will be carried out at lower heads. It is an economy, therefore, to choose a pump with a flat efficiency curve *i.e.* a high efficiency over a wide range of head, even if the maximum efficiency is less. This flat efficiency curve is another favourable characteristic of the screw pump.

In the design of the pumping station and drainage system provision must be made for shrinkage and the consequent fall of the ground levels. The amount of shrinkage to be anticipated must be determined from local conditions. It can be quite considerable: $\frac{1}{2}$ in per year over a long period is not uncommon and the shrinkage in the first few years after the drainage system has been installed will, of course, be in excess of this amount. The time for which shrinkage continues has not yet been determined but it appears to be continuous. There should be sufficient reserve of power in the engines to allow pumping at the increased head and the pump should be capable of this new duty without undue loss of efficiency. The intakes to the pump and the suction bay will have to be low enough to cope with the new conditions. At the same time the level of the station floor must not exceed that permitted by the maximum suction lift of the pumps. The station has to be designed to suit existing conditions and also those to be anticipated in the future, otherwise the useful life of the station will be very limited.

The station floor should however be above flood level or arrangements should be made to prevent flooding of the station. Otherwise failure of the pumps would result in the station being completely out of action throughout the flood period.

The station should be equipped with more than one pump. With the minimum of two, one pump should have double the capacity of the other, thus a pump is always available for emergency and the pumps will operate more often close to maximum efficiency. At the beginning of a pumping period the smaller pump will deal with the flow. As the demand increases the larger pump replaces the smaller and with further increase in demand both pumps operate together and are capable of dealing with the maximum demand if it should be required. When there are three or more pumps they should be identical. This will reduce the capital cost and limit the number of spares to be carried.

Flow must be prevented from the delivery side to the suction side through the pump. Flap gates at the delivery side will prevent this back-flow but if they are heavy the loss in head through the gates may increase appreciably the pumping costs; if they are balanced, in the event of a breakdown during pumping, they may slam and do serious damage to headwall and gates. It is usual to have a vertically lifting sluice valve on the delivery side of the pump. In an emergency this valve is self closing. If the gravity and pumping flumes have a common exit then balanced flap gates are placed at the exit and are held open during pumping. The gates only operate during gravity flow.

CHOICE OF PRIME MOVER

The choice of prime mover is at present between electric motors and diesel oil engines. Steam, owing to operational difficuties, is now obsolete and at the present price of coal is not even competitive. The relative advantages and disadvantages are set out in TABLES 6A and 6B.

Technically there is no doubt of the superiority of the electric motor but the choice depends largely on costs. The terms for the supply of

TABLE 6A

ELECTRIC MOTORS

Advantages	Disadvantages
Low capital cost of station and machinery	Complete breakdown of station in event of power failure
Little attendance required	Such attendance as is required must be specialized
Small in size and weight	High running speed
Few repairs	
Quiet in operation	
Easy starting	

TABLE 6B

DIESEL ENGINES

Advantages	Disadvantages
Cheap to run at low speeds	High capital cost
	Heavy and cumbersome
Minor repairs within scope of average attendant	Require constant attendance when running
	Much auxiliary equipment
	Direct drive limited to horizontal position
	Frequent overhauls
	Storage for fuel oil

current to remote land drainage stations are often unfavourable, with the result that the total annual cost (annual running cost plus loan charges on capital cost) of a diesel station is less than an electrical station. Each case should receive detailed consideration. In practice, larger stations are usually diesel, and smaller ones electrical.

SLUICES AND OUTFALLS

Where control of a river level is required but cannot be attained by the use of a weir then a sluice or battery of sluices is introduced. An area may be short of water during some periods of the year and at other periods may suffer from severe flooding. Thus, while at one time it is necessary to store all the water possible, at others the maximum possible discharge has to be allowed, but a weir low enough to pass the winter discharge would sacrifice a considerable amount of storage. This is a typical use for a sluice gate or, as it is often called, a penning gate or penstock. Where the river level rises above the adjacent land level, which land has been protected by embankments from flooding, there must be some form of

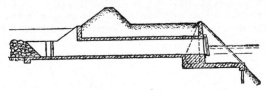

Figure 29. An outfall

control at the outfall (*Figure 29*) of the area to prevent the river flowing up the drain and at the same time allow local discharge from the area when conditions are favourable. The flap gate on the discharge end of the outfall only allows flow from the drain to the river. There is however no control of drain level with a flap gate or valve, so a vertically lifting sluice is often placed at the inlet to the outfall to retain the water in the drain during dry periods.

TABLE 7

LOSS IN HEAD THROUGH AN OUTFALL WITH INCREASING DISCHARGE *

Discharge *cusec*	*Average velocity ft/sec*	*Loss in head (difference in drain and river levels) ft*
55	2·2	0·07
94	3·8	0·18
126	5·0	0·33
168	6·7	0·55
214	8·6	0·80

* 1 cusec = 0·028 cu m/sec
1 ft/sec = 0·3 m/sec

The size of an outfall or sluice opening is more or less arbitrary. With velocities of less than 4 ft/sec (1·2 m/sec) the outfall should be not less than 50 per cent of the free flow area of the drain at maximum discharge. At 6 ft/sec (1·8 m/sec) the area should be not less than 75 per cent of the area of the drain and above 6 ft/sec the outfall should restrict the flow as little as possible. TABLE 7 shows the loss in head through an outfall 5 ft × 5 ft and 55 ft long, completely submerged.

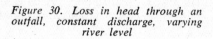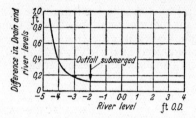

Figure 30. Loss in head through an outfall, constant discharge, varying river level

The discharge through a submerged outfall depends only on the difference in levels at inlet and outlet and not on the actual levels. This is illustrated in *Figure 30*, which shows the loss in head through the above outfall for a constant discharge of 75 cusec for varying levels of the river. When the outfall is submerged at − 2 ft O.D. the difference in level between the drain and the river remains constant at 0·12 ft. The loss in head due to the gates themselves will be specified by the makers. For flap valves and gates it should be about 1 in to 3 in.

While the choice of type of gate is that of the civil engineer the actual design of the gate is best left to the manufacturers. They will require to know *a* the span (clear opening required), *b* conditions of opening, *c* maximum head in one or both directions. Conditions of opening will include whether automatic or otherwise, mechanically or hand operated. and the head against which the gate may have to be opened.

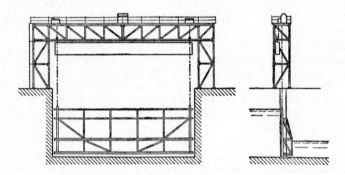

Figure 31. Vertically lifting gate (Penning gate)

Sluices have been developed to deal with almost every condition and the types are numerous and various. Those in common use are vertical lifting gates, flap valves and gates, and tidal doors.

Vertical lifting gates, Figure 31—These gates are lifted clear of the flow if necessary and while normally designed to withstand a head in one direction only can be designed to withstand a head in both directions. They are fully counterbalanced and if power is not available can be lifted by hand. They are made in almost any size and allow free unrestricted discharge. For small heads the gates run on fixed rollers but for higher heads they are usually fitted with free rollers. A modification of this type, often fitted to the tops of weirs, uses radial gates. This allows easy opening of the gates with large differences in head on either side. A small vertically lifting sluice or penstock is illustrated in *Figure 32*.

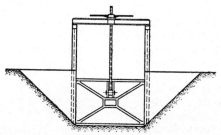

Figure 32. Small vertically lifting sluice
(Penstock sluice)

Flap valves and gates, Figures 33 and 34—These gates are self acting; they are simply hinged at or near the top and slope a few degrees to the vertical. If the level behind the gate exceeds that outside, water passes out through the gate. If the level outside exceeds that inside, the valve or gate is held down on its seat and water cannot pass in or out. They are loose hinged or double hinged to allow easy seating on closure and to offset the effect of obstructions on the seat. They vary in size from the smallest pipedrain to 12 ft × 6 ft or greater. They are very suitable for tidal outfalls and if counterbalanced can be operated with a very small loss in head. The Hillman gate eliminates counterbalance gear by the introduc-

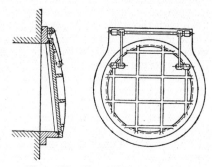

Figure 33. Flap valve (unbalanced)

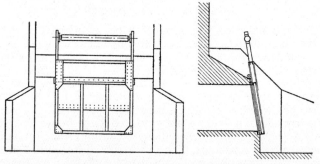

Figure 34. Flap gate (counterbalanced)

tion of air chambers in the gate itself, reducing the net relative density to just more than that of water. Greenheart timber gates also do away with the necessity of counterbalancing.

Tidal doors, Figure 35—These are now obsolete as a form of new construction but many still exist. They are a pair of doors hinged vertically and set V shaped into the river, like lock gates. If the level in the drain exceeds that in the river the doors swing apart and allow discharge. If the river rises above the drain the pressure of water on the doors closes them and tends to seal them more and more as the pressure increases. The arch effect of the V setting allows them to withstand large heads. They demand good craftsmanship and timber in their construction and repair.

Defects

Sluice gates and valves suffer from two main troubles, failure to close owing to timber, stones or other obstructions becoming wedged between the gate and seat, and failure to open owing to deposits of silt outside. Failure to close is most serious in flap gates and tidal doors because these are self operating and it

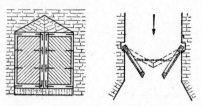

Figure 35. Tidal doors

may be some time before the trouble is observed: it will then be too late to do anything about it as the outside water pressure prevents the opening of the gate and the removal of the obstruction. The risk of being jammed open can be greatly reduced by designing the outfall so that the gate and seating are not confined by the walls or floor. With vertical gates the operator will know immediately that the gate is not shut and by opening it again can usually free the obstruction. For small gates the sill should be flush with the floor of the structure with the apron at a lower level, the only vulnerable spot being the bottom of the vertical guides in which small stones may collect. With large gates or sluices, a raised humped sill can be used to cut down the size of the gates without adverse hydraulic effects. Failure to open is only likely to be encountered when the gates remain inactive for long periods, *i.e.* during the summer. The site of the gates can be chosen to reduce this. They should be placed in the river, if possible on the side of a bend and not set back so that there is a backwater between the gates and the river. The outfall should, if possible, be above the bed of the river. Periodic inspection and removal of the silt by hand are essential.

ECONOMY OF DESIGN

Almost all land drainage works have to be maintained if their original purpose is to be fulfilled. The cost of this maintenance must be considered with the capital cost in determining whether this cost is to be offset by the value of the benefit derived from the works. The acreage of benefit is often the primary concern. This maintenance charge is perpetual but much can be done by good design to reduce maintenance to a minimum. Even smaller works, which themselves may well be classed as maintenance, should be carried out with a view to reducing future charges. Bank reinstatement should always, where possible, fit into some future completely comprehensive river regulation. The work should be finished in such a way as to ensure that there will be no disturbance of the flow above or below the works likely to cause further erosion. Above all, the effect of each piece of work should be carefully noted, and any lessons to be learnt applied to future works.

The ultimate cost of separate works can, by good organization and/or design, be reduced by combining two or more items or types of work *e.g.* the construction of a bank with the excavation of a new channel. When an embankment has to be repaired it is often an economy, although the initial cost may be higher, to clean out the existing drainage system or even to rearrange it to advantage. Under certain circumstances the river can be used to advantage, both to excavate and to deposit material as required. Full consideration should be given to the river as a means of transport and designs amended to this end where necessary.

Much land drainage work has to be carried out far from hard roads and in ground which, by virtue of the necessity for drainage, is soft and marshy. Furthermore the value of the work may be relatively small and cannot allow for elaborate temporary works, the cost of which may be out of all proportion to that of the permanent works. In recent years lighter types of mechanical equipment have become available which have done away with the necessity of slower manual work. Local materials and easily transportable plant should be used wherever possible, and river transport can be economical. When there is likely to be a number of works accessible to the river it may be economical to design and construct special equipment for the purpose.

TYPICAL BANK REINSTATEMENT METHODS

Withy piling—This is suitable in medium flowing streams in districts where withies (three year old rooted willows) are available. It has the added advantage of having a most attractive appearance. One disadvantage is that it requires annual maintenance, in trimming back, and sometimes protection against cattle which eat the new shoots. Stakes, 4 in to 6 in diam, butt end pointed, long enough to give firm penetration and to reach to near the top of the river bank are driven into the river bed, raking about 20° to 30° to the vertical, about 18 in apart along the line of the face of the proposed reinstatement. A maul (mallet) suffices for this purpose. The tops of the stakes are cut off to level. The withies are woven in and out of the stakes, the roots being left to the back. They are pressed down the stakes to the river bed by means of a wooden fork or other suitable tool. When this façade has been built up to water level the back area is filled, the roots being well embedded in the backfill. The operation is completed to the level required. At this stage the bank has the appearance of wattle fencing and relies for stability on the stakes. Very quickly however the withies root and sprout and as, in time, the dead stakes rot away the stability is transferred to the living withies, the roots of which bind the bank together and the shoots successively resist erosion. This method is cheap, attractive and gives a very beautiful effect. It is carried out in the wet. The plant, maul, shovels, wheelbarrows, some planks and possibly a rowing boat are easily brought to the site. The withies are trimmed back each autumn, otherwise they will overgrow the stream. They are not very amenable to being trimmed in the spring.

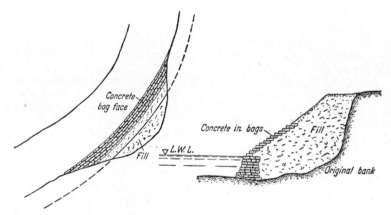

Figure 36. Concrete bagging

Concrete bagging, Figure 36—Concrete bagging is suitable in any river however fast the current, particularly if there are accessible shoals of ballast. The ballast need not necessarily be of first class quality; mass rather than quality is required of the concrete.

The line of the face of the proposed reinstatement is set out and, working from the upstream end where this line joins the existing bank, dry concrete in bags is dropped into the water on this line as carefully as possible to form a footing. When it is possible to stand in thigh boots on this footing the bags are laid and arranged to follow the water surface and brought up in courses, with broken bond, to the surface. The width of the footing will depend on the level of the water above the bed but should be at least three bags wide. The wall will have to be capable of withstanding at this level a head of water equal to the depth. As the footing of the wall is brought up to the surface it is used to carry the bags to continue the work downstream. When the whole length is up to water surface level backfilling is commenced. Another course of bags is laid along the whole length and backfilling brought up to the top of this course. A second course is then laid but is set back 6 to 9 in from the line of the first and again backfilled and so on for each succeeding course as high as is required, usually up to flood level. The appearance is that of a line of steps. With care in the coursing and line, above water level, the work has a pleasant appearance which improves as the bags rot away and leave the rough concrete. The courses should be approximately parallel to the water surface. This form of protection will withstand most severe erosive conditions but should only be used on a good hard stable foundation. In other cases the foundation bagging should be replaced by a loose stone or slag wall, the fill slope made flatter and dry stone pitching added if necessary.

Mattresses—Where deep water and an unstable sloping foreshore exists, large willow mattresses floated and sunk by loading with stone from bags are admirable. This method was pioneered in Holland and is a specialist operation requiring the employment of an experienced contractor.

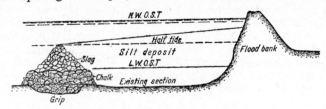

Figure 37. Half-tide wall

Half-tide walls—These form a successful method of bank protection and river training in tidal reaches of rivers carrying a considerable quantity of silt, *Figure 37.*

Again the line of the face of the proposed reinstatement is set out and after excavating a shallow grip from the river bed along this line chalk is deposited into the grip and brought up to low water level. The shallow grip is, however, not always necessary. On this chalk footing rough stone is placed and brought up to half-tide level. The river overflows the wall at each tide and deposits its silt behind the wall so that within a few weeks the whole area between the new wall and the old river bank is completely filled with a firm silt which stabilizes both the river and flood bank. Cross groins are sometimes used to encourage the deposit. Chalk, provided that it is not exposed to air, forms a conglomerate mass and makes an ideal footing. Any movement of the wall is vertical and can be quickly remedied, if necessary, by the further addition of broken stone to the top. Blast furnace slag is particularly suitable for the upper portion if available. It should be brought to the site by barge, which should be fitted with a small unloading crane.

Faggoting, Figure 38—Brushwood is made into bundles and placed, end on to the river, along the line of reinstatement. Each layer is set back from its predecessor and the area behind backfilled. This method is effective for a time but eventually the brushwood rots away. In appearance it is most unattractive but as it is cheap and quick it is quite commonly used. Its best use is as an emergency protection to flood banks where they may be in imminent danger of being eroded through.

Figure 38. Faggoting

Summary—The essentials of all these methods are:

1 avoidance of precise underwater excavation
2 use of flexible construction so that the reinforcement can mould itself to the changing shape of river bed without fear of collapse
3 use of small and easily transportable components
4 use of local materials as much as possible

EXCAVATION

Hand excavation is permissible only if the quanities are small. For larger quantities mechanical excavation is considerably cheaper. For drainage work, where the digging is usually soft and downwards and where long reaches are required, the dragline is the most useful form of excavator. An excavator is known by its capacity when working as a standard shovel *e.g.* a '$\frac{1}{2}$ yd' machine, or by this capacity in cu ft; thus a 'ten' implies a machine with a 10 cu ft capacity when operating as a shovel and is equivalent to a $\frac{3}{8}$ yd machine. In land drainage work, draglines with buckets varying in size from $\frac{1}{4}$ to 2 cu yd, and jib lengths of 20 ft to 70 ft are normally used. It is rarely possible to obtain optimum output. The amount of excavation per yard length of river is often small, sometimes less than 5 cu yd. A considerable proportion of the working time, there-fore, is taken up in moving the machine. If the ground is bad and the machine is working on mats, this proportion increases. The length of jib is determined by the maximum reach required to reach the centre of the river or the full width in the case of smaller streams.

The total cost per cubic yard excavated equals the preliminary charges spread over the total volume of excavation plus the actual digging cost. The preliminary charges are made up of:

a transport charges to and from the nearest hard road to the site
b on and off loading
c conveying machine from point of off loading to working position (a considerable item in drainage works). It may involve temporary bridges, reinstatement of gates, fences *etc*
d cost of conveying fuel to the machine, which again may be high because of the difficulties.

The dragline itself operates at right angles to the cut and is therefore unsuitable for use in narrow ditches and drains. An attachment is, how-ever, fixed to smaller machines to convert them into what is known as a side arm dragline. A cross beam at the front of the machine, with suitable pulley gear, offsets the normal working direction of the bucket from jib top to centre of tracks to a point outside the tracks. The machine can stand at the drain edge and the bucket moves along the drain. Cheap and efficient cleaning and even enlargement of ditches with hedges alongside is possible with this machine.

Excavation in rivers or running water can be carried out upstream or downstream. The advantage of working upstream is that soon after starting the excavation is being carried out in shallower water, is easier and quicker and allows more accurate cutting. However, due to the immediate draw down of the enlarged channel there is a considerable rush of water just where the bucket is working. This and the disturbance caused by the bucket carry away large quantities of material to be deposited again downstream. If the bed and banks are of soft loose material it may well be that reclearing of these deposits is necessary. If the deposit is likely to be within reasonable limits allowance can be made by digging deeper than actually necessary. The swift flow at the change of the old and new sections may also cause erosion of the newly dug batters.

If the excavation is carried out downstream there is little movement of silt and any silt carried down will automatically be removed in the course of the work. The excavation, however, will always be in deep water, no advantage being derived from the enlarged channel owing to the continued hold up immediately above the old channel just where the machine is working. As the work proceeds the water level in the new channel above the effect of the restricted old channel will fall and reveal the raggedness of the batters cut under water. Hand dressing may then be required.

Precise excavation by machine under water or in rivers is difficult and digging within 3 in either side of line or level must be considered good.

With varying water levels, the best method to obtain the required depth is to set gauge boards in the river divided in ft, with the zero of the gauge to correspond to the new bed level. The reading of the water surface on the gauge board is the depth the operator has to dig below the water level. Depths to salient points on the bucket can be readily ascertained and if necessary the lower portion of the hoist rope can be conspicuously marked. The operator then digs until the depth as shown when he throws out his bucket is that shown by the gauge. By interpolation between adjacent gauge posts the operator can dig to depth without check or leaving his machine. The gauge boards can be spaced along the river so that the new bed level between successive gauges does not vary by more than the allowable tolerance if there is to be any difficulty of interpolation.

A considerable quantity of water is brought out with the excavated material. As the material is dumped the slurry tends to run in all directions and can be very troublesome. The ground round the machine can become so soft and muddy that the machine will sink during working and the mats ahead will float, making movement to the next working position a most difficult operation. A certain amount of water can be released by drilling holes in the bucket. To prevent the slurry running on to the machine the dry material above water should be taken first and formed into a bank at the back of the berm. The wet material is then thrown behind this bank, which prevents it spreading to the machine, at the same time increasing the effective disposal range of the machine. It has the added advantage of presenting a tidy appearance and reduces the cost of clearing up.

In river work operators have a tendency to slew one way only. This causes all the wear to be on one thrust bearing with too frequent stoppages for replacement. To avoid this unnecessary delay, machines working along a long stretch of river should be turned end to end at intervals.

PILING

Most land drainage structures have to be built on poor bearing soils and it is necessary to make provision to carry the load, either by spreading it over a larger area or on bearing piles. The problems which arise in this connection however differ little from those encountered in other works, except perhaps that in fine alluvium or peat soils there is a tendency for cast *in situ* piles to be squeezed during formation and the actual finished diameter is less than that anticipated.

Many land drainage structures, however, such as pumping stations, sluices *etc* separate widely differing water levels: it is necessary not only to support the structure but also to prevent lateral movement and to prevent percolation of water from one side to the other. The volume of water which percolates may not in itself be important, but the constant flow of water bearing particles of soil will cause undermining. Percolation is prevented by a cut off wall, generally of sheet piling, *Figure 39*. If an impermeable strata is within reach of the piles a single line of sheet piling will suffice, the position of this line depending on the structure and local conditions. If the impermeable strata is too low to be reached by the piles it is usual to drive two lines of piles as far apart as possible, one at the front and the other at the back of the structure: the length of the piles will vary according to the head and the type of material shown by preliminary borings. The upward thrust of the percolation water should be taken into account in determining the stability of the structure.

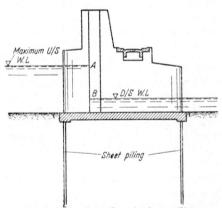

Figure 39. Cut off with sheet piling

Sheet piling is of great use not only for cofferdams and other temporary work but also for the construction of permanent river works. It offers a high factor of safety and can best resist the varying and somewhat indeterminate lateral loads encountered which tend to cause the bodily sliding of the structure. As well as resisting the lateral thrusts it eliminates any danger of undermining due to scour. Driven at the downstream end of any structure it will eliminate the danger of the scour which always tends to take place at this point. Walls of forebays and wingwalls to sluices where scour can be excessive can be cheaply and attractively constructed in sheet piling. Estimation from the rate of corrosion now occurring shows that the expectation of useful durability may be up to one hundred years for the heavier sections of steel sheet piling. For cut off piling which is completely buried the expectation of life is considerably longer. In driving steel sheet piling in running water the driving should commence at the upstream end and continue downstream. For further information on piling see the chapter on Foundations and Earthworks.

CONCRETE IN WATER

Concrete can be successfully placed in still water. It is preferable but not essential to use a rapid hardening cement. The mix should be dry with a large cement content and should not be tipped into the water but placed by 'Tremie' tube to avoid mixing with the water.

MAINTENANCE

The successful continued operation of land drainage works depends on efficient maintenance. While the original design and construction of the works should be such as to reduce maintenance to a minimum it cannot be eliminated entirely. The routine items involved are mainly grass cutting, weed cutting, hedging, removal of dangerous trees, clearing and servicing flap valves, gates *etc.*

Many earthworks depend for their durability on the grass surface. If this surface is destroyed the wind, rain and the flowing water will quickly erode the bare earth below. Cattle should be encouraged to graze grass banks; ramps and fences should be provided and suitable seed chosen to this end. In this way the amount of cutting will be reduced even if the bank has to be made up in places from time to time. Repairs should be protected until the grass has regrown and bare patches should be treated and resown. In tidal reaches cattle must not be allowed to graze on berms subjected to frequent inundation by salt water. Special grasses have often to be sown to withstand the rigorous conditions. If the grass is not cut it becomes rank and the surface becomes spongy and easily eroded. Rank vegetation also offers cover and so encourages infestation by vermin, which can, without it being apparent until too late, completely undermine a bank so that it fails under pressure. A ratcatcher is an essential part of any large maintenance organization. In serious cases of infestation action by specialist contractors may be necessary. In some instances it is essential that new work or repairs should be given immediate surface protection, in which case the banks should be turfed. It is advisable to cut the turfs in the form of bricks, the cut being at the batter angle to the surface, so avoiding all difficulty of laying.

Weeds, growing unchecked in waterways, can quickly spoil a drainage system. In the first place steps should be taken to eliminate as far as possible those conditions which promote weed growth. In digging new ditches and drains the method of having a machine to take out a rough cut and men to follow behind trimming into the bottom must be strictly avoided. The machine should be held back to take out the trimmings. A soft bottom of top soil is the best encouragement to weeds. Conditions which allow the main drains to be alternately wet and dry are also to be avoided. Machine cleaning of ditches and drains takes out the roots and tubers, whereas hand cutting simply removes the tops and often encourages the growth in the following year. Weeds in lakes and other wide waters present a difficult problem. Special flat bottom boats with mechanical cutters have been designed and used by some authorities. Grabs and rakes are used to remove the cuttings. Blanket weed can well be removed by grapples or drags hand operated. The introduction of water snails should be considered as a long term method of keeping weeds under control.

Trees liable to fall into the river should be removed before they actually fall and the bank should be repaired at the same time; otherwise they will possibly fall during a flood and would be carried downstream, damaging weirs and other structures *en route.* All overhanging or trailing branches should be removed; they merely act as collectors of debris which, while not seriously interfering with the discharge, disturb the flow and cause erosion of the bed and banks.

Outfalls and flap valves should be maintained in good order otherwise they will fail to operate in an emergency and considerable damage may result. The expense of constant and efficient maintenance will be amply repaid.

REFERENCES

[1] HOYT, W. G. Studies of Relations of Rainfall and Run-off in the United States *Wat.-Supp. (Irrig.) pap., Wash.* 772, 1936

[2] O'KELLY, J. J. The Employment of Unit Hydrographs to Determine the Flows of Irish Arterial Drainage Channels *J. Instn civ. Engrs* (1955)

[3] HAILE, W. H. and CHEETHAM, H. Flood Prevention Schemes in the Vicinity of the City of Nottingham *J. Instn civ. Engrs* (1951)

[4] STEINBERG, I. H. The Nomograph as an Aid in Computing Backwater Curves *Civ. Engr.* 9 (1939) 365

BIBLIOGRAPHY

WILEMAN, R. F. and CLARK, H. W. Measurement of Discharge of River Basins of White Nile and Nene *J. Instn civ. Engrs* (1946)

LINSLEY, KOHLER and PAULHUS *Applied Hydrology* McGraw-Hill, New York, 1949

RICHARDS, B. D. *Flood Estimation and Control* Chapman and Hall, 1955

LELIASKY, S. *Irrigation and Hydraulic Design* Vol. I. Chapman and Hall, 1955

KING, H. W. *Handbook of Hydraulics* McGraw-Hill, New York, 1954

ALLEN, J. *Scale Models in Hydraulic Engineering* London, 1947

NIXON, M. A Study of the Bank-full Discharges of Rivers in England and Wales *J. Instn civ. Engrs* (1959)

THORN, R. B. *The Design of Land Drainage Works* Butterworths, London, 1959

KLEIN, L. *Aspects of River Pollution* Butterworths, London, 1957

HYDRAULICS OF CANALS AND RIVERS
OF MOBILE BOUNDARY

T. BLENCH, D.Sc., M.I.C.E., F.A.S.C.E., M.E.I.C.

INTRODUCTION

MAJOR reaches of most rivers move material of at least part of their boundary at some stage of flow. Under these circumstances they do not carry pure fluids and they do not have rigid boundaries imposed by an external agency; so the principles of conventional hydraulics, though applicable, are inadequate to describe their behaviour. They form themselves to obey appropriate hydraulic principles and, in addition, to obey laws of sediment transport and of erosive resistance of banks. Accordingly they assume breadths, depths, slopes and changing meander patterns whose magnitudes fluctuate within limits about equilibrium (regime) values dependent on fluid discharge, sediment load, and erodibility of banks. If an engineer attempts to interfere with these values, *e.g.* by dams, barrages, dikes, cut-offs, bridges, nature will proceed to reimpose either the original regime or a substitute that, consistent with the obstructions, obeys the fundamental laws. Likewise, if an engineer designs sediment-bearing channels to conventional hydraulic principles alone they will not, except by luck, retain the dimensions he gave them, but will adjust themselves like comparable rivers to the dimensions appropriate to their discharge, sediment load, and bank material. This chapter deals entirely with the type of channel just described; its subject may be called ' mobile boundary hydraulics '. For the principles of flow of pure fluids in rigid boundaries the reader should consult the chapter on Mechanics of Fluids, Vol. 1. Because the mechanism of transport of sediment is complex mobile boundary hydraulics has developed its quantitative side from observations of the breadths, depths, slopes, and meander pattern sizes to which channels have adjusted themselves to suit imposed discharges; that is, it has followed a course comparable with that of electromagnetism, by observing the relations that hold among measurable phenomena and using the results to define a measure of the imperfectly understood ultimate causes. The phenomena of the subject, the formulae discovered, and their application to river and canal engineering will now be outlined. For a detailed treatment with references and worked problems see ref. 1.

SEDIMENT TRANSPORT
DEFINITIONS

The following common terms require definition:

(*i*) *Sediment* means any material that is denser than the liquid and is transported at any stage of a specified flow. If used without reference to a particular flow it means any material denser than the liquid that, at some period of its history, could have been transported by that liquid.

(*ii*) *Water-sediment complex* is used when needed to emphasize that the dynamical properties of water carrying sediment are affected by the presence of the sediment; the usage is similar to that of the word ' emulsion ' when the dynamical effect of the suspended colloid on the fluid vehicle becomes important.

· (*iii*) *Sediment load* at a section of a channel is, technically, the weight per unit time of sediment passing that section. The term may be used in the general sense of ' material moved by a flow '.

(*iv*) *Sediment charge* is the ratio of load to weight of fluid per unit time passing a section.

(*v*) *Sediment concentration* is the weight of sediment per unit volume or per unit weight of fluid according to the context. It cannot be related to charge unless the relative velocity of sediment to fluid is known.

(*vi*) *Clay, silt, sand and gravel* are of sizes defined in the chapter on Soil Mechanics.

PHASES OF TRANSPORT

There are two major phases of transport of sediment by liquid flow:

(1) *Suspension*—In a laboratory flume with rigid boundary one may observe that sand of suitable size, in small enough quantities, injected into a fluid flow of sufficient speed, will be carried without ever resting on the bed, though particles may strike the bed. So ' suspended load ' may be defined as load that never rests on the bed, and its state is said to be of ' suspension '. Presumably boulder rivers in flood may pass gravel in suspension.

(2) *Bed-load movement*—Extension of the experiment just described, by increasing the size or quantity of the sediment beyond some limit, or by reducing flow speed, shows that material can deposit on the bed where, after building up to some depth, it will be transported in a manner that can be described somewhat generally as a combination of sporadic rolling and hopping, associated usually with dunes. So bed-load movement will be defined ' movement of load that spends at least part of its time in contact with the bed '.

DUNES, SHEET FLOW, ANTIDUNES AND SALTATION

Except as an intermediate phase (below), bed-load movement of sediment is associated with dunes. If a levelled bed of sand is prepared in a flume and a sufficiently slow liquid flow is imposed, the sediment will not move. Gradual increase of flow speed will result eventually in bed-movement which causes the bed to ruffle into moving *dunes;* appreciable continued movement without dune formation seems to be impossible. If no sediment is fed to the flume after dunes start to form, the material that moves in association with the dune formation will become exhausted but the dune pattern will remain. Photos of sand dunes in the desert are exceedingly like those of flume bed dunes. The sand moves partly by trickling up the flat back slopes of the dunes and rolling over the relatively steep fronts, and partly by being whisked up by eddies and projected to the next dune where the impact may cause or help other grains to start on similar expeditions; this jumping or hopping motion is called *saltation* and, although it is rather difficult to see in water (but very easy to see in a wind tunnel), it forms an important part of total bed-load transport. As fluid speed is increased, dunes generally tend to flatten out. When approximately critical velocity (see chapter on Mechanics and Fluids, Vol. 1) is reached the dunes vanish and transport is in a cloud or *sheet* of saltating particles. Further increase of velocity causes *sheet movement* to continue to a limit, which is probably a definite multiple of critical velocity, at which symmetrical dunes very like flat sine curves appear and progress upstream, whence their name *antidunes*. Of course, the actual transport is forward in the scurrying cloud of saltating particles and the reverse behaviour of the antidunes merely reflects the temporary resting habits of sediment particles on the backs of the anti-dunes where they are safe till a retreating face digs them out. It is interesting to note that the water-surface goes down and up with the ups and downs of the dunes, because flow is subcritical, but goes up and down with the ups and downs of the antidunes because flow is supercritical.

Dune formation can be prevented by mixing some gravel with the sand in flumes; the effect seems to be to introduce centres of disturbance out of pitch with the natural wave lengths of the dunes. Confirmation, by sonic sounder, of dunes in sand bed rivers is now extensive; data from gravel rivers and flume experiments on gravel are scanty. There is negligible systematic observation of bed-load movement where size of sediment is comparable with channel depth. However, for practical purposes, there seems no reason to suspect phases of transport other than described; and regime behaviour of rivers shows no obvious change in type when the detailed phase of bed-load movement changes. Experts may subclassify dunes into ripples, *etc.* Of course, in nature, suspension and bed-load movement can occur together and suspended and saltating material become confused.

REGIME AND DEGREES OF FREEDOM OR SELF-ADJUSTMENT

PURE FLUID, ONE DEGREE OF FREEDOM

For later comparison consider a specified discharge of pure fluid passed down a uniform laboratory flume. Kinematically we can imagine flow at any depth with a corresponding velocity. Actually Nature selects one of this infinitude of depths to suit the law of hydraulic resistance, and this law is expressed by one flow formula available from rigid boundary hydraulics. We may say the channel has one degree of freedom, or of self-adjustment of its free fluid surface, and one equation is necessary and sufficient to express it.

FLUID WITH BED LOAD, RIGID FLUME, TWO DEGREES OF FREEDOM

If, in the preceding set-up, a bed load of sand or fine gravel is injected in sufficient charge along with the fluid, part of the sediment will deposit on the bed and build up to a slope steeper than that of the flume. Deposition, on balance, will not cease till the bed built of moving sediment has acquired a slope that permits bed-load at all sections to be the same. Here nature selects depth as before to suit the resistance law of the rather complex moving bed combined with rigid sides and also selects slope to suit the law of bed-load transport. This channel has two degrees of freedom, and two equations are necessary and sufficient to express them.

FLUID WITH BED LOAD AND SUSPENDED LOAD, CHANNEL EXCAVATED IN ERODIBLE ALLUVIUM, THREE DEGREES OF FREEDOM

If the flume is replaced by a canal cut in cohesive erodible soil and water carrying bed load only is injected the case will be as just described but, if the flow conditions are sufficiently severe, the channel sides will erode till the severity has been automatically mitigated. If a suspended load is introduced, and if the channel breadth is great enough, suspended material will adhere to the sides and cause them to grow inwards so as to reduce breadth. In both cases this channel has a third degree of freedom and nature selects breadth to suit a law concerning cohesive resistance to erosive attack. Three equations are needed to express the three laws at work.

If maintenance of the preceding canal is neglected for a relatively long time small irregularities of the sides will develop and show that the artificial straight form is really unstable, for, once started, they will develop relatively rapidly into meanders exactly as in a river. These meanders, given enough time, will progress and cut off and reform—in fact the canal will now be a river of constant discharge—but their average wave length and amplitude will be definite over a long time. Apparently a fourth degree of freedom has developed, associated with erosive attack by curved flow; a fourth equation is needed to express the size of meander pattern involved.

MEANING OF REGIME

In the practical cases quoted a steady condition will be achieved in very different times. In the first case it will occur perhaps seconds after turning on the flow. In the second, a few days will usually be needed before the sediment load entering the head of the flume equals that coming out at the exit. In the third, a year or two would be needed for a channel length of forty or fifty miles. In the fourth, of a neglected canal turning into a 'river', the whole meander sequence might take decades to demonstrate its average steadiness. A natural river with its enormously varying discharge from day to day and from year to year would take even longer and as in the previous case its 'steady' condition is of steadiness about a mean state, just as the steady velocity in turbulent flow is really a steadiness of an average about which erratic fluctuations occur indefinitely. Intellectually there should be no more difficulty in visualizing the acquisition of steadiness in one case than in another. However, the novice and the laboratory worker are liable to think in terms of their experience of rapidly occurring events and become confused; the geologist has no difficulty at all. If imposed conditions are fixed, or oscillate about equilibrium, then steadiness or equilibrium, which includes equilibrium of an average state about which oscillations occur, must result. Canal and river engineers have devised the word 'regime' to replace 'equilibrium' since the latter word's association with laboratory physics does tend to suggest something both clear cut and rapid. 'Regime' suggests considerable freedom of individual behaviour within a framework of laws and has no short-period connotation.

Accordingly, for the kind of channel contemplated in this chapter, the term 'regime channel' will be used, meaning that it is capable of acquiring regime, or equilibrium, eventually by self-adjustment of its non-fluid boundaries if the imposed conditions do not change on a long-term average. And the term 'in regime' will be used with the special meaning that such a channel has actually achieved regime or equilibrium.

IMPORTANCE OF CONCEPT OF DEGREES OF FREEDOM

Realization of the number of degrees of freedom in a case is necessary for the engineer proposing to design a regime channel or to interfere with one. For quantitative design he must have an equation for each degree; for interference the ultimate consequences cannot be forecast without taking them into account, nor can these consequences be assessed without some approximate expression of the relevant equations.

THE FUNDAMENTAL REGIME EQUATIONS FOR CANALS

The ideal type of canal now considered is excavated in uniform cohesive soil, or has formed banks by deposition of similar soil from its suspended load; it has a bed of transported non-cohesive material that moves in dune

TABLE 1

COMPARATIVE RANGES OF REGIME DATA

	Indian canals	Flumes of Gilbert
D mm	0·10–0·60	0·3–7·0
Grading	Log. prob.	Uniform
C per 10^5	0–2 or 3?	0–3,000
Suspended	0–1%	Nil
Water temp.	50–86°F	Prob. 55°F
Sides	Clay, smooth	Wood or glass, smooth
b/d	4–30	1–25
V^2/d ft/sec²	0·5–1·5	1–150
Vb/v	10^6–10^8	10^5–10^6
Q c.f.s.	1–10,000	0·1–1·0
Bed phase	Dunes	Dunes, sheet and antidunes

formation; the discharge of fluid is maintained steady and the sediment charge is also steady; the banks are well maintained and, in particular, meandering is not allowed to start; the fluid is of fixed viscosity and density. A canal of these properties will be found to have a mean bed (after averaging out the undulations of the dunes) that is practically horizontal across the flow, and to have sides that are approximately straight and steeper than 1 upon 1; that is, its average section at a site is trapezoidal. When such a channel has attained regime, observations of the self-adjustment of many similar but not so ideal canals have indicated that the following equations are good representations of ideal behaviour:

(*i*)   *The bed-factor equation*—This is:

$$V^2/d = F_b \qquad \qquad \ldots\ldots\ldots\ldots(1)$$

which defines a bed factor F_b. V is the mean velocity of flow in a section whose depth from fluid surface to the mean bed is d.

In words the equation states the discovery that all channels, of whatever size within the limits of observation (TABLE 1), will adjust to the same value of V^2/d if they have the same water–sediment complex constitution; it is believed that the major factor fixing F_b is the nature of the bed load. Dimensionally adjusted, the left-hand side becomes the Froude number in terms of depth.

(*ii*)   *The side-factor equation*—This is:

$$V^3/b = F_s \qquad \qquad \ldots\ldots\ldots\ldots(2)$$

which defines a side factor F_s. b is the breadth at about half depth, so that bd = cross-sectional area of flow. This equation is not strictly analogous to equation (1). First, it should be dimensionally adjusted by multiplying the left-hand side by $\rho\mu$ (where μ is the viscosity of the water–sediment complex and ρ is the mass density), so that this side appears as the square of a shear stress. Then it states the discovery that V^3/b appears to be a principal measure of erosive attack on banks, so that if F_s exceeds a certain upper limit for a certain bank material then the channel will widen till F_s drops to that limit; and if F_s falls short of a certain lower limit then suspended load will deposit on the banks and reduce breadth until the lower limit is regained. It is believed that the equation has not so specific a meaning if the banks cease to be hydraulically smooth (see chapter on Mechanics of Fluids, Vol. 1). Because of the variability of erosive resistance in practice, and the difficulty of assessing viscosity when there is suspended load, the inclusion of $\rho\mu$ in the definition would not be practically useful.

(*iii*) *The regime slope equation*—This is:

$$V^2/gdS = 3\cdot63\,(1+C/233)\,(Vb/\nu)^{0\cdot25} \qquad \text{..........(3)}$$

in which S is the channel slope, expressed as a fraction, C is the bed-load charge in parts per hundred thousand by weight and ν is the kinematic viscosity of the water–sediment complex. The term in C is a recent addition in which the 233 is approximate and meant to apply only to sand of the mechanical constitution normally found in dune formation on canal and river beds. The original canal data on which the formula is based dealt with such small values of C that the term was practically $1\cdot0$; the C term is purely empirical in the sense that the data behind it are scanty and no special dynamical significance can be seen in its form. The equation is of generalized Blasius form, so is consistent with the self-formed nature of the regime channel boundary. In fact, the equation may be taken to state that the regime boundary is ' smooth ' in the sense of ' formed from the water–sediment complex ' just as ' smooth ' in rigid-boundary hydraulics means ' formed from the fluid '.

These formulae are of the correct number for channels of three degrees of freedom. They are based on the work of Gerald Lacey, with a generalization to allow for sides of different nature than the bed, and the addition of the charge term in equation (3) derived from laboratory data. The range of data supporting them is given in TABLE 1, and their successful application to rivers suggests that the range can be extrapolated to indefinitely large channels; the effect of sides probably prevents extrapolation to small laboratory flumes, and their use for sediment of size comparable with channel dimensions should be treated with caution. The physical possibilities of the formulae are discussed in ref. 1, and the latest work by G. Lacey on his original presentation is in ref. 2.

DESIGN FORMS OF REGIME EQUATIONS FOR CANALS

The designer knows the operating discharge of a canal and has estimates of the bed factors and side factors likely to occur, so he needs formulae that will express b, d and S in terms of Q, F_b and F_s. They are derived easily by multiplying equations (1) and (2) together and by V to get:

$$V.V^2.V^3 = F_bF_sVbd = F_bF_sQ$$

whence

$$V = \sqrt[6]{(F_bF_sQ)} \qquad \text{..........(4)}$$

Insertion of this value in equations (2) (1) and (3) in turn yields

$$b = \sqrt{(F_bQ/F_s)} \qquad \text{..........(A)}$$

(the breadth equation)

$$d = \sqrt[3]{(F_sQ/F_b{}^2)} \qquad \text{..........(B)}$$

(the depth equation)

$$S = F_b{}^{5/6}F_s{}^{1/12}/(1+C/233)\,KQ^{1/6} \qquad \text{..........(C)}$$

(the slope equation)

in which $K = 3\cdot63g/\nu^{\frac{1}{4}}$. In usual canal work precautions are taken to ensure that C is so small that $C/233$ is negligible. K is about 1,800 in cold countries and 2,000 in hot.

PRACTICAL USE OF REGIME EQUATIONS
FOR CANALS

EXPERIENCE

The need for experience by the designer of canals is illustrated from a fairly general problem of designing the canals of an irrigating system comprising all the channels taking off from one main line that, in turn, takes off from a river that has wide discharge variation and a flood season load of all material from clay up to medium sand; such a system might have channels from 10,000 cusecs down to 1 cusec. We may suppose that distributing channels are to run full or closed, but the large branches would have to run part supply at times. Normally the head regulating devices of such a system keep the bed-load charge low enough for the C term in equation (C) to be neglected; they will not prevent some effect of C on F_b (see equation (D)). However, in low river no sediment will enter the system, while in high river all grades will enter except some of the largest if the designer and operators of the headworks are competent; how much

TABLE 2

REGIME CANAL DIMENSIONS FOR $F_b=1\cdot0$, $F_s=0\cdot2$, $v=10^{-5}$

Description	Discharge Q		Breadth b		Slope S per thousand	d Depth		Velocity V		b/d
	cusec	cu m/sec	ft	m		ft	m	ft/sec	m/sec	
Main line	10,000	300	225	69	0·09	12·5	3·8	3·55	1·08	18·0
Branch (>500 cusec)	1,000	30	71	22	0·13	5·8	1·8	2·43	0·74	12·2
Distributary (<500 cusec)	100	3	22·5	6·9	0·19	2·7	0·81	1·64	0·5	8·4
Distributary (<500 cusec)	10	0·3	7·1	2·2	0·28	1·25	0·38	1·13	0·34	5·7

will enter cannot be calculated exactly. Thus, sediment entry will vary from day to day and from year to year due to river changes and due to changes of regulation policy and periodic improvements to design. Viscosity will vary with seasonal temperature and with seasonal changes in turbidity. Channels will not be straight. Maintenance of banks and beds may be poor. Discharges cannot be kept perfectly constant. Some banks will be self-deposited from sediment load so will have fairly uniform resistance to erosion, while excavated banks will have considerable variations of resistance. Head regulators of channels will take more or less than fair share of bed load according to their design and orientation. And so on. Accordingly, the simple conditions under which the regime formulae are stated to be accurate will not be met very well and the actual conditions are not all susceptible to measurement. However, a designer of experience will make first approximations to average bed and side factors to use in initial design and will be able to decide on suitable design discharges in cases of variation; some deviation of canals from design after they have run for some time should be expected and, of course, they must be expected to show some fluctuations about regime when they do attain it. The designer's task is to foresee, as far as is humanly possible, what the channels will want to do, and then design them that way.

EXAMPLES

The following problems illustrate practical matters and calculation methods:

Problem 1—What breadth, depth, slope, velocity and breadth to depth ratio would be appropriate to channels of 10,000, 1,000, 100 and 10 cusecs in a system where $F_b = 1·0$, $F_s = 0·2$, mean $v = 10^{-5}$ and C is negligible?

Straight forward insertion of the given values in equations (A) (B) (C) gives TABLE 2. It is to be noted that large channels have small slopes, high velocities, and relatively (to depth) great breadths, and vice versa, just like regime rivers. Common errors made in ignorance of regime relations are: (i) making the deep-cut main lines steep for 'economy' and the distribution channels flat to attain command of the land; (ii) giving the same 'non-scouring non-silting' velocity to all channels in accordance with tables in hydraulic reference books; (iii) imposing breadth to depth ratios to suit 'economy'. These can all lead to major self-adjustments of channels away from design.

Problem 2—The first 15 miles of a lined canal were built with 140 ft bed width, 1:1 side slopes, and slope 0·09/1,000, with the expectation that it would run 10 ft deep with Manning's n (in $V = 1·49n^{-1}r^{2/3} S^{1/2}$) as 0·015, to keep the bed clear of sediment and to discharge 6,045 cusecs. (This otherwise uneconomic section was enforced by a high water-table.) It was opened during the period when sediment charge was high, run gradually up to full supply, and found to operate successfully. During the ensuing clear-water season branches were completed, offtaking from the main line head reach: when dirty water returned the main line supply was short so the branches were run by 'ponding' at main line bridge-sites equipped with gates. When supply became adequate the main line failed to take its designed discharge of 6,045 cusecs even when filled to the top of the lining; investigation showed that the bed had become covered with sand that refused to wash away. Why did the channel behave in this manne? (The F_b, F_s expected for unlined channels were 1·0, 0·2.)

Solution—Usually this problem will not arise unless the channel is of shape comparable with a regime one with cohesive sides. It is exactly soluble if there is smooth turbulent flow along the sides; and the same solution is probably good enough even if smooth turbulent conditions do not hold. Assuming smooth sides, there are two algebraically equivalent ways of solving the problem. The first is to find V from $V^2/d = F_b$; this gives the velocity at full supply level in the lined section with a small charge of sediment moving along the bed. From V the discharge is found; then Q, F_b, $F_s = V^3/b$ substituted in equation (C) will give the regime slope. If the slope provided is not greater than this then the bed will not clear itself. The second method is to use equations (A) and (B) with b, d, F_b inserted to find Q and F_s. Thus

$$b^2 = 150^2 = (1·0/F_s) Q$$
$$d^3 = 10^3 = (F_s/1·0) Q$$

giving $Q = 4,750$ cusecs and $F_s = 0·21$ as the values that would obtain at full-supply level in the lined channel with sediment just moving along the bed and the section behaving as a regime section. The slope required to correspond is found as in the first method and is 0·097/1,000 against only 0·09/1,000 provided, assuming $K = 1,950$.

Problem 3—A short power canal for 1,100 cusecs has been designed to 20 ft bed width, 70 ft water surface width and 10 ft depth. It has been excavated in a sandy material containing pebbles, and it is believed that: (i) if the bed could be eroded the bed factor of the material in movement would not exceed 1·0; (ii) the sides would stand erosive attack about as well as a clay soil with side factor 0·30. (a) If the water entering the canal is free from sediment, estimate the chances of the canal retaining its section under full supply conditions. (b) If the water entering the canal carried, or acquired, a sand load with bed factor 1·0. what would happen to the canal section in the course of time?

Solution—(a) The actual V^2/d is $2·45^2/10 = 0·6$, which is far enough below 1·0 to suggest that, even though the canal section is considerably different from that on which regime formulae are based, there is no danger of the bed moving. The value of V^3/b is $2·45^3/45 = 14·5/45 = 0·32$, so, if the sides were steep, they would probably be just safe. To obtain some idea of side erosive attack near the bed we might use $2·45^3/20 = 0·7$ for lack of an exact formula; it is high enough to cause grave misgivings. (The author's experience is that the bed would widen.) (b) If bed load, as described, occurred the channel would have to adjust to suit the regime equations so would finish with depth 6·95 ft, mean breadth 60·5 ft (equations (A) and (B)), and side slopes as steep as they

could stand. The slope would adjust to suit equation (C). If the source of load
were erosion of banks, and nothing else, there could hardly be sufficient supply
of bed load to produce final in-regime slope. Where canal side slopes could
erode at the base the released gravel would drop to the bed, the sand would
move a little downstream and deposit so as to increase V there and cause slightly
accelerated erosion, and so on; fine material would probably pass away in
suspension. The more the bed material was allowed to accumulate the worse
the bank erosion would become; early repeated clearances would probably cure
matters cheaply.

ESTIMATION OF BED FACTOR

Just as with estimating Manning's n (see chapter on Mechanics of Fluids,
Vol. 1) for rigid boundaries no exact rules can be stated for estimating bed
factor; experience is necessary. The following will give some guidance
towards obtaining that experience. Firstly, if the size of sand that will be
found on the bed is known, a rough guide is:

$$F_b = F_{b_0} (1 + 0.12C) \qquad \ldots\ldots\ldots\ldots(D)$$

in which

$$F_{b_0} = 1.9 \, (D_m)^{\frac{1}{2}}$$

where D_m is the median size (proportions being by weight) of grain in
milimetres, and C, as usual, is the bed-load charge in parts per hundred
thousand by weight; the formula breaks down when F_b approaches 32.2.
The median size is a sufficient criterion since sand that moves in dunes
along a bed is found to have a fairly standard mechanical analysis (according
to a log probability law); the practical possibilities of knowing C are,
unfortunately, remote. Secondly, if instead of sand the bed has gravel
(rather unlikely in regime canal practice) then the $1.9 \, (D_m)^{\frac{1}{2}}$ of the preceding
formula should be replaced by some multiple of the cube-root of the gravel
size; the user will have to find his own multiple since natural gravels do
not follow a known definite distribution law, so compel him to make his
personal guess at ' prevalent size '. Thirdly, if any channel is available
that seems likely to have a bed factor comparable with that of the projected
channel then that channel should be analysed by inserting its $b, d, S, Q,$
into the regime equations to find what its F_b is; this is the only really satisfactory way of estimating. Fourthly, if long-term records of total load of
the parent channel of the canal are available from a site where turbulence
puts the total load into suspension, one may be able to estimate, with the
aid of experience, the type of load that will enter the channel and, thence,
how much of it will differentiate into bed load. It is to be noted that, in
those natural channels where the total load grades gradually from bed
material size down to something much finer, the bed load is merely a
portion of the total that differentiates out according to rules that are not
yet known with assurance; in a laboratory channel the bed load is either
artificially made uniform or is taken from a real channel bed and there is
no suspended load to cause confusion.

ESTIMATION OF SIDE FACTOR

Because a channel can be in regime for a range of side factors, and because
slope is exceedingly insensitive to side factor, estimation of this quantity
does not usually need to be particularly accurate. For design, side factors
of 0.1, 0.2 and 0.3 may be accepted for fine grained soils of slight, moderate
and high cohesiveness. For gravels a rule that fits river behaviour fairly
well is that the side factor is one eighth the square of the bed factor that
would occur if the side material formed a bed and had negligibly small
charge.

ESTIMATION OF DOMINANT OR FORMATIVE DISCHARGE

In normal irrigation canal practice the bed load charge will be very small, probably C not greater than 2 or 3, and periods of running at considerably less than designed full supply will be relatively short and will occur during short river supply when suspended load is absent. Under these circumstances, bed factor will not tend to alter much for different running conditions (equation (D)), and slope will not tend to change much with stage since it depends principally on the minus sixth root of Q (equation (C)); calculations of rates of bed change[1] show that they usually occur very slowly. Therefore, the designer can usually design for full supply conditions as if the channels actually ran at full discharge permanently. In special cases a canal might have a large (say C about 30) bed load charge —*e.g.* a canal connecting two rivers—and might be subject to considerable variations of both discharge and charge during long periods. Then regime would be established about some discharge considerably less than nominal full supply and estimation of it and of occurrences during fluctuations around regime would be necessary; Problems 4, 5 and 6 illustrate calculation methods. The average discharge may be called 'dominant' or 'formative'.

PROBLEM OF FLUCTUATING DISCHARGE AND LARGE CHARGE

The practical use of regime equations for fluctuating discharge is comparable with the use of the equations for uniform steady flow in rigid boundary hydraulics to solve problems of gradually varied flow, *i.e.* backwater curves, and even unsteady flow if it is not too unsteady. Calculations of the rate at which a channel bed erodes or accretes under usual practical circumstances of canals and rivers[1] show that the process is slow enough to permit an unsteady motion to be regarded as a sequence of short-period regimes, each obeying the regime equations. To illustrate the applicability of the equations one may imagine a canal of steady discharge and sediment charge that is in regime. Suppose now that the discharge is altered permanently to two-thirds but the charge remains unchanged. Equation (C) shows that when a new regime is established the slope will be greater than before, while (B) read with (A) shows the depth will be less even if the side factor were to alter in such a way that breadth remained as before (as could happen if there were no suspended load); so deposition would have to occur on the bed and, while this was occurring, the charge would be less in the downstream reaches than in the head reach. During the very slow process of deposition, say at its start, any particular short reach of the channel might be regarded as in regime at its original slope with the new discharge and it would carry the charge found by solving equation (C) with equation (D). Apparently, in this particular problem this charge would be obtained from what was left over from the head reach after deposition had occurred there, and would grow when deposition reached the section; that is, the channel would 'silt-up' from its head. Even when deposition reached the section the equations could be used, *because the deposition is slow*, if the charge appropriate to each degree of deposition were known. Corresponding problems may be imagined, *e.g.* channel discharge increased, or sediment load removed by an ejector. For continuous variation of discharge or sediment load the solutions will be on the same lines, but with much more mathematical labour, provided rates of change are not too abrupt; thus, to give an extreme example, a channel obviously could not adjust its bed to regime conditions to keep in step with the discharge variations that occurred during the passage of a surge.

ALTERNATIVE FORMS OF EQUATION (C)

To solve problems of the type just discussed, it is convenient to have equation (C) with F_s eliminated, since a fluctuating channel will have a side factor corresponding to erosive resistance of the sides only at the highest discharge; it is also convenient to have a form with Q eliminated. The reader may note that equations (A) and (B) define F_b and F_s in terms of V, b, d, so F_b and F_s can be used in equation (C) whether they have any particular physical significance or not, since equation (C) follows from equation (3), which did not contain them, merely as an algebraic

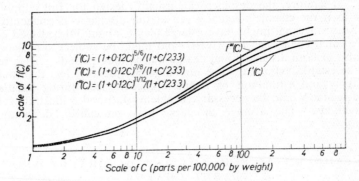

Figure 1. The C functions

manipulation; thus, a channel with smooth rock sides but non-cohesive bed should have its slope formula expressed by equation (C), but F_s would be what V^3/b happened to be to suit the rigidly imposed b and the other equations and would have no relation to the properties of rock. In these alternative formulae it is also necessary to have F_b expressed as F_{b0} $(1+0.12C)$ (see equation (D)) since F_{b0} depends only on the nature of the bed material. So the original equation (C) and the two required alternative forms of it, may be written conveniently as:

$$S = \frac{F_{b0}^{5/6} F_s^{1/12}}{KQ^{1/6}} f'(C) \qquad \qquad \dots\dots\dots\dots(C')$$

$$= \frac{F_{b0}^{7/8}}{Kb^{1/4} d^{1/8}} f''(C) \qquad \qquad \dots\dots\dots\dots(C'')$$

$$= \frac{F_{b0}^{11/12}}{Kb^{1/6} Q^{1/12}} f'''(C) \qquad \qquad \dots\dots\dots\dots(C''')$$

in which

$$f'(C) = (1+0.12C)^{5/6}/(1+C/233)$$
$$f''(C) = (1+0.12C)^{7/8}/(1+C/233)$$
$$f'''(C) = (1+0.12C)^{11/12}/(1+C/233)$$

It is also useful to know equation (B) can be written

$$d = \sqrt[3]{(q^2/F_b)} \qquad \qquad \dots\dots\dots\dots(B')$$

where $q = Q/b$.

    Figure 1 plots the three functions of C against C for easy solution. If the figure is not available the simplest method of using the equations is to solve with $C/233$ assumed zero, and then use the value of $C/233$ from the C so obtained as a means towards finding a better value of C.

SOLUTIONS OF PROBLEMS OF LARGE CHARGE

The following worked problems[1] illustrate calculation methods and some points relevant to assisted cut-offs of rivers.

Problem 4—The section of a long straight channel may be approximated by a trapezoid of 100 ft bed width and sides sloping at 2 upon 1. The bed material is sand of median size 0·275 mm, and the sides may be assumed hydraulically smooth. Mean annual water temperature may be taken at 52·5°F and calculations may be in terms of the corresponding clean water viscosity (kinematic) of $1·35 \times 10^{-5}$ sq ft/sec. Bed slope of channel is 0·14 per thousand. Estimate the discharge, bed-load charge, bed factor and side factor that prevail when flow is at 3·5 ft depth, parallel to the bed, and has occurred long enough to allow the bed pattern to adjust to the conditions, but not long enough to cause erosion sufficient to alter the problem.

Solution—Notice that four quantities are to be found, so all four regime equations will be needed. We cannot start from the sectional equations (A, B) since they contain three unknowns after b and d have been inserted. The appropriate form of equation (C) is obviously (C''). The value of $K = 3·63g/v^{1/4}$ is 1,950; b is 101·75; $b^{1/4} = 3·16$; $3·5^{1/8} = 1·17$; $F_{b0} = 1·0$. So equation (C'') gives $f''(C) = 0·14 \times 1·95 \times 3·16 \times 1·17 = 1·01$, which is outside the range of *Figure 1*; so we might estimate C as 0·1 from the approximate relation $f''(C) = 1 + 0·12 C \times 7/8$ for small value of C. (If $f''(C)$ had been less than 1·0 there would have been no bed movement.) Now $F_{b0} = 1·0$, so F_b, by equation (D), is probably about 1·012, showing that the charge is not enough to affect bed factor appreciably. The value of Q is $1·0 \times 101·75 \times 3·5^{3/2} = 665$ cusecs. Flow area is $3·5 \times 101·75 = 355$ sq ft, so $V = 1·88$ ft/sec, and $F_s = 1·88^3/101·75 = 0·065$, showing that this flow would not erode even loam of very poor cohesiveness.

Problem 5—With the data of problem 4, except that discharge is given as 20 times the 665 cusecs found for it and the depth has to be determined, find depth, bed factor, side factor and bed-load charge.

Solution—The only (C) equation suitable is (C'''); (C') is unsuitable, because we do not know F_s in a problem where a flow has not run steadily for a long enough period for the sides to erode until the side factor drops to correspond to their cohesive resistance. Actually $b = 100$ inserted in equation (C''') would suffice, but for the sake of the exercise allowance will be made for variation of b with d. A preliminary estimate of what d is likely to be can be made from the Manning formula (see chapter on Mechanics of Fluids, Vol. 1), taking the hydraulic radius r as a fixed multiple of d. Then $V \propto d^{2/3}$ and $Q \propto d^{5/3}$ as a first approximation. So d will be about $20^{3/5} \times 3·5 = 21$ ft, and b about 110·5 ft, say 110 ft; $b^{1/6}$ will be about 1·3 per cent more. $Q^{1/12}$ will be $20^{1/12} = 1·284$ times more. Then equation (C'''), in which S is constant, shows that $f'''(C)$ will be $1·284 \times 1·013 = 1·3$ times more than in problem 4 where, because all the C functions are practically equal at small C, it was 1·01. Thus $f'''(C)$ is 1·31, and *Figure 1* shows that C is 3·0. Then $F_b = 1 + 0·12 \times 3·0 = 1·36$, and the accurate value of d from equation (B') is 22·0 ft, $V = Q/bd = 5·45$ ft/sec, and $F_s = 1·45$ which would cause any loam soil to erode.

Problem 6—Answer problem 4 with the bed slope 0·42 per thousand.

Solution—The slope having been enhanced to 3 times that of problem 4, $f''(C) = 3·03$ and *Figure 1* shows $C = 26$. Then $F_b = 1 + 0·12 \times 26 = 4·12$, $Q = (4·12)^{1/2} \times 665 = 1,360$ cusecs, $V = 3·85$ ft/sec, and $F_s = 0·56$.

The reader will notice that great enhancement of discharge has rather a small effect on bed load charge although, allowing for the extra discharge, the increase in load is marked. On the other hand, a relatively small increase in slope has a large effect on bed load charge; this latter peculiarity is relevant to the cutting-off of river bends.

DOMINANT OR FORMATIVE DISCHARGE

The dominant or formative discharge of a fluctuating regime channel, as described previously, could be defined exactly by use of the preceding equations and methods. For example it could be defined as the steady discharge that would move the same total load over an infinitely long time as does the actual fluctuating discharge. Or it could be defined as the steady discharge that would produce the same mean channel slope as actually occurs. This second definition would be practically somewhat easier to use. However, dynamically satisfying definitions generally suffer from the disability that they call for enormous calculation for which the data are probably not available in practical problems anyway. In practice, therefore, a designer normally takes some fraction of peak discharge based on his experience of the general behaviour of channels of comparable type and degree of fluctuation. Except in river problems the fraction would not normally differ much from unity.

FEATURES OF REGIME CHANNEL BEHAVIOUR IN THE FIELD

PREVALENCE OF REGIME CONDITIONS

Although only a proportion of regime canals exhibit all the behaviour discussed in the preceding paragraphs there are actually few channels excavated in soil that do not show some aspects of regime behaviour. Canals fed from reservoirs may start sediment-free but accumulate bed load or suspended load, from which a bed load may differentiate, either by erosion of their own boundary (Problem 3), or from cross-drainages discharging into them, or from wind blown sand. Lined canals carrying load and expected to keep a clean boundary have acquired bed load (Problem 2) on top of the lining, and others have deposited berms on their lined sides (showing they were designed unnecessarily broad). On the American continent roadside drains are notorious for being left unlined, although their slopes are far in excess of regime values, so that they develop into minor canyons. Also the diversion of reservoir or canal spill down valleys whose slope is similarly far in excess of regime is fairly common. Canals dug steep in highly cohesive soil may erode but keep their load in suspension; they are rather special in that side-factor principles have to be used to estimate the bed behaviour, since a bed factor applies only to non-cohesive material. Unless experience has given the answer it is wise to test all channels with soil boundaries, or carrying a sediment load, for possible regime behaviour at some stage of flow.

PROPERTIES OF BED LOAD MATERIAL

Sand that has suffered continued mixing and attrition in bed load movement has a mechanical analysis curve that plots almost straight on logarithmic probability paper, *i.e.* the logarithm of grain size follows the 'normal' (Gaussian or error-function) distribution; approximately 1 per cent of particles will have more than double the median size and 1 per cent will have less than half the median size, the proportions being by *weight* and not by number of particles. Dispersion of sizes will be somewhat more for large median size than for small. Gravels do not follow any presently known simple law. The uniform sands of laboratory experiments do not occur in the field. Sand grains finer than $0 \cdot 1$ mm have terminal velocities of settlement, for usual field water temperatures, proportional to the square of particle diameter, but particles coarser than 1 mm have terminal settlement velocities proportional to the square root of diameter. One consequence of this is that the finer sands are whisked into suspension by comparatively small deviations of velocity of flow while gravels do not go into suspension readily, whence their very different behaviour in ejectors and excluders (below). Another consequence is that formulae like equation (D) cannot be extrapolated outside the sand range. Another, which is also attributed to some cohesiveness, is that silt is not found as bed material unless as part of a cohesive mix. In canal bends the coarser part of bed material moves towards the centre of curvature so does not follow the surface streamline pattern; this peculiarity permits the design of offtaking channels to take coarser or finer bed-material than their parent canals.

In practice coarse bed load may be introduced for short or long times into a canal (*e.g.* by a river breaching in, or by a cross-drainage feeding at intervals); the coarser material tends to move along the canal as a 'bar' or elongated mound that retains its identity for many miles and years. Bed load (equation (C)) is responsible almost entirely for regime slope at a given discharge, and, since charge is usually trifling, the size of the bed material is the controlling factor.

BED LOAD EJECTION

The first major sediment ejector for a canal appears to have been devised by E. S. Crump for the 9,000 cusec Upper Jhelum canal in the Punjab *ca.* 1930. Coarse sediment from cross-drainages in a deep cutting reach arrived in the fill reach about 25 years after canal opening and caused serious rise of regime levels. Surveys showed that the objectionable material moved in long mounds, so the following simple device was built. What was effectively a tunnel, with its roof at designed canal bed, was built across the canal; one end was closed and the other gated; apertures were left along the roof to catch bed load; the gates could discharge into a natural cross-drainage that ran under the canal; when a mound arrived the gates were opened and the mound washed into the cross-drainage. This device was so successful that it was used, with only minor modifica-

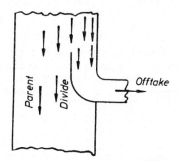

Figure 2. Divide wall located for even sediment draw

tions, as standard for all future main line canals. It does not drop bed factor much in sand-bed canals that have a wide range of sizes in the total load, since (i) the disturbance it produces puts considerable material into suspension (ii) even total elimination of bed material results in very nearly the same size differentiating out of total load. Use of two or three tunnels in sequence down the canal, as a battery, improves efficiency. Despite the poor efficiency as measured by percentage of bed load eliminated in the circumstances mentioned the practical value of being able to reduce bed factor even 10 per cent in a flat canal system is enormous. For gravels the device can be 100 per cent efficient. Water of the order of 5 per cent of canal discharge usually suffices to work an ejector[3].

BED LOAD EXCLUSION

Most successful bed load exclusion depends on the principle that the coarser bed material travels to the inside of a curve. Thus, if a channel takes off from well round the outside of a bend of its parent it will be as free from coarse bed load as is possible. If it cannot be located there then the bend has to be created. Within a canal system one simple way to create curved flow is to build a divide wall to trap the flow that is to enter an offtake so that the nose of the divide wall is far enough upstream of the offtake to be clear of the effect of the offtake draw on the parent; if the divide is located to cut off flow without any disturbance of the approaching stream line pattern the division of coarse bed load will be approximately even (*Figure 2*); if it is located closer to the bank the flow pattern will have to converge into the trap and coarse bed load will be drawn towards the bank and pass into the offtake in excess; if the divide is built father away from the bank the reverse effect will occur and the offtake will draw less coarse bed material. At the Sukkur Barrage (Sind, Pakistan) bed sediment entry to main canals taking off from the river was reduced using the same principle, on the recommendation of Sir C. C. Inglis, by replacing a straight guide bank by a curved one and creating a curved approach channel of which it formed one bank; the main line canals then drew from the outside of the curve so created[4]. Another method is to build a 'table' in front of a canal head regulator so that bed material will run under the table and relatively clean flow will be skimmed off into the canal regulator over the table top; this device is very sensitive to approach conditions, and model experiments have shown that a large excluder may have very much less efficiency than a small one for the same job. Submerged vanes, to divert bed load, can be very efficient for one discharge only. As with ejectors efficiency measured in terms of proportion excluded is small for sands, particularly when there is a total load of wide variation, but the value of a small gain in canals in flat country is great; for gravels efficiencies can be made easily about 100 per cent by the aid of simple models[3, 4].

BED LOAD MEASUREMENT

In practice bed load, defined in terms of bed movement (see Sediment Transport, p 434), cannot be measured as a practical routine when suspended load is present. On rivers, statistical records of what is called 'bed load' are made by suspended load samplers held near the bed; the quantity caught may not be remotely like bed load in its strict sense. References to some special observations are in ref. 1; the correct use of bed load formulae based on laboratory flume experiments may give bed load of canals within about half to twice the truth so far as these references and a few indirect unpublished determinations can show.

IMPORTANCE OF SUSPENDED LOAD IN CHANNEL FORMATION

Although bed load is responsible for regime slope particularly, suspended load is responsible for bank formation and the bed load may be merely a coarse non-cohesive fraction differentiated out of it. The major canals of India and Pakistan have suspended load averaging about 1 per cent by weight, comparable with what might be expected from the U.S.A.'s Colorado river, and are devised either to form their own berms from it or, if in cut, are given artificial berms. The natural deposition of berms and bed from the sediment load may be regarded as a model demonstration of how a river builds a flood plain and is illustrated in *Figure 3*, from Indian practice. In a is the final product; the original bank has been deliberately built to accommodate a larger channel section than will form, and the channel bed has made itself from the sand of the sediment load while the berm has made itself from the fine sand, silt, and clay, so is virtually hydraulic fill such as used to be popular in earth dam construction. In practice the berm formation requires some assistance to ensure that a meandering canal does not develop, and to accelerate depositing. So brushwood spurs are made, as in **b**, at intervals of a couple of times their projection—five times is the limit of effectiveness—with the result that a straight but serrated berm forms as in **d**. In cross-section the berm has a lip adjacent to the flow, as in **b**, when it first forms; this peculiarity exists also in flood plains built from loamy deposit. As a ragged canal deteriorates rapidly, and as berm hollows grow aquatic weeds, condition **b** is remedied by cutting earth from the side slope and depositing it in the hollow as in **c**; the space left by the cutting fills in a few days in the dirty water season. A couple of such cuttings and fillings give dry grassy berms; then the serrated edge is trimmed to leave a perfectly regular canal that is practically breach-proof and will not deteriorate except through long neglect.

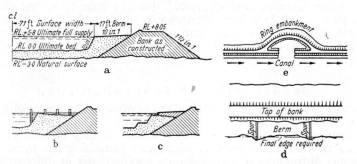

Figure 3. Berm formation. a *Canal in filling reach (a broad berm has been formed with assistance from spurs and maintenance, to contain regime channel breadth);* b *Initial berm formation (canal bed of sand; berm of fine cohesive mixture; top of berm slopes down to bank);* c *First maintenance (excavated edge will reform rapidly even without spurs);* d *Initial berm formation (uneven edge rectified as maintenance continues);* e *Breach repair (berm material deposits between ring bank and canal)*

The power of suspended load containing silt or clay to deposit and form banks is further demonstrated by the standard method of repairing a breach when such a load is available. The method is to build a ring bank round the breach, as in e, so that the enclosed space will fill itself with fine sediment; then the bank is rebuilt over this natural hydraulic fill. Likewise, if a canal has deteriorated by grassy berms growing out, dropping clods into the canal and starting local erosion round the clods so as to cause side-slope collapse, then a standard remedy is to cut the berms back severely to give the canal an increased breadth; suspended load will deposit on the cut banks to make them grow in again regularly and re-establish the original breadth. The same process of side-slope deposition occurs in rivers.

UTILITY OF BERMS

A naturally deposited berm is highly breach resistant. It will hold for some time after the bank has developed a small fissure; it is free from alkali; it has a small but appreciable effect in reducing seepage losses; and it is a line of defence against the depredations of burrowing animals. Even an artificial berm, in a channel in fill or in cut, has the advantages that it allows for imposition of breadth changes within regime limits without interfering with the bank (whose top is often a road), allows a margin for changing breadth without interfering with the bank when designed discharge is increased, allows bank alignment to be smooth when depth of cut varies, and prevents material washed down by rain from entering the channel and causing irregularities that produce vortices that eat into the bank and cause accelerated deterioration. In lined channels a berm has few advantages and may be a nuisance if not sloped upward from the lining edge.

EFFECT OF SUSPENDED LOAD ON VISCOSITY

Suspended load turns the flow into a non-Newtonian fluid, *viz,* one whose viscosity depends on rate of shear. In canal and river work the concentration, usually not over 1 per cent by weight in big rivers, allows the effect to be considered as a drop in viscosity up to about 20 per cent. Where suspensions are high, as in pipe-line transport or small rivers, this simplification will not suffice. A noticeable effect on Indian canals is that if the water becomes suddenly turbid, due to a river flood, the discharge for a given depth in a long channel may increase by 5 to 10 per cent. Laboratory experiments show that suspended load alters the constant of the universal velocity distribution law of rigid boundary hydraulics radically.

OBSERVATION OF SUSPENDED LOAD

Suspended load can be measured[20] with fair accuracy by means of a device that is essentially a metal fish with a pitot-tube mouth and reverse pitot gills, both connected to a milk bottle inside. It may be used to collect samples at individual points, in which case something has to be known about the distribution of sedimentation concentration at different depths, or as an integrator lowered up and down a vertical at slow uniform speed.

DISPOSITION OF SEDIMENT

It is important to realize that sediment cannot be destroyed; it must deposit somewhere. Usually the best way to deal with sediment in a canal system is to design the channels for regime so that they pass the load and do not have to be sediment-cleared periodically; however, if the deposition is likely to be small, clearance of canals may be economic. A common practice is to create sediment-collection tanks along canals and these tanks may actually be beneficial in reclaiming land; if total load is high, say even one tenth of one per cent by weight, the designer should consider whether tanks that have to collect total load are economic when the objectionable bed load is perhaps only one per cent of total collection. Suspended load is usually beneficial to crops, but a load of pure rock flour can be harmful. Load dumped in a storage reservoir may waste reservoir capacity quickly and, as everything but the clay-size material dumps in a delta, the effect of the delta on canal levels upstream (by lengthening the canal by the extent of the delta) has also to be considered. The total load in the Indus system of canals is believed sufficient to raise the whole irrigated area from 6 in to 1 ft per century, in agreement with archaeological evidence on deposition in the whole Indus valley. A useful figure is that, at $C = 1·0$ per hundred thousand, a cusec-year of supply will deposit 8 cu yd at 90 lb/cu ft dry weight (6 cu m at 1,440 kg/cu m).

CHANGES OF REGIME

In irrigating canals, at least, a large sediment load usually calls for distributing channels to be run full supply or to be closed. Attempts to run such channels for several months at part discharge, instead of full rotationally, has shown that sections and slopes can alter sufficiently to cause maldistribution of supply and danger to banks when full supply runs again.

MEANDERING

MEANDERING DEFINED

All channels with erodible banks tend to acquire a configuration, as seen in plan view, of marked sinuosity that *progresses or switches more or less cyclically*. If they actually acquire this state they are said to meander; if they are merely sinuous without changing more or less cyclically (*e.g.* if in inerodible rock) they are said to be tortuous, or to have tortuosity, but they do not meander.

BRAIDING DEFINED

In models built in the simple conditions of laboratory sand trays[21] suppose that a river of constant discharge meanders in its typical sine-curve pattern, and that the discharge is suddenly increased appreciably and held constant at the new value. The sine-curve pattern will be replaced, normally, by a network of interlacing streams that gradually reduce in number till eventually a new single sine-curve pattern of larger wavelength and amplitude emerges. During the transition stage of multiple channels the river is said to be braided. The term is not quite standard, and some authorities call a stream braided if it is merely bifurcated.

PROBABLE CAUSES OF BRAIDING

Multiple braiding appears to be due to large erratic variations of discharge or of sediment load, or to a channel increasing its slope so that it spills repeatedly and forms new courses. This last cause is seen at work in deltas and alluvial fans, which are essentially the same with the one forming into a sea and the other forming into a plain. Accordingly we shall consider braiding as an incipient form of meandering, even if it consists of bifurcating only.

MEANDERING AS A RIVER CHARACTERISTIC

The straight, or mildly curved form of artificial canals is maintained by gentle controlling action, rather like the gentle effort of the steerer of an automobile; however, the natural tendency of the canal, if its sides are erodible, is to meander once it gets free of this gentle control whether it has constant or variable discharge. Accordingly we shall regard a channel as a river, regardless of its origin, if it becomes braided or meanders. Obviously it is then a regime river of four degrees of freedom (see Regime and Degrees of Freedom or Self-Adjustment, p 436).

PECULIARITIES OF MEANDERING

SPILLING AND INCISED RIVERS

For subsequent reference it is convenient to classify rivers as 'spilling' and 'incised'. The typical spilling river is well known from model experiments in pure sand and is reproduced in nature when there is negligible suspended load and no cohesive banks except perhaps at the extremity of the river's meandering swing from side to side. Under these circumstances the river spills widely at relatively low flood discharge so that a definite course cannot be seen. The opposite type of river, with a large cohesive suspended load, builds up banks to nearly peak flood level just as a canal builds berms (*Figure 3*) and so looks like a very crooked canal; even when it spills at very high flood the main course may be clearly distinguishable[1]. The terms are used qualitatively so there is no conventional definition setting a dividing line between the two types.

MEANDER PATTERNS

The spilling river normally meanders in a very good approximation to a sine-curve of double amplitude equal to half the wave length. The incised river in fairly uniform soil tends to assume a form that doubles back on on itself like antisynclinic strata in geology; in heterogeneous soil the form is often zig-zag like a Chinese firecracker; when the unusually large floods are very much larger than the common ones—100-year flood is several times larger than the 2-year one—the loops of the meanders often show sub-meanders developing on them. Geological peculiarities may be responsible for unusual occurrences, such as very long straights with neat curves joining them.

CUT-OFFS AND CHUTES

Perhaps the most striking feature of a meandering river is the formation of cut-offs. The erosion at the outside of a bend tends to progress downstream from year to year and to move out to some definite limit. The actual consequences of this tendency depend very largely on bank resistance, so that the details are different for different cases although the general result is the same. *Figure 4* shows a case where the approach *AB* to a meander loop was straight because the flow had been confined upstream of the approach by bridge training works. The loop *BXC* had grown outward for several years to a shape rather unusual for what was essentially a spilling river, and the chord *BC* had refused to develop into a cut-off. The soil round *B* was relatively tough and round *X* must have been similar. Actually, as the loop was attacking a building area, matters were remedied by making a comparatively slight broadening at the head of the chord and cutting through into under-lying sand; the next large flood turned *BC* into main river in a few days and left the loop *BXC* so heavily deposited that it became virtually an ox-bow lake. This artificially assisted cut-off developed for the same reason as any natural one, *viz* that, at a suitable river elevation, the regime slope by equation (C″) was less than the available slope so it started to erode, and the more it eroded the more excessive, relative to regime slope for its dimensions, did the available slope become.

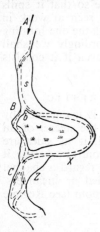

Figure 4. Meander loop with unde-veloped chord

Various possibilities can be visualized in terms of *Figure 4*. Suppose the soil around *B* had been relatively erodible and that moderately high floods had been frequent; then the chord *BC* would have developed long before the loop moved so far to the right, and the meander shape would never have deviated much from a sine curve. Suppose again that *Z* had been a point of resistance but *X* had not, and that *B* was soft, the river incised and the chord channel *BC* absent; then *B* would keep moving down the figure till the river breached through on to itself with a sudden drop[1]. Photos of different cut-offs are in ref. 1.

In the U.S.A. the cut-off of a spilling river is called a ' chute '; it might be regarded as a premature cut-off.

CONSEQUENCES OF CUT-OFFS

Because a cut-off is effectively a canal of slope very much in excess of regime value it erodes violently and, as it degrades, produces a backwater effect upstream that causes erosion there. The products of erosion are carried to the relatively ' in regime ' reach of river downstream, they increase the bed factor, and cause the river to start to steepen there. If an engineer contemplates assisting a cut-off, say for reducing the number of road crossings, he should consider that, except in special circumstances, he will cause flooding and damage to land downstream by deposit of sediment on it and by temporary braiding or enhanced range of meandering there, will cause enhanced bank erosion upstream and may cause higher upstream levels when the effects of downstream disturbances have reached their maximum. Special circumstances can make cut-offs harmless.

VARIATION OF SLOPE ALONG MEANDERS

Slope round bends is greater than along straights, just as in rigid-boundary hydraulics. At low supply the slope variation becomes even more marked because there is scour round the outsides of bends in high supply, and shallow water between bends; so, in low supply, the flow cascades from the elevations into the depressions and, in doing so, moves bed material so that conditions will change even during steady flow in the low-water season. In fact, at low supply the water surface profile is definitely stepped whereas in flood it merely undulates gently. Where channels bifurcate slope tends to be particularly steep because of curvature of flow, reduced discharge and differentiation of heavy material at the nose of divides[5]. These points have to be remembered when measuring slope for regime calculations, when designing heights of flood banks, when considering the safe depth of burial of submarine crossings, and when navigating.

EFFECT OF MEANDERING ON SPECIFIC GAUGES

The ' specific gauge ' at a location is the gauge reading corresponding to a specified discharge and is used to verify whether a river is changing its regime. Specific gauge records fluctuate from year to year even if they show no general trend up or down. If the length between two fixed points on a meandering river, measured along the stream, is recorded periodically, it will be found to fluctuate because of the sequence of meandering, cutting off, and meandering again. This change of length, combined with change of resistance due to change of curvature of flow is a major reason for fluctuations of specific gauge. The change in specific gauge, due to a cut-off in a large river, may have serious consequences to engineering works and should always be considered when designing for safe location of the hydraulic jump on a weir floor. Specific gauge records may be kept advantageously as routine for all gauging sites on meandering rivers on which construction may be done.

POINT BARS

The whole sequence of possible occurrences in the erosion and deposition that constitute meandering in natural rivers is complex and has received some special study by geomorphologists[5, 6]. However, an outstanding feature that can receive mention here is the formation of 'point bars'. In general terms the point bar is the shoal that tends to form on the inside of an eroding bend for reasons including the tendency of bed load to move towards the inside of a curve (see Bed Load Exclusion, p 447). It is often characterized by alluvial ridges parallel to the shore. A point bar would be expected roughly opposite *X* in *Figure 4*, *i.e.* on the downstream portion of the 'point' or 'headland'. The ridges appear to be initiated mainly by large floods, and then evolve to suit subsequent medium and low floods. Consequently air photos show, very commonly, that the bars are crossed by a sequence of these alluvial ridges that, like the rings of trees show abnormal weather, give an indication of the sequence of large floods and thence, sometimes, an idea of the rapidity of meander development.

DEPOSITION IN BENDS THAT HAVE BEEN CUT OFF

When a bend has been cut off sediment will deposit in it according to what is available in the river flow, and the discharges available. If, for example, a bend has been partially filled and is then subjected to a sequence of medium floods that do not pass much flow into it but do carry clay material in suspension the tendency will be for a deposit of clay to build up and, due to alternate wetting and drying, consolidate; this clay deposit could eventually provide a zone of resistance to erosion when the river returns from some other direction and attempts to cut across the old course. On the other hand, if a couple of high floods occurred instead of the sequence of medium ones the bend would tend to fill with sandier materials.

REGIME FORMULA FOR MEANDERING

DEFINITIONS

The following definitions are required:

(i)   *Meander length*—This is the length, measured along the straight path about which it oscillates, of a complete meander bend.

(ii) *Meander breadth*—This is the breadth of a belt tangent to the outer banks of a complete meander bend.

MEASUREMENT OF MEANDER DIMENSIONS

Obviously, in practice, the imperfection of any one meander prevents exact measurement of meander length and breadth. For statistical examination meander length may be obtained by selecting a river reach in which there is a sequence of similar meanders, putting a curved axis of oscillation through them, and finding the mean length of axis per meander. Meander breadth is much less precise since the bank of a river is indefinite and meander breadths vary much more from meander to meander than do the lengths; different observers will make different estimates, so analysis of results must take cognizance of this fact.

THE REGIME MEANDER EQUATION

Statistical examination and the behaviour of models[1] both indicate strongly that, all other causes being equal except discharge, meander length and breadth vary as channel breadth or, what is the same thing, as the square root of discharge. That is:

$$M_L \text{ and } M_B \text{ are proportional to } Q^{1/2} \qquad \text{............(M')}$$

For reasons given in ref. 1, the author recommends generalizing this to:

$$M_L = m \, (F_b/F_s)^{\frac{1}{2}} \, Q_e^{\frac{1}{3}} \qquad \ldots\ldots\ldots\ldots(M)$$

and using it with values of the *meander ratio* M_B/M_L. In it m is a multiplier, usually not much different from 12, that depends largely on hydrograph form and nature of suspended load and covers inaccuracies in estimating F_b and F_s. Q_e is an estimate of the equivalent flood discharge, *viz* the portion of high (about 100-year) flood that occupies the meandering channel, so does not include spill. In this form the equation calls for considerable knowledge of river factors. When that knowledge is absent the formula may be reduced to $M_L = \text{const.} \, Q_{max}^{\frac{1}{3}}$ in which the constant is to be determined from the user's experience; INGLIS'[1,4] value for Indian spilling rivers is 28 and, like multipliers of other equations that are of correct form in Q, fits many rivers that seem quite unlike those for which it was derived but can mislead in special cases. The formula applies well to the spacing of the shoals that form alternately on opposite sides of a river with very little M_B.

MEANDER RATIO

The meander ratio M_B/M_L varies from about 0·5 for fully developed sine curve meanders to a little over 1·5 for very exaggerated-looking meanders; *Figure 5* shows a case with 1·6. These figures are averages for sequences of well-developed meanders.

Figure 5. River with estimated meander ratio 1·6

USES OF THE FORMULA

A major use of the meander equation is in estimating the amount by which a river will try to outflank a bridge or barrage. Any such work has the same effect on a river as an inerodible point in a figure like *Figure 4*; the river tends to collapse on to the obstacle and may develop a full meander breadth to one side of the obstacle before it cuts off and starts straight again. Minor use is to give some idea when engineering action to assist a cut-off to occur is likely to succeed; it will not succeed if the meander ratio is much less than 0·5. Another is to obtain a first approximation, from scaled air photos, of the order of magnitude of the high floods that have formed a river. Another is to estimate the probable limit of erosive attack.

CANAL REGIME FORMULAE APPLIED TO RIVERS

APPLICABILITY IN GENERAL

Regarding a river in general as a canal of large bed load charge and large discharge variation with a fourth degree of freedom to meander there seems good reason to expect the form of the canal regime equations to apply with some minor adjustment to allow for the meandering (this is discussed in detail in ref. 1), subject to the canal proviso that rate of change of discharge must not be too great. However, at first sight, the practical difficulties appear serious. They arise from factors such as: (i) spilling makes the channel section indefinite; (ii) even without spill few sections will be trapezoidal; (iii) with gravel beds F_{b_0} (equation (D)), will vary with stage since the coarsest material will move only at high flood; (iv) bed load charge may fluctuate erratically, may be an unmeasurable fraction differentiated from total load and cannot be measured with any assurance even in simple cases; (v) the effect of meandering on regime slope (linked with deviation of sectional form from the trapezoidal) is not known exactly; (vi) log jams, slides, ice jams, permafrost, tree and vegetation roots *etc* are complications difficult to assess. Actually, sound engineering judgment permits most useful practical problems to be solved with an acceptable degree of accuracy. A major reason for this state of affairs is that, all other things being equal except discharge, we can assert that any two rivers will adjust so that b, d, S, V, M_L, M_b depend on a dominant discharge raised to the powers 1/2, 1/3, minus 1/6, 1/6, 1/2 and 1/2 respectively; this permits an engineer to use observation of a river to predict what most of his interferences will do to it, since the observations give him the otherwise indeterminate multipliers in his regime equations. A further major reason is that if a computor knows the forms of the equation and has acquired a little experience of bed factors and working side factors, the procedure just described can be extended from one river to another with fair accuracy by keeping to formulae in which the bed and side factors occur to small fractional powers (so that moderate errors in estimation are not important in the results). Minor reasons include that some problems of importance do not depend much on poorly known factors, and that a multiplicity of disturbing causes usually produces considerable mutual cancellation—a fact that is equally fortunate in hydrology. The following paragraphs will outline some principal applications; more detail will be found in ref. 1.

THE 'FLOOD BREADTH' OF A RIVER

The flood breadth, b_f, of a river is defined from equation (A) as:

$$b_f = (F_b Q_{max} / F_s)^{\frac{1}{2}}$$

where Q_{max} is peak flood in cusecs, F_b is the bed factor expected of the river at that discharge, and F_s is an assessment of the side factor that would occur in a canalized reach of the river in regime. The fact that no two engineers would be likely to assess quite the same b_f for the same river reach does not alter the utility of the quantity. Q_{max} has to depend largely on what is known of the channel, but is often conveniently defined (when there are good data) as a flood of some specified long recurrence interval, such as 50 years. F_b can be estimated from a visual assessment of F_{b_0} and an estimate of the charge C from the slope formula (Problem 7) after allowing for the effect of meandering (see Variation of Slope Along Meanders, p 453); or it might be found, or F_b/F_s might be found, by working backwards from the data of suitable river reaches of canalized appearance. F_s can be assessed only from experience.

ESTIMATING 'PEAK FLOOD'

To determine, if there are no discharge records, the order of magnitude of the high floods that have carved out a river's channel, the river may be inspected for straight reaches where flow is apparently like a canal's and does not spill during high flood. In such a reach the flood breadth should be the channel breadth at half-depth; then, if F_b and F_s can be assessed, measurement of breadth will permit calculation of Q_{max}. If there is spill then the banks can be produced up to estimated high flood level and the mean breadth assessed accordingly; the discharge calculated therefrom will have to be increased by an assessment of flood spill. Some rivers, particularly the braided ones, afford no suitable sections; incised rivers usually afford many. Useful facts are that many rivers work to a value between 2·0 and 2·3 for $(F_b/F_s)^{\frac{1}{2}}$; a low of 1·25, for rivers of large gravel with banks of the same kind, and a high of 2·75, for rivers of moderate sand charge and highly noncohesive banks, cover most practical cases. The reason for the rather limited variation is that nature usually associates fairly resistant banks with coarse beds, so the quotient F_b/F_s varies less than its components; its square root varies even less.

DECIDING SPANNED BREADTH FOR BRIDGES AND BARRAGES

Hydraulically, nothing is gained by spanning more than a flood breadth since, no matter how much flood plain is inundated, flow concentrates in about one flood breadth. Excessive spans merely present more piers to attack and it may be expected that, eventually, every pier will be equally severely attacked since the river will move across the whole bridged water-way in the normal cycle of meandering. Spanning much less than a flood breadth usually results in unacceptably deep scour round piers and abutments; the decision is essentially one of relative cost of piers and superstructure.

LOCATION OF TRAINING WORKS

The relative positions of training works depend on the size of the meander pattern, so rules can be given in terms of flood breadth to suit the meander equation (M) which gives meander size as a multiple of flood breadth. See Training Works, p 459.

THE 'FLOOD DEPTH' OF A RIVER

In correspondence with flood breadth a flood depth is defined by:

$$d_f = \sqrt[3]{(F_s Q_{max}/F_b{}^2)} = \sqrt[3]{(q^2{}_{max}/F_b)}$$

where q_{max} is found by dividing Q_{max} by the flood breadth or, if F_s cannot be assessed well or if breadth is definite as with a bridge, by dividing by an estimated or actual breadth of flow at peak flood.

USES OF FLOOD DEPTH

The flood depth formula should not be used for estimating peak flood discharge, since depth cannot be measured accurately, compared with breadth, and Q_{max} depends on its cube. Rules for the scour to expect in an *unobstructed* channel can be formed in terms of flood depth; *e.g.* the scoured depth at the outside of a natural meander bend, allowing for bed dunes, may be taken as a multiple of flood depth. Usually F_b has to be estimated from river behaviour at moderate flood, so is a little less than high flood value.

ZERO FLOOD DEPTH

Zero flood depth is defined as flood depth in which F_b is replaced by F_{b0} (see equation (D)). Scour caused by rigid obstacles is expressed in terms of this zero flood depth d_{f0}. The following table gives values of z, the multiplier of d_{f0} to give designed (not necessarily actual) values of scour below high flood level for some principal obstacles.

(a) Noses of spurs or guide banks $z = 2\cdot0 – 2\cdot75$
(b) Flow impinging at right angles on bank $z = 2\cdot25$
(c) Between and around bridge piers $z = 2\cdot0$
(d) Downstream of barrages with hydraulic jump on floor $z = 1\cdot75 – 2\cdot25$

USE OF THE SLOPE FORMULA

The slope formula, in any of its forms (see Alternative Forms of Equation (C) p 444), has to be used on a river with allowance for the facts that (i) meandering causes slope to be much more than the formula states and (ii) river slope cannot change rapidly so sets itself to suit an average condition instead of a peak discharge one. Accordingly, in a general problem, the first step is to obtain the slope along the deep-water channel and then divide it by a factor that is usually between $1\cdot75$ and $2\cdot25$ to obtain the slope at which the river would run in regime at a specified steady discharge with the appropriate bed and side factors, or bed factor and breadth if it were canalized straight. The ratio of this slope to the slope for F_{b0} corresponding to the bed material gives the appropriate $f(C)$ and thence an estimate of the C for the discharge used. From this follows an estimate of the actual F_b. The following problems illustrate procedure, applicability to some of the preceding paragraphs, and the effect of small fractional indices in removing major uncertainties.

Problem 7—A braided gravel stream of obviously high charge is to have its behaviour analysed so as to obtain fair consistence before proceeding to the design of a bridge. The 100-year flood is known to be about 40,000 cusecs, and the median annual flood about 6,500 cusecs. Slope straight down the valley is 0·4 per cent. The bed material suggests F_{b0} might be taken as 5·0 and the few cut banks show bed and side material similar. Estimate (i) the bed-load charge at peak flood, assuming that a definite channel takes ¼ of the total flow; (ii) the corresponding F_b; (iii) the corresponding flood breadth; (iv) the corresponding flood depth; (v) the charge at median annual flood if the flow then occupies a channel of breadth 300 ft.

Solution—(i) Take the deepwater channel length as 1·5 times straight distance and the correction factor to obtain straight canalized regime slope as 2·0. Then the straight canalized regime slope would be $4/3 = 1\cdot33$ per thousand. To obtain the straight canal regime slope for F_{b0}, assume $K = 1,800$ and $F_s = F_{b0}^2/8 = 3\cdot125$ (see Estimation of side-factor, p 442). Then $S_0 = 5^{5/6} \times 3\cdot125^{1/12}$ divided by $1\cdot8 \times 30,000^{1/6} = 0\cdot425$ per thousand. So, by equation (C') the value of $f'(C)$ is $1\cdot33/0\cdot425 = 3\cdot13$ and *Figure 1* gives $C = 30$ parts per hundred thousand by weight. (ii) Then $F_b = 5(1 + 0\cdot12 \times 30) = 23$. (iii) $F_b/F_s = 23/3\cdot125 = 7\cdot35$; $(F_b/F_s)^{1/2} = 2\cdot7$; $b_f = 2\cdot7 \times 30,000^{1/2} = 470$ ft. (iv) $d = [30,000/(7\cdot35 \times 23)]^{1/3} = 5\cdot7$ ft. (v) Using equation (C'''), $S_0 = 5^{11/12}$ divided by $1\cdot8 \times 300^{1/6} \times 6,500^{1/12} = 0\cdot45$; $f'''(C) = 1\cdot33/0\cdot45 = 2\cdot95$ and $C = 22$ by *Figure 1*.

PROBLEM OF THE ASSISTED CUT-OFF

A common river engineering problem concerns the size of channel to cut across a chord such as *BC* in *Figure 4* so that, when the river discharge exceeds a certain amount, the cut will develop of its own accord. Fundamentally the solution is to find the discharge that would give 'in regime' conditions at the slope available in the cut-off if the bed and side factors were as for the river; then the cut is made considerably too large for that discharge. A more precise method, involving more algebra, is to specify that the cut should start running with a charge a certain number of times that of the river and a side factor also a certain number of times more. The working is virtually that of Problem 4 inverted.

SLOPE FORMULA ON TIDAL RIVER

The following two simple problems checked from actual cases illustrate how the slope formula can be used when a river is 'compared with itself' so that complex unknowns vanish.

Problem 8—A tidal estuary was given extensive training works in its upper three-quarters. These caused fine-grained material to build high berms in the comparatively dead water they created; so the estuary lost half its capacity for water at dominant discharge conditions. Therefore, approximately, the tidal discharges at every section of the estuary dropped to about one-half the original values. If the total drop of water level between the ends of the tidal reach of the estuary at dominant conditions used to be 15 ft, estimate what it might become eventually because of the training works.

Solution—As bed and side-factors would return eventually to original values, equation (C) shows that slope would become $2^{1/6} = 1.12$ times greater, so the top end of the estuary would show aggradation of water levels about $15 \times 0.12 = 1.8$ ft.

Problem 9—A tidal estuary split into two branches that had remained permanent features for many years (training works prevented the appoach conditions from altering, so the division of bed-load material could not alter). The median size of bed material in the small branch was found, from many samples, to be 0.22 mm and in the other 0.34 mm. Bed-load charge was known to be very small. The branches had almost the same length and degree of tortuosity. Estimate the proportion of discharge taken by each.

Solution—Accepting F_{b0} proportional to square root of median sand diameter (see equation (D)), and taking equation (C) to apply to each branch with the same correction coefficient for meandering $F_b^{5/6}/Q^{1/6}$ must be the same for both. Therefore $Q_{0.34}/Q_{0.22} = (22/34)^{5/2} = 0.34$.

TRAINING WORKS

SPUR GUIDE BANKS AND MARGINAL BANKS

As meanders progress downstream, cut off, redevelop, and so on, the presence of an obstruction like a bridge in a meandering river results sooner or later in the river folding, or 'concertina-ing' on to the bridge till relieved by cut-off. *Figure 6* shows six . barrages across Punjab rivers of from 400,000 to 1,000,000 cusecs peak floods and illustrates the point. The barrages may be looked on as bridges—they produce no ponding at high flood—and their right and left marginal banks (RMB, LMB) as roadways.

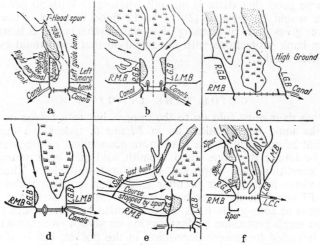

Figure 6. Guide banks, spurs and incipient outflanking

They are provided with right and left guide banks (RGB, LGB) so that the collapse of river does not occur on to the marginal banks but, instead, on to pockets of water whose gentle circulation will not harm the banks. In case a (*Figure 6*) a T-head spur has been built to straighten the river that had folded over to the dotted course marked 1931. In case b the river is temporarily split into two channels (an unstable condition) and both halves are collapsing on to the noses of the guide banks. Case c has good approach banks that refuse to yield, so is not typical. Case d is starting to show the effect at the right guide bank and has experienced it on the left where the channel has died. Case e could be typical of an exceedingly extreme occurrence, but the apparently collapsed course happens to be an old river one before the barrage was built. Case f shows spurs built to prevent the effect. Without spurs to prevent the effect, or guide banks to compel it to occur well upstream, the river must eventually fold on to the road or marginal banks. Generally spurs and guide banks transfer attack from a vital point to an expendable one.

Two dangers arise when there are neither spurs nor guide banks to prevent folding of a spilling river on to the approach road of a bridge across it. The first is that the river will strike the road a long way from the bridge and, in running along the road that has now become the river bank, erode it away. The second is that the river striking the road a long way from the bridge will overtop the road because the road will have been graded to suit the flood level at the bridge and not the flood level a long way upstream. In either case, if the road fails and the site of failure is a good one for a cut-off then a new river may develop through the breach during the flood that caused the trouble and the channel through the bridge will become filled with sediment. The bridge is then described as outflanked, and the engineers may have to decide between making a new bridge and pushing the river back. A fair estimate of the distance by which a bridge can be outflanked in a spilling river is a full meander breadth less the span measured from the abutment adjacent to the out-flanking. If we assume that the effective flow in the meander in a spilling river is half the peak flood discharge, this estimate is $6/(2)^{1/2} - 1$ flood breadths, by equation (M) or, say 3 flood breadths. This figure might be used to estimate the length of revetment needed along a road to a bridge that has no guide banks or spurs. Notice that the bridge causes river swing within two meander belts breadth less one span. For an incised river the amount of outflanking is obviously $1 \cdot 5 \times 12 - 1 = 17$ flood breadths if the incision is so good that there is no spill whatever. With 50 per cent spill the answer would be $1 \cdot 5 \times 12/(2)^{1/2} - 1 = 12$ flood breadths. However, an incised river gives years of warning of its developments and is hardly likely to be given bank protections with the intention that they would eventually become guide banks.

GUIDE BANK LENGTHS

As a spilling river must fold on to the approaches to a bridge or barrage, guide banks must be provided, as in *Figure 6*, unless the engineer is satisfied that he can protect the road more economically otherwise. They need not be longer than one flood breadth, and may be a quarter less if approach conditions are improved by natural obstacles. There is no particular virtue in the rather peculiar guide bank conformations, in plan, shown in *Figure 6*; if the river has a permanent bias, as in c, the banks may be made to suit; guide bank noses rounded to a bellmouth form will not need so much protection against erosion as abrupt ones; bottle-necking as in e is intended to prevent deposition in the pocket, but is of doubtful effectiveness.

LOCATION OF SPURS

An alternative or auxiliary to guide banks is the provision of spurs as in *Figure 6* a, e, f. Essentially a spur is an armoured nose connected to high ground so that the river cannot pass through the connection. If a spur is to prevent folding of the river on to the road it must be located so as to break the meander pattern and prevent the formation of a complete half meander no matter how the river approaches. So the head should be noticeably less than half a meander length upstream of the bridge if there are no guide banks. INGLIS[4] expresses a preference for 0·4 meander lengths. By equation (M) with effective discharge assumed half the peak flood, 0·4 meander length is $0·4 \times 12/(2)^{1/2}$ times a flood breadth of $(F_b \, Q_{max}/F_s)^{1/2}$ or 3·4 flood breadths. So a rough rule could be stated as 'maximum distance to spur = 3 flood breadths in spilling river and 4 flood breadths in incised river'.

PITCHED ISLANDS

In Pakistan and India use has been made of pitched islands to direct a river in a desired direction; one of the earliest applications is described in Ref. 12. They take advantage of the observation that relatively long bridge piers set skew to a river tend to make the river adjust so as to run in their direction; in fact, they are virtually long stone-protected bridge piers without the bridge, and have also been described as T-head spurs minus the shank. Their principle is that a current striking them obliquely causes deep scour along them and this scour, particularly if they are rough, continues for some distance downstream, thus creating the same effect as continuously maintaining a dredged deep channel; to their lee deposition occurs. Thus a 'preferred path' is created in the river and, if it is important enough, the river adjusts to take advantage until some major avulsion, say due to a cut-off, drags it away. Normally a pitched island is built at the edge of a shoal when water is low and comes into operation during flood; thereafter medium supplies keep it operating. The relative advantages of islands and spurs depend largely on cost and circumstances; neither spurs nor islands can normally prevent a river from leaving them, but a spur does prevent the river from entering a forbidden zone, sometimes at the cost of an exceedingly expensive shank.

FLEXIBLE PROTECTION OF TRAINING WORKS AND OTHER OBSTACLES

FLEXIBLE APRONS

Banks for any kind of river training work, and the downstream extensions of barrages, need protection right to the bottom of whatever scour hole will form. Only flexible protection, such as stone, concrete blocks, or, sometimes, articulated concrete matting, is likely to have any permanence on a yielding base. Normal procedure is to build a bank only above a convenient level, lay the protection on its side slope and then lay the protection that will be required for the rest of the bank (after scour has occurred) as an apron (*Figure 7*) on the natural ground. Provided the ground is non-cohesive, the stone will settle to a slope of about 1 upon 2, when it is undercut by scour, and will thus complete the protected bank. The angle to which the stone will settle depends on the properties of stone rolling on stone and not on those of the non-cohesive material underneath; hence the fair accuracy of the slope 1 upon 2. If the ground is cohesive the apron is likely to remain on a cliff as scour occurs; when the cliff fails by sliding, it will carry the apron end away where it will be useless and, eventually, the bank will be lost. Practice has normally been to lay the apron over a length of 1·5 H, where H is the depth of estimated scour below the position of laying; the scour d_s is estimated from empirical rules

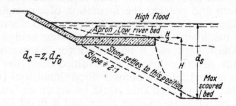

High Flood

Apron Low river bed

Stone settles to this position

Slope = 2:7

$d_s = z, d_{f_0}$

d_s

Max scoured bed

Figure 7. Apron (not to scale)

such as given in Zero Flood Depth p 457. Model experiments by INGLIS[4] show the mechanism of apron launching and demonstrate that the length of laying can be greatly curtailed provided that the proper volume of stone is still given. The volume for a two-dimensional problem is obviously $(5)^{1/2}HT$ where T is the thickness needed on the finally settled slope.

STONE SIZE AND THICKNESS FOR BANK AND APRON PROTECTION

Usually the size of stone used is the same for side slopes and for apron, but strictly the apron needs larger size, since it is liable to cause excessive attack until it has launched to something like its final position. Usually sand-bed rivers are given about 100 lb stone and the side-slope protection is underlaid by a filter layer of gravel that will prevent fine-grained under-lay from being removed by suction from wave-wash or swirl; the apron stone is often wrapped in crates to ensure that it will not wash away before or during launching. Actually, much smaller material will stand on banks in sand-bed rivers if it is well graded, but there are no definite rules as to its size and grading and there is not sufficient evidence to show that it will not be lost during settlement if used as apron under severe conditions. For stability after launching of an apron, 100 lb size or diameter two or three times the diameter of the largest material that moves in the river during high flood, whichever is greater, may be taken as a fair rule for sand or gravel rivers. The value of putting a filter material under an apron on a sand bed is somewhat dubious. The thickness T of the finally launched apron on a 1 upon 2 slope with sand underlay is recommended by INGLIS[4] as $0·06Q_{max}^{1/3}$; on ready made banks at 1 upon 2 slope the thickness, when there is a filter underlay, may be that arising from two single layers of the specified stone size. When very large rocks, *e.g.* 2 or 3 tons, are used in gravel streams or on rock rapids, on top of gravel, an underlay is needed of size that will fill the interstices in the large rock; otherwise the case becomes comparable with 100 lb stone laid straight on fine-grained soil. As the infallibility of stone protection cannot be guaranteed, with present knowledge, at reasonable cost all stone protected works should be provided with a stock of about 10 per cent of the total stone used so as to be ready for emergency. Routine annual surveys plus special ones after severe floods should be made to determine the state of stone protections, and stone that has been lost (this does not include stone that is in the protection zone but has been buried by river deposition) should be replaced and the stock brought to normal.

GEOMORPHIC AND HYDROLOGIC INFORMATION

GENERAL

This chapter, as explained in the introduction, deals essentially with theoretical and applied mobile boundary hydraulics. As with the hydraulics of simple fluids within rigid boundary the mechanism responsible for the laws at work is only imperfectly observable, most real problems are complicated by auxiliary phenomena for which quantitative allowance cannot be made with certainty, and the boundary conditions may make a mathematical solution impossibly difficult even if the conditions of the problem are precise and only the major laws operate. Accordingly, for the best available understanding of river and canal behaviour, mobile boundary hydraulics should be supplemented by facts and theories from geomorphology and hydrology. The former subject provides carefully detailed case histories of river behaviour, laboratory and model experiments to discover fundamental causes and laws, quantitative observations in the field, discussions of geological factors in river histories, and theories by workers of varied outlooks. The latter subject is particularly useful in providing information on river discharge peculiarities, and overlaps into geomorphology at some points. Actually, there is no clear division among mobile boundary hydraulics, geomorphology and hydrology. The following examples illustrate the interconnection.

FLOOD FREQUENCIES

As protection against the highest floods likely to happen is usually expensive, financing agencies appreciate information on the relative costs of projects designed to protect fully against floods of different degrees of rareness. Studies of flood frequency behaviour have shown a fair family resemblance among frequency curves for annual peak floods. In fact, if annual peak flood is plotted on logarithmic probability paper against the percentage frequency with which it is equalled or exceeded, the smoothing curve is likely to approximate a straight line with a slight inflexion in the middle; of course, for obvious reasons, there are exceptions. Accordingly, a useful though improvable criterion of the range of annual peak floods is obtained by extrapolating the frequency fitting curve to a fairly low frequency—say once in 100 years—and recording the ratio of 100-year to 2-year (median) annual flood. Despite the similarity of curve form the range of ratios is somewhat remarkable, but it is consistent with topography and climate. Thus coastal rivers of British Columbia, Canada, show a ratio about 2; small rivers east of the Canadian Rockies in Alberta have a ratio from 10 to 20; the state of Georgia, U.S.A.[13] shows ratios varying from about 2·5 to 5·0 according to definite climatic zones. A low ratio indicates the kind of river that might be described as having a good flood every year, and a high ratio indicates the kind that gives riverain dwellers a sense of false security for years and then produces catastrophic flooding. On the theory of small probability (used as a rough estimate) the odds against a river with ratio 20 producing 2·5 times the highest flood of a 40-year record in the 41st year are only about 7 to 1, so the rather common belief that nothing much worse can happen than has occurred in a continuous 25 or 30-year period can be very wrong in some parts of the world. For applications of regime equations the ratios draw attention to the need for more information on what constitutes a 'dominant discharge' (see Dominant or Formative Discharge p 445); for rivers of large ratio the median annual flood seems suitable. The ratio appears relevant, along with suspended sediment charge and the geological history of the river, to the depth to which high floods can inundate the flood plain. For research a ratio based on annual peaks is obviously insufficient; practically it has the advantage of being fairly quickly obtainable from official records and of being usable in reverse with estimates of peak flood in rivers for which there are few or no records.

RATE OF BED CHANGE

Problems of the rate at which changes will occur in a river as a result of engineering action, or even naturally, are particularly indeterminate. Theoretically regime methods might be applied to an arithmetic integration but there are major practical and computational difficulties; models have shown themselves particularly unreliable although there is hope they would behave better if they could use the same bed material as the prototype[1]. Experience on canals, and geomorphic descriptions[7], gives some guidance. A specific problem might be of fitting a bed load excluder to a canal or an arm of a tidal estuary, or constricting the estuary by spurs, all with the object of obtaining a greater regime depth; the question is whether the canal or arm would clean itself out to the new depth in an acceptable time and manner, or would have to be cleared mechanically. Another might be whether maximum scour would develop round bridge piers in one flood.

RATE OF MEANDER DEVELOPMENT

There seems no way of calculating, even roughly, the rate at which bank erosion can occur; so the rate of development of meandering is equally indeterminate. Field experience and reading in geomorphology[6] are the main guides. A typical problem in whether to bury a pipe-line crossing deep under the flood plain in case the river moves over it, or to leave it at a relatively high level.

FORMATION OF ISLANDS

Some rivers meander in a single channel consistently, some form islands relatively briefly and then one channel takes charge while the other shrinks and the single channel occurs again, some form rapidly changing braids while others form relatively permanent islands or braids, some have single-channel reaches with interposed braided ones. To the engineer the importance of understanding at least the major reasons for these peculiarities is that, for economy and success in locating spurs and pitched islands, he has to know the peculiarities that make a river prefer one course to another. Regime considerations, *e.g.* Problem 9, can answer some of these problems. The number of factors behind them are too large to be discussed here, and all are not yet understood; geomorphology provides many answers[5].

TIDAL ESTUARIES AND INLETS

The currents in tidal waters depend on the tidal oscillations imposed from the ocean, on rivers that may run into them, and on the form and size of the boundary. But, if sediment is transported, the boundary size and form must also adjust to suit the laws of regime. Even without the sediment the problems are complex, but can be solved reasonably well by trial-and-error methods[8]. The solutions can then be tested against regime formulae and adjusted till consistence is obtained; a very simple example is in Problem 8. For simple regime applications it is useful to note that, in estuaries where maximum current velocity occurs at ebb tide, regime equations apply fairly well at low-tide conditions since high-tide results in bringing bed movement to a halt, or at least a major retardation; in inlets such as fiords where the tidal waves are reflected from the closed end the simplest theoretical case is of maximum velocity of flow at half tide. Ref. 9 illustrates adjustment of an estuary size to suit regime laws after training works had been built.

DENSITY CURRENTS

Fluids of slightly different density can retain their identity over remarkably long distances when running 'together'. Thus, the tide will run up a river as a salt-water tongue underneath the fresh, so that a shallow draft tug can be overrun by a large boat that it is towing upstream; a fresh water layer can extend far out to sea and tests of salinity at varying depths can show a relatively sudden change from fresh to salt; the clay fraction in a river can form a dirty-water current that dives down to the bottom of a lake beyond the delta and runs the whole length of the lake to an exit or to form a bed layer that gradually consolidates into clay of very low dry bulk density. This dirty water current is responsible for many natural deposits whose presence affects rivers and its existence makes possible the passage of valuable natural fertilizer downstream of dams to irrigation projects; it does not affect regime relations in practice. Ref. 10 has fundamental application.

FORMATION OF FLOOD PLAINS

The engineer's major interest in flood plains is in estimating to what depth and how frequently they may be flooded, but he may also wish to know roughly what material the river will encounter after it has cut some distance into a plain. The plains are formed partly from bed material and partly from suspended load, and the sequence of floods is highly relevant. Slow geological movements can have effects that may be of prime importance; some rivers have a meander pattern cut deep into the ground because the ground has been rising gradually but the rivers have retained their regime slopes; others hug one side of a valley because the earth is tilting slowly across the valley. Refs. 5, 6, and 11 discuss important happenings and give valuable data.

SUPERCRITICAL STREAMS

Air photos of boulder streams in which flow is supercritical do not show them to have patterns different from subcritical streams. Detailed behaviour is not yet well studied, but the peculiarities of flow noted in rigid boundary hydraulics must be allowed for in interfering with such rivers, and the steep slopes are also reason for caution. Long spurs are liable to have very large differences of head over them; they cannot produce backwater as in subcritical flow; large bed material will be found pushed up at the outside of bends; abrupt changes in direction or sectional form can set up appreciably shock waves or 'jumps'. The size of bed material may be comparable with the depth of flow, so the usual rules for estimating F_{b_0} and regime slope can mislead; however, the regime equations work well so far as variation with Q is concerned and high flood conditions can often fit the regime equations well using F_{b_0} based on the large bed stone and negligible charge.

PERMAFROST IN SMALL STREAMS

In streams that freeze solid, or dry up temporarily, the existence of permafrost does not seem to affect regime patterns as shown by air photos, nor to affect the depths of scour caused by obstacles. However, scour round an obstacle will not develop till the ground has thawed, so the rate of development is slower than in a normal river. Likewise an assisted cut-off opened in summer may develop almost entirely sideways because the frozen ground just beneath the bed is practically inerodible till thawed; thus the cut-off may not become really effective for several seasons.

EFFECT OF ICE ON REGIME

Air photos during the running season do not seem to reveal any feature that can be attributed to freezing; nor does a regime analysis require cognizance to be taken of freezing. In large rivers there seems a tendency for cohesive banks to be eroded to greater breadth within the limit of surface ice, so that there is a small submerged berm. However, the engineering effects associated with the break-up of river ice are important and spectacular; ice jams can cause relatively small discharges to pond up to levels comparable with those of high flood discharge, and bridge piers may have to be designed to allow for impact from miniature icebergs several feet thick and of the order of a hundred feet across. Unfortunately ice engineering has not yet been systematized or made quantitative.

ENGINEERING INTERFERENCE WITH REGIME

Many of man's interferences with rivers demonstrate, in a short time, the actions that have been continuing in nature over long periods. Most of the results could have been predicted from a geomorphologist's qualitative knowledge and could have had their approximate scope assessed from regime equations. For example, the damming of a river removes the bed load and usually alters the dominant discharge; the former effect causes the river downstream to start developing a flatter slope while the latter usually tends to cause slope to increase very slightly. However, the tendency to flatter slope can result in a steeper one if there are steeply inclined strata of relatively coarse material beneath the bed but above the level to which the river would degrade if its bed material were uniform for unlimited depth; of course, the river surface levels must degrade. As the river degrades, its tributaries are left with their ends ' hanging ', so attempt to degrade also, starting from their mouths; if they are in inerodible material they will be left in hanging valleys; if they are in uniform erodible material they will steepen progressively, without obvious discontinuity, and will add their enhanced products of erosion to the main stream so as to retard its degradation; if they are in non-uniform material they may show discontinuity—*e.g.* if the bed is of a single layer of stones (derived from cutting down in boulder clay) on sand, it may cut back in one or more steep faces by aid of approximately the same mechanism as causes waterfalls in rock. Again, the damming of a river causes delta deposits in the lake and, as the delta grows, the river tends to adjust to regime slope through it, with bed material differentiated out of the transported load. Thus, as the lake gradually fills the valley upstream fills also; Indian experience is that the large heavily laden rivers show the sedimentation moving upstream at about a mile a year. This phenomenon is interesting because it is well known to archaeologists and geologists but engineers have made artificial lakes with towns at their upstream ends apparently unaware of the rapidity with which measurable consequences could occur. Yet again the 'improvement' of a river by straightening, associated with the cutting of meander bends, must result in the river tending to acquire the regime slope proper to its straightened conditions, which is less than it had when tortuous; the Rhine provides an example[14]. The products of degradation will normally tend to cause aggradation further downstream, but the actual results will depend on a mass of circumstances different for each case.

COHESIVE AND UNMOVING BEDS

COHESIVE BEDS

A fairly common experience in glaciated regions is to find a cohesive river bed and, on applying regime analysis (to find what it shows), to discover that slopes and sections correspond to what would be expected for a sand bed. Closer examination shows that depths of sand from zero to a few feet are found, at some stages, on the bed at different localities, and that the cohesive material contains a little sand. It seems that such cases are no different, essentially, from those of canals carrying a continuing sand load and excavated in cohesive material that they can erode so as to find place for a sand bed; the difference is that, in these rivers, the sole source of sand is the cohesive material's disintegration. With a sand or gravel load imposed from outside, the depth to non-cohesive material would be comparable with that calculated from formulae for maximum scour to be expected in the sand or gravel at the outside of meander bends; cohesive material found at this depth is actually a common experience. Of course, there are also cohesive beds resistant enough to keep non-cohesive material in suspension, and these will not give explicable bed factors under regime analysis and are not proper subjects for such analysis. The physical point is that an apparently cohesive bed may be a limiting case, so any channel with a cohesive bed merits analysis in the hope that its state may be explicable. If it is, then the results of engineering interference with the regime become estimable.

UNMOVING GRANULAR BEDS

If the slope of a granular bed varies continuously over considerable distances the chances are that the granules move, or used to move, at some stage of flow, even though there seems little present visible evidence of this movement; then regime equations are applicable. In practice the cases of absolutely no movement of granular boundaries are mostly of engineering creation in the form of protected bed and sides, or of rock rapids. The problem then is to decide the size of this large material that will not move under any circumstances. Regime equations are not too helpful, though theoretically they could be applied to select material whose F_{b_0} was considerably larger than the value expected for V^2/d. One difficulty is that not too much is known about bed factors of large material of various shapes and mechanical constitution; another is that the value of V^2/d at which movement will start is not the same as that at which it will continue with vanishingly small load; another is that bed factor seems to depend on relative size when that relative size exceeds a certain limit; another major one is that the flow may be supercritical. For supercritical flow on rapids the author favours an empirical formula, adapted from Meyer–Peter[1],

$$q^{2/3}S^{5/6} = 0.5D$$

where q is discharge intensity, S is energy gradient, and D is the diameter, in feet, of a spherical stone of the same weight as the one that would be just moved for the given q, S. Stones that can bond into each other obviously have a large factor of safety. Another system of calculation is that of tractive force intensity. required to initiate movement[16, 17]; it uses:

$$d = 6 \cdot 4 D_i / S$$

where d is depth in feet of supercritical flow and D_i is the minimum allowable size in inches of the sieve mesh which retains 25 per cent of bed material. Both methods require some means of estimating roughness for full design; one means is to use Manning's equation with $n =$ one forty-first part of the sixth root of D measured in inches. Practical conditions are suited well enough by these rather crude methods of calculation.

MODELS WITH MOBILE BEDS

UTILITY

As a specialized subject, river model making[1, 4] is exceedingly complex and combines art with science. However, with comparatively little equipment or specialized knowledge, simple river models can often be allowed or assisted to reproduce the *types* of situation in which an engineer is practically interested so that he can appreciate the consequences of projected actions. The magnitude of the consequences is not likely, in general, to be predictable reliably from a model, but can be assessed by regime calculations combined with river experience. The *type* of situation is important for two principal reasons, (i) flow near the bed may be totally different from the flow seen at the surface and (ii) the bed conformation keeps changing even in cases of apparently unchanging surface flow. A model shows the consequences of item (i) and permits observation of item (ii). Reason (i) explains why unskilled opinions of the probable effects of training works are often radically wrong; they are based on surface observations.

QUANTITATIVE PREDICTIONS

Although water allowed to develop a passage through a bed of non-cohesive material in a laboratory tray constitutes a regime river the prediction of the dimensions to expect in a corresponding case of a large river is comparable with predicting the proportions of a giant from those of a dwarf. The theoretical possibilities of exact prediction are discussed in ref. 1. Their limitations may be appreciated from the relatively simple case of the rigid-boundary model. Theoretically, such a model can be used accurately for prediction if (i) it is geometrically similar in boundary form, *including the small irregularities that constitute roughness* (ii) if all non-dimensional numbers (Froude, Reynolds, Weber, Cauchy, *etc*), that are physically relevant are the same in model and prototype, and if (iii) this latter condition involves no physical absurdity. A ship model cannot be trusted, theoretically, because its behaviour depends on both Froude and Reynolds numbers at the same time, and the former calls for the model to be towed slower than the prototype and the latter for it to be towed faster; however, as the Reynolds number is not important in the prototype and not paramount in the model, some practical hydraulic arguments plus some experience allow *usable* predictions to be made. In the mobile boundary model the boundary forms itself and follows regime laws that do not give geometric similarity, so the usual rulings of rigid boundary models cease to apply in general. Thus, vertical scale is usually considerably more than horizontal so that, for example, if scour holes round obstacles were to be reproduced to these scales the bed material would normally be required to stand steeper than its angle of repose in water. Accordingly, scour holes should be expected to be distorted so that their dimensions cannot be scaled up to full size; actually the distortion is mainly horizontal and depths are scaled quite well.

JUSTIFICATION FOR A MODEL

Allowing for facts such as that quantitative predictions may be doubtful, that major models may not give usable results for several months or years, that few model makers would make predictions without having many observations of prototype behaviour, and that some river phenomena cannot be reproduced usefully on models, the decision to build a model should be made with caution. The engineer is advised to ascertain whether he could obtain the required results by observing either the river in question or relevant situations in other rivers, and using regime calculations for quantitative results; also whether a simple model (requiring a few weeks) of the type of situation he has in mind would serve his purpose if supplemented by expert advice based on field experiences. An example of justified major modelling with extensive use of field data and observations is in ref. 18.

COLLECTION AND USE OF RIVER DATA

WATER DISCHARGE

Most countries, through some branch of government, have published daily gauge records for several decades at various sites on rivers, and less frequent gauges at other sites and have made discharge records for some of them based on periodic ratings. Methods of discharge measurement are well known, fairly standard, and available in most hydraulics text books and in special publications. Selection of discharge sites seems to be often from immediate considerations rather than long-term ones that aim at establishing long records for areas that may come under development in the remote future. Gauges are usually single, although the river levels on opposite banks are generally different—sometimes very different. Ideally, all river gauging sites merit routine publication of analyses of their data, but such action is uncommon. Individual governments, or sections of governments, have made routine analyses of items such as specific gauges, annual flood frequencies[13], monthly average, peak, and minimum flows; some analyses have been published effectively. The value of such information is as great for construction and maintenance engineers as for research.

SEDIMENT DISCHARGE

For rivers with appreciable suspended load the routine measurement of that load along with the water discharge is vital for reservoir projects and useful for many other purposes. Measurement is now receiving special attention in countries where the cost and implications of sedimentation have become apparent. Methods are detailed in ref. 20.

UNIT HYDROGRAPHS

Some governments[15] have published unit hydrographs of catchments, *i.e.* hydrographs that represent expectation from a uniform storm of some specified duration causing 1 in of run-off from a catchment. These can be used with meteorological data or forecasts to permit accurate flood warning or to estimate maximum flood characteristics for planning retention reservoirs for flood control.

INTERNATIONAL RECORDING OF HYDROLOGIC DATA

There would be scientific and engineering advantages if basic hydrologic data were systematized, to an internationally agreed system, into atlases and almanacs such as those showing climatic, navigational and oceanographic features, or natural resources[19]. Curves of flow duration, sediment load duration and flood frequency, indices relating flow peaks of specified low frequency to catchment areas and peak floods to medians, graphs of hydrograph behaviour, any many other matters are susceptible to atlas representation. At present the river engineer embarking on a project is rather in the position of a navigator who, for lack of systematized information, has to study and analyse original meteorologic and other records before making a journey. The publication of major river investigations by private bodies[22] indicates how international action could disseminate vital information.

REFERENCES

[1] BLENCH, T. *Regime behaviour of canals and rivers* Butterworths, London (1957) (Contains many references)

[2] LACEY, G. Systematic changes in the beds of alluvial rivers, *Proc. Instn. Civ. Engrs Pap.* 1331 (Aug. 1957)

[3] Proceedings of the International Association for Hydraulic Research. Fourth meeting 1951 at Bombay. Various papers, pp 135, 165, 175, 205, 221, 261, 317

[4] INGLIS, C. C. (Sir). The behaviour and control of rivers and canals *Res. Pbl. cent. Bd Irrig., India* No. 13, Simla, 1949

[5] LEOPOLD, L. B. and WOLMAN, M. G. River channel patterns; braided, meandering and straight *Prof. Pap. U.S. geol. Surv.* 282-B (1957)

[6] SUNDBORG, A. The River Klaralven; a study of fluvial processes *Medd. Upsala Univ. georgr. Instn*, Ser. A. No. 115 (1956) (In English)

[7] LEOPOLD, L. B. and WOLMAN, M. G. Floods in relation to the river channel. Pbl. 42 of the International Association of Hydrology. Symposia Darcy. Dijon, 1956

[8] PILLSBURY, G. B. *Tidal hydraulics* U.S. Army, Waterways Experiment Station, Vicksburg, Miss., 1956

[9] INGLIS, C. C. (Sir) and KESTNER, F. J. T. The long-term effects of training walls, reclamation and dredging of estuaries *Proc. Instn civ. Engrs Pap.* 6268 (March 1958)

[10] PRANDTL, L. *Essentials of Fluid Dynamics* Blackie, 1953

[11] LEOPOLD, L. B. and WOLMAN, M. G. River flood plains; some observations on their formation *Prof. Pap. U.S. geol. Surv.* 282-C (1957)

[12] MONTAGU, A. M. R. and UPPAL, H. L. River training and control by pitched islands. Pap. 275, Punjab Engineering Congress, 1945

[13] CARTER, R. W. Floods in Georgia. *Circ. U.S. geol. Surv.* 100, March (1951)

[14] SHULITS, S. Graphical analysis of trend profiles of a certain section of river *Trans. Amer. geophys Un*, 36, No. 4 (1955)

[15] U.S. Corps of Engineers, Dept., of Army Unit Hydrographs Project, CW153, 1949

[16] U.S. Bureau of Reclamation. Hydraulic Laboratory Report No. Hyd. 352, 1952

[17] McKINNON, I. W. Discussion on Qn. 9-Hydraulic Structures *Proceedings of the International Commission on Irrigation and Drainage* 3rd Cong. San Francisco, 1957.

[18] INGLIS, C. C. (Sir) and ALLEN, F. H. The regimen of the Thames estuary as affected by currents, salinities, and river flow *Proc. Instn. civ Engrs* Pap. 38 (May 1957)

[19] *British Columbia Atlas of Resources 1956* Dept. of Geography, Univ. of B.C., Vancouver, B.C.

[20] NELSON, M. E. and BENEDICT, P. C. Measurement and analysis of suspended sediment loads in streams *Trans. Amer. Soc. civ. Engrs* Pap 2450, 116 (1951)

[21] FRIEDKIN, J. F. *A laboratory study of the meandering of alluvial rivers* U.S. Waterways Experiment Station Vicksburg, Miss., 1945

[22] *Rivers Niger and Benne*, Report by Nedeco, North Holland Publishing Co., Amsterdam, 1959 (in English)

COASTAL ENGINEERING

J. VAN VEEN, D.Sc.

COASTS

IN RECENT years International Conferences have been held on two branches of coastal science, Coastal Engineering and Coastal Geography (or Geology). The proceedings of these conferences are available—see Bibliography. Engineers concerned with coasts and estuaries would find much useful information in the geographic and geologic studies.

TYPES OF COASTS

Coasts may be briefly characterized as follows:

1 Hard (granite *etc*), medium hard (chalk, sandstone, limestone *etc*) and soft or loose (shingle, sand, clay). The soft and medium hard coasts give rise to difficulties.

2 Young, middle aged and old (*Figure 1*). Hard coasts keep their young appearance (fjords), medium hard coasts develop spits, tomboli, cuspate forelands *etc* in their middle age, and later on become 'old' cliff coasts. Soft coasts turn old in a few centuries but this does not mean that an equilibrium is established.

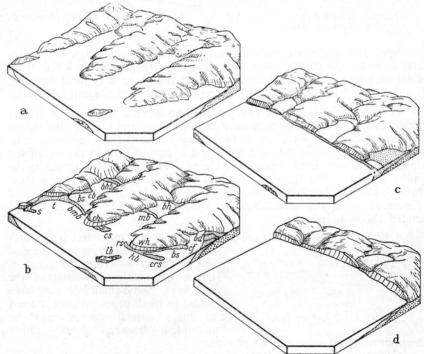

Figure 1. Development of medium soft coasts (D. W. Johnson) **a** *Initial stage* **b** *Youth* (**bd** *bay delta* **bh** *bayhead beach* **bhb** *bayhead bar* **bmb** *baymouth bar* **bs** *bayside beach* **cb** *cuspate bar* **cf** *cuspate foreland* **ch** *cliffed headland* **crs** *compound recurved spit* **cs** *complex spit* **hb** *headland beach* **lb** *looped bar* **mb** *midbay bar* **rs** *recurved spit* **s** *spit* **t** *tombolo* **wh** *winged headland*) **c** *Sub-maturity* **d** *Maturity*

3 Shores of emergence and those of submergence. Owing to the general rise of the sea level relative to land levels by some 300 ft (100 m) or more, mainly as a result of the melting, due to climatic changes, of much polar ice during the holocene period, most coasts are of the submergence type. (The melting of the ice now existing would raise the sea level about 180 ft (54 m).) Coasts of emergence show eroded foreshores and ancient cliffs, or other former shore lines, above the present sea level.

4 Coasts showing accretion and erosion. Coasts recede because of wave and current erosion; the eroded material (shingle, sand, clay) generally causes accretion in the neighbourhood.

5 Hill land coasts. These have cliffs, the hardest parts of which form the capes, while the softer parts are modelled into coastal curves, which are 'suspended' between capes. 'Curves' are formed either by erosion, silting up of bays, or by the horizontal growth of a spit (*Figure 2*). If the curve is not wholly regular there must be a special reason for it. Sometimes erosion is too strong to form curves and the coast then may develop the appearance of the coast of *Figure 3*. Near such coasts there will be deep foreshores which could provide good harbour sites although the intense wave action may prove adverse.

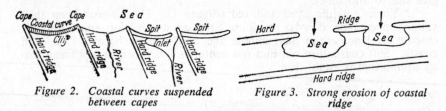

Figure 2. Coastal curves suspended   Figure 3. Strong erosion of coastal
           between capes   ridge

Spits and hooks are built up from the eroded material which waves tend to make into coastal curves; but these remain incomplete where there is not enough shingle or sand (*e.g.* German Bight), or they form anything else but a spit when there is no lee cape (*e.g.* the cape of Skagen, Denmark).

A cuspate foreland like Dungeness is an alluvial cape. It is a huge horizontal ripple obeying the general law of ripples and it is moving slowly eastward because of wave action (not current action) from the west. The shingle is eroded from the west bank and is carried around the top of the ripple to the east bank where it remains. The top of the ripple is the 'alluvial cape'. The lines of growth of shingle ridges on Dungeness show this. A tombola is a bar connecting an off-shore island with the mainland (*Figure 1*). Cuspate forelands, spits, hooks, tomboli *etc* are made up of eroded shore material.

6 Lowland coasts (sand) are shallow coasts and may stretch monoto-

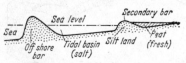

Figure 4. Off shore bars

nously over long distances (*e.g.* the east coast of North America, the coast of Guinea, the south east coast of the North Sea). Some small hills may have resulted in weak capes on such a coast and huge coastal curves may be 'suspended' between them. Other streamlined forms may also be present.

Generally the original slope of the shore has been so small that off-shore bars have formed with shallow basins behind them. Such off-shore bars are formed principally in a vertical direction by wave action, *Figure 4*, but as soon as they have been formed horizontal growths such as spits come into existence. An off-shore bar often bears dunes. A low secondary bar may have formed because of wave action in the basin and behind this bar fresh water may have accumulated, which would cause fen land areas to come into existence. The secondary bar is the fertile silt area which shuts off the low fen district from the sea. The tidal (salt) basins may have partly silted up and in this way a lagoon coast may have formed. Because the tidal basin behind the off shore bar is filled and emptied by the tide, the off-shore bar often has openings at regular distances. Such a bar is transformed into a string of sand islands (*e.g.* Frisian islands).

The coast between Cap Blanc Nez (near Calais) and Denmark is formed essentially of an off-shore bar. In Flanders, that is south of the Scheldt, the original tidal flats behind this bar have since Roman times been wholly filled with sand and clay; but in Western Holland, where the Rhine and Maas provide fresh water, the flats could develop into huge fen districts. The tidal flats on the northern part of this coast are called *wadden* (*cf* ' to wade ').

ESTUARIES

TYPES OF ESTUARIES AND BARS

Estuaries are generally ' sunken' valleys in which marine and river sand and mud have deposited. In these deposits the rivers and tides have scoured channels and creeks. Sometimes, in alluvial plains or in deltaic regions, an estuary has formed due to some low lying peat land becoming a tidal basin, or because some river mouth has become choked and a new mouth has developed. Such estuaries may follow the cycle, young→mature→old, as a result of silt movement along the coast or along the river.

The tidal rise and the area of the tidal basin are of primary importance for the estuary, because the currents which keep the channels in the estuary deep and wide are caused by the filling and emptying of that basin as the tides move in and out. The ' tidal basin' is not, however, synonymous with tidal capacity because the tidal basin is the whole content of the estuary, whereas the tidal capacity is only that part of the estuary contained by the lines indicating the heights of slack water, *Figure 5*. The magnitude of tidal streams through a cross section of the estuary can thus be calculated.

When the estuary has the form of a wide and short basin (*e.g.* the Mersey basin), the tidal capacity will be almost as much as the total body of water contained in the basin between high water (h.w.) and low water (l.w.), because in such basins slack water generally occurs almost at h.w. and l.w.

When there are tidal streams in the estuary of about two or three knots at their maximum, which is generally the case because scouring and silting tend to establish that condition, the slack water will occur one or one and a half hours after h.w. and l.w.

When P is the discharge of the river per tidal cycle and f and e are the flood and ebb discharges in the cross section considered, we have the simple relations :

$$Q = e + f \qquad \text{...........(1)}$$

$$P = e - f \qquad \text{...........(2)}$$

and

$$e = 0 \cdot 5 \, (Q + P) \qquad \text{...........(3)}$$

$$f = 0 \cdot 5 \, (Q - P) \qquad \text{...........(4)}$$

in which Q is the total flow per cycle through the cross section.

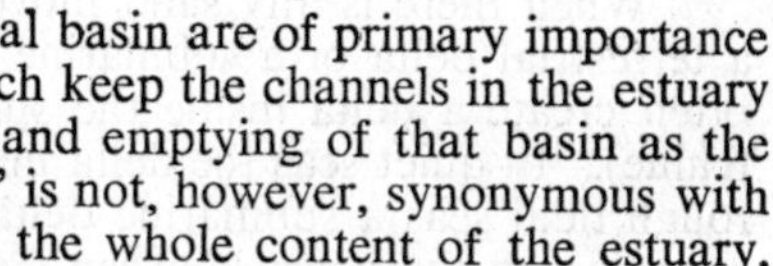

Figure 5. Tidal capacity of an estuary

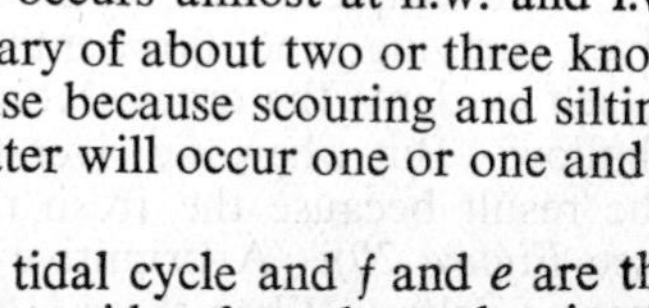

Figure 6. Sand stream in meandering river

As a result of the tidal fill and ebb, sand movements occur. We may introduce the term 'sand stream' here. In meandering non-tidal rivers, the sand stream tends to be straight, brushing the concave bends (*Figure 6*). The bulk of the sand moves near the bottom, the motive power being the current and the turbulence of the water. In bends there is a centrifugal movement at the top part and a centripetal movement near the bottom.

Generally two sand streams occur in estuaries and deltas, one coming down the river from the interior, the other travelling along the coast and often entering the estuary. The latter, called the coastal or littoral drift, can be mainly caused by waves. It may be much larger than the river sand stream. Both sand streams may meet in the estuary, or in front of its mouth. Of course, the sand streams are not continuous steady flows of sand; they are resultants of intricate movements over a long period. Ebb and flood move the sand to and fro in the estuary, and so do waves; but the important thing is that there are resultant sand streams often landward, or across the mouth, of the estuary. The resultant sand streams may not have the same direction as the resulting water streams near the surface. They may be opposed, or at different angles, to the main water streams.

Fine silt also may move differently, following the resultant currents which depend on the relative densities of fresh and salt water. Like salt, marine silt may move far inland. Where marine salt can go, fine marine silt can also go, and is likely to do so.

When there is any sand movement in a river mouth or estuary, either a terrestrial delta or a submarine delta will have formed. The river solids often create a delta inside the spit or offshore bar of the estuary (*e.g.* the Rhine). In quiet seas the delta may extend beyond the general coastline; in rough tidal seas a submarine delta is more likely. Though there are many estuaries on the coast between Calais and Jutland, no river, discharging at this coast, has carried enough material since the last ice period to build up a terrestrial delta in the ordinary sense of the word. The many submarine deltas of that coast consist of marine sands and the same can be said of the English rivers and coasts. There is very little soil erosion in western Europe except in Spain.

The simplest form of a sand bar is as indicated in *Figure 7*. When a river, carrying sand, flows into fresh water, the primitive form of such a bar is self evident; the cross section suddenly becomes very wide and therefore shallow. But when the river flows into the sea an additional factor affects the result because the fresh river water flows over the heavier salt water (see *Figure 20*). A primitive bar may develop into a delta or into a submarine delta. When there is coastal drift the form of the bar or delta will be asymmetrical. A tidal wave running along the coast also makes the delta asymmetrical (*Figure 38*).

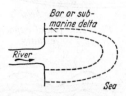

Figure 7. Bar formed by river sand outside the river mouth

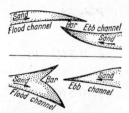

Figure 8. Typical situation of flood and ebb channels

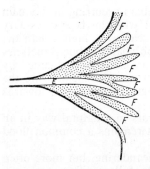

Figure 9. Flood and ebb channels in a wide estuary E ebb channel F flood channel

In tidal waters with sand bottoms the channels can be divided into flood channels and ebb channels: a flood channel is open to the flood and has a bar at the ebb end, an ebb channel is open to the ebb and has a bar at the flood end (*Figure 8*). Ebb channels and flood channels carrying sand will not follow the same course and shipping channels in estuaries often have one or more bars on which dredging must go on. Ebb channels have a tendency to take a different course from flood channels and *vice versa* (*Figure 8*). It is only when special works effect coincidence of these channels that a shipping channel without bars is formed. The reason why ebb channels and flood channels tend to evade each other is the action of sand streams which have a seaward direction in an ebb channel and a landward direction in a flood channel. Each stream deposits sand at its end and forms a bar.

Figure 10. Flood and ebb channels in a narrow estuary—ideal poplar tree type (Scheldt) E ebb channel F flood channel

When the estuary is wide and relatively short there are several flood channels and only one or two ebb channels (*Figure 9*). When the estuary is long and not too narrow the ideal form is like a poplar tree (*Figure 10*), whereas on a lagoon coast the creeks take a form resembling an apple tree (*Figure 11*).

The ideal 'poplar' type very seldom occurs. When it does occur, as in the estuary of the Scheldt, the 'trunk', or ebb channel, provides a good fairway for ships. The shores of the estuary are responsible for this ideal state; they have been fixed at the right places. In all other instances the

Figure 11. Flood and ebb channels in a short, wide lagoon—apple tree form

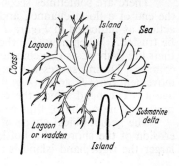

'trunk' is nearly always broken more than once (bars occurring in the main ebb channel). We may call this the 'wild type': with this type of estuary bars occur at both ends of the channels. If the sea bar is higher than the inland bar, we may still call the channel an ebb channel, but sometimes both bars are equally high. A clear picture of an estuary is obtained by showing ebb channels in blue and flood channels in red, schematizing the channels while doing so and increasing the strength of the colour towards the bar.

Cutting off of tidal meanders sometimes occurs in a natural way in an estuary, but generally the initial stage of the cut remains a common flood channel.

Wild types may change their channels by meandering, but more often the depth of their bars, so that shipping has to follow different courses from time to time, *Figure 12*.

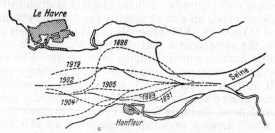

Figure 12. Variations in shipping channel at the mouth of the Seine

The erosive action of the flow of water at bends is the main cause of changes in the ebb and flood channels, a phenomenon we shall call bend action; it is the result of the centrifugal force of the water.

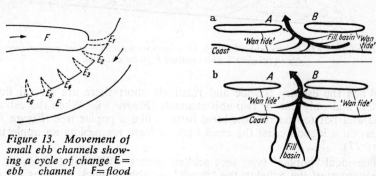

Figure 13. Movement of small ebb channels showing a cycle of change E= ebb channel F=flood channel. The start is at E_1

Figure 14. a, b influence of situation and form of fill basin

There are sometimes secondary ebb channels, originating near a bar at the end of a flood channel, and then shifting after some years due to bend action, as indicated in *Figure 13*. Such secondary ebb channels should not be trusted. When new (E_1) they may be fairly good shipping channels but their life is short, as ebb channels and flood channels tend to follow different courses. During successive stages the secondary ebb channel will show a movement from E_1 to E_6 (*Figure 13*) and after this a new cycle will start over again. The bend which the ebb-water has to follow to reach F becomes more and more sharp, thus causing more and more bend action.

The geographical shape of the tidal basin may influence the place of erosion of the shores of a bottleneck; when the left part of the basin is the larger the right hand island is attacked by the tidal streams and *vice versa*

(*Figure 14*). The action is caused by the centrifugal force of water flowing in a curve. The largest body of water goes with the ebb from the largest fill area and determines the left or right curve.

In the northern hemisphere streams tend to the right shore because of the rotation of the earth, in the southern hemisphere to the left shore; this is of practical importance where the streams are more than about a mile wide.

The wind may displace a river or channel slowly in its most active direction due to wave action on the shore.

COAST AND ESTUARY RESEARCH

The study of the behaviour of coastal waters and estuaries serves important economic interests. They include the saving of dredging expenses, the opening up of harbour and river mouths, the avoidance of land losses by erosion, the gaining of new agricultural land or industrial sites, and a saving on shore defences.

Four different lines of research are required: *1* geological and historical research, *2* research on the site to ascertain the currents and sand streams, *3* mathematical research and *4* research in hydraulic laboratories.

GEOLOGICAL AND HISTORICAL RESEARCH

The general geology of our coasts and estuaries should be known. Borings can be made in the water covered areas and the study of all available historical data should not be neglected. Among the many questions to which answers are needed are the following. How much does the coast recede in a century and what are the fluctuations in this recession? What quantity of material is added annually to the coastal drift because of coastal recession or river discharge, neither clay layers nor mere chalk producing much coastal drift? Does the coastal drift protect the shore? In what direction do the shingle and sand travel? How much is being lost into the deeper parts of the sea? Is there any cycle in the changes of the channels of an estuary? Does the estuary deepen or does it silt up as a whole, and at what secular rate? See Proceedings of Conferences on Coastal Geography.

Sediment petrology is a branch of geology which studies the sand grains heavier than bromide (specific gravity = 2). The origin and deposits of these materials can thus be established as well as the course of the sand and mud streams. Diatoms and foraminiferae may also give some useful information. There are distinct salt, brackish and fresh water diatoms. Geologists often want undisturbed boring samples and borings should reach to the rock bottom, or to a depth of about 120 ft (36 m), which is the depth dredgers can reach.

RESEARCH ON CURRENTS, SAND STREAMS AND WATER LEVELS

Because shore processes are slow the average rate of change can only be decided where exact data are available for a long time. Where such information is lacking, concrete poles should be placed now along receding coasts in order to be able to measure their future annual recession. These poles should be placed every mile or half mile and taken as fixed points on the national triangulation net. The height of the beach should also be measured annually, and more often (monthly or weekly) when the height fluctuations of the beach are wanted. Those fluctuations may be up to three feet or more.

The foreshore should be surveyed periodically and the work can be greatly facilitated by the use of modern measuring techniques, *e.g.* echo sounding, measuring distances by tellurometer (see chapter on Surveying, vol. 1), by making use of portable radio *etc.* Bottom charts can then be prepared, showing the different materials (rock, clay, sand, shingle *etc*). These charts may show the places where silting and scouring occur; the size of the grains of sand must be determined as this gives an indication of the strength of the bottom currents. The engineer in charge of estuaries or shores should have complete records of the nature of the bottom of the whole area in his charge.

The currents and sand movements can be measured from the surface to the bottom under different conditions of wind, tide and river discharge. Different kinds of instruments can be used. The instruments necessary are an echo sounder, a current meter, a bottom sampler, a sand grain meter, salinity meters *etc.*

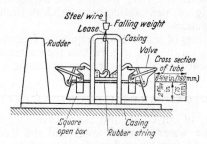

Figure 15. Water and silt sampler

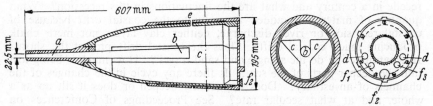

Figure 16. Sand-transport meter (called 'Delft jar') a, b, *nozzle for letting in water.* c, *room between plates.* d, *water-release openings.* e, *air-release opening.* f_1, f_2 *and* f_3, *plugged openings to remove the materials, deposited in the side chambers*

There are two main types of sand catchers, one measuring the sand content of the water, the other measuring the sand transported per minute. For sand content measurement the open tube is placed with its axis in the direction of the current, *Figure 15*. By means of a small weight sliding down the wire suspending the instrument two valves are released which shut simultaneously, actuated by a strong rubber attachment. The content of the tube may be five litres.

The sand transported can be measured in a vessel having a small opening at the front, through which the current flows without any deflection. This can be obtained by means of suction at the back. The idea is that as the flow expands inside the instrument it drops its sand, *Figure 16*.

The volume of sand streams, measured by means of sample takers or sand transport meters, can be checked by comparing the volume of material moved, as taken from the charts. Volumetric comparison of old and recent sounding charts is most useful. If the places where scour has occurred are shown in blue and the silted parts in yellow a good picture is obtained. The scouring and silting quantities must balance each other after geological subsidence has been taken into account. Hydrographic charts show

Frequency curves of floods often assume the form of asymmetrical probability curves (*Figure 21*); when these are drawn on semi-logarithmic paper they produce approximately straight lines. Data collected during excessive storms only should be taken, according to Dutch meteorologists, oceanographers and mathematicians. Far steeper lines have thus been obtained than were accepted in former years (*Figure 21*).

LABORATORY RESEARCH

This kind of research has become a special branch of hydraulic science and is dealt with briefly in the chapters on Mechanics of Fluids, vol. 1, and Hydraulics of Canals and Rivers of Mobile Boundary.

TIDAL ACTION

Engineers dealing with coasts and estuaries should know the principles of tides, but they may find it difficult to master the mathematical details. The principles of tides can best be learned by studying an elementary book on alternating electrical currents. In the Netherlands three different methods are being used to calculate the tides for new schemes: the mathematical method is basic but slowest when no electronic computer is used. The hydraulic laboratory method is quick and can be made reliable, though it should be controlled by mathematics. The analogue computer is handy, especially for mass-computations, such as frequency problems for new schemes. The differences in tidal height found by the three methods will be small.

General analogy between tides and alternating currents:

Electrical current	*Tides*
direct current	stream in ordinary river
alternating current	streams in tidal channel
mixed current	streams in tidal inlet with river discharge
conductivity	conductivity $=\Sigma bh^{3/2}$ (*Figure 22*)
resistance	resistance $=\Sigma 1/cbh^{3/2}$
voltage	head
electromotive force	slope, gradient
capacitance	tidal capacity of basin
condenser	open harbour, tidal basin
self induction	inertia
angle of lag ϕ	angle of lag ϕ
conductor with varying capacitance	tidal channel or tidal river
Ohm's law	Chézy's law: $Q=cb_1h_1^{3/2}a^{1/2}$
First law of Kirchhoff	$Q_1=Q_2+Q_3$ (at a knot of channels)
Second law of Kirchhoff	$M_1=M_2+M_2$ (around island)
Telegraph equation	Lorentz equation for tides

In this analogy b is the breadth of part of cross section, say 30 ft; b_1 the total breadth of channel, h_1 the average depth of channel (the channel has to be considered as having a rectangular cross section); Q the total flow through cross section (ebb+flood per cycle); a the slope of water level; c the constant of Manning; M the motive area = area between tidal graphs of two successive stations (*Figure 23*); l the distance between these stations; ϕ the angle of lag, generally about 0·9 in tidal channels as well as in electric nets.

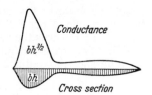

Figure 22. Conductance of a cross section

Figure 24 can be found in all elementary books dealing with electrical currents. It gives the relationship between the vertical and the horizontal tide or streams. The slopes cause the stream currents, the latter lagging ϕ behind the former because of inertia.

A tidal net, containing many channels, receives its impulses from the sea, the boundary conditions being some miles outside the inlet mouths. All components of the tides in any new net of channels can be calculated, the horizontal tide (currents) as well as the vertical tide. The tides which occur when the river discharge is low, normal, high or very high can also be calculated for the proposed net of branches of the tidal delta.

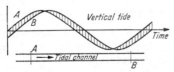

Figure 23. *Motive area between two tide gauge stations A and B*

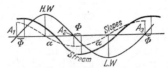

Figure 24. *Relation between vertical tide curves, the slopes, and the horizontal tide*

When the wind effect or storm surge in the sea is of importance the tides in the future net have to be calculated also for high sea levels and low sea levels.

Tides are imitated in an electrical circuit of conductors, condensers, resistances *etc* though there is one marked difference between electrical and water currents: in electricity we have the basic formula (Ohm's law)

$$\left. \begin{array}{l} e=ir \\ \text{with water (Chézy's law) } e=i^2r \end{array} \right\} \qquad \ldots\ldots\ldots\ldots(5)$$

In equation 5, e=electromotive force, or slope α; i=current or flow of water per sec; r=resistance.

Lorentz of Leiden University, when having to calculate the future tides outside the Zuider Zee dam in 1918, did not use the quadratic (hydraulic) law but the linear one, by taking a new constant $k=ci_0$; therefore $e=i^2r$ became $e=ki$ and so the telegraph equations could be used. This linear method can be easily imitated electrically and all components of the tides can be measured electrically or made visible with a cathode ray tube. The more exact quadratic law can also be imitated electrically by using special rectifiers or special valves. An analogue computer has been working at the Hague since 1953 on delta work problems. A new computer, more exact and based on new discoveries, is now being built.

Conductances in the different cross sections vary in a 'wild' estuary, especially when man has used groynes instead of good smooth streamlines. For a steady well-regulated or quiet section of a natural channel, the relation

$$F = \frac{Q}{bh^{3/2}} \qquad \ldots\ldots\ldots\ldots(6)$$

should be more or less a constant. That is, the conductance and the total flow (ebb + flood per tide) should become larger, both in the same degree, when going towards the sea.

For two cross sections, distance l apart, the following formula gives the difference in conductances:

$$b_1 h_1^{3/2} - b_2 h_2^{3/2} = \frac{2 \, ABl \cos \phi}{F} \qquad \ldots\ldots\ldots\ldots(7)$$

where A is the amplitude, B the fill breadth of tidal river, and $\cos \phi$ is about 0·9.

When for navigational purposes depth h is made a constant, we obtain the flare formula of Chatley:

$$b_1 - b_2 = \frac{2,000 AB^2}{Q} \text{ ft/km} \qquad \ldots\ldots\ldots\ldots(8)$$

A ' flare ' is often not advisable, however, when currents due to differences in specific gravity and sand streams have to be taken into consideration. Streamlining, even outside the river mouth, the prevention of the formation of flood channels, the forestalling of a bar *etc* may be of greater interest than a regular flare.

The ' left tendency ' of tidal channels is caused by a tide in the sea coming from the left (*e.g.* the mouths of the tidal waters along the south eastern shores of the North Sea). The theory of electricity (or of tides) can easily explain this (*Figure 25*), because the motive areas will be greater in the left hand channels than in the right hand channels. The co-tidal lines and the amplitudes of the tide define the cross sectional areas of the channels. When the tide in the sea comes from the right there is a ' right ' tendency.

Harmonic analysis is the empirical fixation of the amplitude and phase of the component sinusoids in tidal graphs. Instruments, called harmonic analysers, resembling a planimeter, can be used without much trouble; for learning the tidal components used for actual tide predicting, however, one of the methods developed by tide experts must be followed (Doodson and Warburg).

A tide predictor is a machine in which the component sinusoids are running each in its own phase: one of the famous tide predictors can be seen in the Tidal Institute, Birkenhead, England. This Institute will also undertake the harmonic analysis and prediction of existing tides at any place.

Horizontal tides (streams) can be predicted as well as the vertical tides for any date in the future when the component sinusoids are known, but the wind and other meteorological influences are not taken into account. Near shallow coasts these influences are great.

Harmonic analysis and tidal calculation differ. The first is the analysis of existing tidal curves and prediction of them when no hydraulic changes occur in the channels; the other uses the fundamental law of Euler and calculates new tides in new channels.

Because of the quadratic relation between friction and current the higher harmonics M_4, M_6, M_8 *etc* are produced more and more when the tidal wave travels landward, *i.e.* the front of the wave becomes steeper. These harmonics are called shallow water harmonics. They change in amplitude and phase when dredging is going on, which is when the resistance changes.

A bore is a breaking tidal wave which only occurs where the tidal amplitude is large and the depth is shallow; it vanishes when dredging increases the depth.

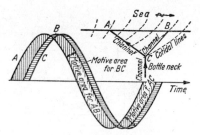

Figure 25. *'Left' tendency caused by tidal propagation from the left*

Figure 26. *A 'Wheatstone bridge' channel (Dutch, 'Wan tide')*

A ' Wheatstone bridge ' channel, *Figure 26* (the Dutch *Wan tide*, wan meaning abnormal, queer) is a place in a tidal channel in which only weak tidal streams occur; generally it is in a channel more or less parallel to the coast. The vertical tides remain normal.

CURRENTS

When measured with good instruments the current velocities are generally highest near the surface, diminishing towards the bed according to the law in which v is the velocity at height h above bottom, q is a figure ($\frown$ 5 to 7), a is the velocity at $h=1$ m above the bottom (*Figure 27*).

This is for homogeneous water, without wind effect. In the North Sea $q \frown 5$; in rivers we find q higher, approximating to 7 or 8. There are other formulae but equation 9 is the most simple and its graph lies about in the middle of the graphs of other formulae sometimes used.

In deep channels there is relatively more scouring because a is dependent on $\sqrt{h}$.

The formula for stream verticals which is used most nowadays is a logarithmic one. The writer does not quite agree with this use, not because the velocities differ so much from those of the parabolic formula quoted above, but because the parabolic formula is more simple and it gives better results as regards the sand movements. The discrepancy of the logarithmic formula is too great near the bottom, where for $h=0$ the velocity becomes $-\infty$, whereas it should be 0.

Much research is being done to try to express the sand movements, caused by currents, in some mathematical formula. The sand content at any point in a vertical line can be expressed by an exponential equation.

Starting from the formula

$$v = ah^{1/q} \qquad \qquad \dots\dots\dots\dots(9)$$

$$N_z = N_a e^{-[C/k\sqrt{(gHI)}](z-a)} \qquad \dots\dots\dots\dots(10)$$

C = terminal velocity of 'mean bottom sand grain' falling through water

$k = 0\cdot4$

g = acceleration of gravity = $9\cdot81$ m/sec

H = depth

I = slope

z and a = percentage of height (relative height)

N_a = sand contents at height a

N_z = sand contents at height z.

Equation 10 is for continuous currents; C is affected by the temperature of the water.

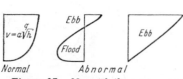

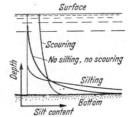

Figure 27. Normal (homogeneous water) and abnormal (heterogeneous water) stream verticals

Figure 28. Silt distribution in stream verticals for scouring, equilibrium and silting

When checked with actual measurements made in the Mississippi and in Dutch waters (tidal or non-tidal) equation 10 has proved better than the formula based on logarithmic stream verticals.

Generally it is found that the total sand content in a vertical varies with v^3 or v^4, which means that the total sand transported varies with v^4 or v^5. If a spring tide current is twice as strong as a neap current the former will transport sixteen to thirty-two times more sand. Tidal channels therefore are kept wide and deep by the scour of spring tides, more than by the scour of the normal tides. Neap tides have little scouring power.

In tidal streams, where silting and scouring change even during the tide, we should not lose ourselves in too much detail. The graph of sand content in a scouring river is markedly different from the graph of a silting one, *Figure 28*.

A sand-laden stream will not pick up more sand than it can carry. This is the reason why bars will not scour. A stream not carrying sand *e.g.* a stream coming through a weir or barrage, is able to pick up its full load. Scour may therefore take place downstream of a patch of rocky bottom, thus originating a sand stream. Narrows (*e.g.* the Straits of Dover) show such a clean rocky bottom with no sand movement above it. Its huge stream is undercharged.

Nevertheless in such regions there may be long and high sand banks lying on the hard bottom in the general direction of the ebb and flood currents. Because they offer little resistance to these currents they have remained in their places during the past centuries. They resemble the desert formation called Libyan dunes, *Figures 29, 30*.

When the sand grains are the right size and the currents have the right velocity a sand bottom will produce huge bed dunes, perpendicular to the general current direction. These submerged dunes may be 20, 30 or even

Figure 29. Cross section of 'Libyan dune'   Figure 30. Top view of 'Libyan dune'

60 ft (6 m to 18 m) high in the southern North Sea and about 3 ft (1 m) in a river of say 15 ft (4·5 m) depth. Generally the height is about 20 per cent of the free depth. The form of these huge ripples depends on the supremacy of either the ebb or the flood. They give an indication in which direction the sand is moving (*Figure 31*). Regular bed dunes can only occur where much sand is available and do not occur when rock, or a clay bottom, is partly exposed to the currents.

Where only a small quantity of sand is lying upon a rock or clay bottom this sand collects into 'barchan' dunes where the current is continuous in one direction, and into long sand banks, resembling Libyan sand dunes, where there are alternating currents.

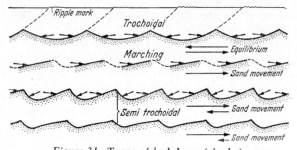

Figure 31. Types of bed dunes (ripples)

In estuaries, ebb channels usually make the best navigable waterways, but in the outer part of a delta a flood channel will be the best entrance. The aim of the engineer is to make the ebb and flood channels combine in such a way that a deep fairway results. Here Nature opposes because of sand movements. The way to attain good results is to forestall bend erosion and excessive sand transportation. The lower Scheldt is a fairly good example of what can be attained by good fixation of the shores. With the Scheldt the sinuous ebb channel or shipping channel is kept in fairly good condition by its protected shores. The flood channels spring forth at every bend of the ebb channel; they serve a local function of filling part of the estuary.

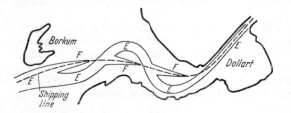

Figure 32. *Channels of the Ems estuary E ebb channel F flood channel*

The Ems estuary was originally also of the ideal poplar type but the Germans decided to make a straight shipping channel and therefore chose the line of the flood channels, *Figure 32*. Nowadays dredging can force almost any solution.

When a non-tidal river branches off from the main river at an obtuse angle the sand will go mainly into that branch because the weak bottom currents (carrying the bulk of the sand) can be deflected more easily than the stronger top currents which flow straight on. The sand may partly settle at A (*Figure 33*). This angle effect provides a means of diverting part of the river sand into places where it is required. The layout of the dividing points of branching rivers or channels should be constructed with care when they carry sand.

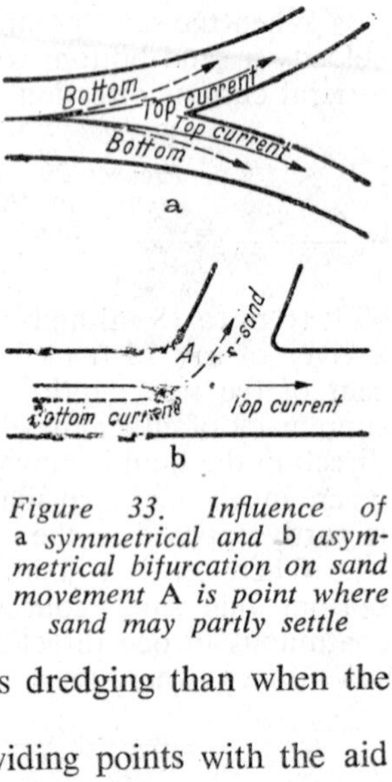

Tidal sand streams can be controlled as follows:

Figure 33. *Influence of a symmetrical and b asymmetrical bifurcation on sand movement A is point where sand may partly settle*

1 by making the fill area larger or smaller. If the flow into the fill area becomes smaller the sand stream will be much more so and this may mean less dredging than when the currents were too strong

2 by making good alignments and good dividing points with the aid of spurs and shore defences

3 by dredging; the new depths attract the currents while those in the undredged concurring (parallel) channels slacken.

The wider and larger the tidal channels, the less man can influence them; if a channel is narrow and deep it is more manageable. Large sea shore currents are extremely difficult to influence. We must accept them as they are, but we should not neglect to study them as well as their results.

Example—In the estuary indicated in *Figure 34*a, there are two flood channels *F₁* and *F₂*. The latter has been diminishing and the former has been increasing, so that it might be expected that *F₁* would become the main shipping entrance. To accelerate this, it is proposed that *F₁* be dredged and that a flank embankment *h* be constructed along the outer bend of *F₁*, that several long groynes be made across *F₂*, and that a groyne *f* would serve to make E flow into F without an intervening bar.

This scheme is largely fictitious but serves well as an example for comparison with an alternative scheme (*Figure 35*b), which has the advantage that a parallel embankment on the high sand bank between F_1 and F_2 would be much cheaper than the groynes *a, b, c, d, e* and *f*, because parallel works are easy to construct and the sand bank is high.

Secondly, the action of groyne *f* (*Figure 35*a) projecting far outside the normal lines would be contrary to the principle of a stream line. A large deep hole would be scoured out, a very bad river portion would result, and *E* and F_1 would not run into each other smoothly.

Thirdly, the parallel embankment *h* should be connected with the shore at the upper end of that embankment, because the tidal area behind it should be filled and emptied from the sea end. The parallel embankment would be expensive, being made in rather deep water. It would have to be protected over the whole length against attack by the currents. It would, therefore, be cheaper to make a parallel embankment on the higher parts of the tidal sands and to construct small groynes of say 300 ft (90 m) length and at 500 ft (150 m) distances apart projecting from the embankment.

The main trouble here lies near the cape at *C* where sand may deposit easily. The estuary should not be too wide there, and the channels F_1 and *E* so situated that they join up. Channel *E* has already in the past moved too far seaward towards *C* because of bend action, so either channel *E* or F_1, or both, have to be deflected to such an extent that they will coalesce.

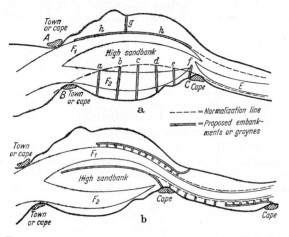

Figure 34. a *and* b *two different ways of training an estuary;* b *is most economical* E *ebb channel,* F1, F2 *flood channels*

The old belief that estuaries must be wide in order to have deep channels is far from correct. Wide estuaries may have large fill basins and therefore several large channels, but too much width means also too much liberty for the ebb and flood channels to diverge from each other. Moreover the ideal is not to have excessive currents and sand displacements, but moderate currents with no sand or mud displacement.

A recent study of the Thames estuary is described in a paper by Inglis and Allen.

One conclusion is that dredged material should not be dumped anywhere in the estuary but should be pumped ashore for land reclamation schemes. (See paragraph on Reclamation, p 502.) The model used for this study even showed the fresh plus salt water currents, and the resulting landward density drift. The 'node or zero point in the estuary', where this landward drift is tending to zero (see *Figure 20*, top-end of salt-wedge) is the critical place where the heavy part of the silt may settle. (In general, this would not mean that dredging would be a maximum at the 'zero point', because fine sea-silt could come much further landward, and, being more voluminous because of excessive water content, up to 90 or 95 per cent, might cause even more dredging.)

The study of the Thames estuary shows clearly what can be achieved by the proper use of models in conjunction with observations made in the estuary itself and mathematical analysis. A good model can serve as a computer for the new tides that will occur in an estuary to be trained or re-formed, and can show density currents and silt movements. Observations in the estuary or the mathematical analysis of tides and sand movements are not, in themselves, sufficient when dealing with estuaries. A model must imitate Nature and model techniques will improve as Nature and its laws become better known.

Though we may expect to be able to calculate sand streams in tidal waters with a moderate degree of exactness in the not too distant future there are some baffling problems, especially in connection with the formation of bars in tidal areas and the formation of bed dunes. We should try to learn by calculation why some estuaries are eroding, while others show accretion; and we should consider whether we can influence the ebb currents or flood currents so that the former may create a larger sand stream than the latter. The mouth of the Scheldt and the lower half of its estuary has deepened more than 3 ft (1 m) in a century (calculated over the whole area of the mouth) and most other Dutch inlets have also increased their mean depth in this period.

WAVE ACTION

The energy of the wind acting on the water is partly stored in the waves. When these break on the shore this energy is partly spent in destroying the coast or in displacing material. Reflections can be calculated, see Proceedings of Coastal Engineering Conferences.

There are three different coastal zones to be considered: those acted on by stream currents, waves, and wind. They are not sharply separated (*Figure 35*a). The wave zone of a coast is most attacked when an open sea front is concerned; in estuaries the stream currents may be the most destructive.

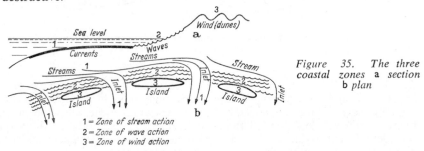

Figure 35. The three coastal zones a section b plan

1 = Zone of stream action
2 = Zone of wave action
3 = Zone of wind action

When a coast has tidal basins the situation of the three zones becomes as indicated in *Figure 35*b. At regular intervals the streams will have broken through the off shore bar, and dune islands may have formed between the breaches.

Waves create strong bottom currents and much turbulence when they break, *Figure 36*: wave action alone can create spits *etc* as can be seen in lakes. Wave turbulence 'lubricates' sand movement by water currents. Wind blowing towards the land causes a surface current in that direction and a bottom current in the opposite direction. This bottom current, especially during storms, may carry much sand seawards. In calm weather some of this sand is carried back by the movement of the breaking waves.

Sand which has been transported during the storm into the deep layers at some distance from the shore does not return; generally the shores lose material and the gains are small.

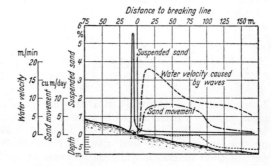

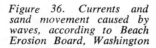

Figure 36. Currents and sand movement caused by waves, according to Beach Erosion Board, Washington

The submarine sand shore requires a certain slope, say 1 in 100, to be in equilibrium. Coastal retrogression will occur when the slope is steeper; such a coast is called a 'poor' coast. When the waves throw a bank of sand on the shore the coast becomes 'rich', temporarily.

Waves may create sand ridges of about 3 to 6 ft (1 to 2 m) high, lying parallel to the coast in the breaking zone. These ridges are pushed up the beach when the weather is calm, *Figure 37.*

Figure 37. Shore and sea ridges or ripples on a sandy coast

Coastal inlets with sand movement have a submarine delta outside the entrance or bottle neck, *Figure 38.* Such a delta does not grow above a certain level, say about l.w., because wave action opposes further accumulation. A marine delta of this kind may protect the lee shore, because waves break on the sands of the delta and they carry some sand from it on to that shore, making it richer. The littoral drift passes over and along the outer side of the submarine delta. Because of this, and because of the protection which the delta provides, the 'head' of the leeward island or coast of such a bottle neck formation may protrude outside the general coastline. The other shore of the inlet shows a 'tail' or common spit.

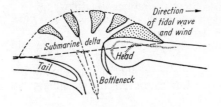

Figure 38. Submarine delta protecting a lee shore against wave attack

When a lagoon is silting up the streams in the bottle neck decrease, because the tidal fill diminishes; hence the size of the submarine delta also decreases and the protection this delta provides against wave action decreases. When the lagoon has silted up completely the submarine delta will have vanished and the coastline will have become a smooth line of sand. Heads and tails will then have disappeared.

Homogeneous sand shores always show smooth lines because action and reaction is everywhere the same over long distances. Some danger of losing land may result when man alters this smoothness by making defence works, harbour entrances *etc.* The size of the channels in a submarine delta, as illustrated in *Figure 38*, depends on the motive areas (gradient of tidal levels, see *Figure 25*).

SHORE PROTECTION

GENERAL

Shore protection probably started with planting willows (fresh water) or other plants. Protection with wooden boards or stones may have followed soon after, but it is said that the Chinese, who in early times excelled in making embankments and river improvements, neglected the underwater part of their defences. This is still one of the main faults of many coast defence works.

The building of embankments seems to have first started in England near Chatham in the 6th century (Dobbie states that Romney Marsh was diked before A.D. 772).

In Holland most of the alluvial land was reclaimed by embankments (dikes) before 1200; but after that year much land was lost again because the level of the land had sunk due to settlement of the soil resulting from better drainage. From 1200 to 1930 more land was lost to the sea in Holland than has been reclaimed from it. The old embankments may still settle 2 ft or sometimes even 10 ft in a century. Settlements of 10 in a year as a maximum have been measured in the delta of the River Po. The cause of this settlement is in dispute. The settlement of alluvial soils may be important.

The embankments of the Low Countries were originally protected by heavy wooden structures and by mattresses of willow boughs below l.w. These costly wooden structures were eaten up by the pile worm after about 1730, which caused much anxiety throughout the country. Stone defence, based *on the principle of grading material* (*e.g.* fine, coarse, coarser, very coarse) was found to be the solution. By this principle sand can be protected by small gravel, and small gravel by coarse gravel, debris, or broken stones, and the latter by stones heavy enough to resist wave attack.

The pores must be as small as possible and be made smaller and smaller in a downward direction. No sand may pass through the pores of the layer of shells or gravel; no shell or gravel may pass through the pores of the coarse gravel; no coarse gravel may pass through the pores of the bigger stones; *etc.* This is the principle of grading and it is of the utmost importance; neglect of this principle has resulted in many failures. Mussels and other small shells should be allowed to cement the stones together.

An example of a defective revetment where this principle has not been observed is shown in *Figure 39*. The defects are:

1 sand will be washed away through the pores of bricks, rubble and basalt.

2 unless there are groynes, or the beach is in equilibrium, the toe of the revetment is not safe; there is no grading to prevent the washing away of sand through the large pores of the toe.

Therefore the method should be slightly changed. Sand is protected by a layer of good clay, this clay is protected by a layer of straw, *krammat*, and above this the layers of rubble (or gravel) and heavier stones can be placed. Straw is not a permanent material, however, as it will rot. The clay must, therefore, be protected with small sized material as well. The wave currents seeking to penetrate the pores must not be able to reach the layer of clay.

When underwater protection of a sandy bottom is needed, the use of willow mattresses is the ancient well tried method. By using reed (with the leaves still on) as the central layer between the willow layers, the *zinkstukken* (willow mattresses) become less penetrable to currents.

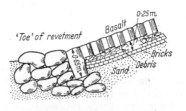

Figure 39. Example of revetment with weak toe

Willow mattresses are of great value in protecting the shore below water level. They consist of a lower grid of fascines consisting of bundles of willow boughs, diameter about 4 in (10 cm), spaced 3 ft (1 m) apart, with an upper grid of the same construction. Between the grids two or three layers of willow boughs are pressed down and bound with ropes. Sometimes a layer of reed (preferably with leaves) is put in the middle instead of a layer of willow boughs; the purpose is to prevent bottom scour under the mattress as far as possible. Instead of willow boughs, other local material can be used such as millet stalks, papyrus, blackthorn *etc.* The total thickness of a mattress is about 2 ft (0·6 m).

Because the closing of the Zeeland estuaries ('Delta-works') would need about 2 million sq m of mattresses and brushwood could not be grown in such quantities, experiments with asphalt sheets, plastics sheets and nylon woven fabric are being made in the Netherlands. Asphalt sheets allow sand to pass through the overlapping seams, plastics sheets do not lie flat on the bottom because of pockets of air underneath; nylon fabric (meshes about 0·2 by 0·2 mm, thickness about 0·5 mm) suited best because air and water pockets cannot form underneath and the sand cannot come through the fine meshes. (This system is the subject of Dutch patents.) Nylon fabric hoses, pumped full of sand, the water escaping through the meshes, are used to hold down the sheets. The first enclosure, at Veere, will need 36,000 sq m in 1960-61.

A general rule is to use local material as extensively as possible. Heavy clay, dredged from the sea bottom in the neighbourhood, may serve as ballast for the mattresses, but this clay may dissolve after some time by molecular action. Also certain stones may crack and split up after some years and such stones and clay should not be used.

The art of making coastal defence as economical as possible is difficult because of the variety of shores and material. Often much rock is wasted by lack of a mattress foundation, which should prevent scouring while the work advances. A sand bottom should be well covered with a mattress or with good layers of fine and coarse gravel before the coarser material of the training wall, which causes a strong current in front of it, is brought into place.

The construction of dams on a rock bottom was carried out with success at Scapa Flow. Crates of steel mesh, 6 ft cube, were filled with rip-rap and placed with the aid of a cable spanning the fierce tidal streams from island to island. Plastic sacks filled with sand were tried in 1957 in the Netherlands with good results (weight of the filled sacks 2 tons). Nylon fabric sacks can be pumped free of sand and the water escapes through the meshes. In the gaps of the Zuider Zee dam heavy barytes stones were used.

When it is desired to construct a dam across a gap with an erodible bottom, a rock apron (or mattress) strong enough to resist excessive erosion should first be laid. In the breaches of the 1953 flood many concrete pontoons (7,000 ton weight each) were sunk at the turning of the tide. The use of large special units is the latest development in closing tidal gaps.

For closing the huge gaps of the ' Delta-plan ', (1955-1980), many large concrete structures may be used which can be shut at the moment of still water.

STREAMLINE PRINCIPLES

One of the main methods of coastal defence is to build artificial capes which can be placed at regular or at irregular distances; for the latter, existing strong points are used. The aim is to divert the streams from the shore *i.e.* to protect the land. Vierlingh (1570) laid down the principle that streams should be gently deflected: ' he who exerts force on water, will have to meet the force of the water.'

Fargue in the second half of the nineteenth century formulated his well known rules for correcting rivers; they were rules bearing on streamlines and their objects were to make the river carry its water, sand and ice rather than to protect the shores of the river, though this was included. On shores of estuaries and coasts, the streamline principle should also be taken into account, especially when the shore itself is streamlined by nature.

Where a series of groynes is built, *Figures 41, 42,* scour will occur on either side if the series ends abruptly. Sometimes a salient point *e.g.* a harbour pier, is specially required and a large deep hollow will be formed just in front of it.

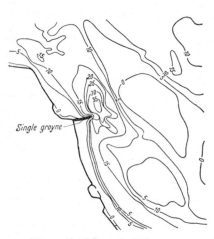

Figure 40. Effect of single groyne

This very simple, self evident, rule of action and reaction is the principle of streamlines. No one would think of fixing an angle section on the wings of a plane with one leg at right angles to the wind, but in hydraulics we sometimes meet with such obstacles. Single groynes create much turbulence and very irregular cross sections with extraordinarily large local disturbances, and they will attract the channel instead of pushing it from the shore, *Figure 40.* Moreover they are costly, because the force of the stream makes frequent repairs necessary.

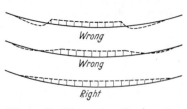

Figure 41. Ways of ending a series of groynes

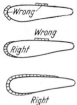

Figure 42. Groynes on an island

The top of the wing of an aeroplane has a lifting function as well as the under surface. In the same way the inner bend of a river can be streamlined with a parallel embankment (revetment) in such a way that it attracts, or keeps, the current so that good navigable depths may be obtained even near the shore of the inner bend. This is, as seen from a theoretical viewpoint, totally different from the irregular depths found along shores defended by groynes.

When the current in a branch of an estuary is not strong enough to cause scour, yet is sufficiently strong to prevent silt from settling, the streamline principle can be neglected to a large extent. These channels make good sites for harbours and industries because extra wide river sections can be made that may remain stable.

The alignment of tidal channels should be in accordance with their breadths as flood and ebb should be led through the same parts of the channels (*Figure 43*).

A good type of a half trained, half natural estuary is the Lower Scheldt. As has been explained already, the reason why the Lower Scheldt has a good fairway is that the shores offer the right resistance at the right places. If the shores of the Scheldt estuary had not been protected, or had been protected in other positions, the Scheldt would have no more navigable depth than the East Scheldt, north of Walcheren, and would be 'wild'. Streamlining was not, however, the object; the aim was to fix the bends.

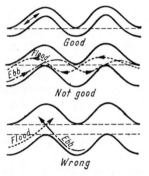

Figure 43. Alignment of tidal channels according to breadth

TYPES OF GROYNES AND OTHER SHORE DEFENCES

There are so many different coasts and so many ways of constructing groynes and revetments that it is not possible to give one solution only. Experiments with the materials at hand have been made on many coasts and have resulted in some method being devised which is economical and successful. These experiments still go on however, a sign that the art of finding the most economical way of defending a certain coast is not easy.

Three main types of coastal defence can be discerned:
1 revetment type
2 groyne type (artificial cape type)
3 small groyne type (using the coastal drift as a means of defence).

Revetment type
The whole shore surface is protected from a low level up to a certain height above high water (*Figure 44*). This is a very costly method. The streamline principle can be followed, so that the stream shows little turbulence near the

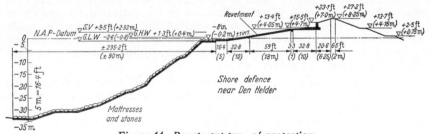

Figure 44. Revetment type of protection

shore, but nevertheless the cost of upkeep is often enormous. The defence works near Den Helder in Holland, shown in *Figure 44*, are the most costly shore defence works in the world; mattresses and stones have had to be added at frequent intervals for more than 150 years. Instead of using expensive Belgian stone an experiment is now being made to use local diluvial clay, dredged nearby. The revetment type of protection should extend further than the lowest part of the channel, when the current is the cause of coast recession. For wave eroded coasts less depth may be sufficient.

When there is a stable beach, or when there are saltings, only the part above the beach or saltings need be protected. But great care should be taken that such a revetment cannot become undermined. Often such a high beach or salting has to be protected by groynes, or if possible with plants. A row of wooden stakes or faggots at the toe may be of some slight use to allow the beach or salting to be lowered a little by the waves without causing damage to the revetment, but they will not stand much loss of beach height.

Waves act fiercely on a revetment as they arrive unbroken. The upper layer of stones should be heavy enough and well placed and keyed, so that only small amounts of water may penetrate into the revetment. Mussels must be allowed to grow on them. Some engineers used to prefer wooden poles sticking about 3 ft (1 m) high out of the revetment in order to break the force of the waves. Most engineers now object to this construction because they consider that the poles are vibrated by the wave action and loosen the revetment.

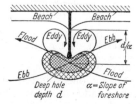

Figure 45. Groyne effects (length of groyne should be greater than d/α)

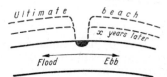

Figure 46. Possible effect of groyne (ordinary Dutch type)

Several experiments have been made using grout for closing the pores, but a rigid closed surface has the disadvantage that large holes may form underneath it. Even on old, well settled embankments, large concrete slabs or a rigid closed cover of concrete are hardly advisable. Asphalt in the pores allows more settling, but the engineer should beware of making a non-flexible, closed surface where the foundation and footing are not very stable. Bitumen filling can, however, be recommended in the case of many old stone revetments.

Bitumen slabs can be made of 13 to 20 per cent bitumen, 70 per cent sand and the rest small gravel. Plants often are activated by asphalt so that they may grow through the slabs; the bottom must therefore be made sterile before the slabs are laid. Reinforced asphalt slabs can be handled by crane but the difficulties are considerable. Nylon fabric can be used under a revetment, see p 493.

Small wave action may be opposed with small means; concrete tiles or clay bricks, or even loose debris may suffice, and grass and weeds should be encouraged to grow between them. Willows, reeds or rushes may be planted to protect the revetment; willows need fresh water, reeds and rushes may grow in slightly brackish water. Saltings or foreshores can be encouraged to silt up to a higher level, see p 502.

Straw thatching (*krammat*) and wood thatching have their uses for temporary defence. *Krammat* is also used as a protection for a clay layer under a stone revetment, but modern practice is to use nylon fabric.

Artificial cape type of groyne

Groynes of the artificial cape type have to be of solid construction and have to be stronger than natural capes. The most important feature of such a groyne is its head. The stones on it must be heavy enough to prevent their being rolled away by the waves and, to prevent the stones settling into the sandy bottom, willow mattresses are needed, or else the principle of grading should be used. The underwater part of the head must be frequently examined and the sea bottom around it must also be sounded regularly.

The length of the groyne, *Figure 45*, must be longer than d/α, when d is the depth to be expected in the deep hole in front of the groyne and α the slope of the sand along the groyne.

If the groyne is made too short, Nature will take material from the shore until it is satisfied, *Figure 46*. Especially with single groynes and strong currents the depth d will become greater and greater and the shore will, therefore, recede more and more.

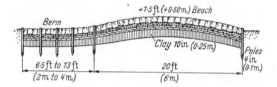

Figure 47. Body of groyne (ordinary Dutch type)

The 'body' of the groyne connecting the head with the shore is of less importance than the head. Its object is to prevent a gully forming behind the 'cape'. In the ordinary Dutch types the body is usually of stone (*Figure 47*) and much attention has to be paid in making this solid enough to prevent waves destroying it. When the beach loses sand, as is often the case, the stone groyne is left as a high unnatural ridge on the beach and, having lost its side support, topples over or has to be lowered. Often a side berm has to be made on both sides to obtain a new streamlined cross section. *Figure 47* shows only one berm; when the right hand beach lowers still further another berm will have to be constructed and when the beach lowers still further the whole construction will have to be made anew. Bitumen should be used to fill the gaps of the upper layer of stones.

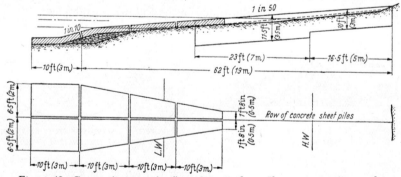

Figure 48. Groyne (new type) using concrete sheet piles as connection to shore

It has been proposed—and there are already some groynes constructed in this way—that the head should be joined to the shore by sheet piles (*Figure 48*). The heads of steel sheet piles have been worn away by the blowing and washing sand, so concrete sheet piles, with a good concrete slab over their tops, are preferable. When a sand beach loses much sand the sheet piles can be driven deeper with a water jet: thus the top of the groyne need not become too high above the beach.

Small groyne

The small groyne, or beach groyne, resembles a fence and is made of wood or concrete, *Figure 49*. Its object is to retain the shingle or sand of the upper part of the littoral drift. When using wood, the danger of pile worm must be considered; wooden groynes cannot reach to great depths. Most engineers would prefer permeable groynes passing some littoral drift. One of the functions of small groynes is to break the waves.

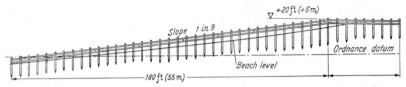

Figure 49. Typical beach groyne to protect shore above low water, Sussex coast

Another method of using coastal drift of sand as a means of coast protection is to pump this sand back to where it came from. In 1938 an experiment was carried out with this method on the Dutch island of Goeree. Considering the costs the results have been fairly satisfactory, as far as experience goes, Since then the method is advocated more and more. Groynes are expensive and rather unnatural.

In shallow, tropical rivers, ' bandal training ' is used, *i.e.* the resistance to flow along the shallow banks of a river is increased by placing small trees, branches *etc* in order to increase the scour at shoals.

There are three main points in making solid groynes, embankments, revetments, training walls and piers which must be considered carefully:

1 the top layer must consist of stones heavy enough to lie steady despite the impact of waves, and they must be well keyed, or grouted with a bitumen mixture

2 the grading towards the bottom must be so gradual that no sand, gravel, shingle or larger stones can be washed out

3 the 'toe' must be sufficiently low down and adequately protected against scouring.

Examples—These points are illustrated in the following examples:

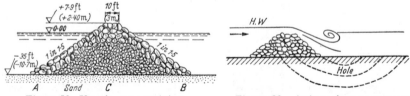

Figure 50. Unsafe stone training   *Figure 51. Action of cross currents*
       dam on sandy bottom   *on wall of insufficient height*

Figure 50 shows the cross section of a training dam laid on a sandy bottom. Where there is a littoral current there is severe scour in front of the groyne or training dam while it is being constructed. This is called 'head action' and is the cause of an unnecessary deep foundation of the training dam. The amount of stone may be two or three times the calculated amount, unless the bed is protected by a stone apron before the training dam is constructed. The principle of grading is not wholly neglected in *Figure 50*. Still, the sand from the bottom will be washed out by wave currents or by stream currents particularly at *A* and *B* and the stones will topple down. Even the central part of the foundation, near *C*, is not safe against being washed out. When a training dam with such large pores is made upon a sand bottom, a mattress should be laid well in advance to prevent scouring by head action and to prevent later scouring because of wave and other currents through the pores.

When there are cross currents at h.w. and the spur or training dam is not made to that height, the water will wash over the structure and cause a deep scour immediately behind it; the training dam will slide into the scour hole. To prevent this the structure should have a mattress where the attack is to be expected (*Figure 51*).

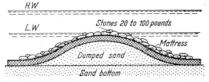

Figure 52. Cheap groyne for a shore with small cross currents and small waves

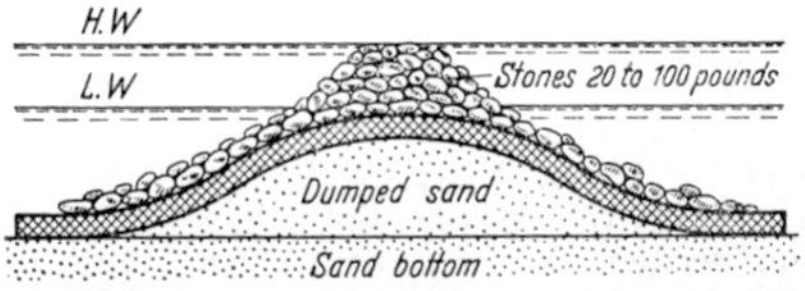

Figure 53. Cheap groyne for a shore with small cross currents and slight wave action. Height up to h.w. or higher

Figure 52 shows a cross section of a cheap groyne often made in Holland. During slack tide, sand is dumped or washed into place and after that this sand is covered quickly with a mattress before the tidal current sets in. These groynes will stand when there is not much wave action and not much cross current, but where cross flow occurs the sand might be washed away from under the mattress.

Because willow boughs will rot above l.w., they should be used only slightly above this level. In order to prevent cross currents flowing over a l.w. groyne a mound of stones can be built upon the l.w. groyne, as in *Figure 53* but such a mound is not water tight. The currents will pass through its pores and the sand may be washed away from under the mattress. This could be prevented by a special layer of gravel or shell as shown in *Figure 54*.

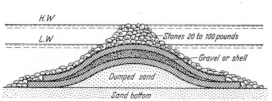

Figure 54. Groyne for a shore with cross currents and slight wave action with a special water tight layer of gravel or shell

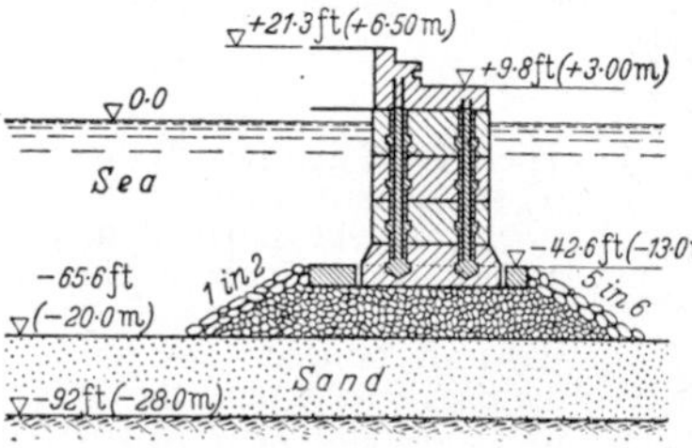

Figure 55. Mustapha breakwater at Algiers before destruction in 1934

For dams parallel to the currents, or nearly so, the sections shown in *Figures 52, 53* might be good enough. These sections, which are comparatively cheap to build, can be used for groynes or training dams which are likely to be shrouded with silt after a few years.

Figure 55 shows the Mustapha breakwater at Algiers which had a reinforced concrete section upwards of 42·6 ft (13 m) depth, but it had a weak foundation. The stones in the top layer were too small and the grading was poor with little regard to the size of the fine sand underneath it. The washing away of this foundation must have been one of the causes of the collapse of the breakwater in 1934.

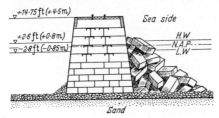

Figure 56. Ymuiden harbour pier

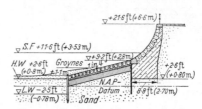

Figure 57. Scheveningen embankment

The harbour piers of Ymuiden (*Figure 56*) are protected against the waves by means of large concrete blocks. Though these blocks have large pores through which the wave currents wash freely, there is a fairly efficient layer of small rip-rap as a foundation protecting the sand underneath. Though the grading was far from correct no serious damage has occurred, but blocks have to be added because they sink into the sandy bottom, a sign that sand is still being washed away from under the layer of rip-rap.

In recent years large concrete tetraeders and 'tetrapodes' (French patent) have been used for breakwaters and for damming rivers and tidal streams. The pores of these tetrapod-dams are relatively small, but underlying layers of rock of the right size and grading should be used, so that neither sand nor rock can be washed out. The use of nylon fabric seems desirable in many cases.

Vertical sea walls like the one shown in *Figure 57* (Scheveningen) are built to protect the higher part of the shores against storm waves. These vertical walls have to withstand earth pressure from the back and therefore should be made stable. They also have to withstand the huge forces of the storm waves. They must not be undermined by the waves, and they must, therefore, have a foundation well below the lowest level of the beach, or they must have a wide stone revetment or 'toe' in front of them. In addition, large groynes are usually necessary to protect the beach and the foundation of the sea wall.

Figure 58 shows a cheaper method of protecting the higher part of the shore by avoiding the vertical walls. The cross section must be sufficiently streamlined.

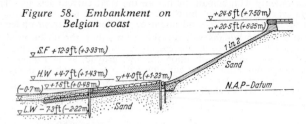

Figure 58. Embankment on Belgian coast

There is no great earth pressure and the waves do not exert such tremendous forces on the construction, so the concrete slab which has to withstand the attack of the storm may be fairly thin, but the toe should be well cared for lest it becomes undermined. There is always the danger that large holes may form beneath the concrete slabs; the sand should, therefore, be very well tamped before the concrete slabs are poured. The toe of the protection illustrated in *Figure 58* is well below the beach level, and the beach itself is protected by large groynes. The waves on this coast (the Belgian coast) are not very large.

Figure 59 shows a mixture of steep and other slopes; the cross section has no simple streamlines. The slope of the sand stands almost vertical at places and the wall protecting this vertical sand is only a thin slab. It is no wonder that the waves proved too strong for this structure. The toe is not extended to a low level, but the beach is protected by long and strong groynes.

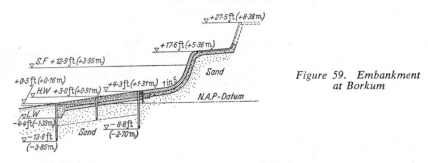

Figure 59. Embankment at Borkum

The question whether to use natural stone, concrete or asphalt for the revetment is an important one in countries where good natural stone is expensive.

Concrete slabs, poured *in situ* or placed by cranes, do not seem to have a great future, as holes may be expected underneath them and the slabs may break. Factory made concrete blocks with hexagonal or square forms are being used more and more for five main reasons:

1 they are often cheaper than good stones

2 they need no keying, as the blocks can be put very close together. The underlayer, therefore, can be fine gravel, shell, or light debris

3 they can be placed by almost inexperienced labour in a third of the time; this reduces the cost greatly

4 they can be made with top surfaces of varying height, so that the waves will break on them, and friction may diminish the uprush of the waves.

5 the sides of the concrete blocks can be made in such a way that any block is anchored by the adjacent blocks.

The concrete must be resistant to sea water and have a crushing strength of 7,000 lb/sq in (500 kg/sq cm). The water absorption should be under 8 per cent and the density 144 lb/cu ft (2·3 kg/cu dm). These figures can be obtained by vibrating or tamping methods.

Blocks for moderate wave attack can be about 3 ft × 3 ft × 1·5 ft (1 m × 1 m × 0·5 m) with a hole in the centre for handling. The joints between the concrete blocks can be filled with asphalt. There are several types of interlocking concrete block revetment, all protected by patents.

There must be a good layer of debris or gravel underneath any revetment in which these blocks are embedded, to prevent washing out of sand and clay.

The newest development is in the more extensive use of asphalt to the exclusion of stone. In Harlingen (Holland) a breakwater was constructed in 1949, the cross section of which is shown in *Figure 60*. The sand for the core was pumped, the length of the breakwater is 2,952 ft (900 m), the height of the top above mean sea level is 23 ft (7 m), the slopes are 1 : 4 on the sea side and 1 : 2·5 on the harbour side. The thickness of the bitumen-sand slab is 10 in (0·25 m) and on the most exposed part 16 in (0·40 m). Above mean sea level the bitumen-sand mixture was poured *in situ,* below that level cranes or other devices put prefabricated asphalt slabs into place. The method is definitely cheaper than stone construction, especially when stone has to be brought from a considerable distance. The cost of this first breakwater was 2,000,000 guilders (£200,000 roughly) for 900 m.

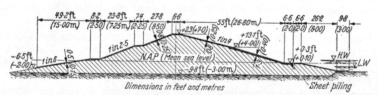

Figure 60. Breakwater at Harlingen

Later, another breakwater of the same type was made for the harbour (naval base) of Den Helder. *Figure 61* shows a promising experiment of asphalt dune-protection, made between the Hook of Holland and Scheveningen after the 1953 flood. The asphalt covering is made more or less like an asphalt road. The level of the top, 7 m (23 ft) above mean sea level is not high, so that the waves may reach the asphaltic slab and the filling of dune sand may become more or less saturated. The slope of the asphalt slab must, therefore, not be steep.

In 1953 several miles of new embankments in Holland were covered with such an asphalt sheet, especially in places where no clay was available. The sheet of asphalt is made *in situ* and covers the whole dike, except the lowest part of the inner slope. Trucks and cars can easily ride on the top of these new dikes and on their outer slopes.

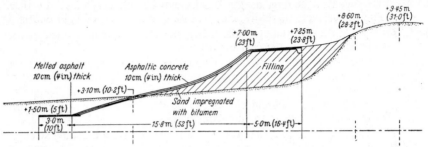

Figure 61. Modern asphaltic dune-defence work north of Hook of Holland

LAND RECLAMATION

Material provided by cliffs receding by erosion may make possible the gaining of much fertile alluvial land. There are three ways of gaining new land:

1 land accretion by using natural means
2 pumping dredgings into a swamp or lake
3 pumping a lake or sea shore dry.

Land accretion by natural means

Land accretion can be stimulated in several ways but generally only a small percentage of the total amount of suspended material in the coastal water is retained.   The principle is to make silt settle by producing still water conditions by stopping currents and wave action as far as possible.

Use of plants—Local plants are easy to obtain and may give sure results when their habits are known sufficiently. Proof of satisfactory growth under varying conditions is needed and it may be necessary to carry out trials in different places over many years. *Spartina Townsendii* is one of the first choices for temperate regions. It will grow in salt, brackish and fresh water but in fresh water rushes or reeds give better results. Both are economic products; there are hundreds of species of reed and it may be possible to select or develop a kind which may grow at a low level.

Reeds are used for mattresses in scouring waters, rushes for floormats, binding vines and cattle food (dried). The quality of that food seems to be so high that Eastern Germany made a law to protect rushes and promote their growth.

Silt trenches—If there is too much wave action along a coast for plants to grow, the age-old method is to dig small trenches (1 ft × 1 ft) which form a grid pattern of about 10 ft × 200 ft (3 m × 60 m). The silt settles in these trenches and by redigging them once a year or more often the small areas are heightened to a level where plants can grow. The method gives a fine homogeneous soil. Thousands of acres have been gained in this way along the coast between the Zuider Zee and the Weser.

Small dams—Dams or embankments are expensive; even when very small ones are proposed preliminary experiments should be made over a long period.

In Germany (Schleswig) and Holland (Groningen and Friesland) large sums are being spent to make shelter by means of willow-filled small breakwaters about 6 ft (2 m) high and 1 to 2 ft (0·5 m) wide, giving a grid pattern with areas of 1,300 ft × 1,300 ft (400 m × 400 m). Ice often destroys the hearting of these small breakwaters and the soil it gives is rather heterogeneous.   Direct economy is out of the question in many places.

High dams or causeways—Sometimes a railroad or a highway is made across an estuary and this causeway creates quietness in the water. Land accretion on both sides may occur, but generally on one side only. The North Frisian islands (Germany and Denmark) have been connected by means of large dams with the Continent. In 1878 the Dutch island of Ameland was connected with the shore, a distance of about 5 miles (8 km), the object being to gain land, but the dam breached soon afterwards, because it was not high enough. The storm piled the water at the western side up to a great height and at the eastern side the water was totally blown away, so that the western water washed over the dam. The top of a dam of this type should be made well above the storm floods plus wave heights, and a road can then be made upon it. The Ameland dam was a total failure partly because its layout was perpendicular to the prevailing storms. The North Frisian dams run east-west.

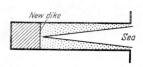

Figure 62. Natural land accretion

Figure 63. Reclaiming tidal flats or shallow bays a *old method* b *modern method*

Further gains resulting from land reclamation (Figure 62)—When 10 per cent at the land end of the fill basin of an estuary is reclaimed the streams in the rest of the estuary diminish; about 10 per cent at the mouth, and much more near the land end. If there is silt and sand in the water the cross sections of the estuary will therefore diminish and the shores will show natural accretion, because the size of the channel is a function of the fill basin. The action of silting in an estuary is progressive. This action, also called the ' method of pinching an estuary from behind ', is quite natural, but it can be accelerated by man, either by planting plants or by pumping parts of the estuary dry.

Narrow rivers and rather narrow ship channels are to be preferred to wide ones. Wide waters show wild, unstable features; the waves are bad for inland shipping; the embankments have to be made extra high because of big waves; and the salt penetrates far into the country because salt and fresh water mix, especially in wide estuaries. There is another advantage in making wide estuaries narrow, namely, the gaining of fertile marine soil.
Gains resulting from dredging—When the main channel of an estuary is deepened, the breadth of the estuary will decrease in a natural way when there is any sand and silt suspended in the water.

Reclamation by using dredging spoil

Dredging spoil is often used to heighten a low shore in order to create a new town district or harbour terrain. This is called ' making work with work '. On the river Scheldt about 5,200,000 cu yd (4,000,000 cu m) are dumped annually in the estuary itself. It seems to be a cheap way but some or perhaps much of this sand is added to the circular sand movements. In such a case dredging may go on endlessly when dumping nearby.

Reclamation by pumping out lakes (Figure 63)

This is often the most economic way of gaining new land. Land accretion is slow and generally requires more capital expenditure and interest charges than the new land can bear. The method becomes costly especially when artificial constructions are necessary to make the silt settle. Formerly labour was less expensive than it is now and much land could be gained by making silt trenches or by using one of the other means mentioned on p 502 but now that machines have become abundant and more economic, pumps can be used. Often when the methods of land accretion are used, the new polder takes the shape of a segment needing a long expensive embankment to protect it (for a relatively short time only). The pumping method, as used in the Zuider Zee, is much quicker and often requires less capital expenditure per 1,000 acres.

The question of the degree of fertility of the soil then arises. Here agricultural experts are needed. Perhaps there is a layer of clay at some depth which can be brought up with a special machine; such machines exist already for layers at a depth up to 10 ft (3 m). Perhaps there is clay in the neighbourhood which can be transported, and so on. The new soil should not be too clayey. An amount of 20 per cent of silt in the top layer (grains smaller than 20 μ) is often considered to be the best soil, but a committee of experts in Holland came to the conclusion that for the upper layer of 2 ft (0·6 m) a content of silt of only 12 per cent was as good. One of the main factors in fertility is to regulate the height of the ground water with extreme care, and to keep this water fresh.

Now that artificial manure is used extensively, sandy soils become more valuable, but the disadvantage of too sandy soil is that it may be blown away. Grass, bulbs and woods can be grown easily on sandy soils.

The planning of large pumped polders can be much better than the planning of the small segment formed polders. The roads, villages, canals, schools, churches *etc* can, and should, be made before the population moves into the polder. Land reclamation nowadays can hardly be else than a government job.

Land has a private economic value (selling value) and a public economic value. In a well populated country the latter is much higher than the former because the land supports not only the owner but the whole community as well. It is the public economic value of land which must be taken into consideration when planning a new polder to be added to the country.

Land reclamation by making sand dikes (Figure 64)

Near the sea, blown sand can be caught by means of rows of fir boughs or reeds, height about 3 ft (1 m). In the course of a few years high dunes can be made in this way with little cost. Sand dikes have been made in Holland

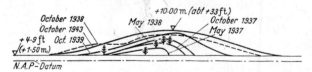

Figure 64. Brushwood hedges for making sand dunes

for several centuries, and much new silt land has grown behind them. The method is simple and inexpensive provided that the situation of the sand dike is well chosen. The new sand dikes have to be fixed with marram grass and other dune vegetation. Here the botanist's advice should be sought. Rabbits and holidays makers are the worst destroyers of dune vegetation.

SUMMARY OF PROMISING RECENT DEVELOPMENTS AND TRENDS

1 The use of specially shaped precast concrete units, called ' tetra-pods ', the subject of French patents, for protection against strong currents and waves (p 500).

2 The use of large concrete structures for closing tidal gaps in embankments, covered by Dutch patents (p 494).

3 The use of mattresses of nylon fabric (Dutch patents) to reduce erosion of a stream bed (p 493).

4 The use of nylon fabric sheets under stone revetments in place of brushwood *etc* (p 493).

5 The surfacing of embankments and the sea faces of sand dunes with an asphalt layer (p 501).

6 Pumping sand on to a denuded beach instead of building groynes (p 498).

7 Extrapolation of frequency curves, *e.g.* of high water.

8 Research into the formation, behaviour and height of waves and the reflection of waves.

9 Methods of predicting the height of a storm surge from the expected wind forces of an approaching depression. (The error found at the Dutch coast has been within 1 ft.)

10 Mathematical methods and the use of electronic computers and tidal analogy computers in tidal calculations.

11 The use of modern electronic measuring and sounding devices for offshore surveys (p 478).

12 The systematic measurement of the settlement of embankments.

BIBLIOGRAPHY

Bibliographies

Association d'Océanographie Physique, Union Géodésique et Géophysique Internationale, *Bibliography on Tides 1665–1939*, Göteborg, 1955; *Bibliography on Tides 1940–54*, Göteborg, 1957. (*Publ. sci. Ass. Océanogr. phys* No. 15 and 17)

Commission on Coastal Sedimentation, International Geographical Union, *Report of the XVIIIth International Geographical Congress at Rio de Janeiro*. New York, 1956

Corps of Engineers, U.S.-Army, *Bibliography on Tidal Hydraulics*, Vicksburg, Miss., 1954. (*Committee on Tidal Hydraulics*, Report No. 2)

Periodicals

Bulletin d'Information du Comité Central d'Océanographie et d'Étude des Côtes (C.O.E.C.), Paris. Service Hydrographique de la Marine, from 1949

Bulletin of the Beach Erosion Board, Washington, D.C. Beach Erosion Board, Corps of Engineers, Department of the Army, from 1947

Houille Blanche, La. Revue de l'Ingénieur Hydraulicien, Grenoble, Association pour la Diffusion de la Documentation Hydraulique, from 1945

Hydrographic Review, Monte-Carlo, International Hydrographic Bureau, 'from 1923

Küste, Die, Archiv für Forschung und Technik an der Nord- und Ostsee, Heide i. Holstein, Küstenausschuss Nord- und Ostsee (Kiel), from 1952. (Published as *Westküste*, Heide i. Holstein, 1938–43)

Rykswaterstaat Communications The Hague, from 1959

Shore and Beach, New Orleans, American Shore and Beach Preservation Association, from 1933

Congresses and Conferences

Proceedings of the First Western Conference on Asphalt in Hydraulics, Salt Lake City, Utah, *Bull. Univ. Utah*, 47, No. 14 (1956)

Proceedings of Conferences on Coastal Engineering, Council on Wave Research, The Engineering Foundation, Univ. of California, Berkeley, from 1951.

Proceedings of Conferences on Coastal Geography (1st 1954, 2nd 1959). National Academy of Sciences (National Research Council Committee on Geography), Washington D.C.

Conference on the North Sea floods of 31st January/1st February 1953, Institution of Civil Engineers, 1954

Transactions of International Navigation Congresses, Brussels, Permanent International Association of Navigation Congresses. (XVth Congr. Venice, 1931, XVIth Congr. Brussels, 1935, XVIIth Congr. Lisbon, 1949, XVIIIth Congr. Rome. 1953, XIXth Congr. London, 1957)

Proceedings of the Minnesota International Hydraulics Convention, Minneapolis, Minn., 1953. (5th Meeting of the International Association for Hydraulic Research)

Other Publications

ALLEN, F. H., PRICE, W. A. and INGLIS, C. C. (Sir). Model experiments on the storm surge of 1953 in the Thames Estuary and the reduction of future surges, *Proc. Inst. civ. Engrs* (1955)

D'ARRIGO, A. *Ricerche sul Regime dei Litorali nel Mediterraneo* (Researches on the Mediterranean Coastal Regimes), Rome, 1936

ASBECK, W. F. VAN. *Bitumen in Hydraulic Engineering; a Book of Reference*, London 1955

Shore-protection planning and design, *Bull. Beach Eros. Bd., Wash.* No. 2 (1953)

Tech. Memor. U.S. Army Eros. Bd. No. 1 etc.

BOER, H. E. and KIELMAN, J. A. *Rivieren, Rijshoutconstructies, Dijken, Duinen en Stranden, Waterschappen, Polders en Droogmakerijen* (Rivers, Fascine Work, Dikes, Dunes and Beaches, Waterboards, Polders and Reclamations), Amsterdam, 1957. (*Weg- en Waterbouwkunde* (Road and Hydraulic Engineering), Vol. III)

BOLDERMAN, M. B. N. and DWARS, A. W. C. *Waterbouwkunde* (Hydraulic Engineering), Vols. 1–V, Amsterdam, 1949–57

BRIQUET, A. *Le Littoral du Nord de la France et Son Evolution Morphologique*, Paris, 1930

BRUUN, P. *Coast Stability* Univ. of Florida, 1954

BURGT, J. H. VAN DER. *Toepassing van Asfalt in Waterbouwkundige Werken* (Application of Asphalt in Hydraulic Engineering Works), Utrecht, 1953. Also in *Bull. Beach Eros. Bd.*, Jan. (1951)

DOODSON, A. T. and WARBURG, H. D. *Admiralty Manual of Tides*, London, 1941

DOODSON, A. T. and WARBURG, H. D. *The Admiralty Tide Tables*, Vols. II and III, London, 1936–7

DRONKERS, J. J. Een Getijberekening voor Beneden-Rivieren (A Tidal Calculation for Estuaries), *De Ingenieur*, 1935

FARGUE, L. Expériences rel. à l'Action de l'Eau Courante sur un Fond de Sable, *Ann. Ponts Chauss* (1894)

FRANCIS-BOEUF, CL. Recherches sur le Milieu Fluvio-Marin et les Dépôts d'Estuaire, *Ann. Inst. Océanogr.*, Paris, 1947

GUILCHER, A. *Coastal and Submarine Morphology*, Paris, 1958

HOYT, W. G. and LANGBEIN, W. B. *Floods*, Princeton, N.J., 1955

HUITEMA, T. *Dijken langs Zee, Rivieren en Kanalen, etc.; Samenstelling, Aanleg, Onderhoud* (Sea, River and Canal Embankments; Structure, Construction, Maintenance), Amsterdam, 1947

Hydraulics Research; reports of the Hydraulics Research Board with the reports of the Director of Hydraulics Research, London, H.M.S.O., from 1947

Interim Reports 1–5 and Final Report of the Delta Commission to the Minister of Transport and Waterstaat, The Hague, State Printing and Publishing Office, 1953–8. (In Dutch; an English translation of the third Interim Report has been published: *Damming Up of Tidal Inlets*, The Hague, State Printing and Publishing Office, 1954)

JOHNSON, D. W. *Shore Processes and Shoreline Development*, New York, rev. ed., 1938

JOSEPHUS JITTA, J. P. *Sluizen en Andere Waterbouwkundige Kunstwerken in en langs Kanalen* (Locks and Other Canal Structures), Haarlem, 1947

KUIPER, E. De Bouw van de Nieuwe Noorderhavendam te Harlingen (The Construction of the New North Breakwater at Harlingen) *De Ingenieur*, 1949

LORENTZ, H. A. *Verslag van de Staatscommissie* (Commissie Lorentz) *ter Afsluiting van de Zuiderzee* (Calculations for the Enclosure of the Zuider Zee), The Hague, 1926

MINIKIN, R. R. *Coast Erosion, an Enquiry into Causes and Remedies*, Dock Harb. Auth., 1950

MINIKIN, R. R. *Coast Protection, a Survey of Beach Stability*, Dock Harb. Auth. 1948–9

NIELSEN and SCHOU. *Atlas of Denmark* Copenhagen, 1949

O'BRIEN, MORROUGH P. Salinity Currents in Estuaries, *Trans. Amer. Geophys. Union*, 1952

POSTEMA, J. A., SCHIPHORST, M. F. A. and SCHRIER, W. VAN DER. *Sluizen, Kanalen, Havens* (Locks, Canals, Harbours), Amsterdam, 1955. (*Weg- en Waterbouw-kunde* ("Road and Hydraulic Engineering"), Vol. II)

Report of the Departmental Committee on Coastal Flooding (Waverley Committee), London, 1954

ROUVILLE, M. A. DE. *Le Régime des Côtes*, Paris, 1946

SCHALKWIJK, W. F. *A Contribution to the Study of Storm Surges on the Dutch Coast*, The Hague, 1947. (Thesis, Utrecht)

SCHÖNFELD, J. C. *Propagation of Tides and Similar Waves*, The Hague, 1951. (Thesis, Delft)

STEERS, J. A. *The Coastline of England and Wales*, Cambridge, 1948

VEEN, J. VAN. *Analogy between Tides and a.c. Electricity*, London, 1947

VEEN, J. VAN. *Onderzoekingen in de Hoofden* (Researches in the Straits of Dover), The Hague, 1936

VEEN, J. VAN. *Research on Tidal Rivers in the Netherlands*, Dock Harb. Auth., 1946

VISSER, J. A. *Bagger- en Grondwerken* (Dredging and Earthwork), Haarlem, 1946

WOUDENBERG, A. *Buiten de Bandijken* (Outside the Embankments), Amsterdam, 1949

EXPLOSIVES

R. WESTWATER, B.SC., PH.D. and G. MORRIS, PH.D., F.INST.P.

BLASTING explosives are divided into two classes, high explosives and low explosives. High explosives detonate with the rapid production of gas while low explosives deflagrate and produce the gas much more slowly. High explosives include all the Gelignites, Gelatines and Dynamites; the only low explosive in common use is Blackpowder. High explosives are initiated by detonators and No. 6 strength is satisfactory for normal conditions. No detonator is required for Blackpowder and it is initiated by safety fuse or electric powder fuses. High explosives containing nitroglycerine are liable to freeze at temperatures below 10°C and special low freezing types are therefore available where low temperatures are likely to be encountered. The use of such types is compulsory in Great Britain.

HIGH EXPLOSIVES

These are available in several different types, but can be divided commercially into two main classes, Gelatines and Powders. With the exception of the straight Dynamites, the velocity of detonation of commercial high explosives when initiated by a No. 6 detonator is of the order of 2,500 m/sec (8,200 ft/sec), but Blasting Gelatines and certain of the higher grade Gelignites can be initiated to 7,500 m/sec by means of primers.

Gelatinous explosives

These have a density of about 1·5 g/cc and good resistance to moisture both in use and in storage. Keeping qualities vary according to the composition, Blasting Gelatine being highest and the low grade ammonium nitrate gelatines the lowest. The maximum life of high explosives varies according to the conditions of storage and climate, and it is difficult to generalize on the maximum period that explosives can be stored. It is good practice to turn over stocks of explosives regularly and, if possible, to use them within a year of manufacture; although with the higher grade gelignites under reasonable storage conditions, their life should be up to two years. All types of gelatinous explosives are suitable for use in bore-holes filled with water, but where the explosive is to be subjected to high water pressures a high grade Gelignite such as Submarine Blasting Gelatine is recommended, and primers should be used for initiation.

Gelatinous explosives are available in a wide range of strengths and TABLE 1 indicates the most suitable explosives for different work.

Powder explosives

The nitroglycerine types of powder explosive have a density of 0·98 to 1·25 g/cc and include the well known class of straight Dynamites. Their resistance to moisture is less than the gelatinous explosives and they are not suitable for boreholes filled with water although they can be used in wet boreholes provided they are fired soon after charging. Powder type explosives do not store as well as gelatines and even under good conditions of storage it is preferable to use them within a year of manufacture. They are available in a wide range of strengths and are used in dry or damp conditions where concentration of strength is not required.

TABLE 2 indicates the most suitable powder type explosives for different work.

508

TABLE 1. GELATINOUS EXPLOSIVES

Class	Explosive	Use
Blasting Gelatine	Blasting Gelatine	Drifting and tunnelling in very hard rock. Open cut work in very hard rock
	Submarine Blasting Gelatine	For underwater blasting
Gelatine Dynamite	Gelatine 90 per cent strength Special Gelatine 90 per cent strength	Drifting and tunnelling in hard rock. Open cut work in hard ground
High strength Gelignite	Gelatine 75 per cent strength Special Gelatine 75 per cent strength	Drifting and tunnelling in average ground. Stoping in hard ground. Primary blasting in quarries. Open cut work in average ground
Medium strength Gelignite	Gelatine 50 per cent strength Special Gelatine 50 per cent strength	Drifting and tunnelling in average to soft ground. Stoping in average ground. Primary and secondary blasting in quarries
Opencast Gelignite	Opencast Gelignite	Removal of overburden in opencast cut work

The above explosives are all low freezing.
' Special ' indicates that the explosive contains ammonium nitrate.
The nomenclature used in the above table represents explosives issued to export markets.

TABLE 2. POWDER EXPLOSIVES

Class	Explosive	Use
High strength	Belex Belex 1	Primary blasting in quarries. Drifting and tunnelling in average ground
Medium strength	Belex 2	Stoping in average ground. General colliery work (non-gassy)
Low strength	Belex 3	Ditching and general agricultural work

Non-nitroglycerine powder explosives

These explosives consist of TNT (trinitrotoluene), ammonium nitrate and aluminium. They have a density of 1·1 g/cc and a velocity of detonation of about 3,500 m/sec. They are available in cartridges, loose powder or granular forms and are widely used in quarrying and civil engineering work where borehole conditions are dry and a high strength, medium density explosive is required. The loose powder and granular forms are generally used where shotholes are to be 'sprung' and where it is desired to pour the explosive into the shothole. For large scale quarry blasting by the heading method the loose powder is available made up in 25 lb (11 kg) tins. These explosives, containing as they do a high percentage of ammonium nitrate, are very hygroscopic and are not recommended for use abroad. In Great Britain they should be used within six months of manufacture, although if in sealed tins they can be kept longer. The best known explosive of the class is Nobel's Explosive 704.

LOW EXPLOSIVES

Blackpowder

Blackpowder is ignited by means of safety fuse or electric powder fuses and while it is not affected by low temperatures it is quickly affected by moisture. It has not the strength of the high explosives and a larger quantity is required for any given piece of work, but the comparatively milder spreading action is well suited to certain types of strata and it is particularly useful in granite quarries where dressed stone is required. It is available either in the form of blasting powder of different grain sizes or in the form of blasting pellets.

BLASTING ACCESSORIES

Safety fuse

Burning speed—90 sec $\pm$ 10 sec per yd (*c* 100 sec/m)

Black single fuse $\Big\}$ for general mining and quarry work
Blue sump fuse

White countered gutta-percha waterproof fuse for use in very wet conditions or under water.

Capped fuses

This is the name given to lengths of safety fuse to which detonators are attached before they are taken to the place of use. They are available in lengths from 2 ft rising in stages of 6 in. Capped fuses are coiled and packed in cartons of ten.

Plastic igniter cord

Plastic igniter cord is a device for lighting safety fuse. It is cord-like in appearance, and when ignited an intense flame passes along its length at a uniform rate. This flame will ignite the blackpowder core of ordinary safety fuse. Two types are made. Plastic igniter cord (fast) has nominal burning speed of 1 sec/ft and plastic igniter cord (slow) a nominal speed of 10 sec/ft. Special connectors are available to ensure the transmission of the flame from the cord to the safety fuse even in the wettest conditions. Electric lighters for igniter cord are also available.

Detonators

Plain aluminium detonators are for use in conjunction with safety fuse; common sizes are No. 6 and No. 8. These give efficient detonation with all types of blasting explosives.

Electric detonators

Electric detonators are suitable for single or simultaneous firing in series or parallel. In fiery coal mines, copper tube detonators must be employed but in other cases the aluminium type are more common. There are two types of detonator assembly: *ordinary*, for use in dry conditions and *waterproof*, for use in wet conditions and/or under water.

Delay and short-delay detonators

For certain blasting operations it is an advantage to have the various charges fired in predetermined sequence, with regular time intervals between the shots, and delay detonators have been developed to meet this requirement.

Two types of delay detonators are made, the half-second series and the short-delay series.

In the half-second series, which is extensively used in tunnelling operations, there are eleven detonators No. 0 to 12 with a standard time interval of $\frac{1}{2}$ sec. They are usually connected up in series, but they can also be fired using parallel circuits.

Short-delay detonators provide a series of explosions with very short time intervals between. Detonators in the range are No. 0 to 18. No. 0 is an instantaneous detonator and the nominal interval between successive numbers from 0 to 4 is 0·025 sec, 4 to 12 is 0·05 sec and from 12 to 18 is 0·07 sec.

The short delay series is of particular importance in quarries and open cast work where ground vibration must be kept to a minimum.

Electric powder fuses

These are constructed on a similar principle to electric detonators, and are used with Blackpowder.

Test fuses

Test fuses and fuseheads are issued in sealed containers for use in the testing of exploders, in conjunction with resistances. This avoids the use of detonators for the purpose.

Detonating fuse

Cordtex detonating fuse is a textile fuse containing a core of PETN (pentaerythritol tetranitrate) and is used for initiating large charges of explosives. This fuse has a velocity of detonation of 6,100 m/sec (20,000 ft/sec) and is particularly useful in quarries where large diameter holes (+4 in) and heading blasting are carried out. Cordtex enables shot-holes to be column loaded *i.e.* the charges spaced in different parts of the shothole, as it will detonate a cartridge when it is running alongside it.

Detonating relays

Detonating relays provide a convenient means of obtaining short delay firing intervals in blasts primed with Cordtex detonating fuse.

The relay is inserted into the Cordtex main or branch line whenever a delay interval is required. The Cordtex line is cut and the cut ends crimped into the open ends of the relay. Detonating relays have a delay period of 0·02 sec and by inserting them into the main and branch lines in suitable positions, any required blasting sequence can be readily arranged.

EXPLODERS

Firing shots electrically can be done either with exploders or from the mains. In Great Britain the most general method for simultaneous shot-firing is to couple up the shots in series and fire by means of exploders. A range of exploders is available, from the single shot Little Demon exploder to the 100 shot dynamo condenser exploder. It is therefore possible to get an exploder to suit any type of work, but in every case the size of exploder chosen should be such that it has good reserve capacity, as by so doing the risk of misfires is much reduced.

In civil engineering jobs the small M.E.30 exploder, which has a firing capacity of 30 shots in series, should give satisfaction. The dimension of this exploder is $6\frac{3}{4}$ x 6 x $2\frac{3}{4}$ in and its weight is $5\frac{3}{4}$ lb (2·5 kg). It is operated by a twist-action detachable firing key and incorporates a device which prevents current from passing through the firing circuit until the armature has reached the required speed. This eliminates the risk of partially misfired rounds due to faulty operation of the exploder by the shotfirer.

The strongest exploder available in Great Britain is the Beethoven dynamo condenser, Mk. II. This exploder differs radically from orthodox exploders in its mode of operation. An a.c. voltage is generated by a dynamo which is operated by the turning of a handle. This voltage is stepped up by a transformer, rectified, and used to charge a condenser to a voltage of over 1,200 V. When the firing button is depressed the condenser is discharged through the firing circuit, firing the shots.

As a safety device a red neon light indicates when the condenser is charged, and the removal of the charging handle discharges the condenser. No voltage is applied to the output terminals except when the firing button is depressed and the charging handle in position. It is important to note that the voltage of over 1,200 V applied to the firing circuit might be lethal under some circumstances and care should be taken that no part of the shot firer is in contact with the firing circuit.

In the field this exploder is recommended to fire up to 100 shots in series. Under ideal conditions it has fired 500.

The dynamo condenser exploder is extremely compact for its performance. It is built on a metal chassis contained in a waterproof moulded bakelite case of external dimensions $6\frac{1}{8} \times 4\frac{1}{2} \times 10\frac{1}{2}$ in and weighs only 10 lb (4·5 kg).

CABLES AND CONNECTING WIRE

Generally shot firing cables are of the twin type and different grades are available according to the type of work required. Details of the different grades and their applications are given in TABLE 3.

To avoid damage to the cable from blasting it is customary to use connecting wire. This is generally supplied in 100 yd reels of plastics covered 23 SWG tinned copper wire.

Only fresh connecting wire should be used to connect the cable to the round of shots. It is bad practice and will lead to misfires if odd pieces of wire are used.

TABLE 3. SPECIFICATIONS OF SHOTFIRING CABLES
(a) *Twin-Core Cables in Coils of* 100 *yd*

Reference	Description	No. of wires and diameter (in)	Resistance per 100 yd of single conductor (ohm)	Remarks
T1	Yellow taped and cotton braided	4/0·018	2·4	Suitable for use in damp locations
T2	Yellow cotton braided	4/0·018	2·4	Suitable only for use in dry conditions
T4	White plastic, 'figure 8'	7/0·0164	1·7	Suitable for use in wet conditions
X1	Tough rubber sheathed	14/0·0076	1·4	Suitable for use under water

(b) *Single-Core Cables in Coils of* 100 *yd*

Reference	Description	No. of wires and diameter (in)	Resistance per 100 yd of single conductor (ohm)
S1	White taped, cotton braided and compounded	3/0·036	0·8
S2	White, tough rubber sheathed	3/0·036	0·8
S3	White, plastic covered	3/0·036	0·8

PREPARATION OF EXPLOSIVE CHARGES

The type of explosive for any particular purpose depends upon the rock to be blasted and the humidity or dryness of the conditions of storage and use. In most civil engineering work nitroglycerine explosives are used in both the gelatinous and powder types. These give a wide range of strength and very little fume on detonation. To get the best results with any explosive the largest possible diameter and weight of cartridge should be used in the borehole. In small boreholes the cartridge diameter chosen should give at least $\frac{1}{8}$ in (3 mm) clearance, but in wellholes *e.g.* 6 in (15 cm) diam, the cartridge size should be 5 in diam. On p 526 some general hints and precautions are given.

Preparation of detonator

Unless an electric detonator is to be used, it is necessary to prepare the detonator with safety fuse, as follows.

If the detonator contains any sawdust from the packaging this must be carefully shaken out.

Cut the safety fuse straight across with a clean, sharp knife or fuse cutter, using a freshly cut end for insertion in the detonator. Never allow the ends to come into contact with damp, oil or grease.

Slip the detonator over the end of the fuse so that the composition and fuse are in contact. Hold the fuse lightly pressed against the composition, but do not screw it. Crimp the detonator gently but securely on to the fuse with approved crimpers.

Preparation of primer cartridge

Detonator and safety fuse—Open a cartridge at one end, make a hole with an aluminium brass or wood pricker in the opened end, and push in the detonator, leaving the top of it projecting. Tie the cartridge paper firmly round the fuse immediately above the detonator.

Electric detonator—Make a hole in the end with an aluminium, brass or wood pricker. Press the detonator lightly into this hole until it is completely buried in the cartridge. To prevent the detonator from being withdrawn accidentally during charging make a hitch round the cartridge with the leading wires.

Detonating fuse—Efficient priming using detonating fuse depends on the fuse being in good contact with the primer cartridge. Two methods are recommended:

1. For large diameter cartridges. Pierce a hole from side to side through the cartridge. Thread the detonating fuse through the hole and tie the short end to the line, making a loop.
2. For small diameter cartridges. Pierce a hole through the cartridge from end to end. Thread the detonating fuse through the hole and tie a knot in the end so that it cannot be withdrawn.

Charging the borehole

Clean out the borehole by blowing out with compressed air. Insert the cartridges one at a time and press each home with a wooden rod. Push or lower the primer cartridge into the hole until it rests against the main charge. Always insert the primer cartridge so that the detonator points to the full length of the charge.

After loading the explosive, insert the tamping or stemming, the first few inches being pressed gently with the wooden rod against the last cartridge. Increasing pressure should be exerted on the tamping as the borehole is filled, the final length being packed as tightly as possible. While the tamping material is being inserted, the leading wires or safety fuse should be held to one side to facilitate the action of the tamping rod and prevent stripping of the wires or damage to the fuse.

Never ram or pound the cartridge into the borehole.

Never bunch or double up the cartridges; choose a size suitable for the diameter of the borehole.

Never use a metal rod.

QUARRYING

Primary blasting

Several methods of quarrying are available according to the nature and condition of the rock to be quarried and the daily output required. The following are the normal primary quarrying methods: *a* benching; *b* springing; *c* medium and large diameter hole blasting; *d* heading blasting.

Benching—This is used for small outputs with shotholes from 3 to 20 ft deep, spaced from 3 to 10 ft apart and with burdens of from 2 ft 6 in to 10 ft. The shotholes are usually drilled with hand-held compressed air machines and give a finishing diameter of $1\frac{1}{2}$ to 2 in (*c* 4 cm) suitable for explosive cartridges of $1\frac{1}{4}$-$1\frac{3}{4}$ in diameter. High explosives of both the nitroglycerine and non-nitroglycerine type are used and from 4 to 6 ton of rock is produced per lb of explosive (*c* 10 kg/g). This method can be used under any rock condition.

Springing—This primary blasting method can be used to produce fairly large quantities of stone, but is restricted to quarries with good vertical and horizontal cleavage planes. It is an unscientific method depending particularly on the skill of the operator, who must judge the number of springing shots required and the size of the final charge from his own experience in the particular quarry. The method consists of drilling holes 12 to 20 ft (4-6 m) deep and firing a successive number of gradually increasing charges to open up cracks in the rock so that the larger final charge can be placed. In average conditions from 3 to 5 springing charges will be required, the first being 1 lb and the final being about 5 lb. In placing the shotholes these should be started from 1 to 2 ft (0·5 m) behind vertical joints and should finish from 5 to 10 ft (1·5-3·0 m) above horizontal joints. The burden should be approximately equal to the depth, and generally only one hole is fired at a time. The most common explosive for springing is Blackpowder, but grain explosives, such as Nobel's Explosive 704, can also be used. This method gives a high yield of rock, generally of the order of 8 to 12 ton per lb of explosive (*c* 20 kg/g).

Medium and large diameter hole blasting

This method is suited to faces above 30 ft (9·5 m). Drilling equipment has been developed to drill holes in almost any type of rock, however bedded and jointed, in diameters from 3 to 12 in. The average yield of rock per lb of explosive is 6 tons (13 kg/g) and this method of blasting accounts for about 80 per cent of all surface blasting carried out in the U.K. Hole spacing and charges for average conditions are shown in TABLE 4.

Heading blasting—This is suitable for any kind of stratum, but the most favourable conditions are when there is a free end with the main cleavage planes parallel to the face. The minimum height of face in this instance should be 50 ft, with the main drive of the order of 0·6 of the height and the maximum distance between chambers equal to the depth. Blackpowder should be used when there is the need of stone for ornamental purposes, and the charging ratio here averages $3\frac{1}{2}$ ton of rock per lb of explosive (7 kg/g), but Opencast Gelignite gives better results for other types of stone work. In this case the average yield of rock per lb of explosive is 5 ton (11 kg/g).

Secondary blasting

Normal secondary quarrying methods are pop shooting and plaster shooting.

Pop shooting—In pop shooting a short hole is drilled into the stone to be broken and a small charge of explosive placed therein. The charge is initiated by a detonator and a length of safety fuse, the hole being stemmed with sand or clay. The depth of the hole and charge vary according to the size of the stone, but the majority of holes are from 6 to 12 in deep and contain from 1 to 3 oz of high explosive or Blackpowder.

Plaster shooting—In ordinary plaster shooting the explosive cartridges, one of which contains a detonator, are placed on the material to be blasted and then fired either bare or preferably covered with clay. This method has been used for many years in a wide variety of circumstances, such as demolition of brick walls, concrete, cutting of steel plates in ship breaking usually under water, also in metal mines and quarries for the breaking of boulders.

The main advantage of plaster shooting is that the material is broken *in situ* and not scattered over wide areas. The main disadvantages are the noise produced and the amount of explosive required. In most quarters the noise effect can be disregarded, but the relatively high explosive consumption has, in the past, kept many quarry managers from adopting plaster shooting for secondary blasting. Where labour costs in quarries are high and mechanical loading is employed, the conditions are favourable to plaster shooting, and, while some rocks are more susceptible to this method than others, it is worth while carrying out trials to study the costs of pop shooting as compared with plaster shooting.

PUBLIC WORKS

Breaking ground

This type of work varies from blasting of small outcrops of rock to the making of large cuttings. The methods available are often similar to quarrying and the same general rules can be applied. According to the nature of the work, different methods will be necessary and different types of drilling equipment will be used, but it is always essential that shotholes should be balanced, that is, the distance of the explosive charge from the nearest free face should be less than the depth of the shothole, and for best results should be equal to $\frac{1}{2}$ to $\frac{2}{3}$ the depth of the shothole. The best depth of hole will depend upon the height of face or depth of cutting necessary and on the type of drilling equipment available, but the deeper the hole the more rock will be produced per ft of drilling.

The most commonly used type of explosive is Special Gelatine 75 per cent strength, the diameter and weight of cartridge being chosen according to the type of drill available. For deeper holes where the rock is very hard it is sometimes an advantage to use a stronger explosive such as Special Gelatine 90 per cent strength for the bottom part of the charge and Special Gelatine 75 per cent strength for the upper part. In such cases, usually large diameter holes, the charge is spaced in the hole with $\frac{1}{2}$ to $\frac{2}{3}$ of the charge in the bottom and the remainder spread higher up the hole, the two parts being separated by stemming. By using a detonating fuse such as Cordtex this system is easily applied because it is sufficient if the Cordtex from the base charge passes alongside and touches the cartridges in the deck or decks. Where detonators are used, a detonator in each part of the charge is necessary and care must be taken in coupling the leading wires.

For average conditions of work TABLE 4 gives suggested hole placements and charges for the different depths of shothole.

Tunnelling

Explosives and consumption—The choice and correct placing of explosives play a most important part in tunnelling work as on these factors depend the amount of rock pulled per round and its suitability for loading by hand or machine. The main requirements for a tunnelling explosive are that it should have a high to medium strength, high density and velocity of detonation, good water resisting properties and a fume on detonation low in noxious gases. These requirements are met by both the straight Gelignites and the Special Gelatines, the former being generally used abroad because of their excellent storage qualities and the Special Gelatines in Great Britain where they can be used within a year of manufacture. These explosives are available in several grade strengths and a suitable grade for the hardness of the rock should be chosen.

For average work Gelignite 62 per cent N/G or Special Gelatines 75 or 90 per cent strength are most commonly used in cartridge sizes of $1\frac{1}{4}$ in diam × 8 in. For very hard rock conditions, the concentration of the explosive can be increased by using cartridges $1\frac{7}{16}$ in diam and these are

TABLE 4.

TYPICAL CHARGES AND BURDENS FOR PRIMARY BLASTING BY SHOTHOLE METHODS

Minimum finishing diameter of hole (in)	Cartridge diameter (in)	Depth of hole (ft)	Burden (ft)	Spacing (ft)	Rock yield (ton)	Explosive charge (lb)	Blasting ratio*	Tons of rock per foot of drilling
1	$\frac{7}{8}$	4	$2\frac{1}{2}$	3	2·3	5 carts †	4·0	0·6
1	$\frac{7}{8}$	5	3	3	3·3	7 carts†	4·2	0·7
$1\frac{1}{4}$	$1\frac{1}{8}$	8	$4\frac{1}{2}$	$4\frac{1}{2}$	12·0	$2\frac{3}{4}$ lb.	4·4	1·5
$1\frac{3}{8}$	$1\frac{1}{4}$	10	5	5	18·5	4 lb.	4·6	1·9
$1\frac{3}{4}$	$1\frac{1}{2}$	12	6	6	32·0	7 lb.	4·6	2·7
$2\frac{1}{4}$	2	20	8	8	95	21	4·5	4·8
		25	8	8	120	26	4·5	4·8
		30	8	8	140	32	4·5	4·7
		40	8	8	190	42	4·5	4·9
3	$2\frac{1}{2}$	30	9	9	180	40	4·5	6
		40	9	9	240	55	4·5	6
		50	9	9	300	70	4·5	6
		60	9	9	360	80	4·5	6
$3\frac{1}{4}$	$2\frac{3}{4}$	50	10	10	370	85	4·5	7
		60	10	10	450	100	4·5	7
		70	10	10	520	115	4·5	7
		80	10	10	600	230	4·5	7
4	$3\frac{1}{4}$	40	12	12	425	95	4·5	11
		60	12	12	650	140	4·5	11
		80	12	12	850	190	4·5	11
		100	12	12	1100	230	4·5	11
$6\frac{5}{8}$	5	50	20	20	1500	330	4·5	30
		60	20	20	1800	400	4·5	30
		80	20	20	2400	530	4·5	30
		100	20	20	3000	660	4·5	20
$6\frac{5}{8}$	6	60	22	22	2200	475	4·5	36
		80	22	22	2800	630	4·5	36
		100	22	22	3600	800	4·5	36
9	8	70	25	25	3300	725	4·5	46
		80	25	25	3700	825	4·5	46
		90	25	25	4200	925	4·5	46
		100	25	25	4600	1050	4·5	46

* Tons of rock per pound of explosive.   † 9–10 cartridges to the pound.

available in weights up to 1 lb. It should be noted that the shothole should always have a clearance of at least ⅛ in over the diameter of the explosive cartridge.

The amount of explosive used in tunnelling varies greatly according to the nature of the rock, the size of tunnel and the fragmentation required. In small tunnels, such as 10 ft × 8 ft (3 m × 2·5 m), in hard rock, the explosive consumption will be from 4 to 7 lb/cu yd (3 kg/cu m), whereas, in the same rock, a 20 ft (6 m) diam tunnel would require about 2½ to 4 lb/cu yd (1·75 kg/cu m). In softer rocks, such as in collieries, 2 to 2½ lb of explosive per cu yd (1·5 kg/cu m) is common in 10 ft × 8 ft tunnels.

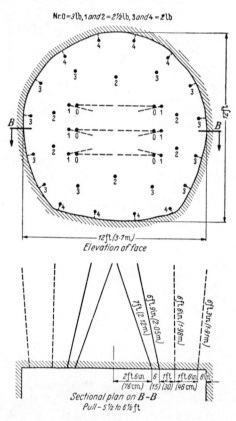

Figure 1. The wedge cut. Scale, 1 in to 6 ft. Explosive, Special Gelatine 75 per cent strength. Cartridge size, 1¼ in by 8 in. The weight of explosive required per hole is shown above the diagram. The figures 0, 1, 2, 3 or 4 indicate the order of the delay detonators

Types of cut—The most important factor in tunnel driving is to get a good 'cut' and the two most common methods are the wedge cut (*Figure 1*) and the burn cut (*Figure 2*). Other types of cut used in special conditions are the drag cut, pyramid cut and the fan cut.

The wedge cut is probably the most commonly used and pulls of 7 to 8 ft can be obtained in practically every type of ground. The burn cut is becoming increasingly favoured because generally speaking it is easier to drill as all the holes are approximately parallel and longer pulls can be obtained than with the wedge type. The burn cut will perform very satisfactorily in hard rock but in soft or spongy materials it is not usually successful as the ground absorbs the explosive force and the cut is not thrown out properly. Examples of these two types of round are shown in *Figures 1* and *2*: the explosive is Special Gelatine 75 per cent strength; cartridge size $1\frac{1}{4}$ in × 8 in; the weight of explosive required per hole is shown above the diagram, and the figures 0, 1, 2, 3 or 4 indicate the order of the delay detonators.

The blasting of a tunnel round involves the blowing out of a cut followed by easers to widen out the hole blown and by a succession of trimming shots to give the required size of tunnel. By using delay detonators it is possible to charge up the whole round at one operation and on the application of the current the delays will fire the round in the predetermined

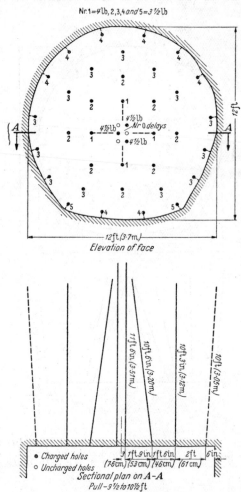

Nr 1 = 4 lb, 2, 3, 4 and 5 = 3½ lb

Elevation of face

• Charged holes
○ Uncharged holes

Sectional plan on A–A
Pull – 9½ to 10½ ft

Figure 2. *The burn cut. Scale, 1 in to 6 ft. Explosive, Special Gelatine 75 per cent strength. Cartridge size, $1\frac{1}{4}$ in by 8 in. The weight of explosive required per hole is shown above the diagram. The figures 0, 1, 2, 3 or 4 indicate the order of the delay detonators*

order. Half second delays are preferable in hard rock and short delays in softer stratified material. If delays are not available a similar effect can be obtained using safety fuse and cutting the fuse to give the proper firing rotation; this method is largely practised in drivages in metal mines but is not recommended for large scale tunnel work as it is most important to ensure that the cut shots fire together and this is difficult with fuse firing.

Delay detonators have the following advantages: *1* increased rate of advance due to *a* less time to do actual blasting, *b* reductions in the time the men are away from the face; *2* safer and healthier working conditions for the shotfirer, who does not have to go back into the tunnel to charge up successive series of shots; *3* less danger from falls of rock, as with only one firing period the men can give the fumes time to clear before going back into the face and any loose pieces of rock can then be seen and taken down; *4* a large pile of debris results after a round has been fired; this is very suitable for mechanical loaders.

Stemming

In all blasting work, good and adequate stemming is essential to achieve maximum blasting efficiency. The best stemming material is damp sand and this can be easily used when the shotholes are vertical, but it is difficult to use with horizontal holes. A good substitute for damp sand is a mixture of sand and clay and, provided the stemming is not too moist, it is very efficient. Clay by itself is an inefficient stemming material but if no other material is available, it should be used as dry as possible. For tunnelling work, where time is most important, stemming should be prepared on the surface and sent to the face ready for use. This can be done by extruding a sand–clay mixture into cartridges about 8 in (20 cm) long and sending these cartridges into the tunnel in wooden boxes. Alternatively, paper bags can be obtained for filling with sand and this makes a useful and efficient stemming material. Where sand is damp, it is advisable to use waxed paper to prevent the bags bursting too readily, and in collieries the paper should be fireproofed.

DEMOLITIONS, METAL AND PILE CUTTING

Explosives can frequently be used for a wide variety of demolition operations, such as demolishing buildings and brick, stone and concrete chimney stacks, railway and road bridges, concrete foundations for engine beds, pile cutting, breaking up machinery and dealing with sunken wrecks. Explosives required for this work depend upon whether the explosive is to be used in a shothole or as a plaster shot. Where the explosive is to be placed in a shothole, any of the normal commercial explosives will be suitable but Special Gelatine 75 per cent strength is commonly used. For the plaster shooting type of job the best result is obtained by the use of a strong high velocity explosive. The best explosives in this class are Submarine Blasting Gelatine and Plaster Gelatine, but the work can still be carried out, though not quite so efficiently, with other explosives. The general methods for the different subjects are given below.

Brick walls

Shotholes—In the shothole method the holes should be drilled dipping at an angle of 30 to 45° and finishing just beyond the centre of the wall so that the explosive charge will occupy a central position in the wall. The holes should be kept as low down to the ground as practicable with the bottom of the holes finishing about two brick courses above ground level as this allows flying debris to be more easily smothered. The holes should be spaced about 1 ft 6 in (0·5 m) apart and the explosive charges should be as in Table 5.

TABLE 5

Thickness of wall	Explosives charge
18 in (45 cm)	Two $\frac{7}{8}$ in diam carts (10 to the lb) 3·2 oz (90 g)
2 ft 6 in (0·75 m)	Three $\frac{7}{8}$ in diam carts 4·8 oz (136 g)
3 ft (0·9 m)	Two 1$\frac{1}{4}$ in diam carts 8 oz (226 g)

Initiation should be by *Cordtex* or electric detonators.

Plaster shots—In the plaster shot method the weight of the explosive charge will depend upon the thickness of the wall and strength of the materials. For thin walls the charge may be strung out as much as possible, but for thicker walls better results are obtained by 'bunching' the cartridges at intervals. For example, for a 14 in wall it is better to bunch two 4 in cartridges together per foot run of wall than to place the two cartridges end to end. Suitable charges are as in TABLE 6.

TABLE 6

Thickness of wall	Explosives charge
4½ in (11·5 cm)	2-4 oz per ft centres
9 in (22·8 cm)	4-8 oz per ft centres
14 in (35·5 cm)	8-10 oz per ft centres
18 in (45·7 cm)	16-24 oz per ft centres

The explosive charges should be doubled for the corners.

For plaster shots on brick walls the easiest means of initiation is by Cordtex detonating fuse which is run along a length of wall making contact with each explosive charge. The charges are held in position by clay or other suitable means.

Stone and concrete walls

Hole placement should be similar, but if possible advantage should be taken of any joints or planes of weakness. In some cases the charges will require to be increased by 25 to 50 per cent. In thicker walls it may be necessary to increase the hole spacing to 2 ft or 2 ft 6 in (0·7 m) making a corresponding increase in the explosive charge per hole.

Concrete foundations

Although these are of irregular shapes and sizes, usually they present a free face or faces and holes should be drilled to take advantage of these. If the structure is in a workshop, engine house, power house *etc*, particular care has to be taken to avoid flying fragments, and short holes spaced close together and charged lightly should be used. For instance, holes 1 ft 6 in to 2 ft deep (0·45 to 0·6 m), spaced 1 ft 6 in to 2 ft apart and charged with a half or one $\frac{7}{8}$ in cartridge will usually break up concrete sufficiently to demolish by wedge and hammer or crowbar. To prevent flying fragments the holes should be covered with old sacks and timber baulks or sandbags. Where there is no risk of damage from the blasting, deeper holes can be used with increased spacing and larger charges.

Reinforced concrete

It is usually necessary to tackle reinforced concrete in two stages, first breaking away the concrete and then dealing with the reinforcement by cutting through with chisel or hack saw, burning with oxyacetylene flame or cutting through with explosive, as described later.

Chimney demolition

Chimneys may be readily felled by firing shotholes so placed as to cut away a sector a little more than half the area of the base of the chimney. The line of fall should first be decided and holes drilled to cut away equal portions of the chimney on either side of this line. This applies where the chimney is circular or rectangular in cross section. With chimneys rectangular in cross section it is best to fell the chimney along a line normal to one of the sides. In general it is often found advantageous to cut away certain portions of the chimney before firing the final series of holes.

In demolition of all buildings, in placing the explosive charges, advantage should be taken of all openings in brickwork or stone work *e.g.* windows, doorways or cracks in the fabric. Also explosive charges should be placed on steel girders or wood frames which might offer support to the walls and prevent collapse after blasting.

Cutting steel plates

For cutting mild steel plates of different thickness the following diameters of cartridges should be used.

For $\frac{1}{4}$ in (6·35 mm) thickness	$\frac{7}{8}$ in diam cartridges
For $\frac{1}{2}$ in (12·7 mm) thickness	$1\frac{1}{4}$ in diam cartridges
For $\frac{3}{4}$ in (19·0 mm) thickness	$1\frac{1}{2}$ in diam cartridges

For under water blasting, as in cutting up submerged vessels, for the given thickness of metal the diameter of the cartridges should be doubled.

To get the best results, it is necessary to get good contact between the explosive and the steel plate. From work carried out, it has been shown that the cutting power of an explosive depends on the area of contact with the metal being cut. TABLE 7 gives the minimum contact required for freely suspended plates.

TABLE 7

Plate thickness	Minimum contact width of Submarine Blasting Gelatine to cut through
$\frac{3}{8}$ in (9·5 mm)	0·6　in (15·2 mm)
$\frac{1}{2}$ in (12·7 mm)	0·75 in (19·0 mm)
$\frac{3}{4}$ in (19·0 mm)	0·85 in (21·6 mm)
1 in (25·4 mm)	1·8　in (45·7 mm)

It will be seen that there is a big jump from the $\frac{3}{4}$ in to the 1 in plate thickness, the explosive evidently being just at the limit of its cutting powers with unstemmed explosive.

The figures in TABLE 7 are for Submarine Blasting Gelatine initiated at high velocity. With Gelignites the minimum contact width has to be materially increased. This is due to the greater power and gas volume of Submarine Blasting Gelatine, giving rise to a more sustained pressure application.

From the above it will be seen that the best results are obtained when the explosive is laid on in such a manner as to give at least this minimum contact width. Wherever possible, in metal plate cutting, tamping or confinement should be used. Stiff clay is better than damp sand as confinement for plaster shooting, probably since it is less readily dispersed. Also, it should be noted that steel is most easily cut against a shearing edge.

Cutting girders

For cutting mild steel H section girders, up to say 18 in by 6 in, a string of $1\frac{1}{2}$ in diam cartridges of Submarine Blasting Gelatine or Plaster Gelatine can be used. The explosive should be placed on one face of the web, and the inner side of both top and bottom flanges. For heavier section girders and girders reinforced with angle iron, the explosive charge should be increased accordingly, taking care to make sure that sufficient explosive is placed on the angle iron to ensure cutting through.

Metal castings

Where these cannot be demolished by the use of plaster shots, 1 in (25·4 mm) diam holes should be drilled and placed according to the thickness of the metal. The 1 in diam of the holes facilitates drilling and is suitable for $\frac{7}{8}$ in diam cartridges. Often it is necessary to chamber the holes before a final breaking-in charge can be used. Where shotholes cannot be drilled mechanically, suitable holes can be burned with an oxygen flame issuing from a small diameter mild steel pipe. The burning of the steel pipe gives the intense heat required.

Metal vessels

Hollow castings such as stills, retorts or drums can be readily broken up by filling the vessel with water and firing a suitable charge of explosive suspended in the centre. A cast iron still, say of 2 in to 3 in (50 to 75 mm) thickness, in metal and measuring 6 to 7 ft (2 m) diam by 6 ft deep, can be suitably broken up by firing a single charge of $1\frac{1}{2}$ lb (0·45 kg) of Special Gelatine 80 per cent.

Boilers can be similarly dealt with by filling with water and firing suitable charges. Here, however, it is a case of opening up the boilers by shearing the rivets and then cutting the metal into suitable scrap with plaster shots. In the case of riveted boilers, however, care has to be taken to guard against flying rivet heads, as these are projected for considerable distances and heights unless adequate protective covering is used along the joints. The boiler is first burst open by filling with water and firing three charges of a Special Gelatine, suspended below the centre line of the boiler. End charges of $2\frac{1}{2}$ lb (1·1 kg) are then placed about 3 ft (1 m) from either end, with a centre charge of 2 lb (0·9 kg).

Pile cutting

Wood piles may be cut by firing a necklace of explosive around the pile, provided access is possible at the desired cutting depth. A 9 in by 9 in wood pile requires say 3 lb (1·4 kg) of explosive, and a 12 in by 12 in (30 cm) pile 4 to 5 lb (2 kg). An alternative method for pile cutting or loosening is to drive down alongside a mild steel tube $1\frac{1}{4}$ to 2 in internal diameter and tapered at one end. The tube is then charged with a suitable explosive charge, say 1 to 3 lb, and fired. In some cases when dealing with wooden piles it may be possible to bore a hole dipping at an angle and finishing say two thirds of the way through the pile. This enables a smaller charge of the order of 12 oz to 1 lb (0·45 kg) to be used for piles up to 12 in or so square.

Cast iron piles of tubular structure can be readily dealt with by filling with water and firing small charges suspended inside. For example, from 4 to 6 oz (110 to 170 g) of Gelignite fired suspended in water will deal with cast iron piles 12 in (30 cm) diam and 1 in thickness of metal.

Sunken wrecks

Explosives find a useful application in dealing with sunken vessels. The blasting operations involve plate cutting, removing obstructions, flattening the wreck *etc.* It is advisable, however, to increase the charges for plate cutting under water as compared with ordinary metal cutting, and the diameter of the cartridges used should be large enough to ensure sufficient surface contact to cut right through the metal. Where it is desired to flatten out a wreck, heavy charges should be suspended in suitable positions in the vessel, while the weight of explosive used will depend upon the size and structure of the vessel.

Example—A vessel of about 1,000 ton and about 200 ft (60 m) long should be levelled down with charges of 200 lb, 300 lb and 500 lb (90, 135, 225 kg) fore, aft and amidships respectively, with a further 50 lb (22 kg) placed through the fire box to deal with the boiler.

OPENCAST MINING

Removal of overburden

In most opencast mining operations the success depends on the efficient and rapid removal of the overburden. This is a fairly simple matter where the workable deposit is comparatively thin and consists of soft shales and clays, but where the overburden consists of harder materials blasting is necessary. An ideal state of the overburden preparatory to removal by excavators is in the form of a loose material and the blasting practice adopted should be such as to reduce the overburden to such a condition that it can be readily removed by the excavating machines available.

The overburden is generally blasted by either vertical or horizontal holes, or a combination of both. In soft or medium hard sedimentary strata, such as shale, horizontal holes generally give good breakage with a ratio of from 7 to 10 cu yd of material per lb (11 to 17 cu m/kg) of explosive used. In harder rock such as sandstone horizontal holes will be satisfactory if they are in, or in the vicinity of, the sandstone, and the sandstone is only a few feet thick, but otherwise vertical holes will be necessary. In some cases a combination of the two will give the best results. The amount of explosive required in these conditions will vary from $2\frac{1}{2}$ to 5 cu yd of rock per lb (4·2 to 8·5 cu m/kg) of explosive.

With horizontal holes the spacing is generally from 12 to 15 ft (3·5 to 4·5 m) and the depth of hole can be anything from 40 to 60 ft (12 to 18 m). The spacing of the vertical holes will depend upon the depth, but generally will vary from 12 to 18 ft (3·5 to 5·5 m) between holes and between rows of holes.

The most common diameter of shothole for opencast overburden removal is 6 in (15 cm) for the horizontal and 7 in (17·5 cm) for vertical holes, and explosive cartridge sizes of $3\frac{1}{4}$, 4, 5 or 6 in diam should be employed. The type of explosive will depend upon the condition, but generally a Gelignite is preferred because of its water resisting properties, though a TNT type of explosive could be used in dry conditions in the softer strata or made up in sealed tin containers where the conditions are wet.

RISK OF DAMAGE FROM BLASTING OPERATIONS

When blasting operations are contemplated account has often to be taken of the possibility of damaging neighbouring structures, and of the distances to which it is essential to move men and machinery during the actual shooting. In some fortunate instances, as for example isolated quarries, the only structures concerned are the buildings associated with the working of the quarry, so that the operator is free to set the degree of risk at any level he may choose since he can balance the convenience and economy of a big shot against possible damage which he himself will have to repair. On the contrary, blasting operations have sometimes to take place very close to dwelling houses and the like, when it is obvious that a quite different degree of care is necessary.

Damage to surrounding structures can be caused by an explosion by three main agents, the action of air blast, the projection of debris, and the vibrations transmitted by the ground. It is assumed that damage will never be caused by structures or machinery being deliberately left inside the area broken by the shot.

In a well designed commercial blast in which the explosive is fired in a properly tamped hole with the quantity of explosive nicely adjusted to the work it is called upon to perform, there should be no air blast and practically no debris should be projected, unless there is an unnoticed geological weakness actually penetrating to the borehole.

Ground vibration

It is unfortunately impossible to stop the generation of seismic waves, but certain simple rules have been deduced whereby the likelihood of damage can be estimated. It is found that the amplitude of the ground motion is very complex, as in an earthquake shock, to which it is in fact closely related. The ground motion is compounded of a large number of parts, some transmitted along the surface of the ground, the so-called Rayleigh wave, and the others reflected and transmitted at the geological beddings of the site. At a distance of a mile from an explosion some of the ground vibration may have travelled through strata several thousand feet deep, and this is made use of in the seismic method of geophysical prospecting. Experience indicates that normal rock formations, for example limestone and igneous rocks, behave sufficiently similarly to allow a common rule to be employed in calculating the permissible quantity of explosive which can be used near an average building, and some typical figures are set out in TABLE 8.

It is found that wet ground, particularly clay, is an excellent transmitter of ground vibrations and a separate column is given in TABLE 8 for wet sites, where the maximum charge allowable is rather less than that for dry sites.

There is little difference in the ground shock produced by equal weights of different types of explosive; to take extreme cases Submarine Blasting Gelatine gives a ground motion only about 15 per cent greater than an equal weight of gunpowder. The minimum ground shock is produced by a charge nicely calculated to the work it has to do; under- and over-charged shots both produce more ground movement.

When a number of holes are fired simultaneously the ground amplitude at a distance is very nearly the same as if a single charge of equal weight had been fired. The use of delay detonators will serve to reduce ground motion.

It is difficult to calculate the dynamic strength of a building because of variations in the conditions of structure, particularly with ancient monuments, but TABLE 8 applies to property in a good state.

This, together with variations in psychological reactions, often makes it expedient to use smaller quantities of explosives initially.

In exceptionally difficult circumstances the wisest procedure is to fire a pilot shot. That is to say, a small quantity of explosive is fired in as nearly as possible the same place and manner as the main blast. This enables the transmitting properties of the site to be found and the degree of risk of the proposed blast to be calculated more accurately.

TABLE 8. WEIGHTS OF EXPLOSIVE WHICH HAVE BEEN FIRED AT VARIOUS DISTANCES FROM ORDINARY BUILDINGS IN GOOD REPAIR

Distance (ft)	Charge (lb)		Caution
	Dry sites	Wet sites	
100	65	15	*These charges apply only to well-stemmed shots, correctly balanced to the work they have to do*
200	250	65	
300	575	150	
400	1,000	250	
500	1,600	400	
600	2,300	575	*Initial trials should, if possible, use explosive charges smaller than the figures quoted*
700	3,000	775	
800	4,000	1,000	
900	5,000	1,300	
1,000	6,500	1,600	
2,000	—	6,400	
3,000	—	14,000	

Damage by air blast

As already stated the generation of air blast can be almost eliminated by close attention to the correct procedure in loading and firing explosives. The importance of this can best be realized by considering the distances at which damage can be caused by bare charges of explosive. TABLE 8 shows that in a normal rock site ¾ ton of explosive could be fired at 500 ft (150 m) with standard technique from an average building on a dry site without risk of damage. Nevertheless a bare charge of this size fired on the surface might break windows by air blast up to 3,000 ft (1,000 m), depending on the effects of ground contours, trees *etc.*

Bare charges are seldom used in civil engineering and when they are they are limited to plaster shooting using 1 to 5 lb of explosive.

STORAGE OF EXPLOSIVES

The storage of explosives is governed in most countries by legal restrictions and in Great Britain by the Explosives Acts of 1875 and 1923 which should be consulted. The following is a brief guide extracted from these Acts and gives some information on the different quantities which can be stored according to the type of store available. In all cases explosives should be kept free from grit or other foreign matter and protected from moisture, extreme heat or cold. No iron or steel tools should be used with explosives.

The Home Office have authorized the storage of explosives under the following conditions.

Private use—Quantity allowed 10 lb and 100 detonators. This method is suitable only for very small users. Application for certificate should be made to the chief offices of police.

Immediate use—Apply to police for certificate covering one purchase of explosive, 10 lb or over, and detonators, for urgent requirements in special circumstances. Details of circumstances for use to be furnished to the police.

Registered premises—The premises must be registered with county council, town council, district council *etc.* Renewable annually. Make application to the police for a police certificate covering the purchase of explosives, for storage under either mode *A* or *B*.

Mode A. For storage up to 60 lb in a separate building specially designed for the storage of explosives, detached from any dwelling house, and at a safe distance (about 16 yd) from any highway *etc.*

Mode B. For storage up to 15 lb in a substantial receptacle inside a house or other building where unauthorized persons are excluded.

Registered premises are useful where consumption is small but regular.

Stores—Licences to be again obtained from the local authority such as county council, town council, district council *etc.* A police certificate is also required to cover the purchase of the explosives. Licences renewable annually. Stores are divided into 5 divisions.

TABLE 9. STORES

Division	Weight of explosive including blackpowder (lb)	Distance from road, path, etc. (ft)	Distance from house, workshop, railway etc. (ft)
A	150	75	85
B	300	75	130
C	1,000	146	292
D	2,000	230	460
E	4,000	352	704

Requirements—The stores must be substantially built with brick, stone or concrete walls and a concrete roof. The outside door should be of steel plate in an angle iron frame and fitted with 3 all-brass locks. An inner timber door with 2 all-brass locks is also required. The stores should be plaster or timber lined and the floors covered with gritless asphalt. If they are licensed for either *B*, *C* or *D* quantities they must have an efficient lightning conductor, and must only be used for the storage of explosives and the necessary tools connected therewith. Certain notices must be affixed therein.

NOTE. In all above cases detonators must be kept separate from other explosives *i.e.* in a separate receptacle or store. Users are *warned* that in all above cases a *police certificate is essential* and is renewable *annually*. These vary as to whether they cover items 1 to 4. Police certificates for store licences should have the *division* under which store is licensed stated thereon. Under The Control of Explosives Order 1953 a *police licence* must also be obtained to cover all purchases of Blackpowder and Safety Fuse.

Magazines—These are licensed by the Home Secretary. Police certificates and licences from local authority are not required. Magazines are only required by very large users.

HINTS ON USES OF EXPLOSIVES

General recommendations for shotfirers

All shotfirers should be officially appointed (preferably in writing). The person making the appointment should be satisfied that the shotfirer is adequately trained.

Smoking or the use of naked lights must not be allowed when handling or working in the vicinity of explosives. There is a hazard with all explosives, but Blackpowder and detonators are specially susceptible to premature initiation by spark or flame.

Take special care to keep explosives and detonators dry.

When firing a round of shots using safety fuse, make sure that the method of lighting allows time for the full number of shots to be ignited and that the fuse lengths are adequate for a safe getaway. Make sure that the fuse is not damp and that it is not damaged during stemming.

When crimping plain detonators on to safety fuse make sure the fuse is in contact with the detonator composition, but never use force or screw the fuse against the composition.

Never crimp the detonator tube on the part which contains the detonating composition. The crimp should be about $\frac{1}{8}-\frac{1}{4}$ in from the open end of the tube.

When straightening out leading wires, do not hold the detonator by the tube. Grip the wires about 3 in from the detonator with one hand and smooth them out with the other—this avoids any pull on the electric fuse.

When inserting the primer cartridge in the borehole, see that the wires are straight. If there are kinks, untwist them gently. To jerk them out may break the wires and cause a misfire.

In charging and tamping take care to avoid damaging the covering of the wires of electric detonators. Stripping the wires during this operation is a possible cause of misfires.

See that the leading wires are long enough to allow good connections with the cable.

Twin-core cables have two conductors, and care should be taken to make sure that the strands of one conductor are not in contact with those of the other. It is good practice to have the exposed ends of the conductors staggered in relation to each other.

In making the connections the bared conductors should be twisted together tightly for a length of about 2 in. The bared conductors should be kept clean. Greasy or dirty wires give poor connections and may cause misfires.

Before finally deciding that a shot has misfired, carefully examine the cable and all connections and test the circuit with an approved circuit tester.

To ensure good insulation in wet holes, see that the junctions are securely covered with insulating tape or joint insulators.

Do not allow electric wires or cable to run near boreholes charged with explosives. Avoid electric shotfiring near overhead power cables.

Do not handle explosives during the approach or progress of an electrical storm.

The handle of the exploder must always be kept in the personal possession of the shotfirer.

Connecting shots is the responsibility of the shotfirer. Do not entrust this work to anyone else.

Before returning to a shot, first disconnect the cable from the exploder and remove the firing handle or key.

Never drag a firing cable along the ground. Coil it carefully and carry it. Take every precaution to prevent kinks. These usually develop into internal breaks, which are difficult to trace.

When using Cordtex always cut the fuse at the reel as soon as the primer cartridge is in position. Make sure that the Cordtex is not damaged during the stemming operation.

Never spring a borehole near another hole loaded with explosives.

Never load a sprung hole until it has cooled from the previous shot.

All explosives produce a certain amount of noxious fumes on explosion. Most 'Nobel-Glasgow' explosives have their ingredients carefully adjusted so that any toxic fumes are controlled and kept to a minimum, and provided that normal precautions are taken for adequate ventilation, especially in confined spaces, no hazard will arise from this source. Certain explosives, however, developed for special purposes are not adjusted in this way, and these should not be used underground or in confined spaces.

BIBLIOGRAPHY

MORRIS, G. and WESTWATER, R. Damage to structures by ground vibration due to blasting. *Mine & Quarry Engng*, April (1953)

TEICHMANN, G. A. and WESTWATER, R. Recent trends in short delay blasting. *Mine & Quarry Engng*, Oct. (1952)

TEICHMANN, G. A. and WESTWATER, R. Blasting and associated vibrations. *Engineering*, April (1957)

BROOK, D. H. and WESTWATER, R. The use of explosives for demolition. *J. Instn civ. Engrs*, 4 (1955-6)

RANKIN, W. W. and HASLAM, R. Modern blasting practice in tunnelling operations. *Civ. Engng, Lond.*, Feb.–April (1957)

WESTWATER, R. and HASLAM, R. Underwater blasting. *Civ. Engng, Lond.*, July–Sept. (1949)

The following are available from Nobel Division, Imperial Chemical Industries Ltd, 25 Bothwell Street, Glasgow, C.2

Blasting in Quarries
'Nobel-Glasgow' Explosives and Accessories
Blasting Practice
Explosives. The Sale, Storage and Conveyance by Road
Electric Shotfiring
'Nobel-Glasgow' Delay Detonators
Detonating Relays for Short Delay Blasting
'Cordtex' Detonating Fuse
Blasting in Agriculture
Plastic Igniter Cord for Quarries
Détonateurs à Retard 'Nobel-Glasgow'
The Storage of Explosives (Overseas Edition)